T5-ADY-402

Seal Family

AMERICAN WILD LIFE

ILLUSTRATED

COMPILED BY THE WRITERS' PROGRAM
OF THE WORK PROJECTS ADMINISTRATION
IN THE CITY OF NEW YORK

Color Photography by
AUSTIN BAYLITTS

1949
WM. H. WISE & CO., INC.
NEW YORK

Copyright 1940, by the City of New York

WISE books are trademarked

Look for the *WISE* old bird!

3491

PRINTED IN THE UNITED STATES OF AMERICA

Table of Contents

FOREWORD v

ACKNOWLEDGMENTS vii

INTRODUCTION xi

MAMMALS 1

FISHES 139

REPTILES 291

AMPHIBIANS 419

BIRDS 463

INDEX 737

List of Color Plates

SEAL FAMILY . . . . *Frontispiece*

BUFFALO . . . . *Facing page* 1

MISSISSIPPI GAR PIKE . . . . . . " " 139

COPPERHEAD . . . . " " 291

TOAD . . . . " " 419

AMERICAN EAGLE . . . . " " 463

Foreword

Chief credit for assembling and verifying the information contained in *American Wild Life, Illustrated*, for shaping the work and bringing it to completion, must go to the staff of writers and editors whose names appear below.

Ralph De Sola, *Editor*

Alexis Chern
William F. Craig
Clifton Cuthbert
Milton Friedman
John Harms
Ben Kagan
Edward Malkin
Ralph Manheim

Joseph Rosner

Of great assistance in the final production phases of the book, which appears to be the only comprehensive and at the same time popular American natural history to be written within the past thirty-five years, were the following members of the Project editorial board:

Walter K. Van Olinda, *Editor-in-Chief*
George Fleming, *Managing Editor*

Frederick Clayton, Director
New York City WPA Writers' Project

Acknowledgments

In the preparation of *American Wild Life, Illustrated* many individuals and institutions have co-operated. We extend to them our heartfelt thanks and deep appreciation for their consistent and open-handed assistance in giving technical advice and in providing illustrations. They are nowise responsible, of course, for any editorial opinions expressed in the book.

We wish to acknowledge a special debt of gratitude to the Mayor of the City of New York, the Honorable Fiorello H. La Guardia, who as official sponsor for the WPA Writers' Project for his city has repeatedly demonstrated his interest in the activities of the project and the welfare of its personnel; gratitude also to the Honorable Newbold Morris, President of the Council of the City of New York, appointed by Mayor LaGuardia to expedite the publication of project books.

To Dr. Willard G. Van Name of the American Museum of Natural History we are particularly indebted for his services as technical consultant to the sponsor of the project. Dr. Van Name's critical comments have been followed in the text and have done much to enhance the value and authenticity of the book.

For their technical advice, and for their help in conducting research, we wish to thank the following individuals and agencies: Dr. Charles M. Bogert, Assistant Curator of Herpetology of the American Museum of Natural History; Dr. C. M. Breder, Jr., Acting Director of the New York Aquarium; the Bureau of Biological Survey of the United States Department of the Interior; Dr. Lee S. Crandall, Curator of Birds of the New York Zoological Park; Dr. Raymond L. Ditmars, Curator of Mammals and Reptiles of the New York Zoological Park; Dr. Eugene W. Gudger of the American Museum of Natural History; Mr. John T. Nichols, Curator of Recent Fishes of the American Museum of Natural History; Mr. Richard H. Pough of the National Association of Audubon Societies.

For the wealth of illustrations displayed we are indebted to: Dr. Roy Chapman Andrews, Director of the American Museum

ACKNOWLEDGMENTS

of Natural History, and many members of the museum staff; Dr. Clinton L. Baker, Director of the Reelfoot Lake Biological Station of the Tennessee Academy of Science; Mrs. Matthew R. Barcellona, Publicity Manager of the Buffalo Museum of Science; the Bureau of Biological Survey of the United States Department of the Interior; Mr. Frank L. Bird of Netcong, New Jersey; Dr. W. Reid Blair, former Director of the New York Zoological Park, and many members of the zoological park staff; Dr. C. M. Breder, Jr., Acting Director of the New York Aquarium, and many of his staff; the Bureau of Fisheries of the United States Department of the Interior; Mr. Walter H. Chute, Director of the John G. Shedd Aquarium of Chicago; Mr. J. S. Daily of Fort Smith, Arkansas; Mr. Henry E. Ditzel, Advertising Manager of Sharp and Dohme; Mr. George L. Dowden of San Gabriel, California; Mr. Adrian C. Fox of Mandan, North Dakota; Mr. John H. Fulweiler, editor of the magazine *Frontiers*, of the Academy of Natural Sciences of Philadelphia; Mr. W. F. Gerecke, photographer of Marine Studios, Marineland, Florida; Mr. Joe Hall of Cincinnati, Ohio; Mr. W. Lincoln Highton, photographer of the Work Projects Administration; Mr. J. W. Jackson, photographer, Brush, Colorado; Mr. L. M. Klauber, Curator of Reptiles of the Zoological Society of San Diego; Mr. E. A. MacIlhenny of Avery Island, Louisiana; Mr. Charles E. Mohr of Reading, Pennsylvania; Dr. Robert Cushman Murphy, President of the National Association of Audubon Societies for the Protection of Wild Birds and Animals, and Mr. Richard H. Pough of that organization; Mr. R. Nelson of Calumet, Michigan; Mr. Liston M. Oak, associate editor of the magazine *Antiques*, New York; Mr. Frank Pagan of Wellsboro, Pennsylvania; Mr. James McAlpin Pyle of Isle St. George, Monhegan, Maine; Mr. A. C. Reneau, Jr., of Independence, Kansas; Mr. John S. Robas, volunteer in the Department of Ichthyology of the American Museum of Natural History; Mr. R. A. Romanes of Alto, Georgia; Mr. William Rubin of Liberty, New York; Mr. C. W. Schultz of Superior, Wisconsin; Mr. Alajos Schuszler, photographer, New York City; Miss Natasha Smith of Berkeley, California; Mr. Lee J. Smits, Director of Publicity of the National Wildlife Federation; Mr. Hans Stecher, Curator of Reptiles of the Staten Island Museum of Arts and Sciences; Dr. A. D. Stoesz of Lincoln, Nebraska; Mr. Freeman P. Taylor of St. Petersburg, Florida; Mr. Richard W. Westwood, managing editor of *Nature Magazine* of the American Nature Association; Mr. Winton Weydemeyer of Fortine, Montana; Mr. Gifford Wood, Advertising Manager of Becton, Dickinson; Messrs. Stacy

ACKNOWLEDGMENTS

and Horace Woodard, producers of the motion picture, *Adventures of Chico;* and Dr. Albert Hazen Wright of Cornell University.

Photographs made by the editor of this book are so credited, and the places where they were taken are indicated by the following code letters which appear under the respective illustrations: (AMNH) American Museum of Natural History; (CPM) Central Park Menagerie; (NYA) New York Aquarium; (NYZP) New York Zoological Park; (NZP) National Zoological Park; (PPZ) Prospect Park Zoo; (PZG) Philadelphia Zoological Garden; (SIM) Staten Island Museum; (SIZ) Staten Island Zoo.

Introduction

In the great Western desert of the United States the earth's thin, green, life-supporting mantle has worn through so that the gaunt framework of our planet shows through. Silica, mica, borax, salt and alkali lie about on the floor of the land, which is corrugated like a great washboard and from which the water has long since evaporated.

Until 1935 this desert, which occupies so many square miles of the West, in the minds of most Americans was little more than the tedious stretch of country between the populous and industrial East and the luxuriant, semitropical fruit-growing land of the Pacific slopes. In that year the desert all at once served dramatic warning that it was on the march. The skies became filled with wind-blown topsoil blotting out the sun even as far east as New York City. Pictures of bony cattle dying of thirst or dust pneumonia found their way into the daily papers. New pioneers hastily left farmhouses crushed and buried by silt in the submarginal lands of the dust bowl, to find a grudging refuge in California or Oregon.

Years before that, the buffalo and the mule deer had disappeared from these great plains; now humans were leaving it. The sight of the weary, dustlined faces of courageous men and women brought home to the American public the conviction that conservation was not merely a luxury advocated by lovers of birds and beasts, or by faddists, but was in fact one of the most vital and immediate concerns of our Nation as a whole.

The necessity for preserving our wildlife has been difficult for Americans to understand. Amid a lush overabundance of every other type of natural resource, this continent teemed with wildlife. Before the transcontinental railroad was built, sixty million buffalo roamed the plains of the United States; now barely five thousand survive, and only in protected areas. The slaughter of the buffalo is rivaled only by the amazingly complete extermination of the passenger pigeon, flights of which at one time "darkened the sun for

INTRODUCTION

hours on end." The Carolina paroquet, the heath hen, the Pallas cormorant, and the giant mink are among the once numerous vanished species. The grizzly bear, the California condor, and the sea otter have become rare. Many other species are fast approaching extinction.

With their swords beaten into plowshares at the close of the Revolutionary War, Americans turned their attention to the great empire west of the Appalachians. Here the topography ranged from high mountain peaks to below-sea-level "sinks," and a generally temperate climate provided an ideal habitat for the most diverse animal species.

During this period of expansion, wanton killing of wildlife was inevitable. Frontier communities of the early days were not served by grocery or clothing chain stores. Among the first of the pioneers to exploit the resources of the wilderness were the fur trappers, whose trading stations were for many years the remote outposts of our civilization. This killing of animals and birds on a small scale soon paled into insignificance when highways and railroads were cut through the forest, providing easy communication with the markets of the East. Then skins, feathers, and even bones, began to pile up in the storehouses. Mills and factories sprang up along the edges of streams to pollute the waters, ever driving the wild creatures to more inaccessible regions. Finally, even these last sanctuaries were invaded by sportsmen with rifles and shotguns, and by the time conservation societies intervened enormous damage had been done.

Conservation today, after its first propagandistic beginnings, is striving to lay the foundations for a long-range, commonsense program to "save our wildlife." Intelligent conservation avoids hit-or-miss meddling in natural inter-relationships, for that may set off a train of events whose end cannot be foreseen. Everyone is familiar with the elementary rule in keeping goldfish—the "balanced aquarium." Simply stated, in the balanced aquarium the plants give off oxygen which is "breathed" in by the fish; the fish then give off carbon dioxide which is assimilated by the plants. Such mutual dependence in a strictly controlled environment is much more complicated in the natural world, where wild things survive and keep each other in a very delicate balance. Spraying petroleum on a swamp to kill off the larvae of mosquitoes, for instance, destroys the swamp as a breeding place for wild fowl, lessens the food supply available for other birds, and wipes out the sustenance of game fishes and amphibians. In turn, the harm-

INTRODUCTION

less snakes which prey upon the frogs and toads are forced to leave the vicinity, and the results of this are immediately evident in an increase of small rodents in the neighboring fields, much to the disgust of the farmers. Ironically enough, moreover, many authorities hold that once the balance of wildlife is upset in this way, the mosquitoes actually increase. Like a pebble dropped in a still pool, the consequences of one such act extend in all directions, in ever-widening circles.

In the past, the boundaries of our national parks have often been changed solely to benefit such private interests as lumbering. Now, however, plans have been drawn up to set aside wildlife ranges where species native to each region may thrive in successive generations. The lesson of the heath hen has been well learned. In 1907 only seventy-seven of these birds still survived. All were on the island of Martha's Vineyard, and it was believed that special guardianship would save them. For several years their numbers actually increased; then an extremely hard winter and an unusual number of goshawks, aided by a fire and a gale, finished them off. In the future, protected creatures will be kept alive in separate localities, so that a natural catastrophe will not result in the destruction of an entire species.

A comparatively large number of the orders of living things is encountered within the borders of the United States. Of the seventeen living orders of mammals nine make their homes here; twenty of the twenty-six living orders of birds; three of the four orders of reptiles; and two of the three orders of amphibians. A fair proportion of the world's fishes spawn along the American coasts and in the fresh-water lakes and rivers of the United States. This book, then, though limited to American wildlife, may be said to be a representative natural history.

American Wild Life, Illustrated is the fourth of a series of books written by the zoological division of the New York City WPA Writers' Project. It offers in popular style the life histories of American mammals, birds, reptiles, amphibians, and fishes. The present volume is actually a natural history of the chordates; that is, those forms of life which at some stage in their development possess a notochord. The notochord is a rod of elastic tissue dividing the creature into bilaterally symmetrical halves. The vertebrates like man and the higher animals and fishes have notochords, but only in their embryonic stages. Later the notochords are replaced by backbones.

Unless otherwise stated, the dimensions given in the text are

INTRODUCTION

average, not maximum. In the writing of the text, the staff has made use of the latest and most authentic scientific papers and articles; it has had the assistance of the many eminent authorities to whom acknowledgments have been made. In addition, the classic sources of information dealing with the natural history of this country have been used extensively. To the degree that the resulting volume is a readable, informative, and up-to-date work on the natural history of this country—something that has long been needed—the purpose of the undertaking will have been achieved.

NEW YORK CITY WPA WRITERS' PROJECT

MAMMALS

AMERICAN BISON

Mammals

On a sultry summer evening a weary wayfarer was crossing the Black Rock Desert of Nevada. Day was swiftly changing to night, and the silence of the high plateau seemingly magnified the long shadows of the yuccas, which spread over the sand like tapering fingers, while the dancing jets of sun made the straight, endless road seem even more desolate. It was almost dark when he stopped and stretched out on the sandy sagebrush.

For a while he lay there watching the end of the day, and then a shrill piercing call like the bark of a dog drifted in on the soft wind. Three pairs of shining eyes peered from behind a cactus, blinking on and off like traffic signals. The wail grew louder and the eyes looked at him steadily.

Coyotes!

He trembled. His throat went dry. He tried to shout, but no sound came and his lips moved awkwardly. As the eyes came closer and he heard the rasping, short breathing close to his ear, he staggered to his feet and fled down the road. The coyotes bounded silently away.

The fear of animals is deeply rooted, paralyzing the senses, numbing the reasoning power of many a man. Large or small, ferocious or gentle, and without apparent logic or foundation in fact, animals almost invariably represent formidable opponents. In the morning our wretched hiker awoke safe and sound. The curious coyotes had not molested him.

Divorced from fear and prejudice, mammals are perhaps the most interesting, harmless, and lovable of all animals. Separated by the bars of the zoo we have admired their graceful antics, their lonely detachment from the crowds of gaping people that surround them, their bold, magnificent bearing. So diversified that they run the gamut of shapes and sizes, mammals constitute not only the highest form of animal life but also the most widespread and diversified. Over the entire globe there is scarcely a region where they do not eke out an existence. They are, moreover, fairly well represented in the United States and only a few of the most outstanding members are not found here. In every instance, with few minor exceptions, they serve, help, and amuse man. Their reward is slight—an occasional kind gesture to the tamest members of the species, a life of toil for others, and in most instances sudden death from the hunter's blazing gun.

Although reluctant to be classified as one, man is the most advanced of mammals, even though this fact may not always be apparent. Nevertheless, he is kin to such diverse species as the tiny, earth-burrowing mole and the half-ton grizzly bear, as well as the largest of all living beings, the ocean-dwelling whale. Set off from all other living creatures by the fact that their offspring are nourished at the mother's breast, or mammae (from which the term mammal as well as mamma is derived), mammals are warm-blooded and backboned, usually covered with hair, breathe air, and bring their young forth alive.

Scampering, running, leaping, digging, swimming, climbing, parachuting and flying, the separate species have the assistance of their specialized limb development. The forelimbs of the swimming mammals such as the otters and seals are webbed; the flying (usually gliding) species are equipped with skin folds extending from the wrists along the sides of the body to form a parachute.

Such modified and specialized physical structures have played an important part in the survival of all the mammals. Even teeth are adapted to the particular diet of the creature. Thus, gnawing rodents have chisel-shaped incisors, while carnivorous beasts such as the cats and bears are provided with prominent canines, essential in killing and disposing of their prey.

In the United States, human progress has been largely instrumental in the destruction and curtailment of the once populous hordes of mammals. The forests and plains where they once ruled supreme have become man's domain, turned to logging camps and farms; great cities have sprung up on their old stamping grounds. The larger animals suffered the greatest losses from the wholesale depletion wrought by man. Pushing westward to the Oregon Trail and El Dorado, the growing torrent of humans invaded and despoiled their natural sanctuaries. Mammals were killed because they were predators; they were killed for food; they were killed for their skins; they were killed for amusement. The buffalo and deer, which at one time numbered in the millions, are survived only by small decimated bands, existing only because of Government protection. Roaming through some of our national parks, they suggest on a small scale the primeval American scene.

In spite of this slaughter, our language is still replete with expressions which show the affection and even esteem with which humans regard the warm-blooded, backboned beasts which stand nearest to them in the evolutionary scale. The dog is "man's best friend"; the horse, "that noble quadruped."

The utility of animals is most apparent when expressed in terms of domestication of such servants and pets as the horse, cow, dog, and cat. All other creatures which man has been unable to tame and exploit in the same fashion as the sheep, goat, and pig, he tends to regard as enemies, and treats them accordingly. Perhaps it is their inability to crowd up to man's fireside, to share his comforts and hardships, that make the other mammals such maligned and ready victims of the trapper and sportsman.

Whales, Dolphins, and Porpoises

Largest and heaviest of all animals known in the past or present is the fast-swimming sulphur-bottom or blue whale. One specimen measured one hundred and three feet. A ninety-five footer was calculated to weigh no less than forty-seven tons. Although such marine monsters are seldom seen off our coasts, a few individuals have been accidentally run down by ships. Their speed averages twelve miles an hour, although fifty miles an hour has been reported for shore distances.

More than a dozen species of whales and as many related species of the somewhat smaller and faster-moving dolphins and porpoises are found in American waters. The length of these creatures varies from four to one hundred feet.

All cetaceans have a flat, horizontal tail terminating in paired flukes. The tail is their chief means of locomotion, and is a common characteristic of all these sea-dwelling creatures which look like fishes but are really air-breathing mammals. Like other mammals they bring forth their young alive and suckle them with milk. Sometimes the young at birth are twenty feet long. Unlike other mammals they are generally devoid of hair except for a few stray whiskers about their muzzles and the whalebone or baleen which is a modified form of hair possessed by whalebone whales. Cetaceans are found in all parts of the ocean and in many seas, and some of the dolphins even frequent tropical rivers. They never leave the water even to breed.

WHALES

THAR she blows, cries the ship's lookout, sighting a slanting water spout against the horizon. The whaler turns and soon all can see by the flat angle at which the spout rises that they are approaching a school of sperm whales.

Presently the boats are lowered, a harpooner in the bow of each. The small craft set out to attack the eighty-foot monster, which with one flip of its tail could send them all to Davy Jones's locker. The whale's eyes are so placed that it cannot see directly before or behind, and the whalers attempt to utilize these blind spots. The harpoons are thrown and stick fast in the whale's thick

WHALE

HUMPBACK WHALE *(Megaptera nodosa)*. Length: 40 feet. Range: Atlantic and Pacific coasts of North America.
American Museum of Natural History

blubber. Sometimes the leviathan, infuriated by the pain, doubles back and smashes or capsizes the boats, but usually it runs away. Though its cruising speed is no more than three to four miles an hour, it can now race along at twenty-five, pulling several boats after it. The giant mammal may sound to a depth of nearly a mile, and then the whalers must rapidly let out lines to avoid being drawn beneath the surface. At length, however, the hardiest whale grows exhausted, permitting the men to close in and kill it with their lances.

After it has been towed back to the ship, the carcass is cut up. It yields spermaceti, a fine oil contained in the head; ambergris, a substance sometimes found in the intestines of whales and used in perfume making; and blubber, the source of whale oil. During their long voyages seamen carved whalebone ornaments, known collectively as "scrimshaw," which constituted one of the first American folk arts.

But these adventurous scenes are things of the past, alive only in the glamorous literature of the sea. In the days when such methods were employed, whaling was a leading American industry. George Weymouth's *Journal of a Voyage to America* in 1605 described Indians fishing for whales in canoes, using bone harpoons attached to bark ropes and making the kill with arrows. Captain John Smith, in 1614, had a permit from the King of England to fish for whales. From 1715 to 1761 the New England fleet multiplied from six vessels to one hundred and fifty, and scoured every part of the ocean. Yankee whalers had the reputation of catching the largest whales with the smallest ships. In 1833 more than one hundred large whaling vessels put out from Nantucket in quest of oil for lamps and machines, and whalebone (provided by blue whales and finbacks) for corset and camisole stays. In 1850 more than six hundred American vessels sailed the seas in the quest for whales. However, after the middle of the 19th century, whale oil was gradually replaced by petroleum, and spring-steel stays were found preferable to whalebone. Though the industry declined, it did not disappear altogether; but the old sailing vessels were largely replaced by steamers, and harpoons were shot from small cannon. Ambergris is still valued in perfume making; spermaceti can be sold at a low price; and whale-meat meal is not only used for cattle feed but is also canned as a delicacy by the Japanese. Today most whaling is carried on by Scandinavian expeditions, each with a factory ship of as much as 20,000 tons and a fleet of speedy killer boats, which make year-long cruises to the Antarctic and bomb their prey. The United States now has but two of these factory ships, which are equipped with machinery for extracting the marketable products of whales.

The sperm whale, which ranges throughout the Atlantic and Pacific Oceans, is black above and somewhat lighter below. The head is large and blunt like an immense battering ram, and indeed the sperm whale, whose flesh is denser than that of other whales, may ram and sink a wooden ship. Most amazing of all battles of man versus whale was probably that of a certain large sperm whale which attacked the three-masted ship, *Essex*, of Nantucket in 1819.

Some hundreds of miles out in the Pacific due west of the Galapagos, the whale swam full-tilt against the bow of the ship and stove in a hole. As the ship began to fill with water the whale attacked again and with a single hundred-ton blow enlarged the opening and sank the vessel.

Formerly sperm whales moved in schools of a hundred or more, but today they are usually seen in groups of about fifteen. Unlike other whales, sperms have a large throat opening. They hunt for giant squid and octopus on the ocean bottom, often a mile beneath the surface, descending at tremendous speed. Scientists have long sought to explain how they withstood the immense pressure. One theory is that the pressure itself enables them to compress their blubber till it is hard enough to protect them.

The spout, which occurs whenever the beasts rise to the water's surface, is composed of vapor and not of water from an internal fountain, as was once believed; the whale is simply breathing out the air used up during its sojourn under water. Unlike other whales, sperms are polygamous. The bull, which is much larger than the twenty- to thirty-foot cow, collects large harems over which he lords it until a younger, stronger bull defeats him and takes his place. Then the battle-scarred old bull is said to become a "rogue" and wanders off by himself.

When hunted, the bull whale will rarely stay to help his mate, but the cows protect one another and the young. In a playful mood, the bulls may raise thirty feet of tail from the water and bring it down with a splash. They occasionally breach, or jump clear of the water, landing with great noise and force on their side or belly.

Right whales average fifty feet in length, but prize specimens from the Pacific may be seventy-five feet. They feed near shore or close to the surface of deeper water. They are slow of movement and not very violent, though capable of smashing a boat with their flukes. The smooth skin of these whales is dark gray or black, but sometimes seems to take on varying color shades. The end of the snout is adorned with a "bonnet"; this two-foot patch of horny matter is a common resting place for little shellfish known as whale lice. These whales were also hunted for their oil and bone. Their name is said to have originated when a whaler, seeing this species in a group of smaller and less valuable whales, pointed and said, "That's the right whale."

The dark-brown bowhead, or Greenland whale, rarely leaves the Arctic waters, where it finds protection under the ice when attacked. The blubber may be two feet thick to protect it from the intense cold, and the whale of this species yields as much as three hundred barrels of oil more than any other. It is rarely more than sixty-five feet long. The head is one-third the length of the body, and the upper jaw is arched. Inside the immense mouth are hundreds of thin strips of baleen, a horny substance providing the whalebone once so highly prized. This baleen strains out the water from the small crustaceans eaten by the bowhead.

Sulphur-bottoms range throughout the Pacific and Atlantic Oceans. The humpback whale is a heavily built creature, averaging forty feet in length with a thin pectoral fin almost one-third as long as the body. It is black above, marbled with white below, and has twenty-six lengthwise folds on its throat and belly. The lower jaw is longer than the upper. Humpbacks are found alone and in groups along the Atlantic and Pacific coasts.

The adult black or brown common finback is about sixty-five feet long. It has a flat head and narrow body, and like the sulphur-bottom has longitudinal folds on throat and breast. It is very active and often plays near ships, either alone or in small schools, in both the Atlantic and Pacific. Its quick, high spout can be heard for some distance. In the Antarctic the finbacks feed on small animals resembling shrimps, known to the Norwegians as *krill*. The whale simply swims through dense, drifting swarms of these larval creatures, effortlessly swallowing them by the thousands.

The bays and shallow waters near the coast of the North Pacific are the home of the gray whales. They once herded there in great numbers, but are now seldom seen. Females average forty feet in length and males thirty-five. They range in color from light gray to black, and have two longitudinal folds under the throat.

To protect whales from complete extermination, twenty-five nations, including the United States, signed the International Whaling Treaty in 1936. This pact regulates the time, place, and kind of whale hunting.

DOLPHINS AND PORPOISES

THE killer has "the appetite of a hog, the cruelty of a wolf, the courage of a bulldog, and the most terrible jaws afloat." This dolphin, declared Dr. William T. Hornaday, is one of the most fearsome creatures of the sea.

The killer will not hesitate to attack even the largest whale, darting about it with flashing rapidity. As the speed of its onslaught churns the water, it snaps at the whale's fins and flukes until the great beast is exhausted. Sometimes several killers make a concerted attack on a whale, clutch it by its lips, and draw it down into the deep. Shortly afterward they leap to the surface. In their jaws are gory masses of their huge prey's flesh and perhaps even its enormous tongue, which is torn out if the whale's mouth is open.

PORPOISES FEEDING.
W. F. Gerecke, Marine Studios

BOTTLENOSED PORPOISES *(Tursiops truncatus).* Length: 9 feet. Range: Atlantic and Gulf coasts of the United States.
New York Aquarium

The chief weapon of this twenty-foot terror is the set of ten to thirteen large teeth. It was long believed to use its sharp, six-foot dorsal fin for ripping open whale stomachs, but recent investigation indicates that this is untrue.

The killer's appetite is fabulous. The stomach of a dead specimen has been found to contain as many as fourteen seals. It also preys upon small porpoises and horse mackerel.

The Atlantic killer, found in all seas, is black in color with splashes of white. The Pacific killer is similar but lacks a white spot over the eye.

The common dolphin, a relative of the killer, attacks smaller creatures, using its fifty small sharp teeth to destroy large numbers of mackerel. Often these dolphins are seen from the deck of a ship as they leap merrily about the bow. Their oily skins glisten in the sunlight when they leap tirelessly out of the water only to dive curvingly back with a splash. The presence of a group of romping dolphins cheers voyage-weary travelers, for it indicates that land is not far away. They are seen off both our coasts.

The back of this slender, seven-foot dolphin's body is usually black, its belly greenish white. Deep grooves extend from the jaws to the tail. The eyes are framed in heavy black "spectacles," and the professorial look is heightened by a sparse moustache of five to seven hairs on each side of the mouth.

The common dolphin is typical of the approximately twelve species of bottle-nosed, spotted, long-beaked, and striped dolphins inhabiting North American waters. They range in length from six to twelve feet, a few species, such as the blackfish, attaining seventeen feet. On the whole, dolphins and porpoises are almost completely devoid of hair. The sleek bodies of these warm-blooded cetaceans have heavy layers of blubbery fat to protect them from the wintry waters and to cushion them in diving. So similar are dolphins and porpoises that it is sometimes difficult to distinguish the various species; moreover, the names "dolphin" and "porpoise" are used interchangeably.

The blackfish has a misleading name, for it, too, is a mammal, not a fish. It bounds in and out of the waters of the North Atlantic and Pacific Oceans in large groups. Sometimes hundreds of these dolphins visit the coast of New England, running aground on beaches, shoals, and sand bars. Dead, they plague the neighborhood with a foul stench. Consequently, when blackfish are sighted, boys sometimes go out in boats to head them inhospitably toward the open sea. Though large and powerful, the blackfish docilely permit themselves to be turned away. The blackfish, sometimes called pilot whale or ca'ing whale, has the blunt head of a small sperm whale.

The most playful member of the group of dolphins and porpoises is probably the common, or harbor, porpoise, also appropriately known as the herring hog. It gracefully twists and turns in the water, leaps out sometimes fourteen feet, or swims in curves—a sort of rolling gallop—so that its arched back flashes momentarily above the surface. This jet black, four-hundred-pound mammal loves to gambol around a moving vessel. Travelers enjoy watching the porpoise rush to the surface and, as if in greeting to the air, shoot out a jet of vapor which resembles a miniature whale spout. The vapor is formed when the warm air from its lungs strikes the cold air. Before submerging, the porpoise fills up with fresh air, loudly inhaling through a valvular opening in the top of its back. The sound produced has earned it the nickname of snuffling pig. Porpoises, which also "speak" to one another by squeaking through that opening, sleep with closed eyes. Sailors report that they are bad eating, cry like babies when harpooned, but can beat a shark in a fight.

Sea Cows

Manatees are aquatic animals which originally had four limbs. However, their hind limbs gradually evolved into a fleshy paddle. These strange marine mammals, closely related to whales, dolphins, and porpoises, are vegeterians.

Besides the American species, several others are known. They have been observed in the West Indies, on the Amazon, along the west coast of Africa, in the Red Sea, the Indian Ocean, and in the waters of northern Australia.

Steller's sea cow, huge relative of the Florida manatee, was discovered in North Pacific waters early in the eighteenth century and completely exterminated within three decades.

MANATEE

THE quiet surface of the water is broken as the female manatee slowly rises for a few breaths of air. An affectionate mother, she clasps her baby to her breast with one of her two flippers. Her body extends half out of the water to permit the young one in her embrace to inhale the life-giving air.

As the mother returns below, the nostrils are closed. The heavy bones of her body make it easy for her to remain submerged near the bed of a stream.

So sluggish are these dark-skinned, blubbery creatures that mossy plants grow on their backs; it is proverbial that grass doesn't gather on fast-moving things. Luckily, their food supply is at hand. With bovine contentment they munch the long-bladed water grasses and consequently have been nicknamed sea cows.

In appearance, however, the manatees certainly resemble porpoises more than cows. Their length may vary from six to fifteen feet, and their weight from four hundred pounds to a ton. The only visible limbs are the two front flippers. The body is clumsy, ending in a heavy, flattened tail which resembles a rudder turned horizontally. Topping this most unprepossessing figure is a grotesque head adorned with a moustache of bristly hairs. The lips are thick, the upper being cleft in the middle, enabling both halves to move

FLORIDA MANATEE *(Trichechus latirostris)*. Length: 10 feet. Range: "East coast of Florida as far north as Daytona, and sporadically along the Gulf coast; has been reported from Corpus Christi, Texas" (Anthony). Almost extinct.
John G. Shedd Aquarium

independently. Manatees eat by clutching grass between the two parts of the upper lip and drawing the morsel inward.

In spite of their size and ugliness, manatees are harmless animals. They were described by J. S. Kingsley as "apparently monogamous and very affectionate." Caring for her young with true parental solicitude the mother suckles her offspring at the milk glands under her flipper. Parenthood is simple for manatees since only one "calf" a year is born to a pair.

Now that the Seminole tribe is almost gone and Florida laws protect manatees from wanton slaughter, the only enemies of these animals are sharks and representatives of museums. These foes, and such unfavorable weather conditions as the severe cold of the 1939-40 winter, have combined to make them comparatively rare. The Indians used to kill them for hides, oil, and food, their flesh reputedly having a flavor similar to pork, and the hides and oil being useful commodities.

MANATEE

In the limpid streams and shallow, brackish estuaries of southern Florida and the Gulf coast, manatees have been taken by men equipped with nets, harpoons, and other suitable weapons. Although they must breathe air to live, they are such truly aquatic animals that their captors must ship them in boxes half-filled with water and supplied with manatee grass.

In an aquarium a manatee becomes tame enough to raise its head out of the water in mute entreaty for food. It moves with the speed of molasses, lying quietly on the bottom of the pool so long that sightseers either ignore it, or anxiously tell the keeper that "the manatee is dead." At five- or eight-minute intervals it comes to the surface for air. Even when the water is drained from its pool, the manatee will open its nostrils to breathe only at such intervals.

Other members of the order of sirens are believed to have been seen by early Asiatic explorers who, noting the femininity of a manatee nursing her child, brought back the original tales of mermaids. How anyone could "stretch" a clumsy manatee into the incomparable beauty of legendary mermaids will probably remain a mystery.

Toothless Mammals

Scientists first observing the armadillo noted the absence of teeth in the front of its mouth and classified it with the edentates, or toothless animals. Oddly enough, the armadillo has more molars than most mammals, but these are set so far back in the mouth as to be invisible at first glance. It lacks front teeth—both incisors and canines. The teeth it does have lack roots and enamel.

Other members of the order, found in Central and South America, include such oddities as the horse-faced giant anteater and the sloths which hang upside down from branches. Fossil remains of ground sloths as large as elephants and prehistoric armadillos, sixteen feet long, have been unearthed.

ARMADILLO

THROUGH cactus, coarse grass, scrub oak, and tangled brush the active armadillo, dangling its long tail, trots about in search of insects. It frequently stops to poke its pointed snout into holes and, when lucky, draws out a meal of ants on its sticky tongue. So intent is the little armored creature on securing its fill of insects that it may bump up against the legs of a man standing still.

An armadillo kills small snakes by rolling on them and pressing the reptiles against the earth with its armored back. Its jerky motions sandpaper the serpents into a helpless state and, softened, they are ready to be eaten. In spite of its usual diet, the armadillo in captivity enjoys a repast of beaten eggs.

The armadillo is quite harmless and is organized more for self-defence than aggression. When alarmed, it can run with considerable speed, but if cornered will roll up into a tight ball, relying on its pliable segmented shell for protection. Against smaller enemies this protection suffices, but wolves, bobcats, and cougars can split the armadillo's shell with a single stroke of their powerful paws.

At home, however, this small mammal, the size of a house cat, is quite safe. Its lair may consist of a hole in a limestone ledge or a burrow in the ground, depending on the region. These creatures are able to dig into sandy soil with startling rapidity, using the well-

ARMADILLO

developed claws of their forelegs. In regions where armadillos abound, their presence can be detected by the tracks they make to and from their favorite drinking place, for they use the same trails over and over again. Though they are frequently seen in the daytime, they are chiefly nocturnal. At night they like to slosh about muddy banks in search of beetles and other large insects.

The Seminole Indians of Oklahoma and Texas hunted armadillos for their meat and hide with specially trained dogs. The hide was made into baskets by cutting off the animal's legs and stuffing them in its mouth. The tail, which is nearly as long as the rest of the beast, formed the handle. Deer hunters are frequently annoyed by the rustling of armadillos in the brush, which sounds very much like the rustling of deer.

The Texas armadillo differs from other members of the family in that its litters run from four to ten, whereas the latter bear but one or two young at a time.

TEXAS NINE-BANDED ARMADILLO *(Dasypus novemcinctus texanus)*.
Length: 2½ feet. Range: Southern parts of Arizona, New Mexico, Texas, and northern Mexico. Scarce.
New York Zoological Society

This species is almost a yard long; half of its length is taken up by the dark-brown tail, which also has overlapping shell rings. The color of the nine-banded shell is black with faint yellowish markings, and between shell and head there protrudes a pair of large, mulish ears.

Hoofed Mammals

Even-toed or cloven-hoofed mammals, especially domesticated pigs, cattle, sheep, and goats, are familiar as the chief sources of meat, milk, hides, wool, and hair. In countries where camels, reindeer, and water buffaloes are common, they also serve as beasts of burden. But in the United States the wild animals of this order, which were once the legitimate target of hungry and ill-clad Indians, today are fast disappearing under the greedy guns of trophy-hunting and law-breaking "sportsmen" who kill for a thrill. The five-hundred-pound Arctic muskox is an important species not found in the United States. This heavy-horned and long-haired cross between cattle and sheep inhabits parts of Canada and Greenland. An introduced member of this order is the European wild boar. Brought here for hunting purposes, it has been liberated in California, New Hampshire, North Carolina, Tennessee, and Mississippi. In the Southern States it has crossed with the domestic razor-backed hog.

A related suborder of ungulates contains the odd-toed or solid-hoofed mammals. This group is not represented in the United States except for the domestic horse, the ass, and their hybrid offspring, the mule. The wild horses of the West were the descendants of animals that originally escaped from the baggage trains of early Spanish explorers.

Hoofed mammals generally feed on herbs, grasses, and other vegetation. The deer, oxen, and sheep are ruminants and chew the cud. The two upper compartments of their four-chambered stomachs serve only as a temporary food depository when the creatures are busy grazing or running from danger. Later the food is regurgitated, the cud is chewed, and finally swallowed. It then passes into the third and fourth compartments of the stomach where digestion is completed.

MOUNTAIN SHEEP

HIGH up in the rugged Sierras, sometimes at an altitude of 12,000 feet, the mountain sheep graze and gambol about, leaping and bounding with sure-footed ease over their mountain domain. Suddenly a sentry catches the scent of some enemy—a cougar, wolf, lynx, or perhaps a man—and emits a shrill snort. Instantly the entire herd of grayish brown creatures is off on the

ROCKY MOUNTAIN SHEEP *(Ovis cervina)*. Length: 5 feet. Range: High mountainous sections of the West. Endangered and not receiving adequate protection, although the Pittman-Robertson Act, sponsored by the National Wildlife Federation, may save the species.
New York Zoological Society

gallop, seeking out dizzy trails that few enemies can follow. Often great chasms interrupt their route, but the sheep bound across without a moment's hesitation.

Many homespun naturalists, seeing these headlong leaps into space, believe the sheep land on their heads, permitting the immense dark-brown horns to cushion the blow. This is not the case. Old rams may weigh upward of three hundred pounds, and it can easily be seen that their horns, which may curve back and outward to nearly fifty inches, could scarcely bear the impact. The lambs, moreover, possess no horns. Actually the sheep break their fall by landing on ledges outflung from the mountainside, striking these natural stairs with their spongy black hoofs. In this way they may descend an entire mountain slope at speeds which appear to be precipitous and certainly breath-taking.

The bighorn bands are on the move most of the year, following their food which consists of twigs, plants, shrubs, and grasses. Even in the intensely cold Rocky Mountain winter, when the jagged slopes are covered with snow, these wild but peaceable animals manage to find food. Sometimes they are forced to paw down through deep drifts of snow in search of grass. With their heavy coats of coarse, stiff hair, they are undismayed by drifts which may reach to their shoulders. Often the sheep will rest in the snow for hours but the flakes beneath them do not melt as the tightly matted hair effectively prevents any loss of body heat. In the spring they will often roam deep down into the valleys, but never for long. They feel safer on their mountain crags.

With the coming of the breeding season, an old ram, presiding over a band of ewes and lambs, discreetly drives the young rams off by themselves. This is common among polygamous animals.

In the spring the ewe, which is smaller than the ram, gives birth to one or two young. These are fully as agile and adventurous as

EWE AND LAMBS OF ROCKY MOUNTAIN SHEEP.
Natasha Smith

their elders, indulging at once in the most difficult ovine maneuvers. Fuzzy fur almost fills the inside of their ears and serves as an ear muff when cold winds blow.

Eleven species and subspecies of mountain sheep are known to inhabit the mountainous sections of western North America from Mexico to the Arctic Circle. Of the seven species native to the United States, two are extinct, while the remainder here and in Mexico, Canada, and Alaska are facing extinction. The color of these sheep varies from pure white to almost black.

As the years go by these creatures are driven higher and higher into the more inaccessible mountain regions. Here they are pursued only by intrepid hunters in an eternal search for heads and horns, and occasionally by the golden eagle, which likes to feast on baby lambs. Keen sentries can detect enemies three to five miles away.

A big-game inventory compiled by the U. S. Biological Survey showed that in 1938 less than five thousand Rocky Mountain bighorn sheep were left. These were for the most part evenly distributed in the national forests of Wyoming, Colorado, and Idaho. In the State of Washington, where they were once common, only ten were counted. The desert subspecies have fared even worse. A total of seven thousand was revealed by a survey conducted in Arizona, California, Nevada, New Mexico, Texas, and Utah.

MOUNTAIN GOAT

THE mountain goat rushes around perilous crags where most men would fear to tread. All the year around, this bewhiskered mountaineer stays up on the highest peaks, scorning the furies of the severest winters. It wears a shaggy white coat of wool, heavy enough to keep out the piercingly cold blasts which sweep the snow-covered heights. Owen Wister described its stamping grounds as "the narrow top of the crumbling slate where the pines were scarce and stunted and twisted themselves into corkscrews so they might grip the ground against the tearing force of the storms."

The sure-footed mountain goat is equipped with sturdy legs and rubbery hoofs which have sharp rims, valuable mountaineering ap-

MOUNTAIN GOAT

ROCKY MOUNTAIN GOATS *(Oreamnos americanus).* Length: 5 feet. Range: Rocky Mountains and coastal ranges of the West. Rare and restricted in range.
Academy of Natural Sciences of Philadelphia

purtenances in maintaining a foothold. It scrambles up the steep, rough slopes with agility and strength, but in somewhat clumsy fashion as compared with the graceful movements of the mountain sheep which shares its habitat.

It treats the top of the world as its castle. Let danger threaten or uncertainty prevail, and this creature instinctively flees upward, higher and higher, to the majestic solitude of almost vertical peaks. Perhaps this is because its enemies have always approached it from below. Consequently, those who regard the shooting of a mountain goat as sport have been advised to approach it from above. The naive curiosity of the mountain goat is helpful to these sportsmen, since it may pause long enough on sighting a man to provide an easy target, a habit which has earned it a reputation for stupidity. Should it escape in time, though, the two-hundred-and-fifty-pound animal can climb far enough in ten minutes to give the hunter a good two-hour chase before overtaking it.

While bears hibernate and mountain sheep seek the shelter of warmer valleys, the mountain goat ambles about its high range, feeding on the mossy lichens which grow over the rocks. Some observers doubt that it eats grass at all, one of the reasons why other animals must descend the mountains in the winter. In captivity it feeds on oats, hay, and sliced carrots.

It presents a striking picture, a study in black and white, when seen standing attentively on a jutting rock or overhanging cliff. Its white body is trimmed with black hoofs and black, outwardly curving, ten-inch horns.

Only in the pairing season, around November, do mountain goats give up their solitary existence. One to two kids are born the following spring and remain for a year with their parents, both of whom are bearded and horned. Except for such a family group—father, mother, and one or two young—no flocks are seen. The males grow to a larger size than the females.

Despite its appearance and name, the mountain goat is not a goat but an antelope, related to the chamois of the Alps and the serow of the Himalayas. Four species and subspecies inhabit the Rocky Mountains and Cascade Range of western North America from Alaska to Idaho and Montana. About thirteen thousand individuals were counted in 1937, two thousand more than had been recorded in a census for 1922. They were fairly evenly distributed in Idaho, Montana, and Washington.

In recent years the only commercial value of these inoffensive creatures has been their horned heads which are used as wall decorations. The Indians of the Northwest wove cloth from the mountain goat's hair, and tanned its hide for rugs.

BISON

WHEN Cortez came to Mexico in the early part of the sixteenth century, he visited the zoo of Montezuma, the Aztec emperor, and there saw an animal which he described as "a rare Mexican bull with a hump like a camel's and hair like a lion's." This was the bison, or buffalo. It is estimated that in those days there

BISON

were approximately fifty million of these "rare Mexican bulls" roaming the plains of North America.

The male bison achieves a weight of two thousand pounds or more; the female weighs about half as much. Both sexes are equipped with horns, which are never shed. The young beast's horns are straight, assuming a curvature with advancing years. The horns are used by the bulls in fighting among themselves for leadership in the herd, and in goring their enemies. Bisons fighting one another employ a wrestling technique that rarely results in fatalities. Other animals, however, are gored by a powerful downward thrust, then thrown high as the bison raises its massive head.

Though the bison's black or brown hair is long, a woolly down at the base gives it a shaggy, matted appearance. The immense head, familiar to every American from its likeness on buffalo nickels, is adorned with a huge, shaggy beard.

AMERICAN BISON BULL *(Bison bison)*. Length: 9 feet. Range: Restricted to game refuges, zoological parks, Indian reservations, etc. Four thousand eight hundred alive in the United States in 1939 only as the result of an intensive conservation campaign.

Academy of Natural Sciences of Philadelphia

Before the arrival of the white man, the bison was a leading source of food, weapons, clothing, and even shelter for the Indians, many of whom wore buffalo robes and lived in tepees made of buffalo skins. The presence of this free food supply greatly facilitated the white man's advance across the continent. As civilization pressed westward, the great herds began to disappear from their grazing grounds. By the early part of the nineteenth century those east of the Mississippi had been wiped out as a result of the spread of agriculture and the heavy demand for buffalo skins. The completion of the Union Pacific Railroad divided the western herd into a northern and southern half. The southern herd was totally exterminated, and by 1895 only eight hundred of the northern herd remained.

With the bison facing extinction, the fight for conservation of this great American mammal began. Early efforts to save the bison were opposed by "practical-minded statesmen," who maintained that the disappearance of the buffalo would make it easier to pacify the Plains Indians, and by the sheep and cattle herders who begrudged them the necessary grazing lands. The Government, however, finally established a few protected herds, largely with the help of the New York Zoological Society and the American Bison Society. Today the number of bison in the United States has increased from eight hundred to about five thousand, and it appears that the animal has been saved for posterity. Occasionally bison have been crossed with domestic cattle. The resulting hybrid, called cattalo, has a heavy buffalolike hide and meat like beef cattle.

In their wild days, bison were migratory in the sense that in winter they would move three or four hundred miles south in search of better grazing and would return north in the spring. Usually the herd moved in single file, following a leader. In these movements the herds often fused into an army of millions. The buffalo trails thus formed invariably pursued the shortest and easiest route, so that engineers frequently used them as a guide in constructing the early railroads. And the condition of the buffalo grass of the prairies indicated to hunters the presence of the great herds.

BISON

In their travels large numbers of bison fell victims of prairie fires, quicksands, and thin ice on rivers. Danger often caused immense herds to stampede, and the animals trampled one another or anything that stood in their path. If the leaders tried to stop before a quicksand or other hazard, the momentum of the herd driving on behind frequently knocked them down to provide a living bridge for the remainder. "The roaring and rushing sound of one of these vast herds crossing a river, may sometimes in a still night be heard for miles," wrote Washington Irving.

Buffalo hunting was a dangerous sport since the bison often stampeded in the direction of the hunter. An experienced hunter would pick off the leader of the herd. Leaderless, the creatures would stand still for a while, not knowing what to do, until a new leader stepped out of the ranks. The hunter would then pick off the new leader, and so on down the line.

ALBINO BISON. A white bison bull is rarer than the sacred white elephant of Siam and was held sacred by the Plains Indians. If they found one in a buffalo herd they were hunting they would abandon the slaughter.

Ralph De Sola (NZP)

A big buffalo, usually a heavy plodding creature, when pursued can tire out three sets of horses and run nearly forty miles in a single day. Its huge heart and lungs seem to provide it with remarkable endurance.

In summer, when bison shed, they are plagued by mosquitoes, ticks, and prickly grasses. Consequently they are forever scratching against trees and boulders and wallowing in the mud. These habits have had a marked effect on the topography of the West. The buffalo wallow became a deep, smooth saucer in the earth, while countless rocks and boulders were worn smooth by the scratching of large herds. Trees in the buffaloes' path were killed by having their bark worn off, and the first telegraph poles erected were knocked down by the weight of the itching beasts.

In the mating season the males and females live together, but in the fall the sexes divide for a time into separate herds. The young are light brown or yellow in color, assuming the dark brown of the adult in their second year. The buffalo is a solicitous parent. When danger threatens, the males form a ring with lowered heads to guard against wolves and other aggressors.

Today but one of the three American species is alive. The plains bison described exists only in game reserves, zoological parks, and a few private herds. The wood bison was known from a small herd dwelling in the Mackenzie River section of Canada, where unfortunately it had hybridized with the plains bison. At the opening of World War II this herd, numbering three thousand head, was killed off as "a war measure." The eastern bison, extinct since 1800, is said to have been black and humpless.

The sole living relative of the American bison is the nearly extinct European bison or wisent.

PRONGHORN ANTELOPE

FLEETEST of American quadrupeds, the pronghorn antelope rarely declines a challenge to race. Uttering a shrill whistle and flashing its white rump patch, it sets out in pursuit of any fast-moving object. Despite its slender, delicate build, the antelope, eve·

when painfully wounded, can outdistance most other land animals. Even a speeding train or auto may arouse its competitive zeal, and one antelope kept pace with a motorcycle traveling forty miles an hour and then, with a triumphant burst of speed, swept across its competitor's path. Another was clocked at sixty miles an hour.

The pronghorn can see moving objects with ease, and its hearing is unusually sharp. It makes little attempt at concealment, relying on its swiftness and its ability to see an enemy first. Moreover, when the animal is frightened or fighting, the white hairs on its rump stand erect in rosette-shaped patches that serve as indentification marks and help night-traveling herds to keep formation.

In years past millions of antelopes inhabited the Great Plains of the West, providing a ready source of food for the Indians who hunted them by various stratagems designed to offset the antelopes' speed. One method was to erect a three-foot fence around a herd. Unaccustomed to such obstacles, the antelope was unable to hurdle the barrier. Then the braves would enter the enclosure and take turns in chasing the beasts. When the pronghorns were exhausted, the squaws went in with clubs to mop up.

As white men began to hunt with guns and erected cattle enclosures on the plains, the vast pronghorn herds were driven nearly to extinction. Many of the survivors fell prey to a cattle disease called fossy-jaw. However, an odor given off by certain skin glands served to protect the antelopes from the flies and mosquitoes that harassed the cattle.

So accustomed were these beasts to the freedom of the plains that when fences were built along the railroads thousands of antelopes piled up against them and crushed each other to death, or leaped through the wires to destruction under the wheels of the locomotives. The descendants of these old-timers, however, have acquired the knack of jumping out of danger. They can clear a five-foot fence with ease, and their broad-jumping record is about twenty-seven feet.

Pronghorns eat sagebrush in winter when the snow covers the grass upon which they subsist during the rest of the year. In severe weather they may even enter farm lands in search of forage.

PRONGHORN ANTELOPE *(Antilocapra americana)*. Length: 4½ feet. Range: Plains and plateaus in the Rocky Mountain area. Owing to the efforts of conservation agencies this species, once threatened with extinction, is now on the increase.
Academy of Natural Sciences of Philadelphia

The hunting of pronghorns was facilitated by their inordinate curiosity. If a man concealed himself they would come to examine a cloth waved at the end of his rifle. Another weakness in their defence was their habit of running in a circle. Even if the hunter cut across the circle to intercept it, the pronghorn continued its route. It seemed to feel that safety lay only in preventing its enemy from crossing in front of it.

At the dawn of the twentieth century only a few thousands were left of these venerable and peculiarly American mammals which can trace their family history to the Glacial Epoch. Today the number of pronghorns, which are the only true antelopes in North America, is somewhat greater as a result of conservation laws. In 1937 one hundred and thirty thousand remained alive.

The branched horns, twelve inches long in the male and barely noticeable in the female, are hollow for half their length. They are shed annually. There is no analogy between the casting and regrowth of this horny sheath and the casting and regrowth of deer antlers in which the bone itself is shed and redeveloped. The pronghorn is the only horned animal which sheds annually, though this is a common feature of antlered creatures. A tuft of hair grows at the base of the antelope's horn and is drawn upward as the horn grows.

In May or early June the female gives birth to two or three fawns. For the first two days the mother conceals them behind rocks, or clumps of grass or cactus. By that time the fawns are swift runners, and after a month they can equal the speed of their parents. Stories are told of does killing coyotes and wolves with their sharp hoofs to defend their fawns.

CARIBOU

HEARING a shot, the caribou or reindeer stands motionless and attentive. This hesitation permits the hunter to take aim and fire again. Only then do the great dark-brown creatures dash away, leaving behind their killed and wounded. Able to run for long distances without rest, even in jagged mountainous terrain, the sure-footed caribou soon leave their pursuers far behind.

Out of danger, they resume their calm, leisurely search for moss. In this pursuit they cover wide areas, for the mountains are poor providers. In stormy weather they descend to the shelter of timbered valleys, but return to the highlands at the first threat of danger from hunters.

The full grown male caribou measures six feet in length and is four feet high at the shoulders. His many-pointed antlers may spread as wide as five feet. The females are smaller than the males and their antlers far less impressive, although they are the only antlered female deer in North America. The buttocks and belly are white in both sexes; the black legs are adorned with a white ring above the hoofs.

The caribou's chief enemies are bears, wolves, and deer bot flies. The swift creature can usually outdistance the bear, and often the wolf, if it receives sufficient warning; but no animal can escape the bot fly. These noxious insects sting through the mammal's hide to deposit their eggs. The developing maggots then feed and grow in the skin, causing intense suffering and sometimes even death.

In the fall all functions including eating are subordinated to courtship. Using their antlers as weapons, the huge males, weighing from two or three hundred pounds, engage in furious battles for possession of the does. By November, when the mating season is over, they are scarred and emaciated.

In the spring the females climb high in the mountains to give birth to their young. Less concerned with the responsibilities of parenthood, the males wait until the snow has melted before climbing to join the family. In the mountain peaks they find the fawns playfully active, following the mother about as she grazes. Unlike the deer, the cow caribou does not hide her young from danger since they are better able to protect themselves.

BARREN GROUND CARIBOU *(Rangifer arcticus)*. Length: 6 feet. Range: Barren Ground region of Arctic America. Only sixteen examples of our native species, the woodland caribou *(Rangifer caribou)*, were alive in 1939. These were on reserves in Minnesota.

Academy of Natural Sciences of Philadelphia

The large mountain caribou, of which there are four species, has been practically exterminated in the United States. Some authorities believe the species to be extinct, although in 1936 one or two herds were reported inhabiting isolated regions of Montana, Idaho, and northern Minnesota. In British Columbia protective legislation has caused the herds once again to thrive; similar legislation lately enacted in the United States may achieve beneficial results.

The woodland caribou, a closely related species, was once abundant in the Northeastern States, but is now extinct in that part of its range. In 1938 a wild-animal census showed that sixteen were known to be alive in Minnesota. This caribou and two other species are more plentiful in northern Canada and Newfoundland. Another relative is the somewhat smaller reindeer—a European animal famous for its legendary role of transporting Santa Claus. Of the eight related species in North America, all are outside the United States. These lightly antlered barren ground caribou are dwellers of the Arctic wastes of Alaska, Canada, and Labrador.

MOOSE

IN SEPTEMBER the northern forest resounds with the bull moose's mating roar which can be heard three miles away. Standing majestically on its long legs and measuring as high as seven feet at the shoulder, the moose during this period is dangerous both to humans and to other males of his own species. When its bellow is answered by a cow moose it rushes noisily through brush and timber to join its future mate. Often, while the seemingly indifferent cow moose, which has no antlers, looks on, the males engage in savage combat for her possession.

The battle begins casually as the shaggy, purplish-gray beasts square off like boxers in a prize ring. Their weapons are their heavy, many-pointed antlers, which may measure more than six feet from tip to tip and, together with the skull, weigh nearly one hundred pounds. The back neck-hair rises in anger. The adversaries spring upon each other suddenly, and the impact is so violent that the moose, weighing twelve to fifteen hundred pounds each, are thrown backward. The advantage is gained only when one combatant smashes the other around to a sideward position. It is then that the winner drives his antlers into his opponent's unprotected ribs or flanks, piercing the lungs, heart, or other vital organs.

COW MOOSE.
Natasha Smith

Rangers, attacked by angry moose, have been forced to climb trees and sometimes remain aloft for hours. In a peaceful mood, however, the moose, largest American game animal, browses through the forest, grazing on soft twigs of willow, birch, spruce, and alders, moving so quietly that hunters are able to ascertain its whereabouts only by imitating the call of a female. The combination of unusually long legs, short neck, and deep chest make it necessary for the beast to get down on its knees to reach the low-lying mosses and lichens. The upper lip of the moose is about three inches long and is moved back and forth at will, thus conveying food to the mouth. In summer the moose is often seen sloshing about the margins of

MOOSE

Maine lakes, frequently thrusting its head beneath the water's surface in search of waterlilies and other aquatic plants.

In May or June the cow moose, smaller than the male, seeks a quiet and isolated spot, and here gives birth to one or two calves,

BULL MOOSE *(Alces americana)*. Length: 8 feet. Range: Northern United States and Canada. "Decreasing under inadequate protection," writes Dr. Robert Cushman Murphy, President of the National Association of Audubon Societies.
American Museum of Natural History

which stand about thirty-two inches high. They are protected and fed by the cow until the second summer, when they measure approximately five feet at the shoulder.

The bear, the cougar, the timber wolf, and man are the moose's enemies. In the winter moose herds trample the snow to make a yard in which they find greater freedom of movement in defending themselves from attack.

Alaskan Indians kill moose for leather and food, but for the most part the great mammal is hunted for sport. Moose heads—particularly those with an unusual antler spread—are a favorite ornament for hunting lodges. A record set of antlers has thirty-four points and a spread of seventy-eight inches. Hunters use a birchbark horn to imitate the call of the cow moose, though there is some disagreement as to the power of this device to lure the animals.

In the United States the species seems well on its way to extinction owing to inadequate conservation laws. A few moose are still found in Wyoming and northern Minnesota, but they are somewhat more abundant in Maine. Lower Canada harbors a considerable number, while the Alaskan moose, a larger variety, is quite numerous in the Kenai Peninsula and Cook Inlet regions. The total number of moose found within the United States in 1939 was only sixteen thousand.

WAPITI

IN THE fall the male wapiti, or "elk," sets out to assemble a harem. He does not bellow raucously like the moose, but utters a melodious birdlike call. Once the harem has been conquered or cajoled, the bull rules over it with an iron hand, constantly challenging any males who may dispute his claim. The bulls often engage in battle at this season, continuing until one is clearly victorious. Antlers locked in viselike grip, blinded with fighting fury, they may meet death by falling from cliffs, or even from starvation.

During the winter the families unite into a single herd to seek pasture in the lowlands. But with the coming of spring the bulls and much smaller cows separate. At this time the males shed their antlers, and growing new ones is at first such a drain on their energies as to leave them weak and almost helpless. The new antlers first appear as knobby stubs, soft and full of blood. They are so sensitive that the bull is in constant fear of hurting them. By the approach of the new mating season, the antlers are full grown, bearing from five to seven points.

The cow wapiti usually bears one spotted calf, sometimes two, but rarely three. She is very attentive to her young, teaching them to lie motionless at the approach of danger, and even to stop breathing for a few moments. The mother's call to her young resembles the bark of a dog.

WAPITI

Wapitis never graze at night. When attacked, the herd will scatter in all directions. It is most difficult to drive a herd of wapitis to any given destination because, quite cleverly, they show a marked inclination to move in the direction opposite the one in which they are being chased.

In small, compact herds, these tawny brown animals stray about the more inaccessible regions of the Rocky Mountains, chiefly within the confines of our national parks. The male's antlers, which may attain a spread of five feet, are lighter and slenderer than those of the moose.

The graceful wapiti has an exceedingly small head and in three of its salient features resembles three distinct animals; it has the ears of a mule, the rolling gait of a camel, and a cowlike body. A full-grown male stands five feet at the shoulder. Its strikingly slender but strong legs support a six-hundred-pound body. A large yellowish patch invariably adorns the rump. Long coarse hairs on

WAPITI or ELK *(Cervus canadensis)*. Length: 8 feet. Range: Western United States and Canada. Increasing where protected.
New York Zoological Society

the neck form a dark shaggy mane. The underparts, head, and chest are dark brown in color.

Formerly the wapiti was plentiful in the eastern United States but was quickly wiped out by the farmer's guns and fences. Even the western wapiti was facing extinction at the hands of hunters and sheep herders until the founding of the national parks, since game never stays in country grazed by sheep. It is a hardy, prolific animal when protected. Protected herds have sometimes grown so large that some of the animals stray into private lands in search of pasturage and are there shot by hunters. Of the five North American species, four are in the United States and one in Canada.

Wapitis are hunted for their delicious meat; for their hide which provides a soft, durable elkskin for shoes and other articles; and for the males' large canine teeth, which are highly prized as trophies by members of the Benevolent and Protective Order of Elks, who have made the wapiti famous as an "elk," although it is not to be confused with the European elk, an Old World moose.

There has been occasional talk of breeding the wapiti commercially, but thus far legal restrictions have obstructed any such development. About 165,000 specimens inhabit the United States today. Many of these are included in the big herds of Yellowstone National Park. They suffer for lack of adequate winter grazing land in the cattle-filled and fenced-off lowland areas, however.

DEER

THE white-tailed, or Virginia, deer prances through the brush with a springy, exuberant step. It begins to gallop by alternating three or four graceful bounds with a leap high into the air. This pace has the beauty of a dance, for the deer's crest of antlers is proudly held high and the bushy white tail is erect, waving gaily and conspicuously.

Unfortunately, it provides an excellent target and many a carefree deer's gallop has been stopped by a bullet. But this most hunted of American big-game animals needs only to hear the crackling of a twig or a rustle in the underbrush to know that the safest place is elsewhere. When it becomes frightened it speeds away, its lithe body zipping along as fast as its legs can carry it, often at fifty miles per hour on short spurts.

This species, most widespread of the family, inhabits wooded glades and open country from the Atlantic seaboard to the Great Plains, and from the region south of the Great Lakes to the Gulf of Mexico. It usually stays outside dense forests, preferring to roam about in bushy glades with enough timber near-by to serve as a sanctuary from wolves and other enemies. It is interesting to note in this connection that the movements of deer in winter largely determine the whereabouts of wolves which find the deer a ready source of food.

VIRGINIA DEER *(Odocoileus virginianus).* Length: 5 feet. Range: Eastern United States. Most hunted big-game animal in the United States.
Ralph De Sola (AMNH)

In some regions it lives in the same surroundings the year around; in others, such as the Adirondacks, it stays near a stream or lake during the summer months and returns to the wooded highlands in the fall. The deer consumes a vegetarian diet of shrubs, grasses, and nuts.

Although protective laws have done much to end the wanton extermination of these shy animals, there are now comparatively few left. Where millions once roamed there are now hundreds. And many of these are preserved only to supply targets for men who wish to shoot the country's celebrated game animal during the hunting season.

When the early pioneers blazed the white man's way through the uncharted forests, the white-tailed deer was not a thing of sport but at times the difference between life and death. Clad in buckskin to ward off the winter's cold, these hardy woodsmen frequently dined upon venison. They were, however, merely following the lead of the Indians who for centuries had feasted upon deer, worn buckskin clothes and moccasins, and fashioned antlers into ornaments.

The female white-tailed deer gives birth to a brood of one to three fawns. As soon as the young are born, the mother hides them from danger for a period of several months, to save them from such enemies as the wolf, cougar, and lynx.

Young deer have white spots on their reddish-brown bodies which vanish after the first five months. By the time it is fully

FAWN OF MULE DEER.
R. Nelson

DEER

BUCK MULE DEER *(Odocoileus hemionus).* Length: 5 feet. Range: Western North America. Effective wildlife management has caused this species to increase in recent years.
J. W. Jackson

grown the male deer will be five feet long, three feet tall at the shoulder, and weigh more than two hundred pounds. Females, devoid of antlers, are built somewhat more delicately, having smaller measurements.

There are eight closely related species of white-tailed deer, whose appearance and habits are rather similar. The species have different mating times, however, depending upon the locality; in the South mating occurs in early summer and the fawns are born in January, while in the North mating is in the fall and the young are born at the close of spring.

Among the barren flatlands, deep gulches, and craggy peaks of the West, ranges a larger member of the family, the mule deer. Also known, incorrectly, as the black-tailed deer, it has a pair of sensitive ears resembling those of the mule. In some parts of the Rockies both species inhabit the same locality.

The antlers of the mule deer, of which there are four species, are pronged while those of the white-tailed are single and undivided. Another distinction is discernible to hunters; when the mule deer flees, its tail hangs while that of the white-tailed variety is flaunted.

DEATH STRUGGLE.
Frank Pagan

The mule deer has sturdier legs, and when it runs makes a series of stiff-legged leaps, landing on all four feet simultaneously. In spite of this seemingly awkward gait, it has both speed and endurance.

Members of the Lewis and Clark expedition first observed this animal on the Missouri River in 1804. They named it the black-tailed deer because of the black patch on its tail. However, a year later the expedition came upon what is known as the true black-tailed deer on the Columbia River. Five species of black-tailed deer are known to range from New Mexico to Alaska.

The U. S. Biological Survey's big-game inventory for 1939 revealed that the most common species of deer was the white-tailed, represented by about seven million individuals—one third of these in Michigan. The mule deer followed with one million two hundred thousand members, while its related subspecies, the Columbian black-tailed deer, had a population of only two hundred thousand.

PECCARY

CARRYING its plump body swiftly on its strong, spindly legs, the collared peccary forages for its food throughout the sun-baked terrain of the Southwest. Untroubled by a fastidious appetite, it seizes upon insects and roots, fruits and worms, toads and nuts, eating all and sundry with apparently equal relish. When it comes to food, the peccary eats like a pig, a habit doubtless resulting from its membership in the swine family.

The peccary is also known as the musk hog because it has a gland under the skin of its rump which emits an evil-smelling musky substance when the animal is angry. Since these creatures roam in herds of eight to thirty, the result of their combined anger would make a skunk seem like a pleasant playmate.

The odor it emits is somewhat of a protective device. But more dangerous weapons are the sharp tusks almost completely concealed when the peccary closes its elongated snout.

To some Texans hunting peccaries furnishes an equivalent of the thrill of the fox hunt. Mounted on horseback, and with a pack of dogs to catch the scent of their quarry, the hunters may be led a merry chase. The pursued animal, however, does not fall into the spirit of the game. Anxious to avoid trouble, it usually tries to give the dogs the slip by dashing into a convenient crevice. It will fight when cornered, using its sharp tusks to advantage. When the men approach, they must be wary that the tusks do not rip the tendons of their horses' legs.

Sometimes the tables are turned, and a man becomes the quarry of the peccaries. If he wounds or kills a peccary, he learns that the band of porcine creatures treats an injury to one as an injury to all. The whole pack may rush him and then, it is reliably reported, the safest place for the man is up a tree. One camper told of being treed by a pack of two hundred peccaries for almost twenty-four hours

COLLARED PECCARY *(Pecari angulatus).* Length: 3 feet. Range: Southwestern Texas, southeastern New Mexico, southern Arizona, and northern Mexico.
New York Zoological Society

after he had shot one; they would not leave, although before running out of ammunition he had killed two dozen.

It would be an injustice to describe the peccary as an aggressive, bloodthirsty animal. On the contrary, it is shy and cautious, preferring flight to fight. It has been made wary by encroaching civilization which has forced it to take refuge in the wilder regions. About forty thousand were alive in 1937.

The peccary's range extends to Central and South America. In the United States it inhabits the forests of Arkansas, the sandy wastelands of New Mexico, the Texas chapparal, and Arizona's cactus regions, accepting perhaps philosophically any terrain in the colorful Southwest where it may dwell in peace.

The flesh of the peccary is eaten in some sections. It is considered a pleasing dish with a flavor close to that of pork. But it can be eaten only if the musk gland is removed as soon as the animal is killed, or the malodorous substance will make the meat unpalatable.

PECCARY

When captured young, the peccary can be made an agreeable pet. Two of them caught by Papago Indians were kept by a woman in Arizona. They were usually gentle and affectionate unless teased or hurt.

The female peccary gives birth to one shoat a year; twins are uncommon. When born, the offspring is a yellowish gray. As it grows older, the color becomes a dark gray except for the light colored collar at the end of the neck.

Fully grown, it weighs about forty pounds, attaining a length of three feet and a height of two and a half feet.

Rodents

The rodents include hares and rabbits; pikas; porcupines; jumping mice; mountain beavers; voles; lemmings, lemming mice; red-backed mice, meadow mice, and muskrats; grasshopper mice, harvest mice, white-footed mice, rice rats, cotton rats, and wood rats; beavers; pocket rats and pocket mice; pocket gophers, woodchucks, ground squirrels, prairie-dogs, chipmunks, tree squirrels, and flying squirrels. This list represents only a mere outline of the varied array of rodent families and species in the United States. Such a vast assemblage is not strange when one considers that rodents include all the gnawing animals, about fifty percent of the total number of species of mammals.

Although the rodents differ from one another in form and function, they may be distinguished from other animals in that they possess four large, chisel-shaped incisor teeth in the front of their mouths. Behind these is a gap, filled by skin flaps, which form cheek pouches for temporarily storing food and preventing indigestible gnawed fragments from passing beyond the grinding cheek teeth and catching in the throat. The chisel-shaped eye teeth are covered with a thick enamel coating and constantly sharpen themselves against one another, the upper set against the lower. In order to prevent loss through wear, the roots are continuous and send forth new tooth structure as required.

Divided into two suborders, the double-toothed rodents (hares, rabbits, and pikas) and the single-toothed rodents (all others such as squirrels, porcupines, beavers, etc.), this interesting group is unfortunately best known to man in the form of domestic rats and mice. Introduced to these shores from Europe in the eighteenth century, these pests have driven out native and less destructive mice and rats in a number of localities. They have been responsible for the spread of disease, and caused untold and unreckoned damage to homes, crops, and food materials. It is estimated that in the United States there is one rat for every person.

Rabbits are almost as familiar to man, and without the justification which there is for the destruction of rats and mice, have suffered as relentless a persecution.

They were spread out in a huge circle over the alkali flats, and were gradually converging on a wire enclosure. Most of them were older men, armed with heavy clubs, but here and there was a youngster who toddled in his elder's footsteps. They advanced slowly and cautiously as if afraid to make any unnecessary noise, and all had their eyes fixed on the sagebrush no more than thirty feet distant. There must have been about two hundred men in the line, farmers and hunters, and there was tenseness in their actions as they gripped their clubs, eager for excitement.

Then it all started. Rabbits were trapped in the enclosure. Thousands of terrified little animals ran wildly in all directions and tried to hide beneath each other's bodies. But the men were swinging their clubs, bringing them down like axes and each blow found its mark, bludgeoning the skull of a rabbit. The children were supposedly not allowed in the death ring, but the few who managed to get by wielded their clubs enthusiastically but inaccurately and only succeeded in cracking the rabbits' skulls, and the half-killed animals screamed in agony until the plateau was trembling with their ghastly, pitiful cries. In the barbaric excitement many mangled bodies were forgotten and left to writhe and squirm and die a slow torturous death. That went on all afternoon. By the end of the day the ground was strewn with thousands of dead and maimed bodies. In the market these carcasses brought in five cents apiece.

This is no fictitious horror tale. It happened in Colorado in 1939, and was graphically reported in *Life*.

Relatively few rabbits, however, are killed for their furs and meat. The greatest number is exterminated for a multitude of reasons which include their diseased conditions, voracious appetites, and their depredations on farm crops.

Fortunately the rabbit is adequately protected against the ravages of man, otherwise it would have been exterminated long ago. Fleet of foot and an excellent high jumper, the rabbit can outdistance most dogs and hunters; it is able to withstand cold with an ease illustrative of its northern origin. But the most important factor in the preservation of the species is its remarkable aptitude for speedy reproduction, breeding several times a year and producing large litters.

JACK RABBIT

AS a group the jack rabbits or hares exemplify the development of speed and jumping ability and hardiness. They can run at the rate of forty miles an hour, so only greyhounds can pace them, and have been known to clear a seven-foot fence. They average about two feet in length and nearly five pounds in weight, although the largest species in the Arctic regions and the western plains may attain a length of three feet and a weight of ten pounds. Matching their greatly elongated hind legs and paws are their ears, capable of very keen hearing. It was these long ears that originally suggested the name of jackass rabbits more than fifty years ago, although they are not really rabbits at all.

Most jack rabbits—that is, hares—display a remarkable capacity to change color with the season, being brownish or grayish above and lighter below in the summer, and pure white in the winter except for the black tips of their long ears. This change is immediately produced by the gradual molting of their coats in spring and fall, the process being facilitated by the three distinct types or thicknesses of hair in the coat. So perfect is the camouflage that in proper seasonal surroundings the animal becomes all but invisible. Thus, as pointed out, even the black-tipped ears which go with the winter pelage help by giving the illusion of a shadow on snow.

JACK RABBITS *(Lepus californicus)*. Length: 2 feet. Range: Western North America.
American Museum of Natural History

Yet strange as it may seem, this power over coloration seems to be connected more with the need of maintaining the proper body temperature than a protective camouflage. For in warm-blooded animals a white coat conserves heat and a dark one repels it, and the jack rabbit appears to be particularly sensitive to sudden changes in temperature, or at least more so than to its invisibility. Thus the mountain jack rabbit, invisible in its white coat on the snow-clad heights, will come down into the valley where it can be plainly seen. Many species suffer intensely in the summer heat and will sit openly in the shade of a pole or tree even at the approach of danger, as though fearful of exposing themselves to the rays of the sun. Even more significant is the case of the white-sided variety, roaming the deserts and semiarid regions of the Southwest. This creature has the curious habit of pulling the white-mottled skin on its sides up to its back when disturbed, the white surface being exposed on the side nearest the intruder. In flight the white side reflects the sunlight with such power that it can be seen for miles around. This is one of the finest examples of directive coloration, the directly opposite effect to camouflage. Apparently this species, which is the most southerly of all, is best adjusted to keeping cool in the hot desert, and hence most in need of conserving heat when its own activity or fear suddenly causes heat to be lost. It does not exhibit a color change comparable with that of the varying hare and related species, but has considerable black mixed in with its fur, especially on the upper side of its tail.

Jack rabbits are nearly all gregarious, wandering about in groups of two to twenty-five. They eat nearly any sort of vegetable matter, preferring tender grasses and such crops as cotton, carrots, and alfalfa. When food is scarce they may migrate as much as ten miles a day in search of a fertile field or suburban lawn. Feeding early and late along trails of their own making, they spend the intervening hours hidden away in the brush.

In some sections of the country they make seasonal migrations for food. Most vexatious in this respect is the black-tailed variety in the Southwest, thousands of them often being found together on a few acres, feeding on fruit trees and grain. This species is also economically most important in furnishing pelts and carcasses. The cunning developed by it in evading the hounds of hunters is shown by the trick it has of doubling back on its trail, leaping as far as it can to one side, and hiding until the dogs have passed by.

As an example of adaptability the white-tailed variety or prairie hare is most interesting. It inhabits altitudes of ten to twelve thousand feet in the Sierra Nevada and Rockies as well as the low midwestern plains. Still more ubiquitous, however, is the varying hare, also known as the snowshoe hare because of the large tracks its furry hind paws make over the snow. These hind paws enable it to escape from predatory birds and such animals as the fox, wolf, lynx, mink, weasel, sable, and ermine, which take a great toll of rabbits and hares. Varying hares are also particularly prone to diseases which greatly reduce their numbers every few years.

Those fortunate enough to come close to jack rabbits have sometimes seen two of them—usually two males—engaged in "boxing matches." The opponents sit upright on their hind feet and spar with their front paws for a few seconds at a time. Then, apparently at the end of a round, they stop and nibble grass blades for a while, until it is time to resume the match. When one is defeated, he dashes away, while the other pursues for a short distance, but soon gives up the attempt.

Jack rabbits begin to breed at the age of one year. Gestation requires six weeks and a litter of two to four is brought forth about every two months except during the coldest weather. The young are concealed in nests lined with fur and almost covered with earth or twigs. During the day the mother leaves them to search for food, returning to nurse them at night. The young are able to see and hop about at birth, and are soon left to fend for themselves.

COTTONTAIL RABBIT

COTTONTAIL rabbits are the common variety of true rabbits. They average about a half foot shorter than the jack rabbits and have no such elongated hind legs and ears. They are so called because of the bushy white under side of their tails. As they scurry

COTTONTAIL RABBIT (*Sylvilagus nuttalli*). Length: 1¼ feet. Range: Rocky Mountain region.
J. W. Jackson

over the fields, the tail goes up, revealing the downy white undersurface, much as in the case of a doe.

Not so large, fast and keen of hearing as the hares, cottontails are particularly fond of hiding in holes and other well protected places. Often these burrows are the deserted havens of other animals such as the prairie-dog or the badger, but any opening will do, even that into a house, provided it is well protected and unvisited by dogs and cats. The cottontails are indeed quite timid, and tame easily when captured. Their dusky hue gives them considerable protection in tall grass and brush, but varies according to season and locality in lesser degree than in the case of jack rabbits.

Cottontails subsist mostly on the inner bark of saplings, shrubs, and their leaves and fruit, as well as clover. Summer is the breeding season, when a pair produce as many as three litters with three to seven young in each. The young are born without a hair on their bodies and with eyes shut, in contrast with the more developed young of jack rabbits, and so require more nursing. Indeed, were it not for this and the other hazards of predatory beasts and a harsh winter season, they would be much more numerous than they are at the rate they reproduce.

There are some two dozen species and subspecies of cottontails scattered throughout the country. Very similar in habits are the three species of brush rabbits and the four of swamp rabbits, whose names indicate their peculiar haunts and resources. In addition there is the smallest of all American rabbits—the Idaho pygmy rabbit which is barely a foot in length and inhabits the sagebrush of the contiguous areas of California, Oregon, Idaho, and Nevada. Because of its nocturnal habits and way of retreating into badger holes, it is seldom seen, even where most abundant.

PIKA

ATTACKED by the eagle, the pika retreats to its shelter in the crevices of weathered cliffs. Here in squeaking, querulous tones it practices the art of ventriloquism. The eagle hunts in vain for the little animal whose shrill cry pierces the somber stillness of the Rockies again and again. Each time the voice seems to emanate from a different point.

Perhaps the only mammal which can throw its voice, the pika, an unusually shy animal, is difficult to observe, and only when alarmed does it betray its presence by a noisy deception of the enemy. But its careless habit of sunning itself and gathering food some distance away from shelter makes it an easy prey of eagles and hawks.

The pika is a vegetarian, its food supply consisting of grasses, goldenrod, fireweed, and berries. These it industriously collects, dries in the sun, and deposits in small piles under stones or against the side of large mossy rocks. Well-worn paths are soon formed by the pika's constant trips to and from the "hay" piles and home.

Equipped with two pairs of incisors which have no cutting edge, the pika munches its hard-earned repast with a horizontal motion of the jaws. Its protective coloration, which varies from pinkish buff to slate at the base of the hairs, blends remarkably well with the background of weathered shale. The feet are white or cinnamon-buff and the broad, rounded ears are brown or gray. Twice each year the pika sheds its colorful soft pelage and usually there is a well-defined line between the new and the old coats. The new fur appears first on the head and progresses evenly backward.

PIKA *(Ochotona princeps)*. Length: 7 inches. Range: Rocky Mountain region.
American Museum of Natural History

This tailless rodent measures seven inches in length. It looks like a cross between a guinea pig and a rabbit. As it moves slowly but noiselessly over the rocks and among its "haystacks," the short body and hairy padded feet never betray its movements. The pika does not hibernate. Each spring the female gives birth to a litter of three or four gay and boisterous specimens.

Of the twenty-six species of the genus, the most common is the Rocky Mountain pika found only on high cliffs. It is known also by such a variety of names as the cony, rock rabbit, little chief hare, tailless hare, and whistling rabbit, names which vary with the locality in which the animal occurs.

WESTERN PORCUPINE *(Erethizon epixanthum)*. Length: 3 feet. Range: Western North America.
New York Zoological Society

PORCUPINE

BACK arched, nose hidden between forepaws, and quills standing on end, the long-haired porcupine is ready to meet the most powerful foe. With one sharp slap of its flat tail, the porcupine forces its needlelike quills into the flesh of its attacker.

The quills are even more potent than needles, since they are tipped with minute barbs which point backward and rip the flesh when withdrawn. These weapons seem to have earned the porcupine a fearsome reputation among its animal neighbors who hesitate to attack. When gnawing hunger drives a cougar after the porcupine's flesh, the reward is meager. Even if the kill is made successfully, the porcupine has a posthumous revenge because its quills stick in the cougar's throat and prevent the beast from eating.

Two fallacies concerning the porcupine are current. One is that it shoots its quills at an attacker as an archer shoots arrows, a feat, alas, which is far beyond its powers. The quills, though, are so lightly rooted that when the animal presses against another object they are separated from the porcupine and the barbed ends hold fast. Another misconception is that the porcupine rolls itself into a ball when danger threatens. Actually it only arches its back and hides its nose, a tender spot, either in a hole in the ground or between its heavily clawed forepaws.

Usually the gait of the porcupine is most leisurely. Unhurried, it wanders about and when the pangs of hunger strike, casually climbs a tree, picks out a convenient branch, and strips off and eats the green bark. Twigs and plants are also included in its diet. The finest treat a porcupine can receive, though, is salt, which means as much to it as sweets do to children. It makes repeated forages on a camp if the smell of salt is present, chiseling through doors and floors to reach an article with the desired flavor. Even things to which perspiration clings, such as ax handles and strips of leather, have sufficient salt to make them valuable prizes.

The creature's home is either a hollow log or a burrow in the rocks. During the cold spells of winter it stays at home, but a slightly warmer day brings it out in search of a suitable feeding tree. On these bright wintry days, its slate-black coat and coarse, light-tipped hair glisten brightly against the whiteness of the snow. Its quills, the longest being in the back and tail, are concealed beneath the hair. The Canada porcupine found in northeastern United States and Canada has a yellowish white tip to its hair; the western species, ranging from New Mexico to Alaska, has hair with greenish-yellow tips. The quills of both species are light in color with dark tips.

Some "sportsmen" suggest that the porcupine be killed with a club, while the attacker stands at arm's length from the quill-filled tail. There is, however, no sane reason for harming this mild creature which is rightfully protected by game legislation. Since the days of the Indians, who used to eat its meat and decorate baskets and moccasins with its quills, the porcupine has been of little economic value to man. But even in modern times hunters lost in heavy forest have staved off starvation by coming upon a porcupine.

JUMPING MOUSE

AT HARVEST time the mowing machine charges down a growing field, scattering chaff and sending up clouds of dry dust. Caught in the path of the roaring, vibrating mechanical monster, the jumping or kangaroo mice leap for their lives.

The wee rodents depend upon the fabulous resilience of their long hind legs to take them out of danger. Jumping ahead of the machine, they are frequently overtaken and killed. The first frenzied hops may cover as much as ten feet of ground, but these leaps shorten to three or four feet as the animal tires. On occasion they have been seen to leap right into the mouths of predacious hawks, owls, foxes, and snakes. But more often they have leaped blindly into pails of water and milk, or over wells and outhouses.

Normally these mice, unlike their Australian namesake, the kangaroo, walk with all four of their five-toed feet touching the ground. They like meadows and grassy spots and may be seen in the daytime during the warm seasons. With the coming of winter

JUMPING MOUSE *(Zapus hudsonius)*. Length: 8 inches. Range: Generally distributed over most of the United States except in the Southeast.

American Museum of Natural History

they make themselves a grassy nest, sometimes a foot or two beneath the surface of the ground, wrap themselves into a tight ball, and wind their long tails around themselves. Usually the nest is placed in the hollow of a tree or in a shallow hole. Occasionally the mother mouse will take over an abandoned bird's nest and in this sylvan couch will bear her annual litter of six young. Here, too, food is stored for winter use. With the onset of very cold weather the family goes into a deep hibernation and in this state has often been mistaken for dead.

The total length of the jumping mouse is about eight or nine inches, of which the tail comprises about five and a half inches. This long tapering member is not merely ornamental but serves also as a prop and balance. With the tail amputated by some agricultural machine or bitten off by one of its numerous natural enemies, the jumping mouse is reduced to ludicrous and pathetic somersaults. The jumping mouse is colored an attractive ochre above, with under parts blending into the most delicate nuances of yellowish-brown.

Sometimes a natural holocaust, the prairie fire, sweeps relentlessly over the domain of the jumping mouse and then not even its remarkable leaps can save it. The ten-foot wall of flame leaps through the brake and what it does not sear and destroy it smothers. About twenty-five species of jumping mice inhabit large areas of the United States as well as Alaska, Canada, Labrador, and Mexico.

However, the life of the jumping mouse is not solely a process of avoiding sharp-knived harvesters, prairie fires, and snakes. It delights in wandering about fields, particularly where the grass is thick and damp. Its entirely vegetarian diet is composed chiefly of seeds and grain. It quickly learns that human beings mean no harm and will permit itself to be fondled.

MOUNTAIN BEAVER

THE mountain beaver is not a beaver, nor does it live in the mountains. It inhabits the damp, forested foothills of the Cascade Range of Washington, Oregon, and California. Commonly known in Oregon as a boomer, it does not boom; in some sections called a whistler, it cannot whistle. This much misnamed rodent and its eight subspecies have been set apart in a family of their own. They are found nowhere outside of North America.

The mountain beaver crawls rapidly through its shallow burrows, coming out only under the protection of night. Sometimes on these evening excursions, this creature, guileless and poor of eyesight, unhappily meets its doom in the path of automobiles, or as it wanders dazedly into a brightly lighted town.

Unlike the gopher and the mole, the mountain beaver constructs its burrows without any apparent plan in soft, moist ground. It conceals the entrance behind a stump or bush. The tunnels are usually about four inches wide, the nest chamber is about a foot and a half across, the ceiling plastered with packed clay and the floor covered with a bedding of dry leaves and grass. Active in winter as well as in summer, the mountain beaver builds tunnels through the snow. During the long rainy seasons the burrows are frequently flooded, and at such times it swims out to seek refuge on the highest and most protected elevations.

Primitive in structure, the male and female cannot be distinguished by casual observation. Their fur covering is an attractive cinnamon or grayish brown, and invariably slate-colored at the base. Both male and female reach a maximum length of about fourteen inches and an average weight of two and a quarter pounds. Almost tailless, and equipped with strong claws for digging, climbing, and grasping, the chubby animals waddle on short legs through the underground burrows and feeding grounds, their long whiskers sensitive to the lightest touch.

Almost any vegetable matter provides food for the mountain beaver. Leaves, bark, ferns, and even the prickly Oregon grape or the skunk cabbage are items on its daily diet, and since it will eat fir and hemlock twigs in the winter, it is rarely without sustenance. Unfortunately for the small farmer trying to establish himself on newly cleared land, this rodent shows great preference for any farm crop, whether it be clover, carrots, onions, or young fruit trees. It often climbs saplings in search of food, sometimes going as high as fifteen feet hacking off branches with its powerful teeth and eventu-

MOUNTAIN BEAVER

MOUNTAIN BEAVER *(Aplodontia rufa)*. Length: 1 foot. Range: "Narrow strip along western part of Pacific States" (Anthony).
New York Zoological Society

ally topping the tree. The animal leaves the stub of each branch which, like the spikes of a telegraph pole, enables it to descend. It then drags the cut branches to the burrow entrance and leaves them outside to wilt before eating the leaves and bark.

Although the burrows of many mountain beavers may be found close together, the creatures do not actually live in colonies. In fact, they seem to resent each other's presence, which is revealed by an odor, strong and musky, like that of the muskrat.

Not as prolific as most rodents, mountain beavers mate in February or March and after the gestation period of one month the female produces a litter of two, three, and sometimes five offspring. They are gray in color, with a disproportionately large head and eyes that are closed at birth.

The Indians of the Pacific Northwest, who called these creatures *sh'ouch, showt'l* and *sewellel,* used their meat for food and their furs for robes. Perhaps because of an old European fear of rodents, or because of their somewhat musky taste, white residents have never eaten their flesh. The furs today have no commercial value.

Before the West was completely opened the mountain beaver carried on its activities unmolested, except for such natural enemies as weasels, skunks, wildcats, owls, and other flesh-eaters. In recent years, however, new food sources, provided by logged-off land and farms, have made it troublesome in certain agricultural districts where it has done some injury to crops, orchards, and even reforestation projects. Farm animals sometimes step into its burrows, irrigation ditches are diverted and plugged by cave-ins, springs are filled with refuse, and its tunnels have even been known to cause road slides. This has led to its diminution in these districts—a simple matter since the burrows reveal its nest, and its guileless nature allows it to be easily trapped or poisoned. In its natural forest haunts, where it is widely distributed, it is not destructive and continues to thrive more or less unabated.

A captured mountain beaver is surly, and during the first hours of confinement will squeal, whine, and even bite if provoked. If caged indoors, it will usually die within a week. If treated kindly and kept in an outdoor enclosure large enough for the construction of its burrows, it responds much like any other pet.

MUSKRAT

THE giant of its far-flung family, the muskrat loves to sit peacefully on its home-made raft in the center of a quiet pond and eat lunch. Here it is safe from such enemies as weasels and wolves. But when a hawk or owl swoops swiftly down, the muskrat slips into the water, makes a slapping sound with its rudderlike tail to warn its fellows, and swims to the underwater entrance to its home.

The residence of a muskrat is made of mud and vegetation piled in a shallow spot. For safety's sake, the passageways leading to it are below the surface of the pond, but the chamber itself is above water, and the roof is ventilated. When there are two chambers in the house, with separate entrance halls, they are believed to be occupied by different families. Safe from most land-dwelling animals, and

MUSKRAT

able with care to avoid birds of prey, the muskrat can do little against such an enemy as the mink which can chase it right into its own home and kill it.

MUSKRAT *(Ondatra zibethica)*. Length: 1½ feet. Range: Most of United States.
New York Zoological Society

The muskrat, which resembles a tiny beaver but is really a big mouse, will valiantly battle with any attacker. Unfortunately, it is a flyweight in the hard world outside the mouse kingdom, since it is not even two feet long and weighs but two pounds. Yet its fortitude is such that it may gnaw off its own leg to escape from a trap.

It eats fishes, frogs, clams, and vegetable matter. In winter, since it does not hibernate, it swims about under the ice in search of such food or almost any other that it can sink its teeth into.

During the mating season the males frequently engage in fights to win some choice female. The young, four to twelve in number, are born in the spring and lucky it is that the families are large because muskrats are preyed upon by a host of enemies including man himself. Dyed muskrat skins are sold commercially as "Hudson seal."

Intermediate between the nine native and popular fur-bearing species of muskrats or musquashes, as they are sometimes called, and meadow mice are the Florida round-tailed muskrats. One species inhabits the northern and central part of the State while another, named the Everglade water rat, is found in the southern portion. Whether it lives in the Okefenokee or the Everglades, however, its habits are the same. In all localities it seems to enjoy the semi-elevated swamp "prairies" where it gathers and eats mosses, grasses, herb stems, and bark. Here too it is pursued by snakes, hawks, and owls. It responds to protection, multiplying wherever so favored.

MEADOW MOUSE AND VOLE

A MUCH more abundant, though far less popular, member of the family of rats and mice is the meadow mouse, also known as field mouse, vole, or field vole. There are probably more of these running around than any other rodent, the various species and sub-species totaling seventy-six. The physical variations distinguishing the species are slight, probably accounted for by the widely different environments which the ubiquitous creatures inhabit.

So rapidly do these six-inch mice breed that, according to some estimates, a single pair would have one million descendants in five seasons were natural destructive forces kept in check. A female may bring forth six litters a year, each of eight young, and in less than a year the young are old enough to repeat the process. To make matters worse, their appetites are enormous; a single adult is believed to eat about thirty pounds of green vegetation yearly. A group of one thousand in a meadow would require at least twelve tons of food a year, it has been estimated. The damage which they consequently do to crops of corn, wheat, and hay, and to orchards, costs farmers millions of dollars annually.

The home of the blunt-headed, thick-furred field mouse is usually a nest of grass and vegetable matter. But specific differences are great, depending on locality, which varies from mountain ranges to lowlands, and from forests to plains and swamps. Some species even burrow underground to establish a dwelling.

Red-backed mice, often called red-backed voles, number more than thirty North American species and subspecies. Of this multitude more than half may be found in damp and cool places in the forests. Usually distinguished from meadow mice by a fairly showy, reddish band along the back, this slender, soft-furred rodent may be seen during both the day and the night, in winter as well as summer. The mother builds a grass-lined nest and here suckles her four to eight young from April to October.

LEMMING MOUSE

THE lemming mouse, resembling the meadow mouse in appearance, is distinguished chiefly by its shorter tail. Most of the twelve species and subspecies are found throughout northern North America in bogs or near ponds.

They are also known as bog mice and bog lemmings. Snakes, owls, hawks, foxes, weasels, minks, and other small carnivorous creatures prey upon them. The habits of lemming mice, however, are not well known. The two long-tailed lemming mice, members of another little-known group more closely akin to the meadow mice, live up in the Douglas fir trees of the West where they feed on conifer needles and seeds.

The true lemmings and collared lemmings are not found in the United States, being confined to Arctic America.

NATIVE RATS AND MICE

GRASSHOPPER mice, harvest mice, and white-footed mice together with rice, cotton, and wood rats comprise our native species. All of these are members of the same family and in many respects they are also related in their habits.

These rodents may themselves be an economic nuisance but they are not nearly so loathsome and dangerous as the introduced species since they do not carry disease.

The fur of the wood rat, for instance, is clean and velvety, and its flesh is said to be wholesome and palatable, tasting better than that of the gray squirrel. The animal lives in wooded and swampy areas where plague germs are not met with as frequently as in the sewers and cellars inhabited by its introduced cousins, the Norway and black rats.

This creature comes by its additional names, trade rat and pack rat, because of its mercantile traits. Whereas most rats and mice simply appropriate goods outright, the wood rat replaces the commodity with what it judges to be a fair amount of some other goods. It will swap rice for collar buttons as readily as collar buttons for rice.

The nest of the wood rat is piled against a rock or placed high in the branches of a tree. It is composed of vegetable rubbish, cactus being favored in regions where it grows. The spines are left intact and facing outward as a means of protection. Contents of some of these nests sound like a pawn shop inventory, since kitchen utensils, watches, tobacco tins, and other assorted junk have been found.

The wood rat eats seeds, nuts, and fungi, and in time of drought finds sustenance and refreshment in the soft, pulpy interior of the cactus plant. Like all small rodents the wood rats form a staple dietary item in the larder of hawks, owls, wildcats, snakes, and coyotes. The white flesh is eaten by some western Indians. About three dozen species and subspecies of wood rats inhabit our country, varying in minor characteristics as they inhabit different locations and environments.

Litters of three to six are raised by the mother wood rat. In northern climes there is only one brood a year, but in milder places several broods are common.

The southern United States, from Florida to Texas, harbors another indigenous rat, the medium-sized, robust cotton rat which haunts the grasslands and open spaces. These rats are active throughout the year and do not hibernate. They are distinctive for their rough, loose fur which makes them resemble overgrown field mice. About fourteen kinds of cotton rats have been described. Superficially, however, they look alike.

NATIVE MICE

Extending from Texas to New Jersey are five species of rice rats. Like the cotton rat, the rice rat keeps to the open grasslands and has a coarse fur. The first young appear in April or May when a litter of three to seven arrives. There may be a later brood.

The grasshopper mouse is a creature of the plains of the West. This soft-furred rodent is rarely seen in the woods. In the deserts, where it reaches its greatest abundance, its tracks and burrows leading to underground workings may frequently be seen in the sandy soil.

In the northern part of their range, which in general is throughout western North America, these scorpion mice, as they are also called, give birth to only one litter a year. In warmer regions several litters of about four young each are the rule. Twelve species and subspecies are known.

The small, dull-colored harvest mice are rarely seen, as they favor warmer localities than most of the United States offers. Their geographical center is Central America. Active day and night, harvest mice do not hibernate. They are not very abundant and hence do little damage to crops. Seventeen varieties of harvest mice manage to survive within the borders of the United States.

They nest on the ground or amid low-growing vegetation. When they cannot find an abandoned bird's nest they fashion one of their own out of grass, and in this seemingly unsubstantial domicile several broods of young arrive each year.

The white-footed mouse, of which there are almost seventy forms, is represented virtually all over North America south of the Arctic Circle wherever there is a sufficient food supply. It stays close to the ground, is active all year around, and sleeps during the daytime.

Quickly recognized by its white feet, white under parts, and hairy tail, the white-footed mouse makes an attractive pet when captured. They have been taught to sing like canaries. The color of the white-footed mouse changes slightly with its environment. Thus, where the animal lives in a wet, rainy region it is dark, nearly black. In dry desert regions it is pale. The food of all forms of the white-footed mouse is strictly vegetarian, consisting mainly of grains and seeds. They are, however, not nearly as great a problem as are the meadow mice.

POCKET RATS AND MICE

THIS family includes the seed-eating spiny pocket mouse of Texas; the fifty-seven species and subspecies of common pocket mice of the midwestern and southwestern States, whose fur-lined cheek pouches are usually bulging with seeds; the elongated hind-limbed kangaroo rats which leap about the warmer portions of western North America and number nearly fifty kinds; and the dwarf or pygmy pocket rats, of which five species and subspecies have been described. Dwarf pocket rats are from the arid regions of California, Nevada, and Oregon.

Little is known about the habits of the various members of this family. Their hind feet are covered with fur to the tips of their toes. The ears also are completely fur-covered.

YOUNG KANGAROO RAT *(Dipodomys ordii)*. Length: 10 inches. Range: Western United States.
J. W. Jackson

INTRODUCED RATS AND MICE

INTRODUCED rats and mice include the common house mouse and three domestic rats; the common, or Norway, rat; the black rat driven out by the Norway rat, but still occasionally trapped in New York City; and the roof, or Alexandrine, rat which has also been driven out by the Norway rat.

These introduced species have made the term rodent almost an epithet. Filthy, plague-infested creatures, their distribution corresponds roughly to that of man upon whom they prey.

BEAVER

INDIAN children once captured baby beavers for pets, according to an old Seminole legend. Finally an agreement was reached by the beaver king and the Indian chief. The beavers then created fish-stocked lakes for the Indians by building dams, and each year they sent the Indians two young beavers as playmates. When the chief died, however, his successor broke the pact and started a war against the animals. As Indian bands approached the dams, the beaver sentry warned his fellows by slapping his tail on the water. The beavers thereupon broke the dams, flooding their enemy. Ever since, the Okefenokee section of northern Florida and southern Georgia has been a flooded swamp, and the beaver uses a slap of his tail to make a warning sound.

This clever little animal sits on its haunches, propped up by its long, flattened tail, and with its chisel-like teeth gnaws persistently at a tree trunk. It can cut through a four-inch tree in twenty minutes. When the tree is ready to fall the beaver scurries out of harm's way.

Carefully the felled tree is trimmed of branches and twigs. Then it is cut into sections four or five feet long. If it is near the water the logs are pushed to the site of a dam which the beaver colony is building.

If the trees along the bank have already been cut down, the beavers demonstrate their mechanical skill by constructing a two-foot-wide canal from the stream to the clump of trees they are

BEAVER DAM. The destruction of dams like these has not only harmed the beaver but has caused the best remaining duck-nesting lands to dry up.
U. S. Bureau of Biological Survey

cutting. Rather than tug the wood several hundred feet they simply shove it into the canal and float it into the stream.

At the dam site the logs are piled one atop the other, twigs and brush are added, and stones are used to fortify the structure which will deepen the water by blocking its flow. Mud is scooped from the bottom near the embankment, making the water still deeper. With their dexterous forepaws the beavers plaster it in the chinks. According to legend, the beaver sucks the air from the wood to make it sink. Sometimes a beaver gathers up an armful of mud from the bank, clutches the mass to its breast, and paddles with hind legs and tail to the dam.

Usually the site selected for the dam is a narrow stream. The barrier has a base of a dozen feet and a height of five or six. In Estes Park, Colorado, beavers built one more than a thousand feet long.

Alluvial plains in upstate New York have been attributed to the

BEAVER

dam-building activities of beavers. For 25,000 years, since the end of the ice age, the animals were blocking up streams. When the water broke through, it spread silt over a wide area. Long before geologists made this discovery, farmers had been calling these fertile plains "beaver meadows."

The beavers' home is built of the same materials as the dam. The size of the house depends upon the number of occupants, a fair-sized one having a circumference of forty feet and a height of eight feet. Built in the pond, it is always provided with underwater entrances, a precaution against such landlubber marauders as the wolverine, but the main chamber is well above the water. The otter, however, can pursue and destroy the beaver even in this moated castle. Deepening the water by damming the stream prevents it from falling low enough to expose the important door to the chamber.

BEAVERS (*Castor canadensis*). Length: 3½ feet. Range: Generally found in the past over most of the United States and Canada. Almost exterminated. Responds to protection.

American Museum of Natural History

Sometimes the beaver's home is a burrow in the bank of the stream, also with an underwater entrance. It has a brush-covered airhole in the ceiling. Legend again has it that bank beavers are inferior technicians, expelled from the group for poor workmanship.

Another purpose which the astute beavers have in making the water deep is to prevent it from freezing solidly in winter. Under the ice, alongside the dam, the colony lays in its store of supplies for the cold months. Excellent at swimming and diving, the beaver leaves home at feeding time, swims under the ice to the cache, selects a morsel for the family, and returns under water. The bark from such trees as the maple, poplar, and linden, as well as roots, grasses, and berries, comprise the cuisine. The beaver stores whole logs, eating the bark and, if necessary, using the wood for the dam. All such labor is done by the beavers themselves; they do not, as folklore has it, employ muskrat slaves.

Although beavers do not hibernate, they are much less active in winter. They have few worries since food is at hand, and the freezing temperature makes their dams and homes impregnable. In February they mate, the female giving birth in May to a litter averaging four young. It is believed that a male and female mate for life. At maturity the beaver weighs thirty pounds, although sixty-pound specimens have been observed.

Most of their work is done at night, especially in localities where they have enemies. And work there ever is, for wear and tear on their structure makes repairs and reinforcements necessary.

These engineers of the animal world are a model of co-operative enterprise in their construction feats. They live together harmoniously for long periods. A colony may persist for centuries; one in the Midwest is believed to be a thousand years old. When a colony becomes too large some of the younger members migrate. The older and more experienced beavers accompany the pioneers to the site of the new colony, assist them with their construction, and then return.

It is because of the value of their velvety fur that the ten once-abundant species of American beavers have been depleted. So important was the trade in beaver skins that a great deal of the early exploration of the continent was stimulated by the search for suitable trading-post locations. The Astor fortune was based on beaver fur and, before capital wealth was thought of in the New World, Indians used the beaver for food and clothing. But Dr. Robert Cushman Murphy writes: "It has been estimated that preservation of the beaver throughout North America, from the Rio Grande to Labrador and Alaska, would have been worth more because of this animal's flood-control operations than the whole historic value of its fur."

The United States Government in 1938 made CCC workers out of a thousand beavers in Idaho. The animals were put to work conserving water and preventing soil erosion by damming small streams, an official tribute to their industry.

POCKET GOPHER

THE pocket gopher trims the bark from trees with its sharp teeth which move with the rapidity and bite of a whipsaw. The booty is stored in the hair-lined pouches of its cheeks and it is these bulging cheek pockets that give the animal its name.

When the vibration of the soil indicates that someone is approaching, the gopher darts into its underground habitation. Here it unloads the stock in its cheek pouches—bark, alfalfa, clover, or other garden products—in a storeroom. One gopher's cache was found to contain more than two bushels of potatoes, proof of its enterprise and thrift.

The tunnel in which the gopher lives is hollowed out with its teeth and the long sharp claws of the muscular forelegs. As the dirt is scooped out, the animal pushes the mound behind it. When the mound becomes too large, the gopher turns sharply about, places its forepaws alongside its face, and pushes the dirt out.

To the casual observer there seems to be neither rhyme nor reason in the planning of the tunnel's route. Each year the gopher enlarges its tunnel, extending its length and building new chambers. When its route is barred by rock, or more tempting soil is discovered off to one side, the gopher changes its path. One very long tunnel, which extended deviously for a mile, was found to end not far from its opening, so circuitous was the route. Since openings are made at short distances where the scooped-out dirt may be deposited, a gopher often leaves a telltale series of mounds littered over a field.

When a gopher goes into its hole, it usually conceals the opening by scattering loose dirt over it. The tunnels, with their intricate system of chambers, may be either a few inches below the surface or as deep as six feet. Normally a gopher lives alone, occupying the underground haunt in solitude, except in the mating season which occurs in early spring. Females give birth to a litter of two to eight young. Some authorities believe that the female bears several litters a year.

Since this rodent has small eyes and limited vision, it is dependent upon its other senses. It is nocturnal, although not completely so, preferring to stay indoors during the daylight hours.

Sometimes such an enemy as the gopher snake invades the pocket gopher's home and then—woe to the poor rodent. If trapped in a narrow passageway and unable to turn around, it will run backwards, feeling its way with an extremely sensitive tail. The gopher is a courageous little beast, apparently ready to fight whenever necessary. But almost all opponents—coyotes, foxes, badgers, weasels, hawks, owls, and snakes—make short work of the diminutive animal.

It is not built for fighting, being one of the bantamweights of the animal world. The species vary in weight from four to eighteen ounces and are from six to thirteen inches long. Moreover, the gopher's poor eyesight gives its opponents a decided advantage. Its color may be almost any shade of brown; it acquires a new coat each summer and winter. When the fur grows, it begins at the neck and works toward the stubby tail, a clearly discernible line marking off the new from the old. The gopher's face is its distinctive characteristic; there are the baggy pouches on each cheek and the face is sparsely bewhiskered, the incisors projecting outside the mouth.

Farmers in every State west of the Mississippi, and in Alabama, Georgia, Florida, Illinois, Wisconsin, and Indiana, would probably vote the pocket gopher the most annoying rodent. Destroying the bark of fruit trees and gnawing out the roots, damaging mowing machines by their mounds in the hayfield, carrying off plant bulbs, living in burrowed-out hollows of southern palm trees, and drawing water from irrigation ditches by burrowing through them, are among the crimes for which rural America dislikes the gopher. But the animal destroys not only farmlands; with apparent impartiality it digs up golf courses, parks, lawns, and airplane fields, the latter becoming hazardous as well as unsightly. And it caused breaks in levees until it was discovered that a gopher could not dig through loose sand.

Defenders of gophers have, however, come forward with the testimony that the burrows help to aerate and drain the soil, a benefit to agriculture. In the mountains where it is abundant, the tunnels help to retain water which otherwise would flow down the slopes.

In some regions farmers, not convinced that the good overshadows the bad, place gopher snakes in the tunnel to kill the little marauders, and also decimate them with poisoned grain and traps.

In various localities the pocket gopher is known as camas rat, pouch rat, cheekpockets, gopher, and salamander. One genus is found in the West and another in the East. The former contains more than eighty species and subspecies; the latter, inhabiting the prairies and plains, numbers but seventeen.

WOODCHUCK

MOTHER woodchuck peers cautiously from the opening of her burrow, sniffs the air for any possible sign of danger, then disappears inside. A moment later she waddles out, still cautious, followed by her brood of five. Like little puppies they shuffle behind the mother, their short legs moving rapidly, their eyes opened for the first time to the wonders of the new setting. Born only about a month ago, they are pathetically clumsy, not sure of their movements. The mother, always alert for the bark of a dog, nibbles the grass, and the cubs imitate her. For the moment satiated, they roll in the soft grass of the meadow, their round heavy bodies resembling little balls of fur.

AMERICAN WILD LIFE

The bark of a dog disrupts the happy abandon of this kindergarten. The mother scampers for the burrow taking in tow her curious and bewildered offspring. They manage to reach the shelter only a few steps ahead of the enemy. Here they are safe. By the end of the summer the young will have learned their lessons, and will become as adept as the mother in detecting and evading danger.

WOODCHUCKS *(Marmota monax)*. Length: 2 feet. Range: Most parts of the United States and southern Canada in favorable areas.
Buffalo Museum of Science

The woodchuck lives in its deep burrow, which is from ten to twenty-five feet long, with the nesting chamber at the extreme end. It selects the site of the burrow on the side of a hill where good drainage will keep its nest dry, and sometimes constructs several openings to provide alternate means of entry and exit. The burrow is marked by scattered mounds of earth on which the creature sometimes sits. In the safety of the underground chamber the woodchuck takes its daily nap, raises its litter, and hibernates through the winter. After gorging itself all summer the animal has enough fat stored under its pelt to carry it through the period of "lifeless" existence from October to March. During this time its temperature is lowered, its respiration weak, and its state that of suspended animation.

Because it supplements its food supplies of roots, shoots of young trees, and forest plants with the richer diet of clover and green vegetables, the woodchuck is perpetually hunted by the farmer. Dogs are its mortal enemies, and even boys find excellent sport in hunting and killing it. The woodchuck is therefore a very shy animal and, being naturally inclined toward laziness, seldom strays far from its burrow. When the hay of the meadow is cut and it is more easily observed, its senses become sharper and it develops cunning traits. At the slightest sign of danger it sits up on its hind legs, pointing its blunt nose in the direction of the enemy, cocking its small ears for the slightest sound. In this motionless pose it resembles a part of the landscape and is difficult to distinguish from the grassy background. If the danger is real it will scamper quickly into its burrow, from which it soon emerges to make another observation. If cornered, however, the woodchuck is a match for any dog its size and will battle fiercely.

The woodchuck, also known as the ground hog, rockchuck, marmot, and to the French Canadians as *siffleur,* inhabits most of North America. It is of little economic value. Of the rodent species, including woodchucks and marmots that are found in the United States, there are more than a score. Short-legged and heavy-bodied, the woodchuck is related to the ground squirrel. Its grizzly coat is red or gray-brown and the under parts are brownish chestnut. The head is usually dark brown; the feet are brown or almost black. Sometimes the fur is distinctly yellowish, as in the yellow-bellied marmot of the Sierras whose coat blends with the brightly colored stones of the mountains. The sexes differ slightly in size, the male measuring about twenty-six inches, the female about twenty-two.

There is a common legend associated with the woodchuck. Ground Hog Day, February 2, sends reporters scurrying to the zoos and parks to watch the famous animal crawl out of its hole to inspect weather conditions. If the sun is shining and the ground hog can see its shadow, so runs the story, it goes back to sleep for another six weeks—for a warm February is believed by weather prophets to portend a late and chilly spring.

PRAIRIE-DOG

THE prairie-dog city is a gay and boisterous metropolis. The avenues, stretching for many miles, are honeycombed with burrows, which constitute nothing less than a subterranean housing development on a gigantic scale. Tiny golden-brown bodies move rapidly and nervously from mound to mound, visiting neighbors, gossiping, and chattering continuously. Explosive sharp cries break the stillness of the western plains. Alert and observant, these rodents stand at the opening of their burrows, perched on their hind legs, cocking their heads mischievously, munching food.

A sharp warning sends the prairie-dogs scurrying to their holes. Thousands of little bodies run helter-skelter, tumble over each other. *Skip, skip, skip,* cry the sentries, and instantly the members of the colony stop motionless at the mound, wait apprehensively for the next signal. Again the skip, skip, skip, is heard, louder this time, more alarming. The bark is taken up by all the inhabitants, carried down throughout the avenues of the colony, as they dive into the holes. A moment later they quickly peer out at the intruder, bark defiantly as long as they dare, and finally disappear into the recesses of their burrows.

Amiable and cheerful, the plump prairie-dog lives in communities which stretch for many miles over the Great Plains. One of these prairie-dog cities observed some years ago was estimated to number four hundred million inhabitants—three times the human population of the United States. Such a town was surveyed and found to be two hundred and fifty miles long and one hundred miles wide. In spite of its numbers each of the animals manages to solve its housing problem satisfactorily by digging a burrow about fourteen feet deep which serves as home, base of operations, and refuge from the enemy. In its lair it cunningly evades the coyote, the hawk, and the eagle. But there is no escape from the badger and the black-footed ferret, for they dig their way relentlessly into the burrow with fatal results for the defenseless prairie-dog.

Measuring only about a foot in length, the squirrel-like inhabitant of these holes possesses an appetite that is better suited to an animal twice its size. It is particularly fond of green vegetation, grasses, and other luxuries of the garden and pasture, and because of its destructive raids has been classified among the vermin, to be hunted and destroyed. Its plump brown body is no longer a familiar sight on the prairies; the prairie-dog has become more furtive.

Against the mortal attacks of spreading civilization the prairie-dog employs an exasperating natural weapon—its fertility. Early in May the female brings forth a litter of young pups which may number from four to eight. By the end of the month these stout new youngsters are up and around, their short tails sticking out proudly behind them, aping the vivacious movements of their parents. The end of the summer finds them full-grown, ready to assume the responsibilities of their existence.

The prairie-dog always sports a well-fed, sleek body, especially when, with the coming of the summer, vegetation becomes abundant. The extra layer of fat it

PRAIRIE-DOG *(Cynomys ludovicianus).*
Length: 1 foot. Range: Great Plains region. Much persecuted.
J. W. Jackson

carries at this season is very useful in the colder regions of its habitat, keeping it warm during the ensuing short period of winter hibernation.

At the beginning of the century, naturalists were completely mystified by the assertion that the owl, the rattlesnake, and the prairie-dog shared the same burrow. This curious belief has since been explained, for it has been discovered that rattlesnakes will prey upon the young of the prairie-dog, while the "dog" itself will make short work of the owl. An explanation of the origin of the legend may be that a hungry rattlesnake will often invade the burrow in search of food. On such occasions the prairie-dog will scurry out of harm's way, and make haste to dig a new home. The placid burrowing owl seeks out one of the abandoned burrows in order to forego the effort of building a home for itself.

Prairie-dogs are also called barking squirrels, burrowing squirrels, and, in some isolated localities, wishtonwish. Six species and subspecies have been described from our western States, where buried telephone cables are covered with a special protective armor to guard them from attacks by these sharp-toothed rodents. A few introduced colonies seem to have flourished for a time in Louisiana, South Carolina, and on Nantucket Island, Massachusetts.

CHIPMUNK

BLACK and white stripes blend into gray as the sparkling-eyed eastern chipmunk bounds over rock fences, through green pastures, and into the shade of a clump of trees. With quick, nervous movements it alertly scours the ground for acorns, nuts, and seeds and seems to gobble up its food hurriedly. But as it continues to forage, its cheeks swell perceptibly, and when they have attained a mumplike contour, the busy chipmunk is off for home. There it unloads the contents of its cheek pouches. The harvest reaped each autumn day is stored in thrifty anticipation of the rainy days of winter scarcity.

For relaxation, nothing is so fine as lolling about in the sun. The frisky chipmunk can sit motionless and silent on a warm rock,

CHIPMUNK

WESTERN CHIPMUNK *(Eutamias quadrivittatus)*. Length: 8 inches. Range: Western North America.
William Rubin

sometimes balanced on its haunches, cheerily singing a pleasant song sounding like *chip-chip-chip*. Occasionally a number of neighbors will get together for five minutes of community singing. Sometimes they merely seem to be gossiping in hushed tones.

As autumn fades into winter, the bushy-tailed chipmunk settles down in his burrow for a prolonged stay. The burrow, inconspicuously hollowed out without telltale mounds of earth to betray it, winds deviously beneath the frost line. The sleeping chamber is generally a niche covered with a bedding of soft leaves and grass. Other compartments are constructed as pantries for the winter's food. The chipmunk favors a crevice in the rocks as an entrance.

The squirrel-like creature has managed to conceal from scientists its mode of life during hibernation. It is not known whether the stores of food in the underground granary are consumed in the cold winter months, or whether the chipmunk sleeps then, using the food during early spring.

Seemingly refreshed after its underground sojourn, the chipper little animal scampers out of doors to greet the return of spring warmth. This is the mating season, and within a month a brood of four to five young are born to the female. They must rapidly learn to shun such enemies as birds of prey, badgers, and especially the weasel which follows them into their burrow. The chipmunk does have its own animal prey, however, relishing tender young birds, insects, and mice.

On the whole, man has been kind to the chipmunk. In seeming reciprocity these rock squirrels show little fear of humans and will approach them in a friendly way. A morsel of food is always a nice thing with which to reward their trust.

About sixty species and subspecies of the chipmunk are scattered over virtually all of the United States. Of these, Say's chipmunk is typical of the western species. It is out in full force early in the morning, scampering about for wild berries and cherries while occasionally calling out, *chuck-chuck*.

TREE SQUIRREL

IN many public parks throughout the East, the gray squirrel has become so tame that it will feed from the hand. "Here bunny, bunny," the boy pleads as he proffers a peanut. The squirrel comes forward gingerly, a halting few inches at a time, takes a firm grip on the nut with its powerful jaws, and makes off in the twinkling of an eye.

Scampering up the rough bark of a tree it runs out on a limb, squats motionless in a semi-erect position, its short forepaws delicately folded inward to its chest. It proudly displays its prize for a moment, then plunges into the hollow interior of the tree. In midsummer and fall the squirrel buries its find in a hole in the ground to refer to it again during the winter.

Related to the five species of eastern gray squirrels, or cat squirrels as they are also called, are three subspecies of western gray squirrels that frequent the pine and oak tree upon whose seeds they feed. Tufted-eared squirrels, of which there are four, are unique not alone in the possession of long-haired ear tufts but also in their showy color pattern, and their propensity for living in the high plateaus of the southern Rockies.

Fox squirrels number ten species and subspecies and are the largest as well as the most variable in color pattern of all American tree squirrels. Inasmuch as they grow fat in the fall they are preyed upon by hunters.

Red squirrels, which replace the gray squirrel in the West, sometimes jump a hundred feet from tree to tree. They flatten their bodies, rigidly extending behind them the tail which steers them in the manner that feathers control the flight of an arrow. They may lose their footing and fall great distances without perceptible injury. As they fall through the air their feet keep threshing about as if they were actually churning themselves along.

The chicaree or pine squirrel, as the twelve-inch red squirrel is sometimes called, is not only agile but hardy as well. When circumstances force it to leave a district it will swim for as much as a mile to get to better surroundings, which may be any place where trees

GRAY SQUIRREL *(Sciurus carolinensis)*. Length: 1½ feet. Range: Eastern North America.
New York Zoological Society

STRIPED GROUND SQUIRREL (*Citellus tridecemlineatus*). Length: 8 inches. Range: Western United States.
J. W. Jackson

are found. Ingenuity, too, plays a role in the survival of this animal. It can snatch campers' food supplies such as bread, peanut butter, and even meat despite many obstacles put in its path. Thieving blue jays watch the red squirrels cache their winter's supply, but the canny quadrupeds may dig false vaults which occupy the attention of the jays, while they scurry off to find a safer pantry. Some specimens have a strongly developed taste for birds' eggs and young. They also eat grasshoppers and other insects as well as seeds, berries, buds, and nuts.

Red squirrels do not hibernate. During the coldest days of the winter they remain in their nests, which may be a grass-lined tree crotch reinforced with smaller branches, or the hollow of a decayed tree. In fact, it is during the cold months of February and March that the red squirrel seeks a mate. In the spring or early summer the young are born blind, with large heads and naked bodies. They are nursed by the mother until some time in August. Both parents assist in feeding and defending them for some months until they are well able to care for themselves. In this connection, it is interesting to note the varying age at which related animals attain maturity.

If the helpless young must be moved, the mother carries them one at a time, grasping the loose skin of the belly while the young curl their legs and tails around her neck.

Among the enemies of the red squirrel are martens, foxes, hawks, owls, wildcats, and numerous other small forest-dwelling carnivores. The squirrels receive, too, the unwelcome attention of many parasites such as fleas, although they make great efforts to keep themselves clean.

Economically the red squirrel, of which there are some eighteen American forms, is somewhat of an annoyance. In reforestation projects it is apt to remove the seeds as fast as they are laid down. It also eats the young buds of flowers and trees. On the other hand, the red squirrel aids the natural balance of the woodland by burying nuts and seeds where they may sprout in the spring.

GROUND SQUIRREL

IN the mountains of Oregon, ground squirrels live in colonies of twelve up to a hundred or more. They give vent to a shrill whistling call when they sense danger. The warning is taken up and re-echoed all over the settlement. By midsummer the ground squirrel has grown very fat. It goes into hibernation early while there are still days of good weather left.

Among eighty varieties of ground squirrels, the thirteen-lined ground squirrel is distinctive for its color pattern. The striped fur blends with the tall grasses in which the animal is most at home, making it difficult to observe.

In the northern part of the ground squirrel's range it may hibernate as much as six months of the year.

Roving antelope ground squirrels are so called because of their habit of carrying the tail high while they run, exposing a white patch on the under side. This is similar to a rear view of the pronghorn antelope. Active throughout the day, antelope ground squirrels carry their food in cheek pouches to their underground storehouses. They rear several families a year and each litter contains from four to twelve young.

While the squirrel family as a whole gets its name from the Latin word *sciurus,* meaning shade-tailed, the tail of the ground squirrel which digs and lives in an underground burrow is shorter and less brushy than those of its arboreal relatives.

GOLDEN-MANTLED GROUND SQUIRREL *(Callospermophilus lateralis).* Length: 11 inches. Range: Forested mountain slopes of the West.
Natasha Smith

FLYING SQUIRREL

THE flying squirrel is infrequently seen as it is only active at night. During the day it rests in a hollow tree. The flying squirrel actually glides rather than flies. It has a fold of skin along each side which is stiffened by a rod of cartilage from the wrist. These flaps, aided by the flat wide tail, permit the squirrel to soar from the higher branches of one tree to the lower ones of another in short flights. About twenty species and subspecies are found in the forests of our land.

Flesh-Eating Marine Mammals

About seventeen species of marine flesh eaters inhabit the offshore waters of North America. Few of these, however, reach the coasts of the United States. Those that do include the eared sea-lions and fur seals. The earless or hair seals, represented by the harbor seal, are found on the Atlantic coast from the Arctic to the Carolinas. The seldom-seen hooded seal occasionally wanders into New England waters from its more northern range.

Although the finlike limbs of these mammals have lost most of their terrestrial functions, the creatures spend much time ashore, especially during the breeding season. The evolutionary conversion of all the walking limbs to swimming flippers distinguishes this suborder of the carnivores from all of its land-living relatives.

Agile moving bodies with long necks, hairless and clawless front flippers are characteristics of sea-lions; clumsy bodies with short necks, hairy and clawed flippers are characteristics of seals. Furthermore, with the exception of the fur seal of Alaska, the seals lack the external ears of sea-lions and the ability to use their hind limbs in forward rotation. Ashore they are almost helpless. Walruses, one species from the Atlantic Arctic, the other from the Pacific Arctic, are ivory-tusked seal-like mammals of large bulk.

SEA-LION

THE California sea-lion floats patiently beneath the surface of the water, with only the dark tip of its nose protruding. A hungry gull, mistaking the nose tip for a fish, swoops down—straight into the sea-lion's waiting jaws.

This stratagem is only one of the incidental means by which the five-hundred-pound mammal procures its food. It swims swiftly along the California coast, gobbling up daily as much as forty pounds of marine life. At one time it was believed to devour huge quantities of food fishes and a campaign to exterminate sea-lions was launched. However, a saviour, Prof. L. L. Dyke, appeared and conducted a painstaking investigation which proved that sea-lions fed mainly on such enemies of fishermen as squids and devilfish. For some reason, probably connected with digestion, the sea-lion also swallows small round pebbles; one specimen's stomach yielded sixteen pounds of stones as well as a number of mollusk shells.

A captive sea-lion displays remarkable aptitude in learning tricks, and has consequently become one of the favorite performers of vaudeville and circus. Balancing large balls on its nose, juggling and barking rhythmically, are parts of its repertoire. One circus group learned to play a few bars of the anthem *America* on tin horns, and were rewarded after each rendition with tidbits of fish. Unfortunately, the quality of their music deteriorated as the act progressed, one sea-lion skipping half of the notes and another stepping the tempo up in order to obtain the reward more quickly.

The sea-lion in its native state and unassisted by man-made instruments barks in resonant tones which often resemble the erratic, rasping notes of an automobile horn in damp weather. The cries, which may range from basso to soprano, are familiar sounds along certain parts of the coast of California, Oregon, and Washington.

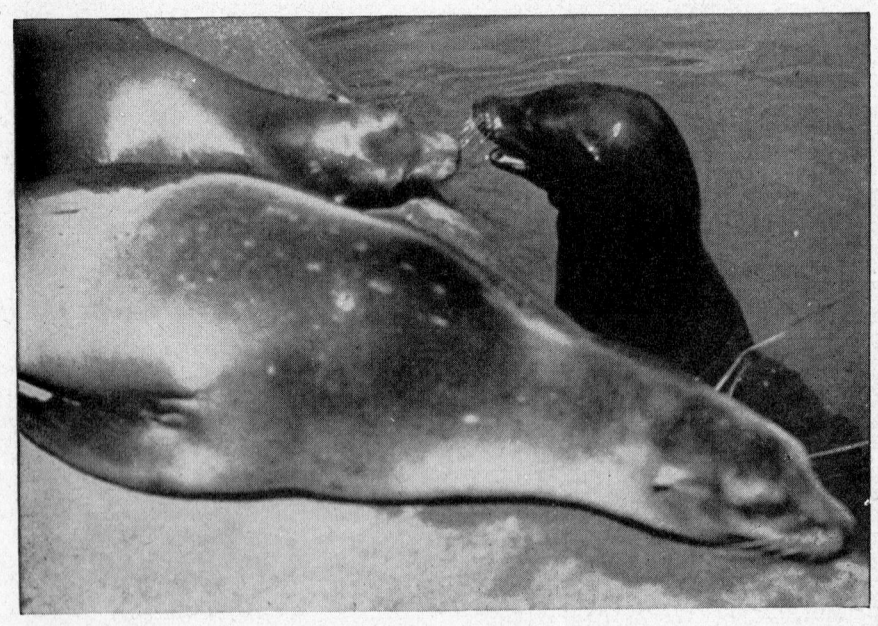

CALIFORNIA SEA LION (*Zalophus californianus*). Length: 8 feet. Range: Coast of California and Mexico.
Ralph De Sola (NYZP)

Here they are both frolicsome and imaginative in their play, spending much time on land. Pups especially do a lot of gamboling near the shore, shaking seaweed, tossing pebbles, and sliding down wet rocks.

If the young male pups are fortunate enough to avoid their main enemies, man and the killer whale, they grow up to attain a length of eight feet, the females being considerably shorter. A crest running from between the eyes to the back of the head also is a male characteristic. The sea-lion's long supple neck, usually held erect, gives it an air of great dignity. When dry, its brown hair is coarse, but becomes sleek and shiny in the water.

During the breeding season the adult males lose their good humor and engage in bloody battles for mates. The piercing screams of the warriors drift far over the ocean as eyes are ripped out, flesh gashed, and lips torn to shreds. Older, weaker males lose the harems built up in their youth to younger and sturdier upstarts. One male may have a controlling interest in as many as twelve females. Females have but one offspring at a time.

A recent sea-lion census taken in California showed that about two thousand remain. Because they are unprotected by conservation laws, sea-lions have been wantonly destroyed in Mexican waters. Huge numbers of them have been killed on their breeding islands and their meat used for canned dog food.

Steller's sea-lion, inhabiting the Northwest coast, is a larger species. Males attain a length of eleven feet and a weight of eighteen hundred pounds. This species replaces the California sea-lion in the northern part of its range which extends from the Farallon Islands to the Bering Sea.

SEAL

ON the rocky Pribilof Islands, off Alaska, the mating season finds the five-hundred-pound male fur seals seizing strategic positions as they await the arrival of the females. When the ladies appear on the scene in early June, furious battles for their possession ensue. The Alaska fur seal assembles larger harems than any other species,

PACIFIC HARBOR SEAL *(Phoca richardii richardii)*. Length: 5 feet. Range: Pacific coast from Oregon northward to Washington, British Columbia, and Alaska.
Ralph De Sola (NZP)

sometimes accumulating as many as one hundred and fifty wives. Consequently, when the smoke of battle has cleared, there are always a number of unwilling bachelors. Some of them may band together in their misery and raid the household of a more prosperous associate. Usually a lucky husband becomes so distrustful that he never leaves the land even for food or drink during the mating season. Within a few weeks his sleek form is reduced to a sadly emaciated state. He barks commands to his females and their broods as he stands guard. His bark can be heard a mile on a clear day.

Mamma fur seal takes good care of her one baby which is born each year any time between June 20 and July 25. She occasionally leaves the baby, who at birth is no bigger than a cat, to spend a few days at sea in search of food. But when she returns, she goes directly to her one pup which she nurses for four months.

Multitudes of fur seals make annual migrations of six thousand miles. They follow the fish schools south to California in winter and return in the spring to the Pribilof Islands where they again set up housekeeping.

They are highly prized commercially. Their coarse, grayish outer fur is plucked out when the pelt is prepared for market, leaving the soft, brown underfur so extensively used in women's coats. However, the dressed fur of muskrats, sold as "Hudson seal," has replaced it as a best seller. Government limitation on the hunting of fur seals has resulted in a steady increase in their population.

Flesh-Eating Land Mammals

The flesh eaters have become the best known of all animals. While such spectacular carnivores as the lion and the tiger are importations to zoos and circuses, native beasts range all the way from the domesticated dog and cat to the massive and ferocious grizzly bear, a furred hurricane when enraged.

All of the foregoing species may be conveniently classified by such well known family designations as cats, dogs, weasels, raccoons, and bears. With the exception of the bears, which are omnivorous, all of the members of these families are carnivorous and without exception prey upon smaller and weaker creatures.

The four-toed or five-toed clawed feet, and large, well-developed teeth fit them for their mode of life. The teeth are divided into small but efficient clipping incisors, large and powerful ripping canines, premolars and molars that shear through flesh and crack bone. The teeth are entirely covered with enamel and are set in short, stout jaws.

Economically valuable because of their fur, the carnivores are perhaps the most hunted of all animals. Where their furs serve no human purpose, they are killed as "harmful vermin."

CANADA LYNX

IN winter the lynx is able to pad about on the snow's surface, its great paws serving as snowshoes, while other less fortunate creatures sink deep in the drifts. Its prominent tufted ears and short tail give it a grotesque appearance, and the fact that its hind legs are much longer than the front ones lends it a strange, ambling gait. At this season the lynx wears a thick, luxuriant coat of grayish fur, interspersed with longer silvery hairs. It is for this valuable pelt that woodsmen trap the overgrown cat.

The lynx leads a shy existence, roaming about alone in the thickest forest and bush country, and consequently is seldom seen. It hunts chiefly at night, but since it is not swift enough to stalk its prey, it usually flattens itself against a limb or boulder to await the coming of an unwary squirrel, rabbit, or game bird. The lynx is famous for its keen eyesight, and the ancients used the term "lynx-eyed" to denote one who was especially sharp-sighted, though, to be sure, some authorities believe the "lynx" of the Greeks to have been the caracal, a long-eared feline of Africa, Arabia, and India.

The Canada lynx preys also on foxes, snakes, and frogs, and is said to kill young deer and mountain sheep by dropping on their back from a tree. This artful animal also obtains food by hijacking. It is most wily in discovering the hiding place where the cougar or mountain lion secretes its loot. In this way it is able to feast on pigs, sheep, or even deer, running no other risk than a chance encounter with the cougar.

The lynx is usually hunted with the aid of dogs which follow its scent; but where dogs are not available or the huntsman desires an arduous sport, he attempts to track the cat through the snow. This may be an all-day job, for the lynx is a master at hiding and at confusing its trailers. The lynx has no fear of water and can swim for considerable distances to throw the pursuer off the track.

WILDCAT *(Lynx rufus)*. Length: 3 feet. Range: Most forested parts of the United States.
New York Zoological Society

In the autumn, when lynxes mate, the males fill the woods with their howling and caterwauling. In the spring the female, somewhat smaller than the male, bears from one to four young in a hollow log or cave. Young lynxes are said to be tamable and to make friendly pets. Like other felines, the lynx is active all year around.

Although this cat's name would indicate Canadian residence it is also found as far south in the northeastern United States as Pennsylvania, whence it occurs westward to the Pacific coast.

BOBCAT

SOME of the lynxes are called bobcats and, except for such superficial differences as the almost complete absence of ear tufts, are more or less like lynxes in habits. Nine species and subspecies of bobcats are known. These range through many forested parts of our country and are encountered in the mountains and on the deserts.

Although the ranges of the two closely related cats overlap, most bobcats are found in warm settled country while lynxes are generally typical of colder and more desolate areas.

Both bobcats and lynxes are often mistaken for overgrown house cats. Critical observation shows, however, that unlike the common cat their legs and feet are larger, tails shorter. Moreover, in wet swampy country wildcats show no dislike of water, while in southern California and Arizona one species exists even in desert country and adapts itself to the dry conditions.

OCELOT

THE tawny, velvet-skinned ocelot or leopard cat makes its home in the trees, walking noiselessly along tenuous branches. This spotted wildcat is most abundant in South and Central America, but stray representatives are still common in the Rio Grande Valley of Texas. In the South American jungles the four-foot-long ocelot's chief prey consists of monkeys. The crafty feline sometimes plays dead in order to attract a band of monkeys, and when they have come too close pounces on a luckless one.

OCELOT (*Felis pardalis griffithii*). Length: 4 feet. Range: Southwestern Texas and northern Mexico.
New York Zoological Society

On the Rio Grande, where there are no monkeys, the ocelot preys on lambs, young pigs, and other small mammals such as rabbits, wood rats, and mice, as well as birds, snakes, lizards, and the like. Its favorite technique is to drop from a tree limb on its unsuspecting victim's back, but it also stalks small wild prey through the woods. Occasionally it raids barnyards to carry off chickens and turkeys. Whatever portion of the carcass the ocelot cannot eat at once is hidden away for future use.

Individual ocelots may vary greatly as to their markings, and a single specimen may be differently marked on its two sides. Similarly, the individuals vary as to temperament. Some captives never accept their fate, remaining vicious and unfriendly; others make tractable pets, permitting themselves to be led about on a leash.

Like the jaguarundi, the ocelot is fond of dense thickets where the thorn-covered chaparral grows and where it is reasonably free of pursuit from its enemies.

JAGUARUNDI

THE brownish-gray, otter-shaped jaguarundi, or cacomitl, is another South American wildcat which has smuggled itself across the Rio Grande in extreme southern Texas. Like the ocelot, this three-foot-long feline climbs about in trees. It pursues its prey, consisting of rats, mice, birds, and rabbits, through almost impenetrable mesquite underbrush. It often goes abroad in the daytime, following regular trails to drinking places. It has been caught by traps set along these trails.

The young of the jaguarundi have been seen in both summer and winter; hence it is inferred that they have no regular breeding time. The jaguarundi is not easily tamed. In its red color phase it is named eyra. But these cats have the same habits, and although at one time zoologists separated the two color phases as two species, today both are recognized as belonging to the same species.

The females of both the ocelots and jaguarundis are smaller than the males and the two cats have many habits in common, although the jaguarundi is more ferocious. Its pelt is not used commercially.

JAGUARUNDI or EYRA *(Felis cacomitli)*.
Length: 3½ feet. Range: Extreme southern Texas, Mexico, Central, and South America.
New York Zoological Society

JAGUAR *(Felis hernandesii)*. Length: 6 feet. Range: Extreme southern borders of Southwest and into Mexico, Central and South America.
New York Zoological Society

JAGUAR

LARGEST and fiercest North American cat, the richly colored jaguar slinks soundlessly behind its prey. Stealthily it glides forward. Then, without warning, it springs, its cruel white fangs bared against the black flesh of its lips. As the dynamic lunge crushes its victim to earth, the jaguar's teeth sink into the defenseless throat.

When the big cat's victim is lifeless, the bleeding carcass is ripped open and the heart, liver, lungs, and breast meat devoured. The jaguar hides the rest of the body under some brush, returning in a day or two for another meal.

After the repast the jaguar uses tongue and forepaws to clean itself. It polishes off the ragged edges of its claws, and cleans them by scratching and sharpening them against the trunk of a tree.

Such helpless creatures as deer, pigs, colts, sheep, or calves are doomed, once their necks are in the clutches of the jaguar's viselike jaws. Even more formidable animals keep their distance from the jaguar which reigns unchallenged below the Rio Grande and along the Mexican boundary of Texas, New Mexico, and Arizona.

It prefers forests and dense thickets, usually prowling about at night. Despite its massive body, its soft paws enable it to move silently as it searches for food. If a large animal is not available, the jaguar will seize lizards, tortoises, and even insects. When it captures a tortoise, it overturns it and neatly plucks the flesh from the shell with its claws. Its lightning rapidity is utilized in fishing, the jaguar crouching along the bank and scooping out fishes as they swim by. It usually ranges near water and is a powerful swimmer.

Where man is concerned, the savage jaguar replaces valor with discretion. Only under stress will it attack a human being. When it does, however, it gives no such warning as a growl or lashing of the tail, but springs suddenly. Stock owners, whose cattle have been preyed upon, track the jaguar with dogs. Sometimes claw markings on trees are a clue that the big cats are in the vicinity. As the dogs close in, the jaguar seeks refuge in a tree or on a high boulder, and is there dispatched with a rifle shot. Few of these jungle cats now remain within the United States although they once roamed as far as Arkansas, Colorado, and California.

Jaguars are monogamous. The females give birth to two or three, sometimes four, cubs in April or May. The males are good fathers, helping to bring in food for the family. When the kittens are a few weeks old, they are able to leave the rocky den where they were born and trot about after their mother. After the first year, the young cubs are able to look after themselves.

Jaguars reach full growth when five years old, although they are able to breed at the age of three. Males are sometimes seven feet long and weigh about two hundred pounds, the females being somewhat smaller and lighter. The fur is a rich tan, profusely decorated above with black spots. The under parts are whitish with small black markings.

The limbs of the jaguar are short and strong and the whole body is a picture of muscular vitality. When the animal runs on its short limbs, its belly is close to the ground. It can maintain great speed only for short distances, a disadvantage which has caused many a jaguar to lose its fine pelt to hunters. Sometimes the jaguar utters deep, hoarse roars as it runs.

In captivity, the solitary jaguar may not even appreciate a mate's company. One savage male in the New York Zoological Park instantly killed a female that had been placed in his cage, by crunching her neck bones.

The jaguar is usually called *tigre* in Central and South America but it appears to be more nearly related to the leopard of Africa than to the tiger of Asia.

COUGAR

STEALTHILY padding along at dusk, the sand-colored cougar, or puma, despite its hundred-and-sixty-pound bulk is scarcely visible against the grayish rocks of the southwestern plateau. In the darkening mountain shadows its eyes shine like coals as it silently approaches its victim. Once within striking distance, it bounds forward and crushes its prey to earth. It has been known to leap twenty feet into the air to land on a branch and to jump twice that distance to the ground.

The great cat promptly begins to gorge itself. When sated, it delicately licks its blood-spattered face and paws and goes off for a nap. On awakening it returns to finish off the carcass or, if the prey is too large, drags it to a lair among the rocks. The cougar's most common victims are deer, wapiti, peccary, and domestic cattle.

Sometimes the cougar conceals itself on the branch of a tree or an overhanging ledge to leap down upon a passing animal. This fierce creature is the second largest of the American cats, the largest being the jaguar. In a fight between the two the jaguar usually has the advantage, but sometimes the puma's greater speed gives it the victory.

Despite its ferocity with animals, the cougar runs from an encounter with man and has thus acquired an undeserved reputation for cowardice. Men hunt the cougar with the help of dogs which rout it out of its daytime lair. The pursued cougar usually seeks safety by climbing a tree. As the dogs encircle the tree, the hunters bring down the "lion" with their rifles. If the cat descends before the men have arrived, it will give a fierce account of itself in battling the dogs. A few inveterate sportsmen have successfully wrestled the puma barehanded.

In the spring the female, who is smaller than her mate, returns to her den, where to the accompaniment of almost human shrieks she brings forth her kittens. The mother cares for her playful young, bringing home a portion of each kill, until they are old enough to shift for themselves. Before the young ones leave her

PUMA *(Felis couguar)*. Length: 7 feet. Range: "Formerly found over practically all of North America as far north as the Great Lakes, Maine, and southern Alberta; now extinct in much of this range" (Anthony).
New York Zoological Society

care, she takes them with her on hunting trips, to show them how it is done.

Once a black bear out for a walk passed the cave of a cougar and her young. Afraid that the bear meant harm to her brood, the puma attacked. So violent was the struggle that finally both combatants rolled down the hillside and were found dead at the bottom, locked in a death embrace.

A baby puma may be trained to become a frolicsome pet but never loses its dislike of dogs. The young have brown spots on their tan fur and resemble lion cubs. As they reach maturity, the color becomes a uniform yellowish or reddish brown with dabs of black and white on the head. The fur is soft and thick.

Cougars, depending on the section in which they live, are also known by such names as puma, mountain lion, *leon*, panther, and its colloquial corruption—painter. Only slight geographical variations of size and color distinguish the eight species and subspecies formerly found over virtually all of our country, but today they are either extinct in many regions or facing extinction wherever they prey upon livestock.

FOX

IN the autumn hunting season the sharp-nosed red fox has ample opportunity to prove its much vaunted guile. Pursued by a pack of savage hounds eager to rend the quarry to pieces, the fox's chief hope for safety lies in trickery. To throw its pursuers off the scent it runs along a wall, crosses a stream diagonally, or dashes over a newly fertilized field. From time to time it doubles back and zigzags to confuse the hounds. When streams are beginning to freeze over, it cautiously tests the ice before venturing across. If the covering is thin, the fox curls its long bushy tail about its paws and sits calmly down on the bank to watch the heavier hounds crash through into the icy water. So inventive is the red fox when hunted that it has even been known to leap on the back of a sheep and ride for some distance in order to break the scent left by the glands in its feet.

The fox shows its intelligence when hunting as well as when hunted. It is a clever poultry stealer, adept at entering chicken coops. It tracks down rabbits, mice, and muskrats with the help of its acute senses of smell and hearing. But it is not above eating

RED FOXES (*Vulpes fulva*). Length: 3¼ feet. Range: Most of the United States and Canada in suitable localities.
Alajos Schuszler

grubs, beetles, and even grapes to round out its diet. The grapes, as we know from Aesop's famous fable, must be strictly sweet. Food surpluses are carefully hidden away for future use. A fox, if unmolested, rarely strays more than five miles from home, except in winter when food is scarce.

The fox shows its true genius in ridding itself of fleas. Taking a stick in its mouth, the fox submerges slowly in a pool of water. As it sinks, the fleas move upward to drier regions. When only the wood remains above the surface, the fleas desert the sinking fox to take refuge on the raft. Thereupon the fox releases the stick, leaving the fleas to their fate.

The fox takes but one mate. In the beginning of spring the two make their home in a den or hole which may previously have belonged to a woodchuck, badger, or skunk. The home is provided with several exits and is kept scrupulously clean. Fifty days later a litter of four to nine is born. For the first nine days the young are entirely dependent on their mother's care. During this time the father is not allowed to enter the home, but spends his time procuring food. Once the pups are able to open their eyes, the parents begin to teach them the many tricks involved in hunting and in evading their enemies. The lynx, wolf, and fisher are the chief animal menaces, but far more dangerous are the traps set by men intent on hanging fox pelts around the necks of women.

The four varieties of red fox are marked by their different coloring. The rarest and most valuable is the silver fox; next in importance is the black fox, which is quite common; the third breed, the cross fox, is reddish yellow in color; the most common is the red fox. These color varieties, however, are known to occur in the same litter and are therefore not accorded even subspecific rank. Five species and subspecies of the red fox inhabit the United States. Related to them are six species and subspecies of the smaller, less clever kit foxes which burrow in the western plains and prairies. The twelve species and their derivative subspecies of gray or tree foxes resemble their rufous relative, aside from their tawny-white color, but their legs are slightly longer. Not as cunning as the red fox, the gray, whose fur is not as greatly prized, is much easier to observe and to trap.

COYOTE

THOUGH the buffalo and the old-fashioned bad men have vanished from the West, the plaintive bark of the coyote or prairie wolf is still commonly heard at night in the mountain and prairie country. These "barking wolves" owe their preservation no doubt to their extreme cunning as well as their small size. Today, it is believed, they are even more plentiful than in the days of Buffalo Bill.

The coyote is smaller than a timber wolf, weighing about thirty pounds. Its soft fur is reddish or tawny gray, sometimes tipped with black. The tail is bushy, the ears upright, and the slender muzzle is sharply pointed. The coyote presents a rather unkempt and ragged appearance.

Coyotes are popularly held to be cowards because they keep out of man's way, yet feed on dead men. At one time the term "coyote" applied to a man was an insult calling for blood. This wolf, however, should not be termed a coward, for in combat with a wildcat it gives a good account of itself. Its "cowardice" is in reality cleverness. Like a crow, the coyote is said to be aware of the presence of guns. It may rest quietly within eyeshot of a man without a gun, but such is its swiftness that an armed hunter rarely can approach within shooting distance. The coyote is also clever in eluding traps and avoiding the poisoned meat sometimes set for it by sheep herders and cattle raisers.

By day coyotes sleep in hollows among rocks or in burrows deserted by other animals. They hunt at night. In summer they subsist chiefly on gophers, mice, rabbits, and birds that nest on the ground. In chasing rabbits they usually work in pairs. It is in the winter, when smaller victims are scarce, that the coyotes form into packs to prey on cattle or sheep, which they harass into exhaustion. Sometimes the coyotes invade barnyards to carry off chickens or turkeys. In former days the pronghorn antelope was a frequent victim.

Only on rare occasions, when a coyote is smitten with rabies, will it invade civilized communities in broad daylight. Such unusual behavior gives rise to a "coyote scare." Thousands of dollars are paid out each year in bounties, in an effort to exterminate coyotes which are sometimes hunted like foxes. The raw pelts can be sold for about seven dollars.

Coyotes mate in February and bring forth a litter of three to ten in April. The pups' eyes remain closed until the eighth or ninth day. At the age of seven weeks they partake of solid food brought to the den by the parents. In the fall the young are prepared to leave home and shift for themselves. Young coyotes are often preyed upon by the great horned owl, the eagle, and the timber wolf. Man, however, is their chief enemy.

There are eight species and subspecies of coyotes in the United States. The males are appreciably larger than the females.

COYOTES *(Canis latrans)*. Length: 4 feet. Range: Western North America.
Ralph De Sola (AMNH)

WOLF

IN a rocky den or hollow tree, a mother wolf gives birth to a litter ranging from three to thirteen. More than a week later the wolf pups open their eyes and see the light of day for the first time. Still helpless, they are cared for by their mother and father who are believed to mate for life. The little wolves behave like puppies during their first months, frolicking, wrestling, and "playing tag."

During their carefree childhood, their mother treats them to such delicious tidbits as crickets which she obtains by overturning rocks. The father also helps provide them with food and spends considerable time doing guard duty outside the family den. He may even offer himself as a sacrifice in place of his children, because he will go within shooting distance of a hunter in order to divert attention from the den.

The pups soon develop keen sight and a sharp sense of smell. No longer satisfied with such small animals as crickets, they develop a lust for the flesh of large animals like cattle, deer, moose, rabbits, and birds. When desperately hungry they will nibble bark and vegetation.

Some wolves hunt alone, others in pairs, but in winter it is common for a family to roam swiftly over the plains in a small pack. Hot on the scent of prey, they give vent to their excitement by a drawn-out, barking howl. They leap upon a victim from the rear, cruelly tearing out pieces of meat while the animal writhes in agony. If edible portions of the carcass remain after the feast, the wolves may return the following day. However, in summer when food is plentiful, they make fresh kills for each meal.

TIMBER WOLF *(Canis nubilus)*. Length: 5 feet. Range: United States except in parts of the Southwest. Extinct in much of its range which extends into Arctic America.
New York Zoological Society

This strong, hundred-pound animal plagues cattle owners with its depredations among livestock. Bounties are offered for the killer, which has learned to keep clear of men and guns. It is even cunning enough to avoid most traps, especially since it prefers warm meat to dead bait. Poison sprinkled on meat has frequently failed to produce results because the wolf will not touch the doctored stuff, leaving it for a less wily, though harmless, creature. Some hunters state that their best season is in late spring during the infancy of the cubs, because if the den can be located, it is easy to kill the faithful parents and capture the helpless offspring.

Captive specimens generally retain their unpleasant disposition. Some at least seem to enjoy nothing better than an opportunity to use their iron jaws on another animal's body. Dr. Hornaday wrote that a wolf in captivity "will watch and coax for hours to induce a neighbor in the next cage to thrust through tail or paw so that he may instantly seize it and chew it off." However, a wolf captured young may be raised with dogs, becoming quite tame.

Zoologists still have not agreed on the classification of American wolves. Those with such names as gray wolf, black wolf, and red wolf differ in color but are structurally similar. The males, averaging five feet in length, are larger and heavier than the females. Wolves are most populous in the Midwest, though their range extends to other sections of the country not completely taken over by urban civilization. Dr. Harold E. Anthony recognizes nine species and subspecies of North American wolves.

The typical gray wolf is also known as the timber wolf and buffalo wolf, the latter referring to its slaughter of buffaloes in those bygone days when the West was "wild." Along the Mexican border it is called *lobo*, the Spanish word for wolf.

BADGER

A SMALL, thick-set, silver-gray creature with a short bushy tail, the badger spends the greater part of the night burrowing for ground animals. The five claws on each of its paws enable it to dig down five or six feet with startling speed. Sometimes the badger

BADGER *(Taxidea taxus).* Length: 2¼ feet. Range: Central States to Saskatchewan.
New York Zoological Society

makes its home in a burrow it has dug while hunting; sometimes it digs a special burrow to live in. Though it is usually active all year, it hibernates in cold regions. Because of its underground existence, the badger is rarely seen.

Their range and their digging bring badgers in contact with prairie-dogs, ground squirrels, gophers, and related burrowing rodents. They feast on all of these as well as on birds, birds' eggs, and sometimes insects.

When these animals were more numerous in the western and central plains, men and horses often broke their legs in badger holes. The badger's constant digging has also made the animal unpopular with farmers and cattlemen. Each badger hole, however, usually signifies the death of one or more rodents that are also enemies of man.

Full protection should be given badgers in return for their rodent-destroying habits. They are especially useful in regions where irrigation ditches suffer from the dike-boring activities of rats.

The badger is monogamous. A litter of two to four is born in late spring in the underground habitation. Four subspecies of badgers are recognized by Dr. Gerritt S. Miller, Jr.

These animals are sly and difficult to trap. If a badger is cornered, its first effort is to dig itself in, seeming to disappear into the earth as if by magic. As a last recourse, the badger will fight to the death, and this gameness on the animal's part has given rise to the cruel sport of badger baiting, in which dogs are set on a cornered badger while the spectators await the outcome.

Dr. Anthony has vividly described the burrowing animal in his *Field Book of North American Mammals:* "A badger that I once came upon as he began digging out a squirrel was only just below the surface and the ejected earth was flying forth in leisurely spurts. The badger sensed my footsteps as I drew near and immediately changed his tempo. Muttered snarling and rumbling began to pour out of the hole, and a geyser of earth leaped up four or five feet into the air. As I looked on, the height of this earth column dropped almost with the seconds and in a very short time the badger was so deep that no more earth reached the surface and the sounds of his subterranean rage were only faintly audible." Other observers have confirmed this.

BADGER AT HOLE.
A. C. Fox

The best shaving brushes are made of badger hair which is used for other kinds of brushes as well. A thick pelt is sometimes used for coat collars and was formerly made into frontiersmen's caps. A courageous, short-legged, and underslung hound has been bred to "badger" the badger. The dachshund or badger hound, an ancient breed developed in Germany, is fast winning favor in many parts of the country where it is appreciated for its keen scenting and tracking powers as well as its elongated appearance.

WOLVERINE

ARCH criminal of nature's underworld, the wolverine cunningly follows the trapper through the forests of the northern United States. At night its dark brown body, trimmed on the sides with stripes of yellowish white, blends with the hazy gray-shadowed snow as it stalks the trapper. As soon as each trap is set, it breaks it open, steals the bait or the captive animal, then destroys the metal mechanism. But the night's work is still unfinished, for though its tremendous appetite has been satiated, it is loath to stop plundering. Until the light of dawn, it continues despoiling the traps, hiding the prey for future consumption.

Not without reason has the wolverine also been called a glutton, and not without reason have stories of its evil spirit and bloodthirsty traits awed and vexed trappers and Indians. Aside from its usual raids on traps it has been known to steal blankets, clothes, and cooking utensils. Even though it has never gone in for housekeeping, in at least one instance it carried off a roomful of furniture. When hungry it is always ready to match its amazing strength against any enemy. Attacking and killing larger animals and, when injured by hunters, fouling their guns are some of its versatile accomplishments.

A gangster of the most rapacious type, the wolverine is truly a triple-threat animal. It can swim, climb the more easily accessible trees, and, in spite of its squat heavy body, run fast enough in the snowbound forest to further its own ends. It is a rare animal and, because seldom seen by the hunter and traveler, tales of its ferocity and devilish cunning have been handed down by hearsay, exaggerated

WOLVERINE *(Gulo luscus)*. Length: 3½ feet. Range: Northern United States. Rare.
New York Zoological Society

and embellished with feats beyond the animal's most ambitious capabilities. Some of these stories may be attributed to the gullibility of trappers, or to the inspired imagination of the casual observer. But in this great garment of myth there still is some patch of truth. Sharp teeth, large curved claws, and a powerful body, three and a half feet long, make the wolverine a potent engine of destruction in its own corner of the world. Mice, ground squirrels, beavers, birds, and fishes are normal staples on its diet, although it does not disdain leftovers and carrion. When an opportunity presents itself it has been known to bring down deer and caribou, and even attack the lordly moose. It is related that even big bears will run off rather than battle with a wolverine.

The day of the wolverine is spent in holes, burrows, or subterranean caves deserted by bears. In March it mates in these hide-outs. Three or four months later the short-tempered female brings forth a litter of two to five precocious offspring. In these maternal months the female, though smaller than her mate, is decidedly more pugnacious, ever watchful over her ill-tempered, savage little brood, and if disturbed does not hesitate to attack even man.

Largest of the weasel family, the wolverine, also known as the carcajou, is highly prized for its useful warm fur. A number of pelts stitched together give excellent service as automobile robes or hearth rugs. Indians have discovered a decided advantage in using this long-haired fur, since it will not frost, and have fashioned it into trimmings and fringes for their garments.

The Californian and Alaskan wolverines are two species related to the common wolverine, differing from it only in color. Their innate instincts for destruction and stealing are fully as great.

SKUNK

A GLOSSY black-and-white coat, tapering into a bushy tail— the kind that one likes to stroke—are but the handsome surface features of the skunk. Unseen, less pleasant to the touch, but so very important, are the glands under its tail. From these hidden glands comes the skunk's sticky, yellow, foul-smelling discharge. That alone has made the skunk notorious.

The animal world knows no more malodorous stench than that which an angry skunk emits. The unpleasant smell may be wafted by the winds for more than half a mile, throwing a pall over even the pastoral fragrance of verdant, flowered country.

This four-legged stench bomb, however, launches its gas attack only under stress. It retreats from open warfare if possible, disliking to disturb the peace. But if it fears danger or is angered, it tries no subtle skirmishes or sly flank maneuvers. Instead it prepares for open battle by turning its back and lifting high its tail. Ready, it fires one barrage of its liquid cannonballs, only two or three drops sprayed a distance of ten feet. The musk is strong enough to burn the skin and may cause blindness if it enters the eyes. At the very least, it has the effectiveness of a screen of nauseating gas. Small wonder that the skunk is considered fearless.

SKUNK

The skunk is little seen because it prowls about at night in search of mice, grasshoppers, and other insects which annoy farmers. Contrary to popular belief, most skunks do not eat poultry; they do, however, worry some farmers because they like to eat the roots of hops, the beer ingredient. One of the skunk's favorite dining places, and the one where it is most likely to be encountered by man, is the garbage pail of a camper or farmer.

Unlike most other animals, its numbers have increased rather than diminished with the encroachment of civilization. The larger mammals which preyed upon it have become depleted, while its food supply has become more plentiful. Most men have adopted, perhaps wisely, a good neighbor policy toward the skunk.

In the daytime the skunk usually sleeps in its den, which may be either a burrow, a deserted woodchuck hole, a cave, or a hollow log. During the winter the handsome catlike animal emerges from its torpor only during spells of mild weather. Six to ten little skunks

EASTERN SKUNK *(Mephitis nigra)*. Length: 2 feet. Range: "New England and Middle Atlantic States; south to Virginia; west to Indiana" (Howell).
New York Zoological Society

are born to the female in the spring. A month or two later, they can follow their mother on foraging expeditions through the forest, walking single file. It is asserted that the last one in the procession can be captured by carefully seizing its tail and lifting it off the ground. Grasped in this fashion, the skunk is powerless to eject its musk.

Young skunks can be tamed and sometimes become amusing pets, although this is not a common practice for obvious reasons. Man is more interested in the skunk's fur than in the animal itself, and many a woman's fur piece or coat has been lifted from the back of the lowly skunk.

Sometimes called the polecat, this twenty-four-inch creature is distinguished by the broad white stripes down its back. The spotted skunk, a related species, is similar in appearance, somewhat smaller, and the white in its pelage is irregularly splotched. In the Southwest it has been called the "hydrophobia skunk" because of the current belief that its bite will produce rabies.

In the United States there are thirteen species of spotted skunks, thirteen large striped skunks, a closely related species in southern Arizona called the hooded skunk, and four species and subspecies of hognosed skunks along the Mexican border.

OTTER

IN winter the frolicsome otters make chutes in the snowbanks near ponds and lakes and slide downward to splash loudly in the water. The air is full of the growling and chattering that everywhere accompany their movements. Sometimes in the midst of play an otter will emit a sharp whistle that can be heard a long distance. As they romp about in the snow, the sun glistens on their shiny brown skins. With their broad webbed feet folded backward, the whiskered mammals are able to slide on their chests.

When the snow melts, the otters slide down slippery mud banks. These are prepared with great care by removing every little stone and projecting root. The bank is made slippery by the water held in the wet fur.

OTTER

The otter is a speedy swimmer and maneuvers with amazing dexterity. Using its sixteen-inch tail as a rudder, it races after fishes, young beavers, and frogs, changing its course as swiftly as a trout. Fishes are grasped between the forepaws and ripped open with the help of the pointed teeth. Usually the head is eaten first. In the last century, when otters were still fairly common throughout the United States, fishermen sometimes reported that, their nets having been raided by otters, their entire catch was headless.

The otter makes its home in a hollow which it digs in the bank of a pond or river. Usually the entrance is under water, and often it is guarded by the gnarled roots of a great tree. The dwelling itself is lined with water grasses and bark.

Though ordinarily found close to the water, the otter can make overland journeys of many miles when its home fisheries are frozen. In mountain regions it negotiates difficult snow-covered slopes in search of rushing streams not yet covered with ice. During the search it may attack domestic or wild fowl, muskrats, ducks, and geese.

So agile is the streamlined otter that, both by land and water, it can avoid the clutches of any animal large enough to fight it. When it does choose to fight, it can easily defeat a dog. Only man can capture it, but in some instances the otter may even elude the intrepid hunter. If pursued in snowy country, it escapes by hurling its body forward and then sliding a considerable distance on its belly. A series of these sudden leaps enables it to outdistance a trapper on snowshoes. Otter fur is durable, and a pelt brings from ten to thirty dollars.

Caught alive, young otters are easily tamed and become good pets. A pack of twelve trained otters exhibited in 1939 by a Minnesota trapper proved to be able "to perform tricks, follow a scent, retrieve pheasants and ducks with the speed of a prize cocker spaniel." All, however, were bred, raised, and trained in captivity. These animals nevertheless have been driven out into unsettled country, although in England they are so well treated that they live almost at the outskirts of large cities and are common inhabitants of the countryside.

OTTER *(Lutra canadensis)*. Length: 3¼ feet. Range: Most of North America. Extinct in many parts of its range.
New York Zoological Society

The otter is monogamous. Each spring from three to five young are born and are hidden in the home until able to protect themselves.

Besides the typical Canadian otter best known in this country from the northeastern and Middle Atlantic States, six other subspecies have been described as the Sonora otter, California otter, Pacific otter, Florida otter, Carolina otter, and the interior otter of the Nebraska region.

SEA OTTER

THE four-foot-long sea otter has the same frolicsome disposition as its landlocked brother. Tossing a bit of seaweed high over its head with one paw, it catches it on the way down in the other paw.

The food consists of shellfishes, cuttlefishes, and fishes. Crustaceans are held in the forepaws and struck together until the shell is cracked open; then the otter sucks out the contents. Kelp and seaweed are eaten when no other food is available.

Sea otters are usually found near a kelp bed, and it is in these beds that the young are born. The parents play with the little ones, which mature at the age of four or five years. Sea otters are able to dive more than three hundred feet beneath the surface when pursued by killer whales and sea-lions.

Today the sea otter, which was extensively hunted for its skin, has become exceedingly rare. A choice skin brought $1,340 in the London market in 1900. A white man is now fined $500 for killing a sea otter. Eskimos, however, whose economic life has for centuries been bound up with the creatures, are not penalized.

The species sometimes seen in a very few localities along the coast of southern California is the southern sea otter which is larger and not as dark as the typical species known from Alaskan waters. In 1938 a herd was observed off Monterey County, California, not only by interested scientists, but also by men eager to capture them for their valuable pelts. Stones, firecrackers, and bullets were used in attempts to pick off the otters. It was reported that a Hollywood actress had paid $4,500 for three pelts taken off the Monterey coast, and the rumor made the future of the small band of otters still more precarious.

WEASEL

A LARGE parasite in its stomach is said to drive the weasel to its unbridled ferocity and wanton killing. There is no beast in forest, plain, or marsh so feared by the host of small rodents and ground-nesting birds. Marmot and woodchuck, gopher and muskrat crouch in their burrows and seem to be safe—but should a weasel appear at the entrance, they are lost.

This terrible little animal, of elongated muscular body, short powerful legs, and strong thin neck, follows like fate wherever its victim may lead. Unbelievably quick, it springs to attack, sinking its sharp teeth into the large veins of the neck. Then it devours the brains and sucks the blood of the victim. The flesh of the carcass is untouched. In a colony of rodents or a chicken coop, a single weasel will continue an orgy of blood letting until it has killed all the occupants.

Utterly fearless, the weasel will march into a trap without suspicion. And then its fury and desperation know no bounds. It puts up a strenuous fight even against insurmountable odds. A story related by Ernest Thompson Seton concerns an eagle which, upon

ERMINE or WEASEL (*Mustela cicognani*). Length: 10 inches. Range: All of North America in suitable localities. Rare.
New York Zoological Society

being shot down, was found to have the skull of a weasel attached by the teeth to its throat. Apparently the bird had pounced on the small animal and nearly lost its life as the desperate weasel sought to administer its typical *coup de grâce*.

Weasels attack animals many times their size and even in the presence of humans may emerge from hiding to have another look at the intruder. It is so speedy that some people believe the weasel can get out of the way of a bullet by dodging as it sees the flash of the gun.

Thirty-six species and subspecies of the weasel are found all over North America and are also known as ferret, stoat, or ermine. The latter name is most properly applied to the family's representative in the Arctic regions, although in its winter coat any weasel might be called ermine. In colder regions winter cloaks the weasel in pure white except for the black tip of the tail, and this fur is highly prized. Normally the soft underfur and long hard outer hairs are brown on the upper parts and white on the under side. The male is somewhat larger than the female, his average length being eleven inches to her nine. Martens and other members of the weasel group also have males larger than females.

Two to three litters a year add to the weasel family. Each litter may contain four to eight young whose mother will defend them with extreme courage.

The natural enemies of the weasel, to be sure, are none too many. Yet horned owls, the fox, the lynx, and larger relatives like the mink and the fisher prey upon it with occasional success.

MARTEN

ALSO known as the American or Hudson Bay sable, the marten, closely related to the weasels, makes its home in the pine and fir forests of the northern reaches of America. Constantly trapped and hunted, the marten is diminishing rapidly although sudden increases in its numbers every two or three years aid it to survive. Hunters regard this increase as a harbinger of great snows. Larger than the weasel, it has all the predatory traits of that animal and climbs about in the trees with the agility of a squirrel. Ferocious and unsociable, martens are rarely seen together except when fighting or mating.

The marten is trapped profitably only from October to April when fur is at its best. While not as fine as the pelts of the Russian sable, its fur is of considerable value commercially. After April the fur begins to thin out and the female is preoccupied with rearing her litter of one to five, which arrives late in this month. The young are blind for the first month or so of their lives.

MARTEN or SABLE *(Martes americana)*. Length: 1¾ feet. Range: Forests of northern United States and Canada. Rare.
New York Zoological Society

FERRET

A LARGE member of the weasel family, the black-footed ferret is the special nemesis of the prairie-dog. The ferret makes its home in the Great Plains where its fat little victim is to be found in large numbers. It enters the abode of the hapless marmot, slaughters the entire family, and takes the hole over as a base of further operations. Strictly a flesh eater, the ferret sustains itself on field mice and other small mammals, as well as birds and their eggs.

The ferret is the largest member of the weasel family, the male reaching a length of nineteen inches, the female being an inch shorter. Little is known of the habits of this animal in the wild state, but under domestication it is most efficient in hunting rabbits in the open and in dislodging rats from inaccessible retreats in buildings. The facility and thoroughness of this carnivore has caused the word "ferret" to be applied to a similar process when employed by peace officers seeking human malefactors in hiding.

FISHER

THE clever fast-moving fisher makes a nuisance of itself by stealing bait from traps set out for the ermine and the marten. It concerns itself very little with the questions of family relationship, frequently killing and eating its cousin, the pine marten, which it pursues through the trees with the agility of a squirrel.

At home in a variety of topographical conditions ranging from swamps to mountain sides, from northern New York State to the Pacific coast, the fisher eats frogs, fishes, dead rabbits and chipmunks, ground birds and even snakes.

In color the fisher varies from glossy black to brown, splotched occasionally with gray or white on the neck, head, and abdomen. Its length may be all of twenty-three inches. It is also called pekan, pennant marten, black cat, and black fox. One species is recognized and is divided into two subspecies. Its pelt is also sought by furriers.

MINK (*Mustela vison*). Length: 1½ feet. Range: Gulf of Mexico to the Arctic Circle in suitable localities.
New York Zoological Society

MINK

SOMEWHAT more robust than the ordinary weasel, the mink is colored uniformly darker and spends much of its time in the vicinity of water where it catches its food. Its home may be a burrow in a bank or a small den in a pile of logs or rocks.

The mink has the characteristic musky odor common to all the members of the weasel family. It is as bloodthirsty a killer as any of its relatives. While it thrives on such helpless animals as rabbits and muskrats, it is fully capable of catching such elusive fish as the trout. It is also known to include snakes, mice, and rats in its diet. The fur of the mink is highly prized as it has uniform color and solid texture. Under parts are a dark brown like the upper parts. The under side of the chin has a white area.

One brood a season comes to the mink family in which there may be as many as ten young born from April to May. When first caught, the mink's rage knows no bounds, but later it may be tamed and will then become an interesting pet. About a dozen North American species of mink are known. These range from the Gulf of Mexico to the Arctic Circle.

RACCOON

ON SUMMER days a raccoon family is sometimes seen sunning itself, high in a tree, where it occasionally expropriates a hawk's or crow's nest for a resting place. The raccoon's fur is a rich mixture of gray, black, and brown with broad bands of gray and black adorning the tail. Black patches under the eyes give the creature's face a masked appearance. The ears are held erect and prominent.

Raccoons go abroad chiefly by night. Usually in small groups, representing one or more families, they forage for fruits, vegetables, small mammals, and birds, raiding farmers' barnyards when wild food is scarce. Good swimmers, they are adept at catching fish; indeed they are often caught by traps placed underwater. They are especially addicted to shellfish, which they open with great dexterity. Before eating a piece of meat or other food the fastidious raccoon must carefully wash it, swishing it about in water until it is a formless pulp. In captivity the raccoon will not touch meat unless there is water to wash it in, nor will it permit its keeper to do the washing. Its specific name, *lotor*, means washer.

RACCOONS *(Procyon lotor)*. Length: 2½ feet. Range: Most parts of the United States, Mexico, and southern Canada.
Ralph De Sola (NYZP)

As a rule raccoons spend the daytime hours curled up in hollow trees. In time of danger they invariably take to the trees and do not venture far from the woods. They are never found in fir forests, because these do not provide the necessary hollows. The animals hibernate in winter, emerging only during warm spells.

The raccoon hunt is a familiar rural sport. A large coon, thirty inches in length and weighing fifty pounds, can give a good account of itself in a battle with dogs, and many a valiant coon hound has died on the field of honor. The raccoon is not a swift runner and takes to a tree as soon as the dogs come too close. Then the hunters either fell the tree or shoot their prey with the help of flashlights. Raccoons have considerably diminished in numbers but seem in no immediate danger of extinction.

The fur was formerly used for the coonskin caps worn by most early pioneers and such caps may still be found in a few sporting-goods stores. Today raccoon is used chiefly for the great bulky coats worn at football games, and as collar trimming.

The raccoon is one of the few American mammals that is without European representatives. Some six subspecies of the common raccoon are distributed over most of North America.

RINGTAIL

RELATED to the raccoon is the rather rare and handsome ring-tailed cat, also known as bassarisk or cacomistle, found chiefly in the Southwest from Texas to California, Oregon, and Nevada. With its long slender body this animal resembles the marten but can

RINGTAIL *(Bassariscus astutus)*. Length: 2½ feet. Range: Parts of the southern and western United States—Oregon to California and eastward to Alabama.
New York Zoological Society

easily be identified by its black and brown tail with its seven white cross bands. Ranchers and miners often keep the fast-moving gray, brown, and yellow cacomistle as a pet because of its talents as a catcher of rats and mice.

The cacomistle is lighter in weight than the raccoon, and its head is much smaller. It lives in the cliffs and rocks of its arid habitat. Three subspecies are known and described as the Texan cacomistle, western cacomistle or Oregon ring-tailed cat, and Nevada cacomistle. All of them are about thirty inches long, strictly nocturnal, nest in tree holes, and bring forth three or four young in May and June. Although they resemble the raccoon family in many external characters, their teeth set them apart in a family by themselves. South of the Rio Grande in Mexico and Central America these animals are more prevalent than in the United States.

BLACK BEAR

WHEN the shaggy black bear awakens from its long winter sleep in April and drowsily lumbers out of its dark cave, its first thought is of food. With slow, cumbersome gait, it roams about, feeding at first only on tender shoots and buds because its digestion is delicate from the long fast. It pauses in its wanderings to scramble agilely up a tree where it munches freshly grown buds.

It gradually resumes its omnivorous habits, partaking of fish, flesh, and vegetable matter alike. With a deft stroke of its paw, it can catch a fish and is itself an expert swimmer. Sheep, pigs, and cattle are slain with ease, providing substantial nourishment, but the bear does not scorn such smaller creatures as crabs, crayfishes, ants, and wasps.

The bear foresakes its leisurely stride in time of danger. It breaks into a clumsy yet speedy gallop, scrambling over rocks and ice with astonishing dexterity. Timid by nature, it becomes a dreaded antagonist when enraged or wounded. In defense of its cubs, the bear is one of the most dangerous of wild animals, attacking furiously with teeth and claws and clasping its foe in a bone-crushing hug which gives no chance of escape.

BLACK BEARS *(Euarctos americanus).* Length: 5 feet. Range: Wooded parts of North America. Rare but would respond very quickly to protection.
Ralph De Sola (PPZ)

Black bears mate in the fall, and the females have one to four cubs in the spring. The helpless infants, no larger than cantaloupes when born, are cared for solicitously by their mother who is willing to lay down her life in their defense. In one litter several color phases often occur, one cub being black, and others brown and cinnamon. There are more than five American species and subspecies of black bears, all of which are superficially alike. About eighty thousand black bears inhabit the United States.

GRIZZLY BEAR

THE grizzly or silver-tip bear, inhabiting the Rocky Mountains, is one of the largest and certainly the most formidable of American game animals. A large specimen measures nine feet and weighs a thousand pounds. Its usual color is a deep brown, frosted with white hairs. Grizzlies do not hibernate, nor do they bother to climb

GRIZZLY BEAR

trees as do the brown bears. They go about singly or in pairs, eating all sorts of food but attacking large prey whenever opportunity offers. In bygone days buffaloes were often killed, and today horses and cattle are still attacked by hungry grizzlies in the Rockies.

The grizzly is reputed to be a most tenacious beast. One hunter relates that a grizzly, which he had shot four times through the heart, continued to chase him over the rough terrain. Although this is doubtful, probably no more terrible opponent exists in the United States than a wounded grizzly bear pursuing an attacker.

Few of them still remain on their former range except in Yellowstone Park and parts of California. Five United States species are known. According to the Bureau of Biological Survey, the estimated grizzly bear population of the country is only eleven hundred. Even the Indians, who used bear fat, thought enough of the bears' economic value to establish safe preserves for them; but one Montana rancher slew eighteen.

BLACK BEAR CUB.
Natasha Smith

Flying Mammals

Bats are not birds, but mammals which nurse their young with milk. Their bodies are covered with hair, not feathers. They are the only flying mammals; others, such as the "flying" squirrel, are really gliders rather than flyers. Even birds do not move as exclusively by the use of their wings as do the bats.

Evolutionists believe that bats developed the ability to fly after a long experimental period of leaping and gliding, but fossil types that would prove this theory have yet to be discovered.

Bats, as the name of the order, Chiroptera, indicates, possess "hand wings." The forelimbs do not terminate in hands but in elongated finger bones to which the sensitive wing membranes are attached. The thumb, however, is usually free and serves as a clutching hook in climbing or supporting the bat when it hangs upside down.

According to legend, the modern bat is a symbol of hypocrisy: a war took place between the birds and the beasts, during which a group of rats pretended to be on both sides and became thoroughly despised. When peace had been established, this group was shunned by the arbiters who finally decreed that since the rats were "two-faced," they should be neither birds nor beasts, but have the body of a beast and the wings of a bird. And, it was further ordered, they should stay out of sight during the hours of sunshine, coming out of hiding only after dusk.

BAT

AT TWILIGHT on mild evenings the bats, looking like giant, winged mice, fly over ponds and streams, fields and meadows. Swiftly they zigzag and dive after mosquitoes, gnats, and other insects. When flying over water they often swoop down, wings flicking the surface to lap up a drop. At times they utter a squeak so shrill and high-pitched that many human ears are insensitive to the sound.

Folklore has made the harmless bat a symbol of mystery and evil. The classic story is that the bat becomes entangled in a woman's hair and cannot be removed until every one of the fair victim's locks is clipped to the scalp. Yet there is no actual record of a man or woman ever having been so afflicted. Many a woman, even in the

BAT

BROWN BAT *(Eptesicus fuscus)*. Length: 4 inches. Range: Most parts of North America.
New York Zoological Society

United States, still hysterically covers her head when a stray bat wanders into the house or garden. Strangely enough this same bat may be about to save her life by catching a disease-bearing mosquito.

Bats may soon be coming into their own, for misconceptions about them are at last being dispelled. In San Antonio, Texas, municipal bat houses have been constructed to preserve the insect-destroying creatures. Studies have also revealed that they possess the homing instinct which leads them to fly many miles back to their roosts.

These creatures seek shelter during the day, most species selecting a cave, hollow tree, or dark unused attic. Clinging to the wall or ceiling they hang head down with wings folded. When they go out at night for food, the females may carry their young with them, or else leave the infants hanging to the ceiling. They cannot endure great cold, and in northern States they develop a layer of fat which furnishes food for either a winter of hibernation in a cave, or for a long flight to warmer areas. Hawks, owls, and snakes are their only enemies.

The bat flies unhesitatingly through the darkest labyrinths. It is commonly believed to be blind. The reputed characteristic finds expression in the phrase, "Blind as a bat." But bats are far from blind and, although their eyes are small, their powers of vision are acute not only at twilight but also during the day. The sense of hearing is also well developed, being even more important than sight for night flying. Keen hearing plus sensitive hairs on the wing membranes help, but possibly the muscle memory or kinesthetic sense is of greatest importance. A bat which had escaped from a laboratory by compressing its body and squeezing through a small crevice, flew at once to the same aperture when after an interval of several days it was returned to the laboratory. In captivity bats quickly learn to associate definite sounds with food, and come to a fixed place for their meals. Soft brown and yellowish fur covers their tiny bodies.

The most common American type is the little brown bat of which there are twenty-four species and subspecies. Thousands may live in one cave, which reeks with the smell of dead bats' bones and guano. With a rapid fluttering of their wings, the bats stream in and out of the cave opening at twilight and dawn. As in other bats the wing membranes are extended by elongated fingers.

With the arrival of early summer, the female retires to the darkest and most secluded part of the cave to give birth to a baby. The newborn clutches the mother's teat, and is carried about in this manner. If the tiny bat falls and is picked up by an enemy, the mother bravely fights, buffeting the assailant with wings and body.

The great northern bat is large and handsome, but is seldom seen, as it flies high and in dense darkness. A tree bat, it spends the daylight hours suspended from branches. Its general color effect is a gray-white with darker tones showing through, but the hair has four distinct layers of color. At the base it is blackish brown, then yellowish brown, then chocolate brown, and finally white at the tips. The under parts are yellowish brown except for a collar of the same tone as that on the back. The membranes are brownish black striped with yellow. About four young are born in each litter.

The California mastiff bat, largest of American bats, has ears so large that they hide the whole head. This brownish-black creature lives in fairly large colonies and often is seen in and about buildings in the Southwest. Sometimes it takes to the hunt before sunset.

The pale, almost white, California leaf-nosed bat has brown wings. A skin growth on the nose is believed to be a sensitive organ of touch useful in guiding the bat on its aerial excursions. A ridge crosses the forehead and connects the ears.

The four species of lump-nosed bats are characterized by a warty growth on the nose. The upper portions of their bodies are brown with lighter patches near the ears. The lower parts are tan tinged with pink. These bats frequent the Carlsbad Caverns of New Mexico in great numbers and are also prolific in tunnels and mine shafts. The lump-nosed, long-eared bat has amazing hearing ability. Sound is so amplified by the large ears that once a scientist shot into a flock and every bat was knocked unconscious by the concussion.

Other species and subspecies of bats in the United States include the silver-haired bat found in all parts of the country; four pipistrelles; three large brown bats; three red bats; two yellow bats, one in Florida, the other in Texas; the evening bat of the East; the spotted bat which has huge ears and is also called the jackass bat; two pale, or big-eared, bats; and four free-tailed bats which have aided mosquito elimination in the Southwest. Dr. Vernon Bailey in *Mammals of New Mexico* has vividly described the emergence of thousands of these Mexican free-tailed bats from the famous Carlsbad Caverns. Dense black clouds of bats, visible two miles away when in flight, return to the caves to hibernate. Here millions, massed together for the winter sleep, may be found hanging from the ceilings. Many of them never awake.

Insect-Eating Mammals

Insectivores, although represented by a number of prolific native species of strongly clawed creatures, are seldom seen because of their burrowing activities. Mouse-shaped shrews, frequently mistaken for mice or moles, do not tunnel as exclusively as do the latter. Occasionally their elongated snouts and close-set rounded ears may be detected moving under dry leaves of gardens, through the litter of the forest floor, or even over the snow. One shrew, the pigmy, is the smallest of all North American mammals. It is less than three inches long, including its slender one-inch tail.

Least known of all mammals, the moles and some shrews are chiefly remarkable for their tunneling. Dr. Robert W. Hegner reports one mole digging a tunnel sixty-eight feet long in twenty-five hours and mentions another one hundred yards long dug in a single night. From these record figures he infers that "to do a proportionate amount of digging a man would have to make a tunnel fifty miles long and large enough for him to crawl through."

Moles are economically useful as insect destroyers and aerators of the soil, but annoying for the ridges they raise in doing this work under lawns and golf courses. Hence they are persecuted by man, more concerned with appearance of grass plots than helping check the insect menace.

Moleskin, a dark brown fur which looks well no matter how brushed as it sets backward as well as forward, is sometimes made up into evening coats. More than nine hundred skins are necessary in the construction of such a luxury garment.

MOLE

AS THE mole delves in the moist earth, its large powerful forelimbs work like the arms of a swimmer. The worm may turn, but the mole tunnels its zigzag course in hot pursuit through tiny grass rootlets, potato patches, and shrubs until it has caught its dinner. Its subterranean course is frequently marked by the roof of its burrow, visible on the surface of the ground.

The mole lives that it may eat, for no other animal has a more voracious appetite. A few hours without food spells death from starvation for this almost sightless six-inch glutton which consumes daily its own weight in insects. It may burrow seventy-five yards in

MOLE

a single night seeking grubs, larvae, beetles, and even meadow mice. The dim, tiny eyes and ears are hidden by overlapping skin which protects them from dirt. Its long piglike snout acts as a wedge.

Seldom seen above the ground, the mole may be easily brought to light. As it advances its tunnel, the moving ridge of earth shows

WESTERN MOLE *(Scapanus townsendi)*. Length: 8 inches. Range: Western Washington, Oregon, and California.
From Audubon and Bachman's "Quadrupeds of North America"

its progress and a hard blow with a spade on the moving soil will daze the tiny miner.

Moles are killed on sight by most people in this country because they disfigure lawns and are believed to eat potatoes and other garden vegetables. The truth is that there are few more valuable animals from the point of view of the agriculturalist. They kill hundreds of thousands of wire worms, cutworms, and harmful insects every year and they do not eat potatoes. In France a fine is imposed on anyone caught killing a mole.

The young of the common mole are born naked during March and April. There is one annual litter usually containing four offspring although the number may vary between two and five. Constructed of leaves, roots, and grass, the nest is placed far down in a burrow, often beneath a stump or rock.

The young of the western mole, which reaches a length of eight inches, arrive somewhat later in May or June. Various species and subspecies of the common mole, of which there are twelve, are found all over the United States. The western mole numbers six forms while the hairy-tailed, star-nosed, and shrew moles number four more species and subspecies.

Energetic and predatory despite their limited vision, moles fight each other to the death. Their sickle-shaped teeth, used normally for cutting and grinding insect food, make terrible weapons.

SHREW

WHILE certain species of shrews are the smallest of all mammals they are a match for any living thing in gameness. When forced to remain in proximity to a shrew, larger animals like mice will exhibit great panic and rush about until exhausted.

Unlike moles, long-tailed or common shrews do not burrow. They scurry under fallen leaves and about crevices in stumps and logs in the forest, emitting piping squeaks, and will race for cover at the slightest untoward sound. In addition to insect fare they will eat almost any animal they can overcome in fair combat or foul. Even small birds fall prey to them. But it is necessity, not gluttony, which makes shrews so voracious, for they can die of hunger in less than half a day.

While the common shrew does not burrow at all, being content to usurp the unused galleries of the mole, the short-tailed shrew will burrow just beneath the surface of the ground in the summer, and under the snow in winter.

Dr. Bailey in *Nature Magazine* relates first-hand experiences with two short-tailed shrews. One of those he captured was given a dead shrew and, surely enough, was cannibalistic. It ate the skin dry, meat, bones, and all, and then used the turned-out skin as a warm sleeping bag in which it snuggled for the night. Another shrew, according to the same author, was musically inclined. He writes, "If I squeaked my lips, or whistled in a high key, he would come to the door of his nest box, wiggle his nose and begin to chipper and squeak. As I led him on he would run into a long vibrating trill, high pitched and birdlike, varied and pleasing as a song. He would sometimes keep it up for a minute or more with nose elevated, mouth open and throat vibrating, with motions not unlike those of a canary."

WATER SHREWS *(Neosorex palustris)*. Length: 6 inches. Range: Northern United States, Canada, and Alaska.
From Audubon and Bachman's "Quadrupeds of North America"

Pouched Mammals

Only native representative of a fascinating although primitive order, the opossum is common in the United States though seldom seen about except at night. After the fourteen to seventeen days of gestation, mother opossum produces her large litter, more of which die than survive.

One-half inch long at birth and nearly helpless, six to sixteen immature young opossums crawl into their mother's pouch, cling with their mouths to her nipples, and feed until big enough to clamber over her back. Then she carries her litter over the fields in search of birds, insects, and fruits.

Not bigger than a common cat, the opossum is the only pouched mammal in North America. Its long prehensile tail together with its opposable hands makes possible arboreal antics that are almost simian.

OPOSSUM

AFTER thirteen days as an embryo, a baby opossum is born. Blind, and with half-developed hind legs, the tiny, half-inch-long creature drags its way along its mother's belly, guided by a streak of milk, to the warmth and security of her abdominal pouch. There it remains dormant for fifty-five days, feeding upon its mother's milk. The young of the opossum are so small at birth that a litter of sixteen might easily fit into a tablespoon.

When the offspring are large enough to emerge from the pouch, but small enough to need their mother's constant attention, she carries them about on her back, their tails twined about hers, their small feet clutching the fur of her back. Over hill and dale, leaping fallen logs, ditches, and rocks, they hang on like steeplechase jockeys.

"Brer 'Possum" has to depend on his legs during the autumn season for then, in preparation for the winter season, he adds a layer of tasty fat under his skin. Southern country folk get out their guns and "houn' dawgs" and go "possum huntin'." Yellow corn bread, browned yams, and 'possum stew are proverbially good.

Caught in the open, the creature makes a beeline for the nearest tree, closely pursued by the yelping pack. In the highest branches of the tree it will hang by its tail presenting a target hard to miss.

OPOSSUM

Sometimes the rifle is disdained and the hunters merely shake the tree until the animal drops out of it to the ground. In such a situation it plays 'possum. Seemingly lifeless, it lies inert, its lips drawn back from the gleaming teeth as might be the case with any dead animal. It will submit inertly to any indignity or torture, the

OPOSSUM *(Didelphis virginiana)*. Length: 2½ feet. Range: "From New York to Florida, and from Atlantic Coast to the Great Lakes and Texas" (Anthony).
New York Zoological Society

thick fur on the chest muffling the motion of breathing. Some people believe it can take so much punishment without blinking an eye because it is frightened into a state of temporary insensibility. But if the hunters relax their attention momentarily, the little actor makes another break for freedom.

When night shrouds the woods in darkness the adult opossum leaves its den and walks slowly and awkwardly on its long, clawed feet, naked ears alert for any suspicious sound. It captures insects, frogs, small rabbits; it may stop to pick berries from a bush; or it may climb a tree to rob a bird's nest of young and eggs, or to eat a ripe persimmon. The long-haired grayish-white animal maneuvers skillfully in the trees, hanging by its monkeylike tail while it uses all four feet to clutch the booty.

The den of the opossum is a bed of grass or leaves made on the floor of a hollow tree trunk. Here it is safe from the tearing teeth of wildcat and wolf as well as from driving snow and rain. Other enemies of the opossum include bears, cougars, coyotes, foxes, and great horned owls.

Generally dull and inactive, the 'possum has somehow captured the imagination of Southerners so that it occurs again and again in their folklore. A favorite tune of Okefenokee swampers is "The raccoon fiddled and the 'possum danced."

As a fur bearer the opossum has reached a place of some economic importance in recent years. Its liking for poultry eggs has made it unpopular with farmers, but in other respects it is helpful to them because it devours large quantities of harmful rodents and insects.

The common or Virginia opossum, found from New York to southern Georgia and from the Atlantic seaboard to the Great Lakes and Texas, has related species and subspecies respectively called the Florida and the Texas opossum. The Florida variety is slightly shorter than the Virginia opossum but is darker and longer tailed. Its range is not confined to Florida but extends to southeastern Georgia, coastal Alabama, Mississippi, and Louisiana. The Texas branch of the family has a tail fully half the length of its body.

FISHES

Mississippi Gar Pike

Fishes

With true Roman arrogance, Pliny, historian and natural philosopher, announced, "Nothing in the ocean is unknown to us." He knew of but one hundred and seventy-six species of fishes. Ichthyologists today are familiar with more than 20,000 species of true fishes, and approximately one hundred or more new forms are discovered each year. There are more species of fishes than the combined species of mammals, birds, reptiles, and amphibians; there are more individual fishes, too, than individuals of all these classes.

Fishes are and have been of great economic importance to this country. Friendly Indians taught the Pilgrim Fathers to lay a fish in the ground with each seedling of corn to aid its growth; the cod meant so much to the mercantile life of Massachusetts that its image today surmounts the flagstaff of the capitol of that commonwealth.

As a present-day source of food, the staple of the Friday meal is still to be had in comfortable quantities, but serious inroads in the supply have already been made. Thousands of edible fishes of the sea together with their eggs and their food supply are destroyed each year by the refuse of oil-burning steamers; in the inland streams the pollution caused by industrial waste has robbed the waters of the oxygen necessary to fish survival. Salmon, shad, and halibut are steadily dwindling in numbers in the depleted New England fisheries. Off the Pacific coast, factory ships from Japan strike at the salmon, while in the Great Lakes overfishing and bilge oil are causing the sturgeon to disappear.

Along the coast of the United States and outlying islands, and in the inland waterways and lakes, at least fifteen hundred species and subspecies of fishes are recognized. They exist in a great variety of natural conditions—some at the surface, others in the midstrata of the ocean depths, while still others grope for their food in the never-abating night of the deep sea floor. Some are rapacious—good game fish, able to give the most avid angler a good fight, like the muskellunge, the trout, and the pike, or those ocean giants, the marlin, tuna, tarpon, and sailfish. Others, like the flounder, move lazily about and are pulled up on the hook as unresisting dead weights.

A safe rule in dealing with fishes is that no rule concerning them is safe. But for the purposes of this book, all vertebrates that live in the water, swim with fins and breathe with gills, will be considered fishes. It is interesting to note in passing that an African fish, the lungfish, is actually able to get its oxygen supply from the air. Thus, although there are really four distinct vertebrate classes—the true fishes with bony skeletons, the sharks and rays with skeletons and skulls of soft cartilage, the primitive jawless lampreys, and the even more primitive lancelets—all will be dealt with together.

True Fishes

By far the most numerous of all fishes, the true or bony fishes are distinguished by the possession of a bony skeleton and a vestigial air bladder, the latter a remnant of the great drought of the Devonian period when fishes were forced to find a means of breathing oxygen from the free air. The true fishes resemble the sharks in the possession of movable jaws and gills supported by gill arches. There are about fourteen hundred species of true fishes in American waters.

The appearance of the first fish on the scene some five hundred million years ago is a momentous event on the evolutionary calendar; the first fish was the first vertebrate. No connecting link appears to bridge the chasm between the vertebrate and invertebrate worlds. There was something tentative about the first fish. Before that the only sea animals with hard anatomical structures were those with shells, like the clams and starfishes. The first vertebrate, while its hard parts were internal, also carried over a protective external armor that plated the fore part of its body. This armor is present in today's fishes only as scales.

In addition to their scales fishes have skins which vary in thickness with the different species. This skin, unlike ours, is alive at the surface. Cells require a liquid medium in which to live, so that land animals all have their exposed skins covered with a layer of dead cells. Even the fish's skin is not in complete contact with the water. A quantity of slime covers the body and protects it against irritants in the water, such as salt and bacteria, fungi, and other parasites; it also acts as a lubricant in aiding the fish's progress in water. Wipe the slime off a fish and it will as a rule become ill. Eels with their slime removed are unable to stand salt water.

In addition to the scales which underlie the skin, some fishes have offensive armament. The surgeonfish carries knifelike scales at the base of its tail. The swordfish is born without its weapon; it acquires that later, losing its scales in the process. The porcupinefish looks and is formidable with its bristling spines.

Fishes are born without scales. At birth they have scale nuclei which barely cover their bodies. As the scales grow, the free end of one scale overlaps the fixed end of the other. These scales grow with the fish, continuing always to cover the same proportion of the body surface. They grow at the edge in the manner of a tree, adding one ring annually. From these rings it is relatively easy to tell the age of the fish and to learn other essential data concerning it. Under the microscope the scale reveals bands or lines of growth. When food is plentiful and the water warm, the fish grows rapidly, forcing the scales to grow at an increased rate in order to keep up, so that the growth rings are spaced farther apart. In winter these rings for the reverse reasons grow close together forming a band called the annual check. When counted, these will tell the age of a fish. A skilled technician is also able to determine from them whether or not the fish has spawned, how many times, and even how long it was at the end of each year of its life.

Protective coloration reaches a high point of development in the fishes. Not only are they able to blend with backgrounds of solid color but they successfully imitate the most intricate color patterns. Even checkerboards present no difficulties for them. Star-shaped sacs imbedded in the skin are called chromatophores. These cells contain pigment in their centers—a different pigment for each cell—red, orange-yellow, or black. The color may be strengthened or weakened on the fish's exterior accordingly as the fish exudes the pigment along the arms of the star or withdraws it into the center of the cell. In the center the pigment can become practically invisible. It is the combined action of the remarkable chromatophores plus a certain amount of fixed coloration in the fish which produces the myriad patterns the skin is capable of taking on. Sharks and rays lack these chromatophores.

Fishes may not see colors as we do, but tests have proved that they can distinguish differences. They have been trained to accept red-dyed food and abjure blue-dyed food, and vice versa.

The lack of eyelids in no way prevents fishes from sleeping. Fishes do sleep—a small Bermuda fish (*Iridio bivittata*) actually covers itself with sand in preparation for repose. Fishes have no outer ears but they hear by means of an inner ear. It had been believed that they were only responsive to sound vibrating against their bodies. But surgical removal of the inner ear diminished these responses.

Fastest fishes are the tuna and related sailfish. They move through water at a conservatively estimated speed of thirty miles an hour. They progress by alternate convolutions of the body culminating in a vigorous motion of the tail. It has been proved that while the fins aid in swimming they are not essential because fishes with their fins removed have shown almost as great an ability to swim and maneuver as before the operation.

Semicircular canals at right angles to each other, filled with a fluid called endolymph, aid the fish in keeping its equilibrium. The lateral line, an organ extending from the gill opening to the tail, is actually a tube beneath the skin which permits the secretion of mucus at intervals along the body. Beneath this there is a trunk nerve which branches off to all parts of the body. It is believed that one of the functions of the lateral line is to warn the fish of s u d d e n harmful changes in temperature.

Fishes can both taste and smell. The catfish smell food from a distance but will not eat it until one of its barbels or taste buds has come in contact with it.

During the Devonian period when inland waters began to dry up, fishes were forced to develop a mechanism that would draw oxygen from the air. The result was an air bladder. This now vestigial organ lies between the stomach and backbone. Sharks and rays lack this organ, whereas in the lungfish it is not vestigial but actively functioning. Among most fishes, however, the function of the air bladder is shrouded in mystery and debate. It seems likely that it has some connection with the hearing of the fish.

DEEP-SEA FISHES (Grenadier at left, batfish center, brotulid at right).
American Museum of Natural History

Reproduction of fishes is carried on in three ways: both female and male may simultaneously deposit eggs and sperm into the water where fertilization and development take place; the fertilization may be internal and the development of the embryo external; or both fertilization and development may be internal.

BATFISH

THE batfish walks like a toad, sits like a toad, and even looks like a toad. It crawls about the ocean floor on its fleshy fins. When it pauses, it rests on its flippers as though they were elbows, while its head points upward. The resemblance is further heightened by bony warts which cover the fish's skin. The batfish ascends to the surface only after dark.

SHORT-NOSED BATFISH *(Ogcocephalus radiatus).* Length: 1 foot.
Range: Coast of Florida, especially about the Keys.
John G. Shedd Aquarium

The batfish group is the most specialized of living fishes. Two representatives inhabit the Atlantic coastal waters. The nine-inch batfish, marked by a triangular head with a long bony snout, is found in the Southeast, infrequently appearing as far north as New York Bay. The short-nosed batfish, twelve inches long, strays among the weeds in the shallow waters off the coast of Florida and along sandy bottoms. The name "batfish" is given in various localities to several other unrelated species.

ANGLER

IF THE angler fish is without a friend in the world, it has only itself to blame. For this strange denizen of the deep lurks in lonely concealment on the ocean floor, not to meet but to eat almost any indiscreet passer-by of suitable size.

The array of items on the angler's menu would put the most elaborate tables d'hôte to shame. Here is one fisherman who does not boast of his skill but nonchalantly snares game of any kind. Rays and flatfishes, whiting and haddock, starfishes and crabs are but a few samples. Its appetite is such that it can eat another fish as large as itself, as at least one flounder learned upon meeting an angler. It eats water birds, too, and when the pickings are scarce it will hungrily gulp down mouthfuls of mud to obtain the minute organisms otherwise beyond reach.

This redoubtable fish is voraciously omnivorous in the full sense of the term. It rises to such heights of epicurean versatility that without a second thought it will swallow—and has—the wooden buoys attached to lobster pots in Massachusetts waters. In Ireland the angler was reported to swallow cork

ANGLER *(Lophius piscatorius)*. Length: 4 feet. Range: Gulf of St. Lawrence to Cape Hatteras.
New York Zoological Society

buoys. The observer who noted this also wrote: "But the most remarkable instance I ever knew of this fish's voracity was its swallowing of a large block of granite used as an anchoring stone for fishing. The only reason I could imagine for its seeming want of taste was that the stone had been used as a block to cut up fish for crab-pots, it being consequently covered with blood, slime and scales."

Waterfowl floating about are seized by the angler in the snapping turtle technique, and it is believed also to swallow live geese. The stomach of one angler yielded seven ducks. Another is reported to have swallowed the head and neck of a loon whose struggles continued until the bird pulled its captor to the surface. Diving birds make especially fine victims, since the angler can seize them when they come under water for food. Its predilection for fowl has given it the name of goosefish, and it is also called allmouth and molligut.

Despite its great appetite, the fish has a weak digestive system which works surprisingly slowly. A fisherman caught one angler whose stomach contained several dozen herrings. The herrings, though swallowed, remained in such a completely natural state, undigested, that the fisherman sold them in the market as if they were a fresh catch. One angler, cut open after it had been out of water for twenty-four hours, contained a variety of fishes which had entered its stomach at least a day before. Yet some of the fishes were as good as new and their flesh seemed to have suffered not at all during the stay within the angler.

All in all, the angler has become quite an unsavory character. Swedish fishermen, for example, believe that if an angler is taken aboard ship someone will die. When one is accidentally caught, they will sacrifice the hook and line rather than raise it far enough to permit them to tear it from the hook. Some Massachusetts fishermen believe that a storm is sure to follow if a goosefish is caught.

Its appearance does not belie the legends, although they are hardly possible. The grotesque body of this recluse is well designed for its secretive life. It is shaped like a comet, a flat ball of a head tapering down to a slender tail. Naturalists have observed that its brownish color blends with the rocks on the ocean floor where most of its time is spent, sometimes completely buried in the mud save for mouth and gill clefts.

The angler's lower jaw juts out like any rocky ledge. From the mouth and various parts of its body a leafy fringe protrudes, closely resembling the sponges and other organisms which border underwater rocks. Further deceptive detail is lent by the uneven surface of its back, and the yellow and black eyes have been compared with "the deserted shell of an acorn barnacle." Even Cicero, two thousand years ago, commented on the realism of the angler's disguise.

The angler is a fish with all improvements. From its back extends a dorsal fin terminating in several filaments resembling bits of seaweed as they are whisked gently about by the water. So thorough is the disguise that passing fishes pause to nibble at the "grass." The angler's eyes keep watch and at the proper moment the unwary fish is swept into the upturned cavernous mouth. This kind of life, in which dinner walks right up to be eaten and need not be hunted, accounts for the fish's sluggish nature.

During the warm months the angler proceeds to shallow water to mate, and in this season comes to the surface to bask in the sun. Then there can be seen, along the New England coast for example, "purple veils" floating on the surface of the ocean. One of these transparent mucous films may be as much as thirty feet long and five feet wide and weigh more than thirty pounds. Its purplish color is derived from a multitude of tiny specks, each of which is a wriggling angler embryo. There may be more than a million small fry in one female's "veil."

When first hatched the young anglers do not look at all as they will when fully grown, for they are shapeless and without a mouth. During one stage of their growth they resemble long-tailed butterflies. When they attain maturity they may be four feet long and weigh as much as seventy pounds. In old age they become more flabby and graceless.

In past years this unprepossessing creature was eaten by Indians and was sold under the name of croan after its head had been cut off. Now nobody cares much for the angler; it is rarely eaten and a champion is yet to claim that it has aesthetic appeal.

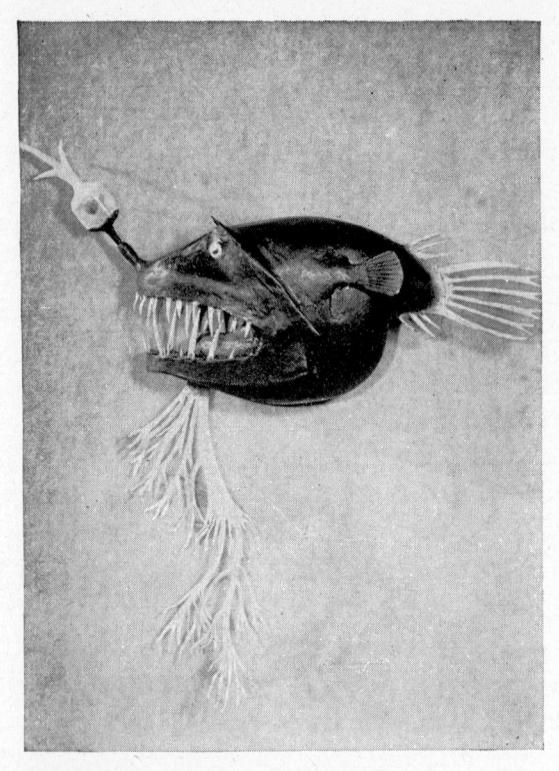

DEEP-SEA ANGLER (*Linophryne arborifer*). Length: 6 inches. Range: North Atlantic.
American Museum of Natural History

If one should want to catch it, however, the angler's tenacity facilitates the process. A man saw an angler near the shore and proffered the butt end of his whip to the fish. The angler seized the whip with such bulldog tenacity that, rather than let go, it allowed itself to be hoisted bodily ashore, still clutching the whip in its mouth.

The angler is found in the Atlantic, north of Cape Hatteras. Other related species, most of them less than a foot in length, inhabit the murky pits of the ocean where they have developed astonishing shapes and physical features. Many of them are jet black and others are a ghostly black and white. Few of them are ever seen except in an aquarium.

One species, the oceanic angler fish, is marked by a forty-inch female whose beacon light at the end of a long tentacle attracts the midget male of four inches. The female weighs a thousand times more than her puny husband. The male attaches himself to the under side of the female, just behind her head. There he lives, incapable of independent existence because he lacks a digestive system and his blood system fuses with his mate's. He loses virtually every function except that of fertilizing his wife's eggs. So perfect is the attachment that it is almost impossible to tell where the body of the female ends and the parasitic male's body begins.

It is believed that the small number of adults and their sluggish life in the ocean darkness make it almost impossible for the sexes to find each other. Therefore, it is conjectured, when first hatched and quite numerous, the young males seek a mate to support them and a few of the lucky ones succeed. These fish nip out a piece of the female's skin, then fasten their lips to the flesh and a permanent fusion ensues. This unique process, practiced by at least one species of the intriguing anglers, is perhaps but a hint of the unfathomed mysteries of daily life in the unknown depths of the ocean and about which we are only beginning to learn.

OCEAN SUNFISH

LIKE a pancake tilted on end, the huge ocean sunfish moves sluggishly through the water. Sometimes it comes to the surface, turns over on its flat side so that part of its body is above the water, and basks in the sun as it drifts aimlessly about. Its pectoral fin sways above water like a signal buoy as the waves wash the flat deck which is the fish's side. The sunfish has been credited with leaping about like a porpoise, though its bizarre physique seems ill-adapted for such a pastime.

It is also known as the headfish, since it appears to consist only of a gigantic head without a body. A record specimen was ten feet long and eleven feet high. Such giants weigh as much as a ton. One report from Sydney, Australia, describes a sunfish, which was killed by a steamer's propeller, as ten feet long, fourteen feet high, and forty-four hundred pounds in weight.

This creature shows no signs of fear of man and will swim alongside a boat. It does not bite at bait like most fishes, so that it must be caught by driving a harpoon into its body. One big fellow was harpooned and thereupon proceeded to sink slowly but steadily as the rope was played out. When the end of the rope was reached, however, the fish continued to sink with such determination that the bow of the launch was pulled down. Finally, to the great relief of the aspiring sunfishermen, the rope broke and the catch disappeared.

On another occasion a harpooned sunfish refused to accept attack quite so passively. Its physical protest was so vehement that it nearly wrecked the launch. Another boat was dispatched and another harpoon sunk into the valiant sunfish. Still it fought on, buckling and tossing about in the foaming waters with the desperation of any animal at bay. Only after a continuous tussle of three hours did it finally succumb. The sunfish is said to utter grunts or groans when hauled out of the water.

According to Dr. Bashford Dean, part of the sunfish's life is probably spent in deep water. Consequently its shape may be the result of great pressure, since fishes under such conditions tend to

OCEAN SUNFISH *(Mola mola)*. Length: 8 feet. Range: All coasts but particularly in temperate and tropical seas.
New York Aquarium

develop huge heads and weak trunks. The sunfish has virtually no spinal cord, a three-foot specimen possessing one of only a fraction of an inch.

Without a visible tail, the fish instead has simply an uneven rim of pliable flesh, which is of slight use in propelling it through the water. Its tough, leathery skin is scaleless and covered with flat spines. The slimy coating of the skin is host to a number of parasites which prey upon it, and little suckfish set up housekeeping in its gill cavities. Under the skin is a layer of gristly material several inches thick; the skeleton has been described by Dr. C. M. Breder, Jr., as "degenerate to the consistency of cheese." The large dorsal and anal fins are quite similar and provide most of the motive power in swimming.

The flat body bulges in the center and front and is thinner at the edges. The mouth is small, for it is about the width of the narrow body, but the powerful beak is equipped with solid teeth. The sunfish is a brownish-gray color above and a dusky white below.

It ranges along both coasts where it feeds upon such creatures as jellyfishes and small crustaceans. Its slowness precludes any possibility of its preying upon fast-swimming neighbors. This fish frequently comes near the shore, and occasionally one is found stranded on a beach. It does not trouble man and is itself of no commercial value, though the Japanese relish its liver.

Young ocean sunfish are so unlike the adults that they were formerly believed to be another species of fish. They are odd, spiny little things, spheroidal in shape.

A related species, the king of the mackerels, is also of cosmopolitan distribution and is sometimes observed along the Atlantic coast.

PUFFER

SILENTLY cleaving the water, the lithe, menacing form of a shark speeds straight toward the meek little puffer. An unhappy ending for the puffer seems imminent and inevitable as the onrushing shark ominously nears. But by the time the shark arrives, the puffer's fishlike figure has been transformed, as if magically, into a large

PUFFER or SWELLFISH *(Spheroides maculatus)*. Length: 10 inches. Range: Atlantic coast of the United States.
John G. Shedd Aquarium

globe. The frustrated attacker finds it as difficult to eat the puffer as it is for a boy with hands tied to eat an apple bobbing about in a pail of water.

The invulnerable puffer can now disdain its ferocious antagonist, if it should so desire. It has gained immunity simply by swallowing water, thus inflating its abdomen until its body is a ball with a dangling tail. This ingenious creature, also known as the globefish and swellfish, can fill up with air when it is threatened by some foe near the surface. Having achieved the contour of a balloon, it turns over on its back, its distended belly sticking out above the water, and permits the waves to toss it gently about as though it were a bit of driftwood.

The defensive swelling of the puffer usually occurs when it is removed from the water. If the puffer is contrary, however, and does not puff up, it can be so persuaded by tickling.

When an occasional puffer, despite its protection, is swallowed by a large fish, it immediately gnaws its way to freedom through its captor's body. The little fish emerges hale and hearty, while the escape tunnel frequently causes its persecutor's death.

Most puffers have a scaleless skin covered with close-set prickles. Some, however, have spines—the chief characteristic of the related porcupine fish—so that they are doubly protected. Moreover, the flesh of some puffers is poisonous, remaining so even after being cooked at high temperature. Although puffers are eaten in Japan, a proverb declares that before partaking of a puffer one should make one's will. The brilliant colors, which a few of the species possess, may be considered protective insofar as they are an advance warning to possible attackers. The versatile puffer is said to growl like a dog.

The ten-inch northern swellfish, which burrows in the sandy coasts as far north as Maine, lays tiny eggs in the summer. The eggs cling to the first objects they touch. In four or five days the young are hatched, but look nothing at all like the adults. By the time they are one-quarter inch long, though, a resemblance is discernible and they acquire the ability to swell up to the size of a pea.

Usually found in shallow water near the shore, these puffers are believed to go to the bottom of deeper water for the winter.

The swellfish eats crustaceans, worms, mollusks, shrimps, and crabs. The latter is attacked only by a gang which makes short shrift of a blue crab, since the swellfish's jaws easily bite through the victim's shell. A swellfish, single-handed, rarely summons up enough courage to brave the nips of the crab.

In color this puffer is green above, and has yellow or orange sides and a white belly. About seven other species of puffers range in the coastal waters of the Gulf of Mexico, the Gulf Stream, and the Atlantic Ocean from Texas to Maine. The smooth swellfish, attaining a length of two feet, is one of the largest.

PORCUPINE FISH

THE slow-swimming porcupine fish need never run from its enemies. Equipped with the puffer's swelling trick, it is further protected by the quills which are responsible for its graphically descriptive name.

When it puffs up, its long barbs stick out threateningly. It would be a very foolish fish indeed that tried to swallow such a ball of barbed wire. Sometimes a group of porcupine fish, facing attack, huddle together so closely that they resemble one large, quill-studded fish.

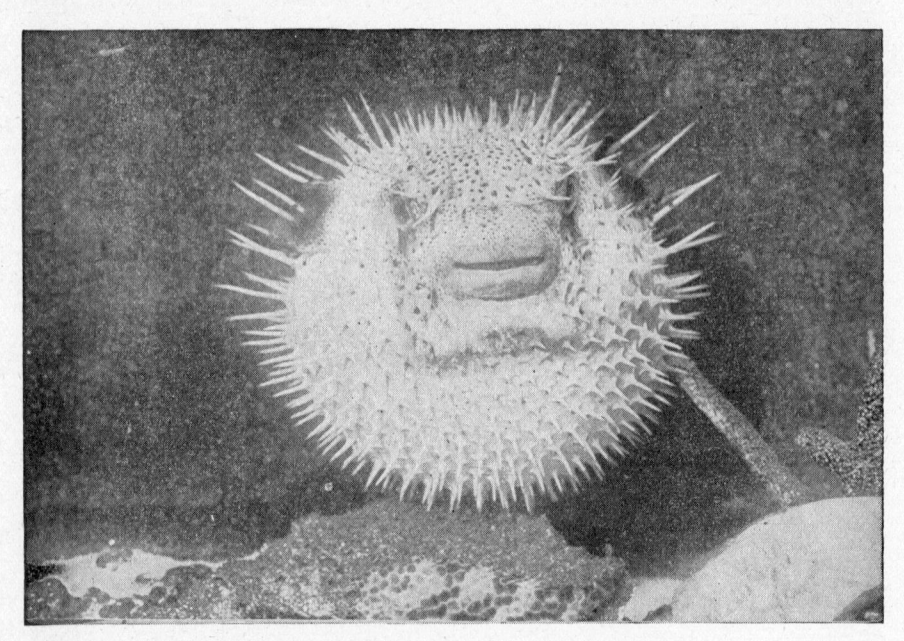

PORCUPINE FISH (*Diodon hystrix*). Length: 3 feet. Range: Tropical seas north to Florida and lower California.
S. C. Dunton, New York Aquarium

Natives of the South Seas attest the protective value of the porcupine's armor by using it for war helmets. In Japan it is often used for lanterns. The back of the skin is cut out, a candle is placed inside, and the dried skin is suspended from a wire. When the candle is lighted, the flame shines through the taut skin with a soft glow.

The porcupine fish of tropical seas, found off Florida, attains a length of three feet. It is used for lanterns in the West Indies as well as in Japan. It is also preserved and sold commercially to curio-collecting tourists.

The spotted boxfish and smooth boxfish are other species occasionally sighted off the southern coast. The most common porcupine fish of the species in this country is the spiny boxfish which ranges in the Atlantic as far north as Cape Cod. This ten-inch fish is olive or brown above, with dark stripes on its back and sides and a yellow-tinted belly. It is a bright-eyed creature of such pleasant disposition that in aquariums it feeds out of keepers' hands.

TRUNKFISH

ENCASED in a hard, armored shell, the trunkfish paddles slowly and laboriously through shallow salt waters, almost scraping the bottom of the ocean. Its movements are extremely sluggish, primarily because the rigid bony box, formed by a fusion and solidification of the scales, prevents even the slightest flexion of the body. Only the lips, the dorsal and anal fins, and the stem of the tail are capable of independent motion. Even the gill openings, which are essentially narrow vertical slits in the carapace, remain stationary. The hard cover acts as an excellent protection against enemies.

COWFISH *(Acanthostracion quadricornis)*. Length: 1 foot. Range: South Atlantic and Gulf coasts.
New York Zoological Society

The full-grown trunkfish reaches a maximum length of one foot, but the few young specimens which have been found about the Atlantic coast of the United States are less than an inch long. The immature trunkfish is spheroidal in form, but later develops its angular, shell-shaped body. In appearance it resembles an irregular shell with a hump protruding from the back. The eyes are large and somber; the mouth is extremely small.

The trunkfish moves through the water by means of the dorsal and anal fins, flipping them slowly like the blades of a propeller. Most of its time, however, is spent on the bottom, where it sits motionless and seemingly unconscious, feeding on hydroids and other soft-bodied invertebrates.

Because its functional body processes are sluggish and underdeveloped, the trunkfish can live almost two hours out of water without any apparent ill effects. It is sagacious enough, however, never to take the hook, and anglers who like its soft fragrant meat must resort to the net in order to capture it. An excellent dish when prepared properly, the trunkfish is baked or roasted in the shell and eaten like lobster.

Essentially a tropical species, the trunkfish ventures northward in the summer although it is commonest in Florida waters. One of the related species, the cowfish, comes as far north as the Carolinas. Three others, the smooth trunkfish, the common trunkfish (smallest of the species, measuring nine inches in length), and the shellfish (largest size recorded—sixteen inches) are all found near Florida.

FILEFISH

ECCENTRIC and somewhat obtuse, the filefish glides in and out of reefs, nibbling on marine growths or calmly munching on pieces of coral. Its mode of existence is placid and unhurried, its movements awkward and blundering.

Related to the triggerfish, the filefish is grotesque in appearance as well as habits, and has been mischievously labeled fool fish. Its brownish-gray, sixteen-inch body is depressed and angular. The mouth is small, and clearly visible are sixteen distinct conical teeth,

FILEFISH

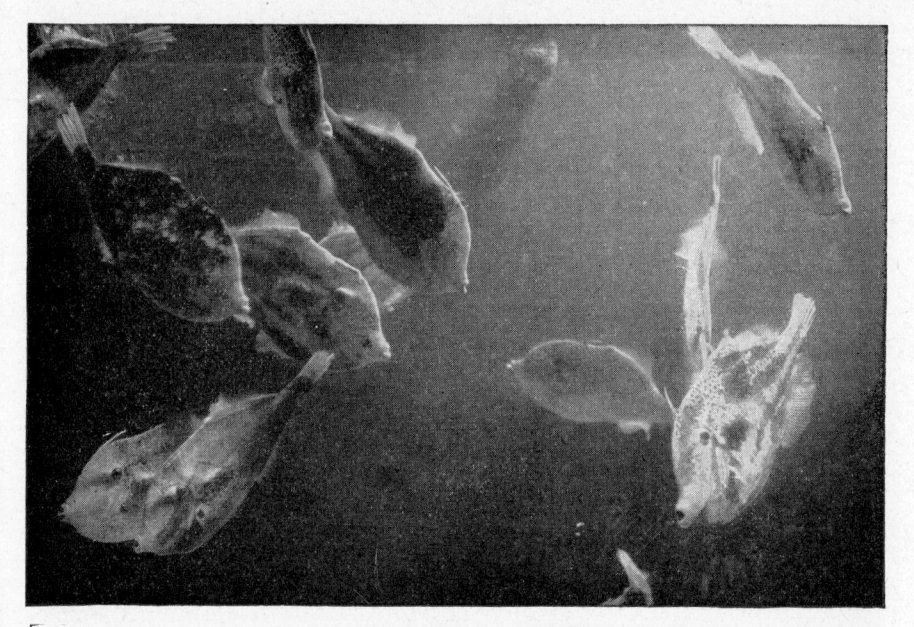

ORANGE FILEFISHES *(Ceratacanthus schoepfi)*. Length: 2 feet. Range: Cape Cod to Florida.
New York Zoological Society

so sharp and strong that the filefish can easily bite off and masticate a piece of hard coral, and even pierce the shell of a mollusk in order to extract and swallow the occupant. This accomplishment, incidentally, has been a source of annoyance to pearl fishermen who claim that the filefish is injurious and detrimental to their work.

Its peculiar characteristic, the one from which its name is derived, is the rough, granular quality of its skin, which at one time was used like sharkskin (shagreen) as an abrasive to perform the work of ordinary sandpaper. Back of the first dorsal spine is a prominent erectile spine, which the filefish can lower and raise by means of a smaller projecting bone directly behind it. A peculiar locking device makes it possible for the filefish to keep this spiked fin erect for long periods of time, and thus avoid being swallowed by a larger fish.

The filefish was known to the ancient Greeks and Romans who considered it pugnacious and possessed of the devil. As late as the latter part of the nineteenth century, its meat was considered highly poisonous, and all those who ate it were supposed to be seized with paroxysms which affected all the muscles of the body and caused death. It is safe and appropriate now to state that both of these beliefs are unfounded. It is true that the meat of the filefish is bitter and offensive, and therefore valueless as food. The filefish itself is a sluggish meek creature, formidable in appearance but not at all vicious.

Although the range of the filefish is restricted mostly to tropical waters, six species have been observed on the Atlantic coast as far north as Maine. The gray filefish, one of the rarer West Indian species, infrequently wanders near and about Florida. The fringed filefish, the smallest of the American species, reaching a maximum of eight inches in length, is common in Florida waters. The common filefish is the most widely distributed of the species and has been found as far north as the coast of Maine. The orange filefish roams the Atlantic coast waters from Maine to Texas. The unicorn filefish has occasionally traveled north to Massachusetts. The scrawled filefish, the-largest of the species (three feet in length), has been found in the offshore waters of South Carolina.

TRIGGERFISH

RESEMBLING the filefish, a somewhat related species, the triggerfish possesses a similar spine-locking mechanism. The two spines situated on the back are so complicated in structure, that once the triggerfish erects its spear-shaped first dorsal fin, it cannot be folded down even if pressure is exerted. An application of force will result only in breaking the appendage off completely. If the smaller spine is depressed, however, it will unlock the fin, and both will automatically fold back.

Primarily a tropical fish, the triggerfish is found mostly in the offshore waters of Florida and Key West, although several species have been observed as far north as Massachusetts. The four species found on the Atlantic coast are the common triggerfish, the bluestriped or queen triggerfish, the spotted triggerfish, and the ocean triggerfish, largest of the species, attaining a maximum length of two feet.

SHARKSUCKER

Colored brown or gray, the body of the average twelve-inch triggerfish is deep and compressed. Its incisor teeth are large and projecting, and the two spines on its back, acting like a trigger, are responsible for its name.

Unlike that of the filefish, the meat of the triggerfish is considered a delicacy. Before cooking or broiling it, the common practice is to remove the leathery skin, which comes off in one complete strip.

SHARKSUCKER

HITCHHIKER of the high seas, the remora or sharksucker attaches itself to the body of a large fish or sea turtle, and rides unmolested on the abdomen of its powerful companion. It is able to perform this unique feat by means of a sucking disk on top of its head which takes the place of the spiny dorsal fin found in other

QUEEN TRIGGERFISH *(Balistes vetula)*. Length: 1½ feet. Range: Massachusetts to Florida and the West Indies in the Gulf Stream.
John G. Shedd Aquarium

fishes. So strong are the adhesive qualities of this large laminated suction plate, that the remora cannot under any circumstances be pried away from its host. Tests have shown that by means of its suction plate this foot-long perpetual companion of the shark is able to lift as much as twenty-four pounds. Moreover, the greater the pull applied backward, the more the rough teeth of the disk are imbedded into the body of the fish, making it virtually impossible for the sharksucker to release its hold. Thus in many instances the sharksucker has actually parted with its tail, simply because it had no choice but to hold on to the shark.

SHARKSUCKERS *(Echeneis naucrates)*.
Length: 2 feet. Range: Comes north from the tropics on both coasts as far as San Francisco and Cape Cod.
New York Zoological Society

In spite of this dependence, the remora cannot be truly classified as a parasite, since it uses the shark, seal, whale, barracuda, and sea turtle for locomotion only. Its ride stealing causes little annoyance to the larger hosts and only tends to retard somewhat their swimming speed. To the sharksucker, however, this association is indispensable, for it feeds on the debris left by the shark, carefully overlooking those morsels which its carrier particularly likes. Although it invariably uses larger marine creatures for locomotion, the sharksucker is an excellent swimmer, and can easily overtake and even surpass the shark.

The adhesive phenomenon of the sharksucker has been utilized and exploited by fishermen for at least the last four centuries, Dr. E. W. Gudger has discovered. Remora fishing was recorded by Columbus on his first voyage to the Americas. The method of catching sharks, seals, and even large sea turtles with the sharksucker has changed but slightly since then. The common practice is to fasten a leather thong or rope about the sharksucker's tail and fling it into the water. The sharksucker immediately and almost uncannily races for the prey and clings to its abdomen, then both the victim and the living fish hook are pulled out of the water. Once the sharksucker is no longer submerged it is easily disengaged from the fish. The practice of fishing by means of sharksuckers is carried on in Cuba and Colombia sporadically but is more common in northern Australian and East African waters. In the New World localities this unique type of angling has been observed by the editor and his father and reviewed in the *Bulletin of the New York Zoological Society* and in *Copeia*.

A distinctive, yet ill-defined, trait of the sharksucker is its ability to change color instantaneously. While riding with the shark it is usually black with white stripes, or jet black; placed in an aquarium tank by itself it clings to the glass front, and turns gray. It is obviously not a protective device since it is difficult to imagine black and white stripes being anything but conspicuous.

Five species of the sharksucker are found on the Atlantic coast of the United States, as far north as the coast of Maine. The sixteen-inch barracuda remora, or the louse fish, follows the barracuda north to the Carolinas. The common sharksucker, the largest of the remoras (reaching a length of three feet), is often found as far north as Massachusetts Bay, attached to shore sharks and tarpons. The foot-long swordfish remora has been seen near the coast of Maine. The spearfish remora comes from the West Indies and ranges to Cape Cod. The sea turtle remora, fifteen inches long, trails sea turtles even to cold Massachusetts waters, far from its tropic home in the Caribbean.

GOBY

SPENDING a major part of their existence in burrows, crevices, and even inside sponges and large fishes, the gobies comprise an exceedingly large and diversified family of carnivorous fishes.

Among the smallest of fishes, the goby is peculiarly adapted for this form of commensalism—which literally means eating from the same table—both because of its diminutive size and the presence of the ventral sucker on its back which makes adhesion to living organisms possible. The goby profits from this relationship by receiving its food supply, consisting mostly of debris, from the animal which has involuntarily given it a home whether it be a sponge or a fish.

Living close to the bottom in both fresh and salt water, the goby is extremely tenacious and is able to survive in spite of its natural handicaps. Many of the species never leave the shelter of burrows originally made by crustaceans, while others remain perpetually

SERGEANT MAJOR *(Abudefduf marginatus)*. Length: 6 inches. Range: Atlantic coast of tropical America, sometimes found in Florida waters.
John G. Shedd Aquarium

in comfortable chambers inside the sponge. One specimen was discovered curled up contentedly in the gill chamber of a shad, unmindful of the cramped space. The more advanced species, however, cling to loose stones and shells.

One of the great handicaps the goby must overcome is its poor eyesight for the eyes are mere vestiges covered by skin, and some of the species are completely blind. The scales are either non-existent or feebly developed. The mouth is small, and the rather elongated body, usually colored brown or green and conforming to the background of water plants, measures approximately two inches in length, although the size varies from half an inch to several feet.

During the breeding season the male searches for a shell which is to serve as nest. Usually it seeks out a cockle or small scallop, turning it over so that the concave side faces downward. Brushing the sand away with its tail, it bustles in and out of the chamber through the tunnel-shaped entrance, cleaning and polishing the nest, finally cementing it with fine loose sand. When the nest is ready, it ventures forth in search of a female.

Fierce and pugnacious are the males during this mating interlude, staging spectacular combats for the possession of the females. In pugilistic fashion they move at each other, cautiously at first, then finally grappling and biting viciously. The victor spreads his fins and glides before the female, displaying his colors as he heads her to the nest. While the female lays the eggs, the male keeps a perpetual watch over her.

Although they are primarily tropical fishes, twenty-two species of the goby are found in the salt and fresh waters of the United States. Most of the species inhabit the offshore waters of Florida, Key West, the Gulf of Mexico, and the south Atlantic coast.

DEMOISELLE

DEMOISELLES constitute another flashily colored group of tropical fishes, smaller in size than the butterfly fishes but with similar habits. They, too, dwell amid coral reefs and in the United States two species are found—one off the coast of Florida, and the other off southern California. And some are able to change colors; the beau gregory, which becomes a dusky shade in captivity, may be transformed into a beautiful blue and yellow when excited. The sergeant major, with orange stripes, is another member of this group.

FLYING GURNARD

ONE of the wonders of the world of fishes is the flying gurnard, most versatile in its means of locomotion. Here is a versatile fish, swimming prosaically through the ocean, gliding through the air like a soaring bird, or walking along the floor of the sea on a pair of "legs."

The gurnard seeks safety by prowling about the bottom, hidden among the rocks and dense sea grasses. The long forefins resembling claws, hook into the sand or grass and are used to pull the fish along. When it walks thus, its body is held high, horizontal, and it may move forward, backward, or sidewise. The pectoral fins are used as hands which move pieces of coral and seaweed as it searches for food. As the fish marches about, it is kept steady by a pair of balancers which prevent it from falling over on its side.

When it is sighted by a foe it unhesitantly heads for the surface. A kick of the tail makes possible a take-off, and the body of the fish leaves the water and glides upward. The second part of its forefins spread out into large, bluish-colored fans which support the fish's brief aerial maneuvers. For fifteen or twenty feet the gurnard glides above the surface of the water, but then it must return to its native element for it does not really fly nor does it have the power and agility of a flyingfish. It may, however, leap out of the water again for a short trip if some danger still lurks below. The large "wings" are also used as a raft, buoying up the fish so that it can float on the surface.

This odd creature, whose gray body is shaped like a long, low racing car, broad in front and tapering in streamlined fashion to a pointed tail, inhabits the Gulf and the Atlantic as far north as Massachusetts. It is about a foot long, though there have been specimens of eighteen inches. A closely related family includes the sea robins.

RED-WINGED SEA ROBIN *(Prionotus strigatus).* Length: 1½ feet. Range: Cape Cod to Virginia.
John G. Shedd Aquarium

Its body is encased in hard scales which may be razor-sharp. The top of its head is covered with an armor of bony skin. There is one case in which a flying gurnard, butting a sailor at the wheel of a vessel, knocked the man unconscious by the force of the impact with its hard shell.

Dr. William Beebe, noted explorer of marine life, has had rare opportunities for first-hand observations of these interesting fishes in their native haunts. He wrote: "When wearing a diving helmet and sitting quietly on the bottom of a coral reef three or four fathoms down, I have seen small gurnards, individuals measuring from two to four inches in length. These swam slowly, and frequently alighted gently on a sprig of coral or on a sponge, examined it carefully, and then took off again. Specialized as these little beings are, they are no recent innovations, and from the moment when I was making notes about them upon my zinc plate at the bottom of the sea, back to the time when the earliest flying gurnard flew over and walked in Eocene seas—all this is a matter of not less than fifty million years."

LUMPSUCKER

IN the cold waters of the North Atlantic dwells the lumpsucker, or lumpfish, noted for its odd shape and for the peculiar character of the male of the species, which exhibits the most touching maternal devotion. Its name is explained by the lumps on its heavy body and the sucker formed by its fused ventral fins. It is also called the paddlecock because the lumpy crest of its back somewhat resembles a cock's comb.

When this odd fish wearies of swimming about the rocky bottom off the coast, it pauses for a few minutes by applying its suction apparatus to a stone or ledge to which it thus can cling. It ventures out to open sea, too, propelling itself with its tail. Although the lumpsucker swims well, it is awkward in its movements and is so lacking in grace as to be compared with "a clumsy woman running." At sea it may adhere to a buoy for a respite, or it may even steal a ride by fastening itself to another fish. A net cast in deep water once brought up a lumpsucker attached to a mackerel, but ichthyologists have suggested that the attachment may have been due only to the lumpsucker's fright at its plight in being caught in a net with the larger fish.

When its sucker is applied to some object, the fish may exhibit the tenacity of a bulldog. Once a lumpsucker was placed in a pail containing several gallons of water, whereupon it fastened itself to the bottom. The fish, standing on its head, was seized by the tail and pulled—and up came fish, pail, water and all, for the lumpsucker would not let go.

Spawning occurs from February to June, and the female lays from 80,000 to 136,000 eggs whose color varies from brown to red or yellow. The eggs cling to the side of a rock and are at once bade adieu by the mother who departs without concern for her brood.

In steps the father who is prepared to make every sacrifice to guard the eggs until his young are hatched. This parental process was closely observed by Dr. Theodore Gill, among others.

The male lumpsucker's vigil is so faithful that he rarely eats during this period of forty days or so. When the eggs are laid in shallow water they may be exposed at low tide, but the father does not leave. Instead, he lies down on his side, nose pressed up to the clump of eggs, and absorbs enough water to keep fit until high tide. He may be left stranded in water too shallow even to float him, but he does not shrink from his responsibility. Should someone lift him and place him a few feet away, he will immediately wriggle back to position, snout just a few inches from the eggs.

When the eggs are unprotected by the blanket of the sea, they are preyed upon by starlings, sea gulls, and rats. Sometimes a heavy sea will sweep the eggs from their perch and scatter them about. But as soon as the turbulent waters have subsided, papa lumpsucker dashes about to find his lost charges and bring them back into the fold.

The father not only stands faithfully at his post, but also fans the eggs and spurts water into the clump to ensure aeration for all the eggs. He may press his head into the midst of the mass to permit water to trickle through.

His concentration upon his duties is amazing. A crab was once placed among a mass of eggs and the fish maneuvered persistently until he was able to seize the intruder. The crab ordinarily would have made a tasty dish, but

LUMPFISH *(Cyclopterus lumpus).* Length: 1¾ feet. Range: Rocky shores of North America as far south as Cape Cod.
New York Zoological Society

the lumpsucker seemed oblivious to such personal satisfactions. He simply carried off the crab in his mouth, dropped it some distance away and promptly returned to his nest.

Despite his solicitude the lumpsucker can do little to defend his nest from adversaries more potent than small crabs. None too sturdy a fish, he is further weakened by his long fast, and his weak jaws and small teeth are of little use in combat. Some students are of the opinion, however, that the lumpsucker can kill a wolf fish which invades the nest, by attaching itself to the intruder's neck and then biting and worrying it to death; other observers, though, are skeptical.

It has been observed that difficulties arise when two females lay their eggs close together, for then both males attempt to exercise proprietary rights. The victorious father unceremoniously sends the other about his business and proceeds to maintain a solitary vigil. The crestfallen loser slinks away and seems broken in spirit. Should he inadvertently venture near the eggs, the lucky father leaves them to drive away the dispossessed parent who appears terrified and glad to retreat.

When the young are hatched, they have the use of the characteristic suction apparatus. The diminutive fishes cling to anything convenient, including seaweed and even one another. As they grow they feed upon crustaceans, worms, and shell-less mollusks. And they are preyed upon in turn by rooks and carrion crows which stab their sharp beaks into the fishes and eat their livers. Lumpsuckers are not eaten by man in the United States, though they are considered a food in Scotland, Greenland, and elsewhere.

This dull greenish or brown fish ranges along the Atlantic coast as far south as New Jersey and is occasionally seen in Chesapeake Bay. It is less than two feet in length and weighs about thirteen pounds at its largest.

The related spiny lumpsucker, which travels only as far south as the coast of Maine, is covered with large warts in disordered array, while the tubercles of the common lumpsucker are in rows. A Pacific Ocean species, found in Puget Sound, Washington, is the only other lumpsucker in the United States.

SCULPIN

EVEN the neophyte angler has little difficulty in landing the sculpin, so voracious and indiscriminate is its nature. Lying motionless on the bottom of a lake or river, it will bite greedily on any bait, which in no case is intended for its capture, and when it is thrown back and given an opportunity to profit by its first mistake, it will readily bite again just as soon as the hook is lowered.

It is because the sculpin has practically no commercial value that its unhesitating determination to swallow the hook is so disconcerting to fishermen. The sculpin is valued only for lobster bait, although in some sections of New England it is used as a base for chowder. Its somewhat repulsive characteristics, however, combined with the fact that a major portion of its food supply comes from scavenging, make the sculpin an absentee from the epicure's table.

The average length of the sculpin is approximately ten inches, although the species vary in size from the four-inch hook-eared sculpin to the sea raven which measures twenty-five inches in length. All the species are characterized by large spiny heads, wide gill openings, and slender tapering bodies. The mouth is enormously large, and the jaws are armed with small sharp teeth capable of inflicting deep gashes. The naked skin is usually colored reddish brown above and grayish below, although the coloration varies with the bottom on which the fish happens to lie. Prominent on the back are the separate spiny and soft-rayed dorsal fins and the large, fan-shaped pectorals.

The sculpin will eat practically anything that is within the reach of its large mouth. Its diet consists of crabs, shrimps, sea urchins, crustaceans, worms, prawns, gastropods, copepods, and the fry of other fishes, including alewives, cunners, eels and lances, silversides and tomcods. An eager and useful scavenger, it lies close to fish wharves, lobster cars, and sardine factories, where it gobbles up all the debris and refuse dumped into the water.

In spite of its greediness, however, the sculpin is an extremely sluggish fish. It prefers to lie perfectly still, hugging the sandy bottom of shoal waters, and it is really a great effort for it to rise even a few feet to snap at bait. Its mode of locomotion through the water is slow and deliberate; its motions are undulating, and the great pectoral fins are spread like bat's wings. When drawn out of the water, it flattens its head, grunts and gurgles—but not contentedly. Some of the species inflate themselves when molested, and if they are thrown back into the water in this enlarged condition, they are

EIGHTEEN-SPINED SCULPIN *(Acanthocottus octodecemspinosus)*.
Length: 1½ feet. Range: Atlantic coast from Labrador to Virginia.
New York Zoological Society

unable to expel the air at once, but must float helplessly for a long time until the body reaches normal proportions.

Sculpins begin to spawn in November and continue until the end of February. During this period of courtship the slender males gather in schools on sandy or weedy bottoms, where they eagerly await the females. The eggs are fertilized externally and are discharged in clumps. The incubation period varies with the temperature, and usually takes from four to twelve weeks.

Perhaps the most familiar of American fishes, the sculpins are found in the Atlantic and Pacific Oceans as well as in rivers and such inland waters as the Great Lakes.

In the Pacific Ocean there are more than twenty-five species of the scaled sculpins, and at least three of the same species are found in the Atlantic. Scaleless sculpins, also known as miller's thumbs, of which there are more than fifteen species, make their habitat in those fresh waters of the West that drain into the Pacific. In the middle northern and eastern States, in rivers draining into the Great Lakes, the Atlantic Ocean and the Gulf, there are more than ten species of the scaleless sculpins. Some of these are confined to the Great Lakes.

The five species of the daddy sculpins are generally confined to the Atlantic coast offshore waters. The lake sculpins are found in the deep waters of Lakes Ontario and Michigan. The great sculpin is restricted exclusively to the west coast from Puget Sound north.

SURGEONFISH

UNIQUE among fishes is the tang, for it is equipped with a sharp, moveable spine resembling two razor-edged knives. It is because of this strange double-threat weapon that the tang is more commonly referred to as the surgeonfish, lancefish, doctorfish, and *barbero* or barber. Situated on both sides of the tail, or caudal fin, the blades are turned forward and drop into a sheath, and are capable of inflicting sharp gashes on both fish and man. The surgeonfish is extremely ill-tempered and quarrelsome, and when two or more specimens engage in warfare they frequently wound each other mortally in amazingly brief time.

Short, deep, and steep-headed, the surgeonfish is related to the triggerfish. Its teeth are long and pointed, and, according to Dr. Gudger, "are attached to the base of the membrane in such a way that they can be easily turned to the right or left, or bent backward." Its compressed body is covered with fragmentary scales, the mouth is small, the eyes set far back on the head. The coloration of the surgeonfish is usually brown; in one instance, blue; the adult reaches one foot in length.

Three species of the surgeonfish are found in the offshore waters of the Atlantic Ocean bordering the United States. The blue surgeonfish or blue tang ranges from the West Indies to Key West and sometimes north to Woods Hole. The ocean surgeonfish inhabits the same area. The common surgeonfish, the most numerous of the species, is found mostly about Florida, and infrequently as far north as Massachusetts.

BUTTERFLY FISH

WHEN butterfly fishes are out of their native haunts their brilliant, decorative patterns flash conspicuously. They are almost indiscernible, however, against the gaudy coral reefs of tropic seas. Their designs seem to run the gamut of the color scale, but a variety of dark markings serve to obscure the form of these rapidly moving fishes.

Because of their small size and lack of fighting equipment, they are forced to rely upon their speed if danger threatens. An additional defense is their structure, a thick body armed with spiny fins, which renders them difficult to swallow.

Some butterfly fishes are marked with a spot resembling an eye. The four-eyed butterfly fish, which wanders as far north as Massachusetts, has a black "eye" ringed with white on each side of its tail. It is said to swim backward occasionally so that its tail appears to be its head. Then, if trouble is in the offing, it reverses and swims normally, full-speed ahead. This maneuver bewilders most pursuers, for the fleet butterfly fish speeds away in a direction just opposite to the one in which it had been moving.

The common butterfly fish, whose range also extends to New England, is somewhat similar but the spare "eye" lacks the white ring and is placed higher on its body. It feeds upon the smaller organisms of the sea. It, too, like the four-eye, picks the parasites from the bodies of other fishes. It is even believed to pluck parasites from the teeth of other fishes which hold their mouths open for this dental operation with obliging patience.

A diminutive creature, the common butterfly fish is rarely more than six or eight inches long. It is a yellowish gray, marked with a black band on the side of its head. According to Dr. Breder, it is

ANGELFISH

"a typical reef species, flitting about from place to place in a rather butterfly-like fashion."

BLACK ANGELFISHES (*Pomacanthus arcuatus*). Length: 2 feet. Range: New Jersey southward to the West Indies.
New York Aquarium

ANGELFISH

THE larger related angelfishes rarely travel farther north than Florida. The queen angelfish, which attains a length of two feet, is considered a good food fish. It wears a gaudy dress, its striking colors dominated by blues and yellows. The most common species in this country is the two-foot-long black angelfish which has even been found as far north as New York.

About ten species of these two far-flung groups of fishes are found along the coasts of the United States.

SPADEFISH

ANOTHER relative, the spadefish, is esteemed as a food. It attains a length of three feet, though two is more frequent, and a weight of twenty pounds. It outshines the butterfly fish, for it is able to change its color from white and black, to black and white stripes. The young have black bars on a silvery body, but the bars fade with age, and as the fish grows older the skin assumes a darker tone. It then presents a grayish appearance with darker gray stripes. Its fins are spiny, and it is much prized as a food fish.

SPADEFISHES (*Chaetodipterus faber*). Length: 2 feet. Range: Cape Cod to Brazil.
W. F. Gerecke, Marine Studios

The spadefish of the Atlantic coast, ranging from Massachusetts southward, browses about rocks and pilings in search of crustaceans and worms. The female, which spawns from June to August, is very fertile and discharges a million ova during the breeding season. It is accordingly very common.

This fish, also known as porgy and moonfish, is especially abundant in the Southeast although it is common up and down the Atlantic coast. One species of spadefish dwells in the Pacific south of San Diego, California.

DRUM

DISTINGUISHED by their croaking sounds, the drums are represented by a large variety of fishes, embracing more than a score of species. Included in this classification are the weakfishes, silver perches, channel basses, kingfishes, and ribbonfishes, as well as the croakers and drums. Varying in size from the six-inch star drum to the four-foot-long species of sea drum, they are found along the Atlantic coast from Cape Cod to Texas, in the offshore waters of southern California, as well as in fresh waters from the Great Lakes to Texas.

The drumming sound, produced by the swim bladder, is more audible in the male, and is probably used to attract the opposite sex.

The drums constitute an important and valuable group of food fishes. Although the flesh is coarse, it is nevertheless tender, and the flavor has been described as delicate. Especially throughout the

SEA DRUM *(Pogonias cromis).* Length: 3 feet. Range: Atlantic and Gulf coasts.
New York Zoological Society

South, and particularly in Florida, the food value of drums is held in high esteem.

The most abundant and best known of the drums or croakers is the black or common sea drum, one of the largest food fishes of the United States. Most common drums weigh twenty to forty pounds, although they have been known to reach more than one hundred and forty pounds.

Sluggish and slow of movement, the common drum lies close to the bottom, and with the aid of its long sensitive barbels, which protrude from its lower jaw, seeks out mollusks and crustaceans—most important items on its diet. The scales are large and silvery, and are utilized in Florida in making "junk," or fish-scale jewelry such as flower sprays, necklaces, and bracelets.

The fresh-water drum is found in streams between the Great Lakes and Texas, but is most abundant in Lake Erie and Lake Michigan. Often reaching four feet in length and a weight of sixty pounds, the fresh-water drum is known from the North to the South progressively as the crocus, white perch, gray perch, and the thunder pumper.

The black croaker, roncador, little roncador, and yellow-finned California kingfish, all related species, are found in the offshore waters of southern California.

PILOTFISH

LIKE a sinister shadow, the pilotfish trails the shark, awaiting an opportunity to feast on some of the food morsels which may come its way, occasionally attacking the parasites with which the shark is infested. Patient and determined in its movements, it follows its benefactor for days, never letting it out of sight. Contrary to popular belief, the pilotfish does not lead the shark to food, nor does it announce approaching danger, but plays the detective only to satiate its hunger, for it will follow a vessel or a floating barrel just as eagerly.

Known also as the rudderfish and shark pilot, the pilotfish is cosmopolitan in all warm waters, but during the summer wanders

PILOTFISHES *(Naucrates ductor)*. Length: 2 feet. Range: Cape Cod to the West Indies.
New York Zoological Society

along the Atlantic coast as far north as Cape Cod. Its bluish body is stout and elongated, reaching a maximum length of two feet.

Closely related to the pilotfish are the skipjacks and the amberjacks, and other species of tropical distribution, which also, like the pilotfish, range northward along the Gulf Stream as far as Cape Cod. A Pacific coast species, the yellow-tail, or white salmon as it is also sometimes called, is abundant about the Santa Barbara Islands of California.

BLUEFISH AND SERGEANTFISH

TWO families closely related to the shark pilot, found in the same range, are the bluefish and the crab-eating sergeantfish or cobia. Familiar to the angler as well as the epicure, the bluefish is unquestionably the most ferocious, destructive, bloodthirsty fish of its size in the sea. It has no rivals in daring, fight, and willfulness. According to Drs. D. S. Jordan and B. W. Evermann, it "can jump higher, come down quicker, dive deeper and stay under longer than any other salt-water fish." When hooked it fights the angler with that graceful, undefeated, and undaunted courage exhibited only by such large game fishes as the tarpon.

Traveling in schools, bluefishes wander capriciously, staying close to the surface of the water.

Sighting a school of herrings, mackerels, alewives, butterfishes, or cunners, the bluefishes plow through the helpless victims with the precision of a mowing machine. They rip and slash through the thickly packed school with a ferocity unequaled by any other sea animal, leaving in their bloody trail a mass of mangled carcasses. Even after their initial hunger pangs have been satiated, bluefishes continue to destroy their prey, often disgorging what they have already eaten in order to eat more.

Estimates of the destruction caused by bluefishes vary, but all are staggering in their vastness. The bluefish in their four months of roaming about the coast of Maine either consume or destroy more than twelve million fishes. Drs. Jordan and Evermann claim that the billion bluefishes which are found along the Atlantic coast south of New Jersey, destroy a total of ten billion fishes daily. Other estimates have credited individual bluefishes with destroying one thousand fish a day.

The average weight of the bluefish is three to five pounds, the maximum is twenty-two pounds. Its stout, graceful, and extremely powerful body is colored deep blue above, silvery below. The nose is pointed, and the molar teeth are sharp and menacing.

The flesh of the bluefish, which is sweet and tender, is prized throughout the United States. More than twenty million pounds of bluefish are used yearly for our food supply. One of the popular methods of catching the bluefish is called chumming. For this process a mess of fish is left to rot, then ground up and thrown into the water. The bluefishes, if any are present, immediately congregate underneath this oily, putrified, floating layer, gorging themselves with the delicate, evil-smelling carrion. A large net is then cast and they are hauled in by the hundreds. This unappetizing food does not destroy their flavor in any way.

The sergeantfish is a strong, swift fish. Also called the crabeater and cobia, it superficially resembles the sharksucker and attains a length of five feet. The black stripe along its side is responsible for its common name.

SNAPPER

SNAPPERS constitute an important and highly valued food element. So abundant and prolific are these active predatory fishes, that in some instances a team of six men have caught as many as a thousand in a few hours. Taken mostly about Florida, Key West, and the Gulf of Mexico, they have been packed and shipped to many parts of the world. Of the dozen species found along the east coast of the United States, all the snappers, with the possible exception of the schoolmaster which is supposedly poisonous, are considered game fishes, and the eagerness and determination with which they take the hook and still put up a fight when caught, have made them prizes worth seeking by anglers.

DOG SNAPPER *(Lutianus jocu)*. Length: 2 feet. Range: Florida Keys and the West Indies.
New York Zoological Society

Equipped with a large mouth and long sharp teeth, the snapper appears ferocious as it glides through the warm waters, and indeed its disposition matches its appearance. It is quarrelsome and voracious, destroying mackerels, alewives, and many smaller fishes upon which it mainly feeds. In size the snapper ranges from one to three feet and reaches a maximum weight of thirty-five pounds. Its coloration reveals every hue of the rainbow, and the shadings and pigmentations are so vivid that they have been widely utilized in marine paintings. With the exception of the gray snapper, which is dark green and gray, the diversity of colors includes rose, red, yellow, crimson, silver, black, green, and blue.

Snappers always travel in schools, usually close to the surface of the water, but this characteristic varies somewhat with the individual species. The red snapper, for instance, is found in deep waters, the gray somewhere between. In July and August they are so numerous that the immediate waters take on their coloration.

Two of the most important and widespread species of the snappers, which inhabit the offshore waters of the Atlantic Ocean and the Gulf of Mexico, are the gray snapper and the red snapper. The gray snapper, the more abundant, is found off Florida, where it is known as the mangrove snapper, and occasionally wanders north to Long Island. The red snapper inhabits a similar range. Excellent as food fishes, more than ten million pounds of snappers are caught annually in the Gulf of Mexico, landed at Pensacola, Florida, where they are packed in ice and shipped throughout the United States.

GROUPER

HUGE, ugly, and vicious-looking, the groupers appear to embody a peculiar accentuation of the more dour characteristics of fishes. There is the bulky but short body shaped like a blimp, looming with the same mysterious calm; a face that is even more than usually sullen because of the wide arc of thick lips formed by the protruding lower jaw and bulging eyes; and the general coarseness of scales and nondescript coloring. In the giant species, ranging in weight from fifty to six hundred pounds, the impression is truly formidable.

In habits the groupers also command respect. They prey on all sorts of smaller fishes, especially mullet, and on crustaceans. Now

GIANT GROUPER OR SPOTTED JEWFISH (*Promicrops itaiara*).
Length: 8 feet. Range: Florida to Brazil.
New York Zoological Society

and then their voracious appetites lead them to swallow a hooked fish, line and all, and a struggle ensues that the angler has not expected. As a rule, however, they are hard to catch as they stay close to the bottom in deep water. The red-bellied variety, weighing around forty or fifty pounds, is mostly snared. An excellent food, it is shipped in goodly numbers from Florida to Cuban markets, since it stays alive two or three hours after being caught, but requires solitary confinement during that period because of its viciousness.

Most species spawn in bays and inlets and salty river mouths during May and June. They are known by a variety of common names such as rock hind, yellow-finned grouper, spotted grouper or jewfish, Nassau grouper, *cabrilla* or red hind, and speckled hind. In all they comprise about two dozen species. One of these, the soapfish, is so called because when handled it exudes a soapy mucus from its skin.

The red and giant or black groupers are abundant off Key West and in the Gulf of Mexico, the red variety occasionally running as far north as New York. The Bermuda grouper, the smallest, is confined to the waters off Key West and the Bermudas. The much prized California giant grouper or jewfish, the largest food fish on the Pacific coast, ranges from the Farallon Islands to south of San Diego.

SEA BASS

MOST numerous of game fishes on the Atlantic coast are the sea basses, the fisherman's staple catch. Although not as game as the fresh-water basses nor as prized as many another ocean variety, they are nearly always around to reward the most luckless angler. And familiarity has not bred contempt, thanks to their firm sweet flesh that makes the finest chowder or broiled fish entree.

They are found usually in shallow water around reefs and sand bars close to land. Here they feed on the innumerable invertebrates

ROCK SEA BASSES *(Triloburus philadelphicus)*. Length: 1 foot. Range: Coast of South Carolina.
New York Zoological Society

SEA BASS

SEA BASS *(Centropristes striatus)*. Length: 1 foot. Range: Cape Ann to northern Florida.
New York Zoological Society

on the bottom in company with porgies, flounders, tautogs, snappers, and grunts. The interval between tides brings great numbers together in these haunts, making them easy to catch.

A clue to their hardiness is found in their low body temperature —about equal to the surrounding medium. Naturally sluggish, they go into deeper waters in the winter to remain virtually immovable until spring. For the same reason they live long in captivity and are ideal for shipment in large quantities over great distances. Before putting them into wells, fishermen puncture their air bladders with an awl driven through their sides, to counteract the lack of pressure which causes them to float.

During July and August they spawn. The males acquire bright colors and a large lump on top of their heads during this season.

Two species are found on the Atlantic coast, the northern type ranging from Cape Ann to Charleston, and the southern from that point to the northern part of the Gulf of Mexico. The northern variety averages one and a half pounds, attaining a weight of four or five pounds at times; the southern is smaller, averaging only about a pound.

On the Pacific coast, three kinds of black and rock bass are known. The black bass, averaging about five pounds, ranges from San Francisco to Cerros Island, being especially numerous around the Santa Barbara Islands. It is called *cabrilla* by the Italians and Spaniards, and *lockee cod* (rock cod) by the Chinese. A large variety of rock bass, averaging about five pounds, is found from San Pedro south to Magdalena Bay; a smaller, spotted variety is very numerous off San Diego.

In all, the sea basses, including the various *cabrillas* or rock basses, squirrelfishes, phoebes, rockfishes, and the like, comprise some eleven species. Families related to the sea basses include the big-eyes of the West Indian tropics, which sometimes travel with the Gulf Stream to Cape Cod; the flashers or tripletails found along the Atlantic coast from Cape Cod southward; and the *Xenistius* of the lower Pacific coast, which does not even possess a common name.

BLACK BASS

A POWERFUL swimmer which can leap five or six times above the water when hooked and is plentiful in nearly all lakes and streams, the black bass is the amateur angler's chief delight. It is a peculiarly American fish, being not only native to the country, but embodying the fighting qualities of our pioneers. Confined originally to the St. Lawrence and Mississippi basins, it has been introduced to Cuba, Europe, and South Africa, and its adaptability to all sorts of conditions detrimental to the trout, promise to make it even more of a game fish in the future.

Both small- and large-mouthed species, of which there are three in all, average about two and a half pounds, but occasionally reach a weight of six or seven pounds or even more. They may easily be distinguished by the length of the upper jaw, that of the small-mouthed type extending to just below the eye, and that of the other far behind it. The large-mouthed variety is the more hardy and widely distributed, being found in both cool and warm rivers, streams, and lakes, while the small-mouthed type occupies cool waters only.

They eat insects, larvae, frogs, and especially crawfishes. The large-mouthed variety is partial to minnows, and larger specimens will go after a sunfish, perch, trout, or pickerel. Even rats and snakes have been found in their stomachs. It is this voraciousness that makes them responsive to all manner of fishing.

No small factor in their numerical superiority is their reproductive capacity. A male will fertilize eggs of several females during a spawning season. Females have been found to carry 17,000 eggs, and, while not all are deposited at one time, the greater portion are, so that nests with 10,000 or more eggs are not unusual. And their breeding habits are no doubt the most elaborate of any game fish.

The male is the more important element in homemaking. When the temperature of the water rises above sixty degrees—that is from March to June, depending on the latitude—he will select a protected spot among the reeds and root out a depression about eighteen inches in diameter. This he will line with small stones around the edge and partly fill with large ones in the center. Then, guarding his territory from ingress by any other male fish, he merely waits until the female arrives. She succumbs readily after a short courtship of advancing and retreating with raised fins, and finally, as she circles about the nest, deposits her eggs. After fertilizing them, the male throws her out, and waits for his next mate.

When the nest is suitably full, after several courtships, the male stands guard, fanning the eggs to keep them free of fungus and to aerate them. The half-inch fry hatch in two or three weeks, depending on the temperature of the water. Then father deserts them, not, however, without first eating a few himself. By autumn the remaining fry are from two to six inches long and the following year mature. But many an accident may happen before then; indeed, the eggs are often killed by oily water or a sudden change in temperature. In the latter case the adults disappear by burrowing in mud or hibernating in rock crevices. This is an important fact to be considered in black-bass fishing, for when the temperature of the water falls below fifty degrees they become inactive.

BLUE-GILLED SUNFISH *(Helioperca incisor)*. Length: 1 foot. Range: Great Lakes to Florida and the Rio Grande.
New York Zoological Society

SUNFISH

LOLLING along the bank of a small stream or pond, bamboo poles set out and cans of worms ready to replenish the hook on the line, many a truant lad has learned the delights of the sunfish. Not as large as the bass, but active and abundant, it is easy to catch. Goggle-eyed and vividly speckled, it is a sight truly warming to the heart of a boy and especially palatable at a campfire.

Although never weighing more than one and a half pounds, the many varieties are well protected by strong spiny fins on back and under side. Hence they thrive in the company of much larger fishes. Streams and ponds too warm for trout or landlocked salmon or too small for bass are their special domain. The common variety, about eight inches long and spotted with red, thrives in clear quiet waters. Its flesh is tastier than that of perch.

In the spring the females dig nests in the shallow water near the banks, a foot or more in diameter and three or four inches deep.

Many nests are often found together. After the male fertilizes the eggs, the female guards them until they hatch. An early drought, however, may leave them high and dry.

The common sunfish is found in the Great Lakes and coastal streams from Maine to Georgia, also in the headwaters of the Mississippi. Among the other species the long-eared kind inhabits coastal streams from Maine to Louisiana; the blue type, the Great Lakes and coastal streams from New Jersey to Florida and Mexico; the beautiful strawberry or calico bass, the Great Lakes, the Mississippi, and streams of the Carolinas and Georgia; the warmouths, Lake Michigan, the upper Mississippi, and lowland streams from Virginia to Texas; the Sacramento perch, the Sacramento and San Joaquin river basins; the rock bass, the Great Lakes and Mississippi River; the mud bass, coastal streams from New Jersey to North Carolina; and the crappie, the muddy bayous of the lower Mississippi. In all some thirty-seven species of sunfishes, bream, and the like inhabit the United States.

White bass belong to a closely related family, the *Moronidae*, and comprise four species. The striped bass and yellow perch are common along the Atlantic coast from Maine to Florida. The former has been introduced into the Sacramento River of California, while the latter ascends streams and frequently becomes landlocked in ponds. In the Great Lakes lives the white or silver bass which often is also encountered in the upper Mississippi and Ohio river valleys. Throughout the lower Mississippi the foregoing is replaced by the yellow bass as far north as Cincinnati.

PERCH

PERCH may not offer the greatest sport, but in numbers and rapidity with which it can be taken it comes near to constituting the fisherman's ideal. A hundred in an hour or two is not unusual for one line, and more than a thousand have been hooked with two in a couple of hours. Indeed, a half dozen hooks are baited with worms, minnows, or grubs at a time when they are running well—which occurs in both summer and winter. The reasons for this are the extreme gregariousness of the species—it travels in large schools and when one disappears all the rest follow—and its voraciousness, leading it to take the eye of its own species when offered as bait.

Nearly all species like cool clear waters with a certain amount of depth and current. Hence in season they are found usually in

YELLOW PERCH *(Perca flavescens):* Length: 1 foot. Range: "Nova Scotia to the Great Lakes and upper Mississippi Valley; south to North Carolina and central Ohio; introduced on the Pacific slope" (Schrenkeisen).
New York Zoological Society

deep pools under hollow river banks, near mill basins, rapids, and in the eddies of dock piles and bridgeheads. They grow torpid in freezing water, but can stand a temperature as low as thirty-eight degrees. When the water grows sufficiently warm in April, May, and June they seek shallow places in which to spawn.

The females carry from eight thousand to fifty thousand eggs which swell their ovaries at this time. As large as poppy seeds, they are deposited like beads on a sticky interlaced string six feet long and two or three inches wide. This mass clings to a twig or stone on the bottom and, if not eaten by birds or aquatic animals, hatches in a week to ten days. The young usually stay together till fall.

PERCH

The vivid tints of this graceful fish, which make it one of the handsomest of all fresh-water species, become accentuated in the spring, especially in the males. Most beautiful of all is the yellow perch, dark olive in tone with bright gold setting off dark patches on the sides and ruddy hues delicately etching jaw, belly, and fins. This, together with its well-proportioned body and intelligence, makes the species an aquarium favorite. The somewhat larger and more slender pike-perch is a lighter olive or greenish brown and heavily mottled with yellow lines and blotches and darker hues. Its distinctive feature, however, is the large glassy eye, whence the name

PIKE-PERCH *(Stizostedion vitreum)*. Length: 3 feet. Range: "Great Lakes region and upper Mississippi Valley; north to Assiniboia; east to Vermont and Pennsylvania; south to Georgia and Alabama" (Schrenkeisen).
John G. Shedd Aquarium

wall-eyed perch. The sauger or sand perch is very similar, though smaller and lacking the prominent eye. It is gray above and so brightly checkered on the sides that it is also known as the rattlesnake pike.

The perch family, an advanced bony type, though boasting fossil remains dating from the Tertiary period, is specialized for defense.

Hence it can live with impunity among larger types and is a menace to carp and trout. It has sharp spines in its long forward dorsal fin and soft rays in the rear one, while a good portion of its scales harbor microscopic barbs. In addition its forked tail and the forward position of its pelvic fins make it a strong swimmer. Its rather long mouth armed with sharp teeth, especially exemplified in the pike-perch, fit it for preying on smaller fishes. A conspicuous lateral line nerve aids it in judging current and temperature changes.

The pike-perch, which returns to shallow waters in the winter and can be caught in large numbers through the ice, and the yellow perch are the only important game species. The yellow perch, also known as the American perch, ringed perch, raccoon perch, yellow ned, river or lake perch, is distributed throughout most of the fresh waters of the eastern United States. The pike-perch averages about three or four pounds and the yellow perch between one and two, though heavier examples of both have occasionally been hooked. Their meat is firm and tasty, especially if the fishes are caught before spawning, and the pike-perch is so important a food fish that the Government maintains extensive hatcheries devoted to its propagation. Both fishes abound in the Great Lakes and upper Mississippi region; on the Atlantic coast the yellow perch runs from Labrador, and the pike-perch, walleye, or wall-eyed pike, extends from the Great Lakes region and upper Mississippi eastward to Vermont and Pennsylvania and southward to Alabama and Georgia. A related species, the blue pike, is confined to the Great Lakes region. The sauger perch, of which there are two species, is found in the Great Lakes and in the upper Missouri, Mississippi, and Ohio Rivers.

DARTER

THE brilliant little darters in nearly all the shallow brooks, streams, swamps, ponds, and lakes east of the Rockies attest that minnows are not the only small fishes. Compact creatures with elaborate fins matching their bright yellow and blackish hues, they appear to be in reality small perches adapted to fresh-water streams too shallow and too swift for larger forms.

Their habits tend to confirm the anatomical evidence too. Lying perfectly still against the current on a rocky bottom two or three feet below the surface, they will dart out suddenly for a distance of one to two yards when disturbed, with great commotion. But after a dozen such efforts they are too exhausted to continue darting and may easily be caught in ones' hands. Some species in the family are progressively specialized toward a quiescent life and are most frequently found buried in sand; others are encountered in weedy and slow-moving brooks as well as in quiet ponds and stagnant swamps.

From one to five inches in length, darters feed on insects, crustaceans, and offal. They are believed to breed in spring and hibernate by burrowing into the mud in winter. There are more than one hundred species in this country. Of the two most important varieties, the log-perch is the largest, and the tesselated darter the most numerous. Neither, however, appears to be of any economic value.

POMPANO

EPICURES pay tribute to the pompano as the finest food fish of river or ocean. In spite of such popularity the pompano hesitates to put in a public appearance and refuses to bite on hooks, no matter how temptingly they may be baited. One veteran fisherman could recall only two instances in forty years when a pompano was caught on a hook. They are therefore secured, minus the thrill of angling, in nets cast along the Gulf of Mexico and Mobile Bay, and are often sold for as much as one dollar and fifty cents a pound.

In the spring pompanos grouped in large schools invade the Gulf coast. They are rarely visible, for they swim well below the surface, but occasionally they flip out of the water and their bodies then flash momentarily in midair. The schools may spend weeks outside the bays, approaching shore only at high tide when the fishes are able to prowl among the sandy hollows in search of shellfish. When the pompanos finally enter the bay, the schools are disbanded, and each goes its individual way.

The pompano is not a fighter; it feeds on such things as mollusks, crustaceans, and perhaps the young of other fishes. Its small teeth are valueless in combat and even these disappear as the fish grows older. Consequently, the pompano is easily preyed upon by sharks and porpoises.

It attains a length of eighteen inches and a weight of eight pounds, though two pounds is average. Of the five species found off the east coast of the United States, the largest is the great pompano, or permit, of Florida, which is three feet long and weighs twenty-seven pounds or more.

POMPANO (*Trachinotus carolinus*). Length: 1½ feet. Range: South Atlantic and Gulf coasts.
New York Zoological Society

The pompano is a warm-water fish appearing off the Massachusetts coast only in the summer. Its range during the year extends south of Cape Cod and along the Gulf. Its peregrinations may depend on the weather, for if a region has an untimely cold spell the fish promptly moves along to a more seasonable clime.

The appearance of these fishes has caused them to be compared with "silver dollars swimming about on their edges." Dr. G. Brown Goode, observing one in an aquarium, also wrote: "It was the only fish I have ever seen which appeared to possess the power of becoming phosphorescent at will. At night we could trace its nervous movements by occasional gleams of light, as the fish, turning one side toward us, touched with the other the floor of the basin."

PORTUGUESE MAN-OF-WAR FISH

ON THE surface of the open sea floats a six-inch cask, filled with air and topped with a colorful sail which can be raised or lowered. This picturesque contraption is a species of jellyfish, known as the Portuguese man-of-war, and it wanders about guided only by the grace of the waves and the winds.

There is more to this creature, however, than first meets the eye. From the cask are suspended long dangling tentacles which may extend thirty feet below the surface of the water. When small inhabitants of the sea wander among these tentacles they are paralyzed by stinging cells surrounding each and drawn up to the feeding man-of-war to be devoured. These cells are the most potent of any sea dweller's and the creatures which come into contact with them are doomed. While the cask can be handled with impunity, any per-

PORTUGUESE MAN-OF-WAR AND POR-
TUGUESE MAN-OF-WAR FISHES (*Physalia pelagica* and *Nomeus gronovii*). Length: 8 inches (fish). Range: Warm seas and northward to Cape Cod.
American Museum of Natural History

son becoming entangled in the coils will receive a series of sharp burning stings.

This wanderer, however, is generally accompanied on its aimless peregrinations by a little fish which has consequently become known as the Portuguese man-of-war fish. It is the only creature which is not affected by the stinging cells. When the fish is beset by danger, it dashes immediately among the tentacles of its partner, the jellyfish, and is completely immune to the stinging cells. Should some intrepid attacker dare to follow, such indiscretion results in death, since it becomes a meal for the jellyfish.

Reciprocity seems to be the keynote of the relationship between the two. The jellyfish protects the little fish which, in turn, is believed to serve as a lure to bring other creatures into the jellyfish's clutches.

As many as twelve fish have been found among the protective coils of a single Portuguese man-of-war. These mutually helpful creatures range along the Atlantic coast, mostly in warm regions. They are found as far north as Massachusetts, and sometimes the jellyfish, carried there by the warm Gulf Stream, is left stranded on the shore.

Some Portuguese man-of-war fish are quite tiny, but they may grow to a length of eight inches. In color they are light brown above, silvery below, and are adorned with large brown spots on their sides.

DOLPHIN

THE long sleek body of the dolphin throws off glints of yellows, blues, and whites as it streaks through the dark-tinted sea. Probably no other fish can move so swiftly, and few possess the beauty and grace of this streamlined speeder.

All its resources are brought into play when it is actuated by the driving pangs of hunger. Then this six-foot fish zooms along like a projectile and near the surface seizes such of its neighbors as silversides, lizard-fishes, and flyingfishes. After it has eaten, however, it may relax and move about lazily.

DOLPHIN *(Coryphaena hippurus).* Length: 6 feet. Range: Atlantic and Gulf coasts.

American Museum of Natural History

This inhabitant of the open sea is sometimes caught by sailors in midocean, though such occurrences are rare and due more to fortuitous circumstances then design. It is considered to be good to eat, and yet it is also believed to be poisonous at times. In olden days seafarers had a strange way of arriving at a decision on this matter. After the fish had been cooked, a bit of silver was placed in the pot; if the silver turned black it was a sure sign that the dolphin was poisonous; if not, the tasty flesh could be eaten.

The dolphin is brilliantly colored, with light green dominating the white or gold of its under surface. It is marked with spots and lines of bright blue, purplish blue, yellow, and black.

From James Montgomery's *Pelican Island* comes this tribute in poetry to the dolphin's beauty:

"A shoal of dolphins tumbling in wild glee,
Glowed with such orient tints, they might have been
The rainbow's offspring, where it met the ocean."

In times of stress, or when it is dying the spectacular colors of the dolphin undergo striking changes and its rainbow pattern becomes still more beautiful.

The common dolphin, which should not be confused with its mammalian namesake, spawns around the West Indies in spring. It ranges from Texas to the Carolinas and is occasionally found as far north as Cape Cod. Another species, the small dolphin, has been observed off the coast of southern California.

SAILFISH

SPEEDIEST of all swimmers probably is the sailfish. One of the most specialized of the mackerel tribe, it has been timed with stop watches as covering one hundred yards in three seconds, or at the rate of sixty-eight miles an hour. When in the water its chief feature—the huge dorsal fin or sail—is neatly tucked into a slot in its back, and the long ventral and shorter pectorals, both fins at-

PACIFIC SAILFISH (*Istiophorus greyi*). Length: 6 feet. Range: Pacific coast of Mexico and lower California. Related species are found off Florida. Depleted as the result of overfishing.
American Museum of Natural History

tached at the breast, are pressed against the body, giving the fish perfect streamlined smoothness from the elongated point of the upper jaw to the powerful crescentic tail. So great is its momentum that it has been known to jump across forty feet of water, and it can easily outdistance its chief enemy, the shark.

The function of the sail has so far baffled scientists. The fish basks in the sun at the surface of the water with it outstretched, so it may absorb heat or serve as a sense organ. In landing from vigorous jumps, too, it should be of value, and indeed such a brake would seem logical in a speed king.

In any case, the sail identifies it as one of the most picturesque of all fishes. This is particularly true of the Atlantic coast species, smaller but far more striking than those of the Pacific. The sail is a lavender hue, darker purple at the tips and dotted with half-inch purple spots. The back is a deep blue, and the belly and lower sides a silvery white. In the center is a bright green stripe. Blue dots and dashes give the effect of faint vertical lines on the sides. The bill is dark purple near the tip and blue where it joins the head, and the large opalescent eyes have triangular purple pupils.

The sailfish, one of the large game fishes, whose depredations on smaller, more edible species have led to the development of its capture within the last few decades, is more important in providing sport than food. It is an extremely spectacular fighter and hard to hook, though of much less stamina than the larger and closely related marlins and swordfishes. When sighted by means of its protruding caudal or sail fin or the presence of flyingfishes and predatory birds, strips of bait cut from bonitos are lowered on a long line and the teaser dragged around a circle at a trolling speed of from two to six miles an hour.

Like the swordfish, the sailfish first strikes the bait with its bill as though to maim it; hence it is necessary to wait before pulling in. When hooked it will strike out, and shortly begin to jump and walk on its tail. Like the marlin and swordfish, it has been known to turn on its tormentors and attack their boat.

Although little is known about the breeding habits of the sailfish, it is probable that the Atlantic species spawns in shoals near the

Gulf Stream during the summer, since schools of young are found nearby the following winter. Many of these necessarily succumb to larger fishes before reaching maturity. The full-grown Atlantic species averages between forty-five and fifty-five pounds, while the more slender, less colorful form from the Pacific runs at least twice as heavy, and has been caught up to one hundred and eighty-two pounds. The Pacific sailfish ranges from Cape San Lucas, California, to Peru; the Atlantic from Woods Hole, Massachusetts, to the Gulf of Mexico. A Florida species is sometimes distinguished from that of the Atlantic.

MARLIN

KNOWN as the acrobat of the sea, the marlin offers one of the toughest and most thrilling fishing experiences to the expert big-game angler. Like the sailfish, it is especially given to jumping and tail-walking—a habit contracted in its efforts to dislodge parasites—and it can continue its flips and sallies a good deal longer than its relative. It is usually heavier, too, averaging several hundred pounds, and at the end of a thousand-foot line taxes the ingenuity of the expert with its violent maneuvers.

In form it is midway between the sailfish and swordfish; that is, it has a somewhat elongated dorsal fin, in which the high point of the swordfish's corresponding member is drawn out to the rear but with no such elaboration as in the case of the sailfish. It is more slender than the swordfish, too, although less so than the sailfish, while the bill or sword is of medium length. It is the resemblance of this latter member to a marlinspike that has given it the name of marlin or spikefish.

Much sought after, the fish is as yet little known, because of the expense and difficulty entailed in capturing it. It is believed to spawn during the summer, but its migrations are a mystery. Hooked specimens have frequently been accompanied by one or two others that refused to take bait, but when landed, were found to be females full of roe. This devotion of mates, which may cause the accompanying fish to leap up the side of the boat as if to see where its consort has gone, has led to the belief in their strong family affection. That the male often lets the female take the bait, however, is rather prosaically accounted for by the fact that he is much smaller.

Three or four chief species are generally recognized: the white, striped, blue, and black marlins. The striped and black species found on the Pacific coast are respectively more or less commensurate with the white and blue varieties on the Atlantic coast, the white species merely having a square-cut dorsal fin and the blue a higher one. The meat of the white and striped species is darker and much less tasty, too, than that of the blue or black varieties. This is fortunate, for the latter are more difficult to catch thus increasing their value to commercial fishers.

BLUE MARLIN (*Makaira ampla*). Length: 9 feet. Range: West Indies and off the coast of Florida. No longer common.
American Museum of Natural History

The striped marlin of the Pacific has a gray-green back, paler sides with faint purple vertical bars, and is somewhat larger, smoother, and more slender than the black variety found there. The white marlin of the Atlantic is said to be the greatest jumper and have more stamina than the black variety, which some believe is only the old female of the blue variety.

Though generally trolled for near the surface, the marlin frequently strikes blind or from the bottom. It never taps the bait, but takes it off a distance in order to devour it safely. It requires considerable practice for the angler to judge the moment when the hook has become set and the time is ripe to strike. Even after a long tussle the fish has so much power that it is generally harpooned when brought alongside the boat before being gaffed and hauled up.

Pacific coast marlins range from the Channel Islands of California south, the black species being commonest off Central America, but neither being found in water colder than seventy degrees. On the Atlantic coast marlins range from Massachusetts to the Gulf of Mexico.

SWORDFISH

FLAYING to the right and left with its long, flat, sharp bill through schools of small fishes, the swordfish first mangles or kills its prey and then returns to devour it. The sword, an elongation of the upper jaw that sometimes reaches a length of four feet, is a formidable specialization that takes the place of teeth, since the swordfish, unlike its close relatives, the sailfish and marlin, has none. So powerful is this blade that it has been known to cut through the planking of boats and lacerate the fishermen within.

A large fish with considerable girth and an evil temper, the swordfish is more often harpooned than caught with rod and reel. It is only when it has been wounded that it grows desperate enough to attack boats or sound with such force as to bury its bill up to the eyes in the bottom sand and muck of the ocean floor. Most of the stories of large wooden ships being punctured by swordfish are attributed to the round-sword spearfish, however, rather than the more common broadbill type.

The difficulty of snaring the swordfish in a sportsmanlike way is not only due to its aggressiveness but also to its poor vision and even poorer sense of smell. The juiciest mackerel or squid bait are passed by most of the time unnoticed. Thus when found finning—sharp dorsal and tail fins protruding from the surface of the water

—boats can approach quite close and drop their lines of bait, but the big fellows nine times out of ten miss the morsels. If hooked, they are slow and methodical in their tactics. Sometimes a swordfish will tow the fishing boat many miles, even as long as a day and a night.

One of the finest of food fishes, the swordfish is sought as much for commercial as sporting reasons. Especially in demand is swordfish liver which at the peak of the fishing season has been found to be a hundred times richer in vitamins A and D than the standard cod-liver oil. The value placed on swordfish as food is the more remarkable in that of all fish it is one of the most infested with parasites and worms. No less than seven species of worms—including round, fluke, and tapeworms—five crustacean parasites, and several species of sucking fish—including the swordfish remora—infest its body. This is why it jumps out of the water at times. Considering what pink pork can do to human insides, it is well to cook swordfish thoroughly.

SWORDFISH *(Xiphias gladius)*. Length: 15 feet. Range: Atlantic coast from Newfoundland to Florida, in the Pacific off the coast of southern California.
Freeman P. Taylor

Young swordfish have been found only in Mediterranean and Japanese waters in winter, and this offers the only clue to their breeding and migrating habits so far. In the young both upper and lower jaws are prolonged, and teeth are present; these with the vertical bars on the sides disappear in the dusky, purplish, scaleless adult. In the adult the high-pointed dorsal fin is well back near the center of the body and ventral fins are lacking.

Swordfish have a world-wide distribution, mostly in waters warmer than fifty degrees. Only sperm and killer whales and the larger sharks can overcome them. The common broadbill is found in the open sea of both the Atlantic and Pacific coasts, in the Atlantic mostly between the Carolinas and Newfoundland, and off the coast of California from the Santa Barbara Islands to San Diego.

MACKEREL

IN THE common lowly mackerel, the streamlined form of the most modern fish first became standardized, leading to a host of powerful torpedo-shaped allies. The essential of their form appears to consist of perfect simplicity and symmetry of line from the tip of their pointed mouth to their powerful widespread tail and compact body. There are no impeding protuberances anywhere, except the essential fins and tail keels.

Although hunted as food by both man and beast, the mackerel is still plentiful, showing the hardy adaptability of its type. It migrates in large schools south in winter and north in summer in search of small crustaceans and fishes, especially spawn. It can stand a temperature of forty degrees and lives in shallow as well as deep water.

Mackerel spawn in deep water along the coast of Long Island and the New England States during May and June. A single female carries as many as half a million eggs, a fact which partly accounts for their profusion. The eggs are deposited in the water where they are immediately fertilized by the male; they then float near the surface aided by the oil globule within each. The young hatch in a few days if all goes well, and grow to a length of six or seven inches by fall. They reach full maturity in four years—a foot in length and weighing about a pound.

The gannet is the chief enemy of the mackerel, swooping down on them in the open sea. Fishermen have found these birds so glutted at times that they could not rise from the water, having first to disgorge several full-sized mackerel in order to do so. Porpoises, whales, mackerel sharks, dogfishes, bluefishes, and cods also relish mackerel. In the case of the young, squids are the greatest killers, darting among the schools to snatch them up. Often, however, the fry are too quick and wary, and to lure them back the squids will sink to the bottom and become invisible by changing their color to that of the sand. But the fry may retaliate by luring the squids so far inshore that they become stranded.

Closely allied to the common species, which rivals the cod in food value, is the chub mackerel. It is also blue above and silvery below, but has indistinct spots below the lateral line as well as the irregular black lines about it. The Spanish and Sierra mackerels differ in having contiguous dorsal fins, rows of golden spots on the sides, and a more slender form. The Monterey Spanish mackerel is similar but unspotted. The Pacific mackerel, with variable color bars on its back and separate dorsal fins, approaches the chub mackerel, while the frigate mackerel is distinguished by its corselet or keel (large scale development) at its breast and larger size.

The common mackerel is found in the open seas on the Atlantic coast from Cape Hatteras to Labrador; the Sierra mackerel, from Santa Monica, California, to Peru; the Atlantic Spanish mackerel, from Florida south; the Monterey Spanish mackerel, in Monterey Bay, California; the Pacific mackerel, from Alaska to Cape San Lucas; and the frigate mackerel, near San Pedro, California.

TUNA

WHEN a big tuna gets hold of a hook and line there's no telling what may happen. It may take you for a ride forty or fifty miles out to sea until you're stranded for lack of gas, or it may run over the rocks and inshore reefs. One thing, however, is certain; the angler is in a dilemma, since—according to the experts—there is no stopping the fish at the outset and all you can do is hang on, while at the same time the tuna's spirit must be broken by never allowing it a moment's peace. It is strictly man against fish and even with the strongest of tackle man does not always win.

TUNNY *(Thunnus secundodorsalis).* Length: 8 feet. Range: Labrador to New York.
S. C. Dunton, New York Aquarium

Such fighting qualities make the tuna one of the world's greatest game fishes. Built like a mackerel, it reaches a large size in the bluefin tuna, also known as the horse mackerel, leaping tuna, or great tunny, which achieves a length of fourteen feet and a weight of sixteen hundred pounds in the Atlantic where it is most numerous. Every season the old-timers vie with one another to better the world's record catch for rod and reel, which now stands at nine hundred and fifty-six pounds. It is the younger tuna weighing between three and six hundred pounds, however, that make the best fighters. All the best technique of big-game fishing is used in trolling with flying fish bait, feathers, jigs, plugs, outriggers, and kites serving to keep the bait away from the boat because the tuna has become boat-shy.

Most species appear on the coast in spring and remain till early winter, when they suddenly disappear, presumably to spawn. Eggs and larvae of the bluefin have been found in the Mediterranean and mid-Atlantic at depths of from eighty feet to half a mile. This species is known to migrate from the Mediterranean to Norway and throughout the Gulf Stream. In the summer, schools of bluefin several layers deep also come up the Gulf Stream on the Atlantic coast to the herring nets of Nova Scotia where many are taken. The young of the smallest species, the oceanic skipjack, have been found near Japan in the summer.

All of them prey on smaller fishes which they herd together and snap up on the edges. Crustaceans and the animals of the plankton are also important as dietary items. The large bluefin also eats bonitos and smaller dog sharks. Its only real enemy is the killer whale, which it can apparently spy, for it will flee from it at a distance of several miles. Its hide is harder and tougher than that of the broadbill swordfish, and short iron poles are used to harpoon it, rather than wooden ones.

The yellowfin tuna is similar to the bluefin, except for the yellow stripe along the side from eye to tail in place of the blue, and a longer pectoral fin. Its maximum weight is around four hundred and fifty pounds, and the average much less. Allison's tuna is believed to be merely another, probably older, yellowfin, since its elongated dorsal and anal fins, reaching as far as the tail at times, intergrade with the lengths found in a large number of yellowfins. In life the yellow stripe of this variety is a brilliant golden hue, but at death quickly vanishes. For its weight the yellowfin is said to be an even better fighter than the bluefin, and its meat is also better. It is the favorite game fish on the Pacific coast.

The oceanic skipjack is about two feet long and reaches a maximum weight of fifty pounds. It has four or five horizontal stripes on the lower sides and irregular purple bars on the back behind the second dorsal fin running obliquely to a point above the lateral lines. It lacks scales except on the pectoral fins and has more gill rakers than other members of the family. It often appears in large leaping flocks pursuing sardines and anchovies. In Japan a strip of its flesh smoked after boiling is a condiment used in every household. The black skipjack is similar except for the black stripes on its back and sides and somewhat smaller size. The bonitos or striped tunnies are also similar, but their first dorsal fin is longer and contiguous to the second.

The bluefin or leaping tuna has a world-wide distribution; on the Atlantic coast it ranges from Newfoundland to Florida, and on the Pacific from the Columbia River south. The yellowfin is found from Point Conception, California, to the Galapagos Islands; and the black skipjack, which is thrown back when caught because of its poor flesh, from Lower California north to Cape San Lazaro and along both coasts of the Gulf of California. Of the three species of bonitos on the Pacific coast, only one ranges as far north as California and this northern variety is chiefly confined between Santa Barbara and Magdalena Bay, although occasionally reaching Puget Sound.

ALBACORE

FISHING for the albacore has been more carefully planned than that for any other fish. This is because in the first place it is the prize "chicken of the sea" or white tuna that is canned by the million pounds yearly; moreover, the fish is extremely erratic in its migrations, so that its seasons and abundance are irregular. Secondly, it has extremely good vision, and is usually very hungry and active.

Large powerboats insulated with cork and equipped with storage tanks and ice for several weeks' voyaging leave the ports of the warm waters on the Pacific coast where the albacore is found. The crew catches live bait of sardines and anchovies the night before they start trolling for albacore or keep a fresh supply in a box astern through which sea water is constantly pumped. When far enough out at sea, the fishermen, moving along at top speed, drop rag lures or jigs about a hundred feet astern, and hold them just below the surface where the fish generally swim.

As the fishes strike they throw their glistening steel-blue bodies after the lures in frantic leaps and the boat is quickly stopped. the lures pulled in, and dip nets full of live bait dropped overboard. This is known as "chumming the fish" to hold them near the boat, while poles with baited hooks are sent over into their midst. The fishes take the free bait rapidly and all hands work at top speed to garner the harvest while they can, for the fishes may disappear as suddenly as they came. However, between fifty to a thousand pounds may be caught before this occurs and trolling is resumed.

Since 1916, when about thirty million pounds were canned, the abundance of the fish has greatly declined. In 1928 albacores brought three hundred dollars a ton, and in recent years between 300,000 and 700,000 pounds have been caught annually. In its mysterious migrations the fish has been reported as plentiful in Hawaii and Japan while scarce here. Tagging experiments by the California Division of Fish and Game are under way to learn more about them as well as the migrating habits of other tunas.

The fish averages about twenty pounds in weight, reaches a maximum of eighty. Its only anatomical distinction from the bluefin is its long saber-shaped fin which extends back to the anal fin. The species is largely confined to the shore of southern California where it is most abundant from May to December.

BARRACUDA

LARGE canine teeth that fill huge jaws and effectively complement its predatory habits, make the barracuda one of the most powerful and ferocious of all fishes. The salt-water counterpart of the fresh-water pike, its long wedge-shaped head extends one-fourth of its total length, and its crocodilian jaws occupy half of this distance with a series of fangs, knife-edged middle blades, and rear grinders. In addition, it is insatiably curious, strikes at anything that splashes, and is extremely difficult to see, owing to its ability to change color in conformity with that of its momentary background.

Averaging between three and four feet in length, it is built like a long cylinder, streamlined for speed, but at the same time sturdy and powerful. Head-on, it has the ferocious aspect of a bulldog, because of its protruding lower jaw and teeth. This impression is emphasized by the usually half-open mouth, a part of its highly specialized biting apparatus. In the middle of upper and lower jaws are great breathing valves allowing the escape of water or forcing it backward and out through the gills. Thus, unlike most fishes, the barracuda can keep its mouth wide open in expiration, and accommodate its huge teeth, Dr. Gudger has explained in his study of the species.

On top, the fish is dark green or blue with two spinose fins, the first of which has five rays and is depressible in a groove directly over the pectoral fins. The rear dorsal fin is directly over the anal fin. The sides are silver or yellow and the belly white. Dark bars and blotches mark the back and sides, veiling the body form. The hues of the fish change as it lies at the surface near buoys, coral heads, wharves, and wrecks or frequents the bottom.

In the West Indies and Florida, the great barracuda, which attains a length of seven or eight feet and a weight of nearly one hundred pounds, is feared more than sharks. The latter are prone to scurry off at any disturbance in the water, but the fearless barracuda is forthwith attracted. While stories of its eating humans have a basis of truth, the fish does not appear to be overfond of human flesh. Nevertheless, it always takes a trial bite of everything in its

GREAT BARRACUDA *(Sphyraena barracuda)*. Length: 5 feet. Range: South Carolina to Brazil.
S. C. Dunton, New York Aquarium

path, and one snap of its heavy jaws leaves wounds that can easily be fatal.

These great barracudas are particularly ill-natured and inclined to fend for themselves. When not particularly hungry or perhaps just for the sport of it, one of them will herd schools of a hundred or more smaller fishes into a bay or shoal, flicking its crescentic tail slowly from side to side like a hunting cat while patrolling for hours at a time. No captive dares make a dash for liberty until the captor is distracted or, having digested a previous meal, breaks into the herded mass for another repast. Although they will eat anything, barracudas are partial to sardines, anchovies, silversides, and mackerels as well as their own young.

Spawning usually occurs in the spring. In the case of the California barracuda, which is a metallic black-gray above and is about three feet long, the females come inshore to discharge their eggs near kelp beds. A little more than a millimeter in diameter, the yellowish eggs are fertilized immediately by the males, and then left to the mercy of currents. The emerging embryos grow rapidly till December, and resume their growth the following spring. In the second summer they are already large enough to spawn lightly.

Because of their curiosity and fearlessness, the barracudas take the bait of trolling spoons, red or white rag lures, or live fish readily, and fight and leap vigorously when hooked. Indeed, it is the most popular summer small-game fish in California. Its flesh is considered poisonous. Many explanations of this tradition have been offered, but it appears to be based largely on the quickness with which the soft flesh decomposes in the tropics. Its omnivorous habits, too, may have something to do with it, though it is singularly free of parasites. Young ones are said to be quite tasty.

Twenty or more species, all belonging to one family and genus, are recognized throughout the world. On the Atlantic coast there are three tropical varieties, ranging from South Carolina and Florida to Brazil, and one northern variety, which is the smallest and only about a foot long, known from Cape Cod to Cape Fear. On the Pacific the California barracuda runs from Puget Sound to Cape San Lucas, and from the Gulf of California to Panama. It is smaller and by no means as fierce as its Atlantic relatives. Although exceedingly voracious it has never been known to attack man.

ESCOLAR

A RELATIVE of the mackerel, the escolar is similarly built, and has a rich brown color from its excessive oiliness. It frequents waters at least four hundred fathoms deep.

This deep-sea habit is undoubtedly made possible by the protection afforded by its oily flesh. But little is known beyond this of its habits because of its dark and distant haunts. The oily skin is presumed to make it difficult to grasp, if not noxious to larger fishes; the oil itself has purgative value.

About thirty inches long, the fish is marked by a first dorsal fin that is much lower than the second, irregular scales, and a lateral line nerve. It is found principally in the deep waters of the Atlantic.

CUTLASS FISH

SHAPED like a long metallic scabbard or sword, the cutlass fish is one of the oddest forms of all salt-water life. Its narrow silvery sides are highly compressed, and on its back one continuous shallow fin tapers with the body to the finless point of the tail. The head with its wide neck and pointed snout resembles the handle or knob of a cutlass. It is also known as the hairtail or snakefish.

A specialized descendant of the speedy mackerel tribe, the cutlass fish may at first appear devoid of the swiftness characteristic of its near relatives. It exemplifies, however, the speed obtainable by another type of locomotion than that usually found in fishes. Like the eel, it moves through the water in a number of wavy motions, made possible by its long body and flexible vertebrae with their numerous muscle segments, instead of the single twist employed by most fishes. This is the extreme opposite of the stiff body motion of the trunkfish which uses its tail as a scull.

Along with its excessive slimness goes apparently a peculiar sensitivity to cold. Cutlass fishes off Florida have been found benumbed in water still above freezing, and in New Zealand they are known as frostfish because of the great schools that swim ashore on cold nights as though temporarily crazed. They have a habit of swimming near the surface and at the mouths of rivers or bays, and jumping. These habits make them good biters, and their flesh is edible.

Although they attain a length of five feet at times, the average specimen measures between twenty-five and thirty inches. On the Atlantic coast they are found chiefly off Florida and in the Gulf of Mexico, although occasionally as far north as Sandy Hook. On the Pacific coast they are found principally around Santa Catalina Island.

MULLET

SWIMMING head down close to the bottom of the ocean, the mullet scoops out a mouthful of mud and a few moments later expels the coarser portion of the sand by sifting. The minute organisms retained by this straining process constitute the mullet's entire food supply. The thick-walled stomach functions like a grindstone during feeding, enabling it to absorb only those portions of the vegetation which are easily assimilated and digested.

The mullet is considered a splendid food fish, especially in the South where it is taken in great numbers and frequently preserved by salting. In Roman times it was praised as the greatest delicacy man could procure, and limited quantities of this precious fish were sold for fabulous sums. Its use now, however, is common, for it is abundant in bays, lagoons, and all sheltered waters.

Related to the silversides, most mullets are marine fishes, but some of the species occasionally enter brackish and fresh-waters. They invariably swim in large schools, roving near the shore or sandy spots near rocks. Extremely furtive, the least disturbance will send them scuttling under seaweed or any other protective covering. When frightened or cornered they jump or skip over the surface of the water in seeking shelter.

The mullet reaches a maximum length of two feet. The coloration is either dark blue or red and the sides silvery. During mating season in the early spring, the fins assume a reddish tinge. Spawning is carried on by one female and two males, which flank her on each side and discharge their milky sperm at the same time the female lays her eggs. Late in July the young reach a length of one inch and feed on plankton until they mature.

WHITE MULLET *(Querimana curema)*. Length: 2½ feet. Range: Cape Cod to Brazil.
New York Zoological Society

Five species occur in the warm waters of both the Pacific and Atlantic Oceans as well as the Gulf of Mexico. The common or striped mullet, found all over the world, occurs in this country on the Atlantic coast from Cape Cod to Florida, and on the coast of California from Monterey to San Diego. Found in schools with it is the blueback or fan-tail mullet which comes as far north on the Atlantic coast as Massachusetts. The range of the white mullet is from Cape Cod to Florida; the red-eye and fan-tail inhabit the offshore waters of the Florida Keys.

The name "mullet" is given to the members of two families which are not at all related.

SEAHORSE

THE seahorse is invariably the most popular and fascinating attraction at any aquarium fortunate enough to be able to display this phenomenon of the sea. Curiously resembling a tiny steed but also possessing a monkey's tail and a kangaroo's pouch, the seahorse seems most unfishlike as it moves through the water in an upright position. In swimming it moves slowly in a dignified, sedate manner, vibrating its dorsal and pectoral fins which are situated on the back of its head and resemble large overdeveloped ears.

Most frequently, however, the seahorse may be seen resting on the bottom of the ocean, or aquarium tank, clasping a stalk of seaweed with its prehensile tail. A solitary and somewhat unsociable creature, it seems to resent any familiarity even by its own relations, and when annoyed it will frequently nibble at the intruder's tail.

When early explorers first saw this tiny creature, they believed it to be a colt of one of King Neptune's sea steeds, in adult size perhaps as large as a pony. Even today many people who have never before seen this fish, and have gained a preconceived picture

SPOTTED SEA HORSES (*Hippocampus punctulatus*). Length: 5 inches. Range: North Carolina to Brazil.
New York Aquarium

of its size, are disappointed to find it so diminutive and inconspicuous, but are inevitably recompensed and delighted by its graceful and seriocomic movements.

The seahorse seldom exceeds five inches in length, and the smallest species, the dwarf seahorse, is but two inches long. The body is covered with bony ridges which produce the effect of an external skeleton. The eyes function independently of each other; consequently the seahorse is able to detect danger from all directions. It feeds exclusively on minute living organisms, and in captivity refuses to deviate from its accustomed delicate diet. Lack of proper and suitable foods, such as soft-bodied marine creatures and small crustaceans, make it exceedingly difficult to keep the seahorse alive for any considerable length of time.

Since its method of locomotion is necessarily slow and methodical, and its progress is always impeded by tides, the seahorse is at all times at the mercy of enemies, who are numerous and include all fishes. Its only protection is the coloration of its brownish body, which blends with the eelgrass and seaweed where the seahorse spends most of its existence.

Reproduction is accomplished in a most peculiar manner. The male is equipped with a brood pouch in which the female deposits her eggs. After a year of incubation, during which time the eggs hatch and mature, the fry is expelled from the pouch, never to return to the bed and board of their father.

Four species of the seahorse are found in the warm waters of the Atlantic Ocean and the Gulf, and at least one species inhabits the southern portion of the Pacific coast north to San Diego. On the Atlantic coast seahorses sometimes venture north to Massachusetts, and many specimens have been taken in New York Bay.

PIPEFISH

ALTHOUGH it is related to the seahorse, and its method of reproduction is similar, the pipefish is peculiar in its own right, and does not in any other way resemble its first cousin. Nor is it as individual in shape.

The pipefish is found among the seaweed and eelgrass along both our coasts, most frequently drifting to sandy shores and muddy creeks. It is a long, slim, bony creature, sometimes measuring twelve inches in length, although the average size is generally four to five inches. Its protective coloration blends remarkably with the eelgrass, to which it usually attaches itself with its tail. It is especially difficult to detect because of its varying coloration which ranges from bright green to gray and sometimes dark brown.

Like the seahorse, the female pipefish lays her eggs in the pouch of the male, where they hatch and mature. Eight species of the pipefish are found in the offshore waters of the Pacific coast, and twelve on the Atlantic coast from Texas to Massachusetts.

Families related to the seahorse and the pipefish include the trumpet fish of southern Florida; the slinky cornet fish of the same region and occurring as far north as Long Island; and the snipe fish, representative of an Old World family, which is accidental on our North Atlantic coast.

STICKLEBACK

THE stickleback is a ferocious little creature, indiscriminately attacking friend and foe alike. Fortunately for the other inhabitants of the sea, it seldom exceeds four inches in length, and is therefore formidable only to small fry and the eggs of larger fishes, although in battle with its own species it is fierce and unyielding.

It is during the mating season in the early spring that the stickleback becomes most pugnacious. Bedecked in brilliant nuptial colors which generally run the gamut of all shades of red, the male builds a cylindrical nest of reeds and seals all openings but one by means of mucous threads secreted by the kidneys, and spun in a network like the spider's web.

When the nest has been completed and waterproofed, the male seeks out one or more females and induces them to deposit their eggs into the conical opening. But no sooner are the eggs laid than the usefulness and necessity of the females are over, at least as far as the male is concerned, and they are forthwith driven away from the

FOUR-SPINED STICKLEBACK *(Apeltes quadracus)*. Length: 1½ inches. Range: Maine to New Jersey, in salt water only.
S. C. Dunton, New York Aquarium

nest and not allowed to approach it under any circumstances. Should the female become anxious about her brood and foolishly attempt to hover near by, the male does not hesitate to kill her. The eggs incubate in ten days, when the male destroys the nest, but continues to stand guard over the young until they are fully matured.

The four-spined stickleback, smallest of the species, is but an inch long. Its body is ovoid and compressed and heavily armed for both offense as well as defense. A distinguishing feature is the large sharp spine on each ventral fin. Voracious and ill-tempered, it does considerable damage among the eggs and fry of large fishes and crustaceans. In turn the stickleback is preyed upon by most fishes which share its habitat.

Of the eight species found in our country, most sticklebacks inhabit salt and brackish waters. The widespread two-spined stickleback is found in shallow bays and estuaries, some members ascending streams; the common eastern stickleback is abundant about New

England; the brook stickleback is found mostly in the Great Lakes region and in fresh waters from New York to Kansas; the Lake Superior stickleback and the nine-spined stickleback inhabit Lake Superior; the seven-spined stickleback is restricted to the Kennebec River, Maine; the four-spined stickleback is found in salt water from Maine to New Jersey; and the Pacific stickleback is common in the Pacific Ocean from California to Alaska.

FLATFISHES

NATURE has endowed the ovate flatfish with startling and inimitable characteristics, which have made it a strong contender for the mythical title of the freak of the sea. Because it is a well-known and universally used fish, these seemingly natural deformities pass unnoticed, are even taken for granted. But the twisted head, the bulging eyes set close together on either the right or left side of the body, the alternate light and dark coloration of the scales, and its clumsy sluggish mode of locomotion in a leaning position, are all incontrovertible evidence of its digression from the normal.

When hatched, the flatfish is devoid of these peculiar and at first unnatural traits. Its eyes are set on both sides of the body, and like other fishes it swims in an upright position. Two or three days later, however, the flatfish begins leaning to one side. The bones of the head twist, and the eye on the under-surface migrates to the upper side, finally joins its mate. A month later it is as misshapen and sluggish as the adult, and either rests on the bottom or swims with the dark side facing upward.

The body of the flatfish is strongly compressed laterally. The upper side is dark brown, the lower side white. Found in both the Atlantic and Pacific Oceans, the flatfish group includes the flounder, halibut, fluke, and sole. With one exception all are considered food fishes, and in most instances are propagated artificially by the Government in order that their present abundance may not too quickly be depleted.

The most commonplace and also the most abundant of the flatfishes is the flounder, widely distributed along the Atlantic coast from Maine to South Carolina. Its prolific powers are indeed formidable, for one female lays on the average of one million eggs in the brief spawning season from February to April.

Spawning is carried on at night, and the eggs, in spite of their great numbers, are heavy and adhesive. The fry are hatched four or five months later, usually in August, and measure approximately two inches in length.

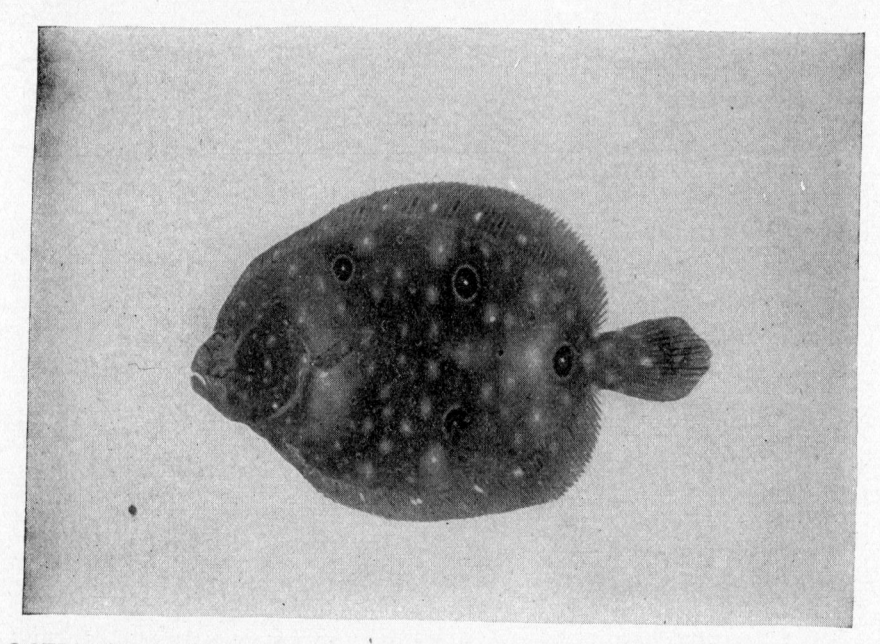

OCELLATED FLOUNDER (*Ancylopsetta quadrocellatus*). Length: 1 foot.
Range: South Atlantic and Gulf coasts.
John G. Shedd Aquarium

The flounder feeds on shrimps, mollusks, and small fishes. Like all flatfishes, its body is elliptical, and the usual size is twenty inches, the weight seldom exceeding five pounds.

A major part of the flounder fishing is carried on in the winter and spring, although the summer flounder does not reach the peak of its abundance until the end of spring. During both seasons large quantities of winter and summer flounders are taken and sold throughout the United States.

HALIBUT

THE halibut, one of the largest of food fishes, attains a length of more than nine feet and a maximum weight of seven hundred pounds. The normal size, however, is more apt to be about two hundred pounds, and the common specimens taken by local fisheries actually weigh no more than twenty-five or thirty pounds.

Because it is abundant and reasonably priced, and because its meat is savory, especially that of the female, the halibut is generally considered to be one of the most valued food fishes in the world. In recent years, however, it has been rapidly decreasing in numbers and the United States Bureau of Fisheries has had to resort to artificial propagation in order to maintain a normal and well-balanced supply.

The range of the halibut extends from the Arctic to the northern portions of both the Atlantic and Pacific Oceans. Primarily a fish of the cold waters, it migrates in roving bands, preying voraciously upon such fishes as the cod, haddock, rosefish, sculpin, hake, herring, capelin, and on crabs, lobsters, clams, and sea birds.

FLUKE

THE fluke, also known as the dab, rusty flounder, yellow-tail, sand dab, mud dab, and rusty dab, is found from Cape Cod to South Carolina along the Atlantic coast. It is a widely distributed species, reaching a maximum length of four feet and a weight of twenty-six pounds. In general, its habits resemble those of the foregoing flatfishes.

SOLE

FOOD substitutes are common and the layman in many instances does not know what animal or fish may be disguised under an exotic or innocuous designation. Thus, when one eats "fried filet of sole," one is really eating winter flounder and not sole at all. Genuine "filet of sole" is a European dish.

Found mostly about Florida, the American sole or hog choker spends its existence in shallow brackish water at river mouths, sometimes ascending the rivers to fresh water. Essentially a small flounder, the sole seldom exceeds six inches in length, and may be distinguished by its rounded nose. Although it is eaten in some sections of the country, the sole has little commercial value.

CODFISH

FROM an economic and historical standpoint, codfishes are one of the most valuable and prized groups of food fishes in the world. Inadvertently they have played an important part in the colonization and development of North America, and particularly the northeastern portion of the United States. The white settler was almost entirely dependent upon an adequate supply of fish in order to subsist, and the prolific codfish served this purpose admirably. The importance of the cod extends beyond the coast of the United States, for no less than five countries, including Canada, Newfoundland, France, Portugal, and the United States maintain large cod fisheries.

In weight as well as in value, no other group of fishes even remotely rivals the abundance of the codfishes. In the thirty year period from 1896 to 1925, on the Atlantic coast alone, the annual catch of cod averaged more than one billion pounds. No recent estimates are available, but according to reliable sources the present annual catch is considerably more than one hundred million pounds.

To offset this constant heavy depletion of its ranks, the codfish must reproduce rapidly. Fortunately this is an accomplishment of which it is master. An average female cod produces three million eggs from October to April. A large female weighing more than seventy pounds is capable of depositing more than nine million eggs. After fertilization the eggs hatch in seventeen days, and in three years the fry are fully matured.

But even this phenomenal fecundity is insufficient to maintain the supply of codfish at a normal level, or even render it immune to gradual extinction. Fisheries, it seems, are its greatest enemies but it must also contend with such natural foes as sharks, dogfishes, and blood-sucking parasites.

The most prominent members of the codfish family are the cod and the haddock. Both are important food fishes but the cod is more valued because of its tremendous size, attaining a length of six feet and a maximum weight of two hundred pounds. The average cod, however, is about twenty-five pounds, and specimens weighing more than one hundred pounds are exceptional. The coloration is usually gray or brown, and the long body is covered with fine scales and spineless fins. Projecting from the body are either three dorsal and two anal fins, or two dorsal fins and one anal.

The cod is found in the North Atlantic Ocean south to Cape Cod. A strong, swift swimmer, it habitually travels in schools, searching for small fishes and crustaceans. Its diet is extremely diversified for besides eating herrings, mackerels, menhaden, alewives, worms, and mollusks, it has also been known to swallow oil cans, rings, rubber dolls, and scissors.

Other codfish species include the wall-eyed cod and the Wachna cod, found in Puget Sound; the pollock which inhabits the North Atlantic Ocean south to Cape Cod; the common cod and the tom-

COMMON CODFISHES (*Gadus morrhua*). Length: 4 feet. Range: North Atlantic south to Virginia.
John G. Shedd Aquarium

cod, found as far south as Virginia; the California and Pacific cods of the Pacific coast; the ling, whose range includes the rivers and lakes of New England, the Great Lakes region, as well as the Missouri and Columbia River basins.

There are at least a half dozen related species of hakes and cusks which are distributed for the most part along the middle and North Atlantic coast, with at least one species inhabiting the Pacific Ocean.

FLYINGFISH

SKIMMING the surface of the sea like skipping stones, flyingfishes intrigue the ocean traveler with their graceful form and curious behavior. Little does the traveler realize that this maneuver is not mere play but a matter of life and death when the gaping, tooth-filled jaws of a hungry barracuda threaten. It is only because of this menace, however, that alone of all fishes, this species has developed a remarkable ability to remain in the air for an extended period. More tasty than other species to a host of powerful predators, flyingfishes are relentlessly pursued not only by the ferocious barracuda but by leaping tunas, sailfishes, swordfishes, marlin—even the mammalian dolphins and porpoises—as the big-game angler well knows. And because of their ability to fly, they have been able to survive in the midst of enemy-infested tropical waters—the most elusive fish to man and beast alike.

Yet, strange as it may seem, even flyingfishes do not really fly in the manner that most birds do, that is by the locomotor power of their wings. They merely glide much like a motorless plane, with their wings comparatively rigid. Thus, with the possible exception of a tiny fresh-water species, they have no real muscular development in the pectoral region such as would be required for rapidly flapping wings. What power they have is merely that furnished by the long lower lobe of the tail which oscillates like a scull to give the necessary momentum in the take-off. Then they head into the wind with outstretched fins, these merely acting as elevators and stabilizers as in airplanes—a limitation quite natural since they are primarily adapted to swimming.

FLYINGFISH

FLYINGFISH.
Davis, Nature Magazine

So perfectly constructed on modern aerodynamic principles are flyingfishes that as Dr. C. M. Breder, Jr., who has studied and observed this family for fifteen years, shows, pioneer airplane designers would have profited more from the study and imitation of this fish than any of the birds used as models since the days of Leonardo da Vinci. Now after all the years of costly experimentation and error, modern planes resemble in structure most nearly the anatomical features of a flyingfish.

This is especially true in the case of the two most specialized species of this fish, in which the principles of speed or lifting power are emphasized in the monoplane-like single-wing type and biplane-like double-wing type respectively. In the former, too, the body of the fish is more flattened and square-shaped like the fuselage of a Bellanca, while in the latter it is thinner and more streamlined like the round fuselage of a Lockheed.

Because of their gliding flight, flyingfishes are entirely dependent on the direction and strength of the wind, much as a motorless plane or even a motored plane at the take-off. They turn into the wind as a weather vane does through the effect of their body keelage, stabilizers and cambered wings. While the gliding mode is particularly adapted to large bodies because of the mechanical difficulty of attaining sufficient wing vibration in heavy forms, the flyingfishes do not exceed eighteen inches in length, largely because of the difficulty in rising from the water with obstructing appendages—the chief difficulty of hydroplanes. The flyingfish has a good deal less wind resistance than the plane, however, due to its mucous covering and lack of landing gear, and in rising and alighting can stretch its wings to a perfectly horizontal level for the maximum lift or brake effect. Because of its adaptation to water, moreover, the flyingfish is not particularly disturbed by a failure of wind or stability, merely flipping off another wave with a powerful swish of its tail as it loses altitude or somersaulting into the water as a gust upsets it.

YOUNG FLYINGFISH *(Cypselurus cyanopterus)*. Length: 1½ feet (adult). Range: Tropical Atlantic as far north as the Florida Keys.
S. C. Dunton, New York Aquarium

The illusion of true wing flapping in these fishes is undoubtedly due to rapid rolling from side to side while in flight. So strong is the illusion, that the controversy over the nature of its flight has waxed warm periodically even among scientists. None of the arguments put forth have overcome the anatomical evidence or aerodynamic principles involved, however, as demonstrated in motorless planes and such large soaring birds as vultures, hawks, condors, and albatrosses. In the case of the minute fresh-water flyingfishes which appear to have more adequate pectoral muscles for wing propulsion, observation and tests are still inconclusive. Perhaps some day slow motion pictures of the larger species may settle the matter to the satisfaction of even the most skeptical layman.

Essentially tropical, flyingfishes roam in large schools north to Florida, and on the Pacific coast to the Santa Barbara Islands, although a few hardy specimens have been observed as far north as Newfoundland. More than ten species are found along the Atlantic coast, especially in the Gulf Stream and off the Florida coast. They average about ten inches long, are marked by a blunt snout and translucent pectoral fins, and include both vegetable- and animal-feeding types. The smallest is Monroe's flyingfish, two inches long and distinguished by two long fleshy barbels dangling from its chin. On the Pacific coast there is at least one species, the California flyingfish. It is the largest flyingfish—eighteen inches in length—and is considered good eating, although not extensively so used because of the difficulty encountered in catching it. Most specimens eaten are taken accidentally as they land aboard ships at sea instead of in their native element.

HALFBEAK

THE halfbeaks are less versatile than the flyingfishes but are able occasionally to leap out of the water and glide in the air for several feet. A distinguishing characteristic of the halfbeaks is the enlargement of their lower jaws, which are as long as the jaws of the silver gar. The upper jaw is short and stubby, and the teeth are small.

The halfbeaks are slender fishes colored a translucent bottle-green and tinged with silver; the under parts are black. They are herbivorous and feed mainly on green algae. All the five species found about the Florida Keys or infrequently straying north to Massachusetts are uniformly small, and seldom exceed one foot in length.

PIKE *(Esox lucius)*. Length: 3½ feet. Range: Northern North America.
New York Zoological Society

PIKE AND MUSKALLUNGE

THE pike is a terrible nuisance to the neighbors because all the pike eat as much and as often as possible. Some of the big brothers in the family are hardy fighters, terrorizing other fishes but delighting combat-loving anglers. And, big or little, they all are satisfactory food fishes.

Giant of the group, the muskallunge may grow in length to eight feet and weigh one hundred pounds.

The greenish or grayish pike, whose protruding lower jaws give their countenances a sullen cast, lurks in ponds and slow-moving streams. The hungry fish conceals itself behind vegetation or logs until a victim is marked for slaughter. Then it shoots forward, teeth bared, and in the twinkling of an eye the unsuspecting passer-by is nestling within the pike's stomach. Fishes, amphibians, and even young waterfowl are preyed upon by the pikes which are not intimidated by superior size.

Because of its voraciousness, the pike is easily caught. It is so greedy that one mouthful at a time does not suffice if two mouthfuls are at hand. A pike has been known to grab for a baited hook, while the tail of an undigested fish, which it was still eating, dangled from its mouth.

The large muskallunge multiplies the greediness of the smaller pike. Specimens have been caught which were crammed so full of other fishes that hunger alone could not account for such gorging. There have been accounts of numbers of fishes, slashed or with pieces of flesh torn out, floating still alive on the surface of a lake. These mutilated victims of viciousness have been laid at the doorstep of the piratical muskallunge. It is even said that smaller fishes "are constantly leaping from the water in terror of this formidable foe." As though in retaliation, fishes, amphibians, and waterfowl destroy the muskallunge's eggs.

MUSKALLUNGES (*Esox masquinongy*). Length: 6 feet. Range: Great Lakes region; upper Mississippi Valley and northward.
John G. Shedd Aquarium

The same kind of reciprocity figures in the relationship of other pikes and their neighbors. On one occasion a small common pike was caught and cut open, since it seemed unusually stout. In its stomach was a large mud minnow. The mud minnow was dissected and within it was found a two-inch pike. The story ends with the opening of the two-inch pike, revealing that it had eaten a smaller mud minnow, which was still recognizable despite its vicissitudes.

These pirates have their boosters, however. Izaak Walton paid the pike the supreme tribute of declaring that it was a fish "too good for any but anglers and honest men."

Pikes live in aquariums in apparent happiness. But now and then they race about in such fury that they crash into the walls of the tank and smash their noses.

Seven species of this family are found throughout the eastern and central States. They vary in size from the huge muskallunge of the Great Lakes and the North to the little, twelve-inch, banded pickerel found east of the Alleghenies. The common pike, or pickerel, is four feet long and weighs forty pounds; it is found in the Great Lakes and northeastern States.

CATFISH

WITHOUT so much as pausing to question whether an object is animal, vegetable, or mineral, the catfish is likely to gulp it down. Such complete lack of discrimination and refinement in table manners prompts more befitting comparison of the catfish with a pig than with a cat. And, as with a pig, its appetite fattens it for the slaughter, since the catfish is used throughout the country as a food fish.

The list of items on a hungry catfish's menu—and the catfish seems always hungry—would cover several pages. It eats peaches and watermelons, weeds and wheat, mollusks and clams, fishes and their eggs. Special treats may include slops from ships' galleys and sewer outlets, or perhaps a dead rat.

It prowls about the bottom of the river, foraging continually. Sometimes it sinks into the mud so that only its forehead and the

CATFISH

BULLHEAD CATFISH *(Ameiurus nebulosus)*. Length: 1¼ feet. Range: Maine, the Great Lakes, and North Dakota; southward to Florida and Texas. Introduced into many western rivers.
New York Zoological Society

barbels are visible. In this ambush of ooze it awaits some unwary passer-by which will perceive the catfish, if at all, too late for action. When eating such prey as clams, the catfish cracks the shells in its mouth, swallows the bodies, and discards the broken halves.

Dinner time for this fish is any time. It is, however, mostly nocturnal in its regular feeding habits, and fishermen have found that it is best caught after sunset. It usually bites avidly on a hook baited with fish or meat, and some species seem to be encouraged to try the hook after other fishes begin to bite.

This hardy creature ranges in rivers and lakes throughout the country, living at ease in stagnant, muddy waters which fit in well with its sluggish nature. It is not put out even if the air supply diminishes, for it casually comes to the surface for refills and it survives even when its water home dries up temporarily, lying leisurely and carefree in a mud clod as it awaits better and wetter days. During the midwinter this dusky-colored fish seems to hibernate by imbedding itself in the bottom.

In such an unattractive environment do the young catfish first see the light of day. The female lays her eggs in a clump which adheres to a convenient object, and at once the male begins his faithful vigil. He fans the eggs with his fins and forces water through their mass. He also sucks the eggs into his mouth and then forcibly ejects them; this process is continued for a while even after the young have been hatched.

It was observed that the fry in an aquarium tank would eat bits of liver thrown to them. Sometimes the parents would seize the liver to which a group of their offspring was clinging. Although meat and offspring both were taken into the fish's mouth, it swallowed only the meat and spat out the young fish. Another observer reported, though, that when the father catfish sucks the fry into his mouth, the tendency to eject them decreases daily, and more and more of them enter their parent's mouth without ever emerging.

The most important species of catfish is the blue cat of the Mississippi Valley and Gulf States, which may attain a length of five feet and a weight of one hundred and fifty pounds. Other species are smaller, down to those weighing only a pound or two. The well-known small catfish, or common bullhead, found in the East and Middle West and introduced into western rivers, weighs only a few pounds; it is a favorite with boys and novice anglers, since it almost begs to be caught by accepting any kind of bait with eagerness. Due to their abundance and size, several species of catfish are important commercial items. They are sold in the market at an extremely low price and have consequently been called a poor man's fish.

Their only resemblance to a cat is in the whiskers which adorn the sides of their mouths. The whiskers vary from a single strand on each side to a moustache of several wisps. These fish are also marked with the barbels which extend upward from the top of their snouts.

Three species are ocean dwellers along the Atlantic and Gulf coasts. These are the gaff-topsail catfish, found from Cape Cod to Texas, the sea catfish of the same range, and the white catfish which reaches New York.

DACE

The United States is host to thirty-six species of catfish in all. Many of them are widely appreciated for their tasty flesh, despite their unsavory feeding habits. But when it was suggested that the catfish be introduced into England, the magazine *Punch* replied with some pungent stanzas:

> "Oh, do not bring the Catfish here!
> The Catfish is a name I fear.
>   Oh, spare each stream and spring,
> The Kennet swift, the Wandle clear,
> The lake, the lock, the broad, the mere,
>   From that detested thing!
>
> "The Catfish is a hideous beast,
> A bottom-feeder that doth feast
>   Upon unholy bait;
> He's no addition to your meal
> He's rather richer than the eel;
>   And ranker than the skate.
>
> "They say the Catfish climbs the trees,
> And robs the roosts, and down the breeze
>   Prolongs his catterwaul.
> Oh, leave him in his western flood
> Where the Mississippi churns the mud;
>   Don't bring him here at all!"

DACE AND MINNOW

DACES and minnows and their numerous allies swarm in nearly all the rivers, streams, ponds, pools, and lakes of our country. Although only a few inches long and among the tiniest of fishes, their nesting activity is more elaborate than any. For days and days in the spring the male, who is usually larger than the female, scoops out a pit in the bottom of the stream, and builds a gravelly ridge two or three inches high, a foot wide, and from one to eighteen feet long, on the upstream side parallel with the current. The current washes a sand trail on the other side of the pit and thus both sides are protected.

This nest is usually placed in protected spots along the banks. Other males or other fishes if not too large are kept away by a display of brilliant colors and horned tubercles which cluster on the male's head, fins, and tail at this season of the year. Usually it does not come to a fight, for a short swim side by side with several ceremonial bows and feints are sufficient to ward off the intruder and protect the nest.

RED-BELLIED DACE *(Chrosomus erythrogaster)*. Length: 2 inches. Range: St. Lawrence River to northern Alabama, chiefly west of the Alleghenies.
John G. Shedd Aquarium

When the nest is finished, the females waiting patiently near by approach, several at a time and timidly. They scurry away as soon as the male moves toward them. Again they come near, and finally one has the temerity to enter. After swimming side by side a moment, the male lies down in the pit, and as the female approaches he flips her into an upright position by a quick movement of his head; in this position he presses her tightly and she then deposits several dozen eggs into the pit.

DACE

The female floats belly up as though dead, while the male watches the eggs descend. Then she swims off. The male fertilizes the eggs, and covers them by scooping up stones in his mouth and dropping them at the head of the pit. This done, he awaits another female, and the same process is repeated. Sometimes the original female returns, but more often she patronizes several nests before her hundreds of eggs are all discharged. Thus each nest has a great

SHINER (*Luxilus cornutus*). Length: 7 inches. Range: North America east of the Rockies except the southern Atlantic states and Texas.
John G. Shedd Aquarium

variety of eggs reflecting the different sizes and characters of the females, and no doubt insuring greater fertility.

Spawning finished, one continuous ridge covers the pit and its eggs. On the lowest level are larger stones, and toward the top smaller ones, the final layer being one of gravel and mud, which seeps through to fill up the crevices below. Thus the eggs are afforded plenty of room though well hidden and protected from the current. Yet the housekeeping male does not relax his watch.

Only when the ridge's scoured gravel and stones have merged their form with the muddy bottom through the action of the current several days later, so as to be virtually unnoticeable, does he swim off and look for food.

To be sure, all this care does not always prevent destruction of his handiwork. Other fishes, especially larger ones, may go rooting about the bottom and discover the appetizing eggs. Since many of these small fishes build their nests in the same places about the same time, they often use the materials of one already finished to reinforce their own. And of course when the embryos begin to emerge from the ooze in the warming waters, many things can happen to them. But the father has literally left few stones unturned in doing his share.

Agility as well as patience are prime characteristics of these smaller fish. The word dace is believed to be a corruption of dart. They have especially good reason to be swift, too, because their bright silvery sides make them very noticeable to pike and perch. Among the most beautiful is the horned dace of the East, whose mating habits have been most closely studied and form the type for this group. It reaches a length of about a foot in the male, though averaging eight or nine inches, and is considered good sport with fly and worm-bait fishing.

Like all the dominant fresh-water fishes of today, this group is provided with a special inner ear connection with the air bladder, which is believed to make them very sensitive to movement and temperature, since its function as a pressure balancer is not utilized in their native shallow waters. Minnows also have one of the quickest breathing rates of any fish, respiring about one hundred and fifty times a minute. Because of their power of changing color to that of the environment, anglers often paint the inside of tin cans holding minnow bait white, thus insuring conspicuous bait for pike and perch.

All the fish in this group have teeth only in their throats, and a short intestine, which correlates with their insectivorous diet. Most of them catch mosquitoes and flies that fall into the water from overhanging foliage along the banks. Vegetable matter does not appear to be digested, although they are exceedingly omnivorous within mechanical limits and take nearly everything offered when in captivity. They eat nothing during the winter, hibernating in groups at the bottom.

Tradition makes the tench or tinca the physician among fish, because of the alleged curative properties of its secretions or bones. Its immunity from attack by the pike, however, has been disputed since its use as effective bait. Another related type is the bleak, two species of which are found in the Columbia River and northward; the hard tubercles of its skin have been used in Europe in the manufacture of false pearls known as *essence d'Orient*.

Daces and minnows comprise by far the largest family of fishes, including more than three hundred and fifty species which are distributed throughout the fresh waters of our country. They reach their largest size in the West, in the dace of the Columbia, Sacramento, and Colorado Rivers—four to six feet; and in the East in their close relative, the fallfish, which is about eighteen inches long. They are also known locally as chubs, shiners, breams, gudgeons, flatheads, and stonerollers, although most of these names are wrong applications of the names of quite different European species.

CARP

MORE tenacious of life than any other fish except the eel, the carp has spread far and wide over the streams, ponds, lakes, and rivers of the country since its introduction from Europe in 1877. Its hardiness is no doubt partly explained by the fact that it is the basic or generic type of the small fresh-water fish. It came originally from India and China, traveling westward with the progress of civilization to Europe where it has become legion since the Middle Ages.

Such is the tradition for long life in the case of this fish that works of natural history written abroad during the eighteenth and nineteenth centuries attribute a span of one hundred and fifty years to it. This is now considered an exaggeration, but a natural one in view of the unusual longevity displayed by it under the most favorable artificial conditions. In the wild state, it is not believed to live much more than fifteen years.

As food its value has been greatly enhanced by this tenacity to life. It remains alive for many hours out of the water and can be transported long distances without spoiling. As it is a fairly bulky fish for its size, weighing from four to sixteen pounds though only seven to thirty inches long, its food value is considerable.

The carp is also exceedingly reproductive. A female of four or five pounds carries a half million eggs; one of sixteen pounds, two million or more. These are dropped in groups of four or five hundred at a time and adhere in clumps to rocks or reeds near grassy bottoms of banks, as groups of males surround one female fish, pressing her to help in their extrusion. The tiny yellow capsules show spots in five or six days that turn out to be the eyes of the embryo. The fry break through in from twelve to sixteen days and, after absorbing the egg yolk, seek food among minute rotifers and crustaceans and, later, mosquito larvae. At the coming of winter the young carp

LEATHER CARP *(Cyprinus carpio)*. Length: 2 feet. Range: Introduced into Europe and America from China.
New York Zoological Society

already weigh a pound if well fed, and at the end of the second summer, three pounds. By their third summer they are sexually mature.

The males develop warts on the back and head, as well as brilliant hues, during the spring mating season. These appear to aid them in battles with rivals and in holding the female. A few days before spawning they rise to the surface repeatedly, and gradually become excited. In pursuing females they lash the water with their tails, leap into the air, and become so oblivious to danger that they can easily be caught. Even the most sluggish sport on the surface at this time.

This behavior seems to be connected with the great mortality occasioned among them at this time by male toads and frogs. These, also sexually excited, often attach themselves to the heads of carp, clutching them as in the embrace with a female, and press their forelegs into the fishes' eyes, causing blindness and death. The wily carp, called the water fox by Izaak Walton, is for once at a loss to such an extent as to belie its sobriquet.

After awakening from the winter hibernation, the carp first seeks the yellow and white water lily seeds and water grasses. Thereafter it is omnivorous, though primarily a vegetarian and habituated to the bottom. It has pharyngeal teeth like all fishes of this group and a long intestine correlated with its vegetable diet.

Besides being used as food, the carp is of value as an exterminator of the trematode worms which cause fluke disease in some sections of the country. It is also a good small-game fish in the quiet contemplative tradition of the old-fashioned angler. Early in the morning or late at night is the best time to catch carp; worms or grain make good bait.

Among the improved or hybrid types developed from the original common species is the scaled carp, with regular concentric scales; the mirror carp with only three or four rows of large scales on its sides; the leather carp without scales except on the back, and a very thick, soft skin; and the gold carp, the favorite aquarium pet of olive-bronze hue, better known as the goldfish of which many exotic hybrids have been developed.

SUCKER

SUCKERS, a widely distributed form allied to the carp, are native to North America, with the exception of two species found in China. This strange segregation is explained by the hypothesis that it came north with the carp from the tropical East, and crossed over to this continent via the Bering Sea and Alaska, when a land connection existed.

The name sucker is thought to come from the slow, greedy habits of the species. It attains a length of two feet or more, is quite variable in color. Tapeworms four times as large as the sucker and one-fourth as heavy have been found in them. Although immobile and unattached, the internal parasites take up so much room as to displace the internal organs of the fish. These parasites can be absorbed into the human body and cause serious anemia, if fish so infected are not thoroughly cooked.

SMALLMOUTH BUFFALOFISH *(Ictiobus bubalis)*. Length: 3 feet. Range: Mississippi Valley and southward.
John G. Shedd Aquarium

The white or brook variety is most common from New England to the Columbia River. The seventy-five species, widely distributed among our rivers and streams, are locally known as silver carp, carp sucker, black, long-nosed, or mountain suckers.

The buffalofish is so called because of the hump on the nape of its neck, simulating the profile of a buffalo. It is the largest of the suckers, running three feet long and weighing fifteen pounds or more. It feeds chiefly on small crustaceans. The four species are found for the most part in the Mississippi River region and in larger streams everywhere. Suckers constitute an important food in the Ohio and Mississippi basins, where bottom lines heavily leaded and baited with soft cheese or raw cotton are used in fishing for them.

MORAY

A LITTLE fish swimming carelessly through the warm waters about a coral reef may well be completely oblivious to any danger in such placid surroundings. But from a crevice in the reef there suddenly emerges the tooth-studded mouth of a green moray and the fish is snapped up. Then the mouth is withdrawn and the setting regains its peaceful air until the moray strikes again.

The full stature of the moray is revealed when it decides to leave its ambush for awhile. It slithers out in the undulating manner so typical of eels, looking for all the world like a heavy-bodied serpent. But it glides effortlessly through the water, completely devoid of the somewhat sluggish motions of its reptilian counterpart. When the moray returns to the reef its sinuous body is coiled as it snuggles in its nesting place, and uncoiled when it departs.

The six-foot green moray, largest of the family, is a fearsome creature when it stretches out to full length and opens its gaping jaws to exhibit a set of sharp, curved teeth. A fisherman, pulling one into his boat by mistake, may precipitately decide to leave the boat in sole possession of his erstwhile captive. The decision may be a wise one, since the green moray has a strongly muscled lower jaw to reinforce its teeth, and is inclined to be pugnacious. Moreover, its bites may have a toxic effect.

GREEN MORAYS *(Gymnothorax funebris).* Length: 6 feet. Range: Florida Keys to Brazil.
New York Zoological Society

This moray, covered with a thick leathery skin, is usually a brilliant green color, although it may be brownish or grayish. The green is effected in an unusual manner, for it is not the actual body color of the moray. The fish actually has a bluish-slate skin which is covered with a yellow mucus. But the combination of blue skin and yellow slime produces the green, just as the mixture of these two colors in any elementary art class gives a green blend. The mucus which covers most fishes is transparent and, indeed, the absence of yellow in the slime may account for the brownish or slate-colored specimens which have been observed.

A number of tales of the related moray of the Mediterranean have descended in classical literature from ancient times. Pliny mentions a friend of Emperor Augustus who ordered a slave thrown, not to the lions, but to a pond full of morays. Yet it is also recorded that morays were kept as pets by aristocratic families who bedecked them with jewels, and even stalwart Romans grieved when these pets died. This was carried to such extremes that Cicero could write that they "deemed no moment of their lives more happy than when these creatures first came to eat out of their hands." Caesar presented six thousand of these fishes to his friends in celebration of one of his victories.

Morays are mostly found in warm southern waters. The green moray, which touches the United States only about the Florida Keys, is not eaten in this country, though relished in Bermuda. Three species of spotted morays, which are usually two or three feet long, extend to Charleston, South Carolina, and the snapper banks near Pensacola, Florida, where they are used as food. Another species, the deep-water moray, is found off South Carolina and occasionally reaches New England; while the California conger eel, a moray, ranges off the southern coast of California.

EEL

A LIVE eel is often regarded as an unsavory character, an opinion based to some extent upon the snaky way in which it slips through the water. But actually the slippery, wriggling, smooth-bodied creature has a romantic history of its own, though it was not until recently that the aura of mystery in which it had been enshrouded was dispelled, revealing the glamor of this scorned fish's life.

The thrilling migrations of the adventurous salmon, which have made it a star in fishdom, are, oddly enough, the eel's forte too. The serpentine fish, however, unrolls the salmon's film in reverse. For in the autumn adult eels throng the aquatic avenues leading to the sea, and in the spring it is the young eels which make their way back upstream in great hordes. After long study it was learned that the migration in the fall ends far out in the Atlantic. Southwest of Bermuda are the spawning grounds of the eel, and in the ocean depths the female lays her eggs and then, it is believed, dies.

Soon after, in midwinter, the exciting career of the young eels, or elvers, begins. As soon as they are hatched they begin to work their way back to the coast. In the larval state they were once considered a distinct species; they are flat and have the outline of a cigar. The elvers are so transparent that "laid upon a printed page, they offer practically no obstruction to reading."

When the elvers reach the coast they have developed out of the larval period. In the brackish waters of the bays they lose their transparency and acquire a black pigmentation. With unflagging persistence the two-inch fishes begin their upstream journey.

They work their way inland over falls, dams, and other barriers in such vast numbers that an observer could scoop up fifteen hundred in a small net. They may clamber over damp rocks, and it is even believed that they may make overland treks; at least that is one explanation for the presence of eels in ponds devoid of inlets and outlets. Only the females, however, go as far as the stream's headwaters; the males call a halt to the grueling voyage much sooner.

At the age of three or four years the common eel develops small scales. It is further marked by a pointed snout and a large gaping mouth. Fully grown, it may attain a length of five feet and a weight of sixteen pounds. When it is six or eight years old, its return journey is started. It stops eating and its skin becomes a silvery color. As it retraces its steps, it travels at night and rests during the day. When it departs, it never returns; at least adult eels have not been observed making the springtime upstream jaunt.

The common eel's color varies with the type of bottom on which it dwells. It is, however, usually a mud-brown color above, lighter brown below with a yellowish-white belly. The eel not only inhabits slow-moving streams, but also the racing waters inhabited by trout. On the whole, its home is determined by the presence of food rather than the type of water.

The eel is another of those omnivorous creatures to which epicureanism in food is foreign. Its menu is determined not by taste but by availability, and it eats any animal food, living or dead. It not only preys on small fishes, shrimps, crabs, and crustaceans, but also eats refuse.

It is best caught by fishermen at night, although its appetite may cause it to be taken during the day. Since it eagerly takes bait of any kind, little proficiency is required to land an eel. And, of course, the eel plays its part in the eating habits of many people.

EEL

This voracious fish is believed to be responsible for the destruction of great numbers of shad and herring in the streams along the Atlantic coast. In some sections of the country, where fishing is done with gill nets, the eel's depredations are considered enormous. When the gill nets are drawn up they may contain only the skeletons of the catch, the eels having devoured the flesh of the other trapped fishes.

The common or American eel, which ranges east of the Rockies, is the only species of true eel in the United States.

The related conger eel has been known to attain a length of eight feet and a weight of fifty pounds, though this is rare. Unlike the common eel, it is an oceanic resident, ranging the Atlantic south of Cape Cod, but not entering the fresh-water streams. It, too, goes far out to sea to spawn, and the female dies upon the completion of this task. A related species is taken at Pensacola, Florida.

COMMON EELS *(Anguilla rostrata)*. Length: 4½ feet. Range: Gulf of St. Lawrence to Brazil.
New York Zoological Society

Other eels are the spiny and long-necked eels of the Gulf Stream; the deep-water snub-nosed parasitic eel found off the Grand Bank; the duck-gill eels of the Pacific, three species of which reach the coast of southern California from the tropical Pacific; the two worm eels of the Florida Keys and the Gulf coast; the snipe or thread eels of the deeper coastal waters of the Atlantic and the Pacific; the snake eels, also deep-water forms of the tropical Atlantic, at least ten species of which have been taken and identified off the south Florida coast.

WHITEFISH

GENERALLY considered to be one of the most important freshwater food fishes, the chubby fat whitefish lives habitually in the deeper waters of lakes and rivers. At one time the whitefish was enormously abundant in the Great Lakes, but because of extreme overfishing its numbers have been considerably reduced, although millions of pounds are still netted and marketed annually. These are caught in submarine trap nets sunk in the deepest parts of the lakes where at one time the fishes were safe. Recently some attempt has been made by those States and Provinces bordering the Great Lakes to restrict this type of fishing and thus conserve the valuable food fish for posterity.

The average weight of the whitefish is four pounds, but some of the species, notably the broad whitefish, reach a maximum weight of thirty pounds. Its body is ovoid and compressed, olive-colored above and white at the sides, the head small and short.

During the spawning season from October to December the whitefish migrates to its breeding pond, which in most cases is situated a great distance from the rivers and lakes it normally inhabits. When it reaches shallow water, the female deposits from ten thousand to seventy-five thousand eggs. If not molested by natural enemies such as the mud puppy, the common yellow perch, crawfish, and waterfowl, the eggs hatch in two to three weeks. The whitefish does not reach full maturity, however, until the third or fourth year.

More than thirty-five species of whitefishes, also called lake herrings, are found in the rivers and fresh-water lakes of the United States, particularly in the Great Lakes and their tributaries. Families

LAKE WHITEFISHES *(Coregonus clupeaformis)*. Length: 2 feet. Range: Great Lakes region northward. Becoming rare.
New York Zoological Society

closely related include the graylings, smelts, and argentines. A great quantity of whitefish is propagated artificially by the United States Bureau of Fisheries.

SALMON

THE salmon is perhaps the gamest, most publicized, and most familiar fish in the United States. It has been photographed, described, and studied extensively. The annual migration of the salmon which it resolutely makes to reach the headwaters of the river where it was first hatched, only to spawn and die, have long been sources of wonder and admiration.

Racing upstream, the moving solid silvery mass of salmon is truly epical. This dramatic journey of wriggling, fighting fishes is comparable in splendor with the treks of great herds of buffalo across the prairies during the early part of the nineteenth century. In its eagerness to reach the spawning ground, the salmon is motivated by an impulse so irresistible that it will not be stopped by any obstacle or hazard. Even when its passage is blocked by a high dam, it will leap up into the air in order to surmount the barrier, and it will either succeed or die.

The migration begins in the spring. Millions of salmon simultaneously begin their long strenuous journey upstream. Unerringly, and guided solely by instinct, they point for the headwaters of the home river or cold mountain stream and will travel two to three thousand miles in order to reach their destination. Fighting the current, leaping over waterfalls, wriggling through shallows, and skimming the swift rapids, they move forward on the perilous journey through day and night, seldom stopping to rest, never turning back. Usually during the early stages of the migration the female selects a suitable male companion, invariably choosing the larger and sturdier specimens, although this choice is by no means final as the eventual mating and spawning may be carried on by two or more males. Once in the fresh-water stream, the salmon seldom take food, consequently get progressively thinner and weaker as they ascend.

Man-made dams have been a source of extreme torture, frustration, and even death to the salmon. When no passage was provided for them over or about these gigantic obstructions, the undaunted salmon attempted heroically, but vainly, to hurdle them, and usually perished from exhaustion. Now the Government has built salmon ladders or stairs at a few dams which enable them to leap gradually upward by stages.

When the salmon reach the headwaters, the thin emaciated female lays about nine thousand eggs, and one or two males immediately fertilize the roe with sperm. Males generally fight for the privilege of fertilizing her eggs, and it is not uncommon to see two or three males hovering beside the female and pressing their bodies

SALMON

to her side. Once fertilization has been completed, the female covers the eggs with a layer of gravel.

Few salmon survive the ordeal of swimming upstream and spawning. The majority die in or about the breeding waters, and most of the hardier specimens who have managed to recuperate and begin their migration back to the ocean fall prey to bears, beavers, farmers, and fishermen. Very few salmon have been known to spawn more than once.

With the death of the old salmon, life begins anew for the next generation. The eggs develop in about two weeks, and the fry remain on the bottom of the stream, fed by the vegetation brought to them by the current. Gradually they learn to use their fins in swimming, and manage to evade natural enemies. In a few months hundreds of millions of tiny salmon move rapidly about the spawning grounds, and in two years, measuring but a few inches in length, they begin to descend the rivers. Here natural enemies and dangerous obstacles take a tremendous toll, and only a small portion of the young salmon manage to reach the ocean, where they spend the next three or four years.

A full-grown salmon weighs approximately twenty pounds. Its body is elongate, covered with cycloid scales; the large

SALMON LEAPING WATERFALL.
U. S. Bureau of Fisheries

247

mouth is equipped with jaw teeth. In its early stages, while still swimming about the spawning brook, it feeds on aquatic insects and worms, but in the sea it is voracious, attacking herrings, anchovies, and other marine animals.

As a food fish, the salmon is one of the most important in the United States. During the period of colonization, settlers found it abundant in the rivers of New England. The Indians also depended upon salmon during the lean months, usually smoking the fish and storing it from year to year. In the ten-year period ending 1936 more than ten billion pounds of salmon were netted in this country and much of the supply was canned, smoked, dried, and frozen. Most of the salmon canneries are on the Pacific coast from Washington south to California, where the salmon is most abundant and at its best.

Seven species of salmon are found on the Pacific coast, mostly from Puget Sound north to Alaska, and occasionally south to San Francisco. The largest of the species, the chinook, also known as the spring salmon and king salmon, reaches a maximum weight of one hundred pounds, and has an average life span of four to six years. The pink salmon is the smallest and most numerous of the species, with an average weight of four pounds.

A dwarf landlocked form of the salmon inhabits the lakes of Oregon, Washington, and Idaho. On the Atlantic coast, the common Atlantic salmon is not so abundant, and its range is restricted to the North Atlantic Ocean south to Maine. An eastern landlocked species is found in the lakes of Maine and New Hampshire.

Salmon may soon be threatened with extinction as the result of overfishing; Japanese factory ships operating in American coastal waters add a new peril to the already depleted salmon fisheries.

TROUT

ABUNDANT in clear, cold mountain streams, the trout is the most desirable fish from the angler's standpoint. Both because its meat is tender and flavorous, and because it invariably puts up a valiant fight when hooked, the trout is the most highly esteemed

BROOK TROUT *(Salvelinus fontinalis)*. Length: 1 foot. Range: "Maine and Labrador to the Saskatchewan, south in the Alleghenies, largely introduced into western streams, but not native west of the Mississippi except in Minnesota and Iowa" (Schrenkeisen).
New York Zoological Society

game fish in the United States, and trout fishing has become a national pastime.

The trout spends most of the day hiding among rocks in deep pools, under logs, or beneath branches; sometimes it lurks in eddies and pools and at the foot of rapids. It takes the fly well, and when hooked it leaps vigorously through the air. In its unmolested moments it feeds mostly on insects such as May flies, stone flies, midges, and black flies, and on fresh-water crustaceans and fish eggs.

The average length of a trout is about ten inches; the average taken and recorded weigh about a pound. The coloration is green on top and white below. In the spring they migrate to small streams, and when they reach the breeding grounds pair off and both move to a gravel riffle. Flexing her tail against the bottom and turning from side to side, the female digs a two-inch nest. After the preliminaries of courtship the eggs are laid and fertilized simultaneously, the entire process taking about two seconds.

More than thirty species of trout are found in lakes and rivers of the United States, particularly in California, Oregon, and Washington. These include the cut-throat or Rocky Mountain brook trout, the widespread rainbow trout, the golden trout of the high Sierras, the hardhead or steelhead of the West coast ranges, the brown trout—a European form introduced in America—the deep-water lake trout of our northern States, the eastern brook trout, the bull trout of the Pacific slope, and many related species.

HERRING

THE herrings constitute the most numerous of fishes in existence. Distributed throughout the whole of the North Atlantic and Pacific Oceans as well as the Gulf of Mexico, and even ascending rivers and lakes, the herrings have often been called King Herring because of their preponderance in our fisheries. Actually billions of herrings swarm the seas throughout the year. According to Dr. Julian S. Huxley, three billion herrings are taken annually in the North Sea and on the Atlantic coast alone, and this tremendous haul weighs no less than one billion five hundred million pounds.

As food the herrings are used perhaps more extensively than any other fish or animal. They are especially tender and tasty during spawning season when they are netted in great numbers and marketed throughout the world to be pickled, smoked, salted, dried, packed as sardines, used for bait, converted into oil, and otherwise adapted to a variety of uses to suit the tastes and needs of different localities.

The body of the herring is elongate and compressed, measuring approximately fifteen inches in length, although the dwarf herring, the smallest of the species, found mostly about Key West, is but two inches long. The coloration is generally steel blue on top, silvery white below.

Living a great distance from shore, and usually keeping close to the bottom, herrings always travel in schools. Their enemies are numerous and potentially destructive, for the herrings are attacked by most predacious fishes including the cod, haddock, salmon, pollock, hake, dogfish, albacore, as well as such marine mammals as porpoises, seals, and finback whales. Particularly destructive and vicious is the silver hake, which makes a practice of driving herring schools ashore, thus leaving them stranded. The food supply of the herring consists primarily of minute organisms such as are found in plankton, and small crustaceans.

HERRINGS *(Clupea harengus)*. Length: 1 foot. Range: North Atlantic to Cape Hatteras. No longer abundant in our coastal waters.
Ralph De Sola

The herring comes inshore to spawn, and its eggs incubate in ten to twelve days, while the fry does not mature for three to four years. Herring, found on both coasts, with some species ascending streams, lakes, and rivers, number ten species. Included in the suborder with herrings are the mooneyes of the midwestern and southern rivers and lakes, numbering three species. On the Atlantic coast, ranging from Florida to Rhode Island, is the thread herring and the mossbunker or menhaden, which is also found in the Gulf and includes three species. Menhaden are caught in great numbers by specially constructed vessels, taken ashore and converted into a rich fertilizer. Of the round herrings, at least three species are found off our eastern coast. The gizzard or hickory shads which are found not only on both coasts but also enter streams and often are landlocked, number six species.

SHAD

DURING the colonization period of America, the shad was so abundant that it was found in every fresh-water stream on the Atlantic coast, and in the spring astounding numbers choked the mouths of rivers, swimming in a seemingly endless mass to the headwaters in order to spawn. The abundance of the shad is now a thing of the past, a natural wonder perhaps never again to be witnessed.

The shad is an extremely delicious fish, and from the earliest times it was caught in vast numbers. So greatly was it overfished and destroyed, that as early as the beginning of the twentieth century it was necessary for the Federal Government, and even various States, to institute artificial propagation in order to save the species from extinction. The method employed proved to be highly successful, and the United States Bureau of Fisheries was even instrumental in introducing the shad into the Pacific Ocean where it may now be found from San Diego to Washington. A contributing factor greatly responsible for the destruction of the fish is the industrial pollution of streams and rivers, which takes a tremendous yearly toll of shad.

Like the salmon, the shad migrates from the sea to the rivers during the spring breeding season in order to reproduce, and, in many cases, dies of exhaustion shortly after spawning. Extremely prolific, the female deposits from sixty thousand to one hundred and fifty thousand eggs which hatch in six to ten days.

The shad roe is considered a great delicacy and in order to obtain it the fish is still netted extensively throughout the United States. The body of the shad, colored bluish above the silvery at the sides, attains a length of two feet and an average weight of four pounds. Three species are found on the Atlantic, Pacific, and Gulf coasts although the center of their abundance is considered to be along the

Atlantic coast line between North Carolina and Long Island. In the Hudson about two million pounds of shad are taken every spring. If four pounds is taken as an average individual weight, males or buck shad being somewhat lighter and females or roe shad a bit heavier, this figure indicates a net haul of 500,000 of the silverbacks.

SARDINE

SMALL and defenseless, the sardine is destroyed by predatory fishes, caught in large numbers by man, but still manages to survive and reproduce so plentifully that it seems in the aggregate to suffer little from these losses, and even to this day it is extremely abundant.

No other fish is taken in such vast numbers in the United States as the sardine. The annual commercial catch averages more than five hundred million pounds, most of which is ground into meal or oil, packed in cans and shipped to many parts of the world.

The sardine seldom measures more than ten inches in length. Its coloration is dark blue above, silvery below, and at night when large schools of sardines roam through the sea, they appear luminous and can be seen a long distance. Their flesh is dark and extremely oily.

Abundant on both our coasts, five species of sardines are found in the offshore waters of the United States.

ANCHOVY

RELATED to the herring, the tiny anchovy is abundant in all warm waters and is found on the Atlantic, Gulf, and Pacific coasts. Its color is silvery white and its translucent body is elongate, never exceeding seven inches in length, and usually measuring but three inches. The lower jaw is extremely long and opens to the rear of the head.

Anchovies swim in large schools, occasionally entering rivers. In spite of their diminutive size, they are carnivorous, feeding on small fishes, copepods, and other marine organisms. They spawn from December to June and the newly laid eggs are left to float in the water, whereupon they are carried out to sea.

Twenty species of anchovies are found in the offshore waters of the United States, and at least one of the species, the striped anchovy, enters our rivers from Cape Cod to Texas.

TARPON

THE tarpon is one big-game fish which, when hooked, has no hesitancy in counterattacking fishermen and boats. Leaping out of the blue depths like a silver flash with the great eyes at the top of the snout glaring grotesquely and yawning mouth showing the blood-red cells under the expanded gill covers, its long, heavy body is a terrifying sight. It can rise with powerful force fifteen feet above the water and thirty feet across. Should it land on a deck, as it frequently does, spars, railings—anything in its path—give way in a splintered mass, as the occupants of the boat seek shelter from its teeth and heavy flops. Men have been severely injured or knocked overboard and even drowned in these forays.

So sensational is the sport offered by this species that it has long been known as the most dangerous and prized kind of catch. Few of the larger ones are caught by rod and reel because of the difficulty of playing them out by exhausting leaps far enough from the boat, and their ability to shake off hooks or entangle and break leaders in their movements through the air. They must be dispatched promptly, despite their endurance, because sharks abound in the warm waters where they are found.

They are also feared by commercial seine fishermen because of their fierceness when they find themselves caught in nets meant for smaller fish. Such diabolical power and ferocity have their source in the symmetrical, streamlined shape of the fish despite its size, which at times reaches a length of eight feet and a weight of several hundred pounds. A decadent type dating from the Cretaceous period, it belongs to the oldest division of the modern bony fishes. In addition to its protruding lower jaw, unmodified vertebrae, soft-rayed fins, and long bony plate between the halves of the lower jaw, it has such useful modern adaptations as a sensitive lateral line nerve, forked tail, and lunglike air bladder with a primitive duct leading

TARPON

YOUNG TARPON *(Tarpon atlanticus)*. Length: 6 feet (adult). Range: Gulf and southern Atlantic coasts.
S. C. Dunton, New York Aquarium

to the throat. The depressible dorsal and anal fins, the great armor-plated eye sockets with the fat-encased eyeballs to withstand pressure and cold at two hundred fathoms, the widely dilated pupils which admit light rays far down, and great silvery scales of the skin to reflect illumination, as well as the layer of mucus covering them which facilitate speed, are other features in this combination of useful old and new evolutionary characters.

Most interesting is the long, loose, last ray of the short upright dorsal fin. When the fish jumps this ray attaches itself through the suction of its concave under surface to the side of the body toward which it is moving, thus indicating the direction of its leap. Because of its great circular scales, from one to three inches in diameter, which are marketed as curios in the South, the fish has a bright metallic sheen when alive, and is also known as silver fish and *grande ecaille*. Above the lateral line it is bluish.

As a member of the sensitive herring family, this species is very responsive to sudden changes in temperature and other disturbances. No specimen was ever kept in an aquarium until 1936, because of its inability to survive shipment or for lack of proper water. In this connection it is interesting to note that it feeds voraciously on cutlass fishes, an extremely compressed fish which is most sensitive to cold water. Mullets, sardines, shrimps, crabs, pinfishes, and sea catfishes are also eaten by tarpons.

The tarpon will travel a hundred miles up fresh-water rivers in search of small fry and other prey. Fairly large ones, indeed, are often found in landlocked lagoons or muddy pools far from their ocean habitat. This is no doubt made possible by the air bladder which enables it to live in muddy and sulphurous water, much like some of the older types of fish confined to such a medium because of receding waters during a past geologic age. The younger specimens are commonly found in these coastal creeks and pools, their shiny scales contrasting oddly with the murky water.

TARPON LEAPING.
Julian A. Dimock, American Museum of Natural History

Spawning is understood to occur in the open sea near the coast rather than inland. This is because the young are believed to pass through a larval stage before becoming true fishes. At any rate, the ten million small eggs of a large female indicate the sea-spawning habit, while a larval stage would account for the fact that the newborn have never been seen. The larva is an inch-long semitranslucent ribbon with only the line formed by the swim bladder and eye spots noticeable in water. After hatching it is believed the larvae are swept inshore by currents and later as young fry reach the inland lagoons before the receding waters leave them, well protected and supplied with food. A length of a foot is probably reached after the first year, two the second, and at maturity the fish averages between four and five feet. The male is smaller and more active than the female.

Two species, each representing a different genus, are found in United States waters. The tarpon proper ranges from Long Island to Brazil, being especially numerous off Florida, where it is found in schools of twenty to several hundred individuals. The so-called ten-pounder is a small relative ranging from Long Island to the West Indies. Most anglers return the fish to the water, although fresh young are said to be tasty if fried, baked, or boiled. The world's record catch—one of two hundred forty-two and one-half pounds —was taken in Panuco River, Mexico, in 1934.

Gar Pike and Bowfin

We now come to the orders of more elementary fish, differing from the true fishes in several characteristics.

The gar pikes and bowfins are members of the order *Holostei*. Their skeleton is bony, but they are distinguished by the possession of ganoid scales which are hard and composed of a layer of shining enamel.

BOWFIN

AS a nest builder the bowfin has few if any equals. In the spring breeding season, the male of this species scoops out a hole about two and a half feet in diameter and nearly a foot deep. The nest is placed in a weedy portion of the water near the bank, so that weeds line the sides, float above, and roots cover the bottom. In his work the male has two little horns or nodules on his snout to help him out, much as in the case of the smaller horned dace, which is also a good nest builder, though of another kind.

At this time of the year the usual bronze color of the male bowfin becomes tinted with green and orange, the fins becoming as vivid as aquatic plants. There are also reticulated markings on the sides which resemble the shadows of the plant leaves floating overhead. A tail spot consisting of a black dot or eye with an orange circle around it is, however, the chief mark of the male. It also has its camouflaging value in resembling images on the shallow bottom during the day when its possessor is most likely to rest from his long labors. For this species is largely nocturnal in habits, building and hunting at night.

In spawning the male courts the female by circling and taking her snout in his mouth, which is as near as a fish comes to kissing. Then they lie side by side, quivering with fins and tails for fifteen to twenty seconds. After that eggs are usually found. This is repeated four or five times with the same or other females, until the nest has several layers of eggs containing from two to five thousand individuals. Should any other male intrude at any time, the mating male pushes him out with his snout.

BOWFIN

For the eight to ten days necessary to hatch the eggs, the male continues on guard, moving slowly above the eggs and fanning them with his fins to keep dirt and fungus spores away. The tiny larvae are a fraction of an inch long and attach themselves in circular swarms to the roots of the nest by means of the adhesive organs on their snouts. After nine more days their snout organs and yolk sacs begin to disappear while fins develop; then they begin to swim in circular swarms, with the center immobile for considerable periods, and feed on insect larvae and the smaller crustaceans. Finally they grow bold enough to follow the male parent outside of the nest for more and larger food, and experiments have shown they do this largely by scent. These schools remain together for several weeks, always guarded more or less by the male parent who has a peculiar habit of splashing his tail on the surface to warn them of any impending danger.

The bowfin is one of the hardiest species and very abundant in its range. Its tenacity is probably due to the fact that it is a very generalized, coarse type closely related to the ancestors of the modern bony fishes which comprise ninety per cent of all living fishes. It can live

BOWFINS *(Amiatus calva)*. Length: 2 feet. Range: Great Lakes and Mississippi Valley to Virginia, Florida, and Texas.
New York Zoological Society

in muddy and foul waters and even stay alive out of all water for some time because of its lunglike air bladder, which indicates the early adaptation of sea forms to land life later stabilized in the amphibians. In addition, it has a large mouth, with long sharp teeth; smooth scales and round soft rays characterize its fins. The long dorsal fin with forty-eight rays is its distinguishing feature, giving it a figure that suggests the arc of a crescent.

The female is duller and darker and grows to a length averaging about two and a half feet, or about half a foot longer than the male. The latter appears to be more numerous, however, especially at the breeding season. They are quite voracious, eating crawfishes, pickerels, and aquatic insects. Because of their nocturnal habits and preference for deep water outside of their breeding period, they are seldom seen. When active they can usually be noticed by the bubbles they emit when they rise to the surface from time to time for fresh gulps of air. Experiments have shown this access to air a necessity to the fish, and even the swarms of small fry rise regularly to the surface for this purpose, causing a rustling sound like rain drops.

The bowfin or mudfish is rather a nuisance to anglers because of its ability to bite through lines with its long teeth. Its meat is too tough to be edible. The one species in this family is found in sluggish streams and lakes from the Great Lakes and the Mississippi Valley to Texas, Florida, Tennessee, and Virginia.

GAR PIKE

PROTECTED by a coat of mail and teeth-filled crocodilian jaws, gar pikes hark back to that dark and distant time when huge dinosaurs roamed the land and their contemporaries—the armor-plated, boneless monsters of the deep—were just beginning to give way before the more agile bony fishes of today. The gars' heavy scales are found in only one other surviving type of fish, though often among the fossils of archaic forms. They are living anachronisms. Their survival is probably due to their close approximation to the modern fishes in such features as a bony skeleton and fins, a spiral valve of the intestine, and a lunglike air bladder.

ALLIGATOR GARS *(Lepisosteus spatula).* Length: 10 feet. Range: Lower Mississippi Valley from above St. Louis. In the larger streams.
New York Zoological Society

So tough is the coat of the gars that no fishes in their range can cope with them. Even the efforts of man are often futile in subduing them, for since they cannot be hooked in their bony jaws, the use of special tackle and bait which they swallow is necessary. The plates of the skin are so hard, at least in the larger specimens which grow ten or twelve feet long and weigh several hundred pounds, that they cannot be pierced with an axe. The only way to kill these monsters is to cut their throats or strike a well-aimed blow on a vulnerable spot back of the head—provided, of course, one can get that close.

In general, their form betrays the sluggish hulks of primeval types, being thick and powerful, although cylindrical and elongated, with round tail fin, and small dorsal and anal fins at base of the tail and abdominal fins. In color they are mostly a dirty mottled yellow-gray above and paler below. This gives them a resemblance to logs as they float on the surface of muddy bayous or streams, or rest in nooks near the bottom. On either side of the long flat jaws, like those of a swordfish or alligator, are rows of sharp teeth, the outer row having the largest ones. At the very tip of the bill, the upper jaw protrudes, allowing the foremost teeth in it to overhang the lower jaw and form convenient grappling hooks.

In habits, too, the gar pikes live up to their awe-inspiring appearance and ancient lineage. Moving warily upon their prey, or lying in wait at the head of currents and caves, they are a terror to fish life, eating everything from insects and crustaceans to the larger pickerels, pikes, and basses inhabiting their waters. Many bass have been exterminated by them to add to the woe of fishermen, and they will even seem to flaunt their immunity by devouring the catch hanging over the side of a boat. They are rather nocturnal in their habits, however, staying in deeper water or shady nooks during the day and frequenting the shoals to feed when the sun has gone down.

In winter the species hibernates at the bottom in an inactive state. As soon as the water grows warm it moves to the head of quiet pools and bayous—usually in schools—to spawn. The female's eggs are deposited in sticky clusters on stumps and shrubbery in the water, and immediately fertilized by the milt or sperm of the male. The young of the most common or long-nosed species have suckers on the upper jaw by means of which they attach themselves to roots and stumps until developed sufficiently to swim freely. They have a broad black band running lengthwise on the sides, which breaks up and disappears later. They feed voraciously on larvae, smaller crustaceans, and fishes, and unless they are themselves eaten, reach a length of a foot and a weight of several pounds by their first winter.

The tendency of gar pikes to come up for air is probably a manifestation of their close relation to the lungfishes and amphibians in the character of their breathing apparatus. Their cellular air bladder represents the earliest change from gills to the lungs of higher vertebrates. No doubt this is why they can thrive in muddy water or in ditches and pools where there is hardly room enough to turn around.

Although their meat is said to be palatable if properly cooked—Negroes and Indians have long relished it—gar pikes are not generally favored as food. The roe, in particular, is considered poisonous.

Their gills, however, harbor the larvae of the prized fresh-water mussel used in making pearl buttons and similar items. Indians have also utilized their enamel-covered, diamond-shaped scales for arrowheads. As for game, there are few fishes that can offer the resistance and obstacles to capture that gar pikes can, especially in the case of the largest, the alligator gar, which has been known to attack man.

The common or long-nosed species grows to a length of six feet, although the average taken is much smaller. It is found in the Great Lakes and the Mississippi Basin, and the coastal streams from Maryland to Florida and Louisiana. The short-nosed gar has a broader, flatter snout one-third or less longer than the rest of the head, and a single row of large teeth in the upper jaw. It grows to a length of three feet, and is found in the Great Lakes and the Mississippi Basin. The alligator gar has a still shorter and flatter snout, rougher scales, and a greenish-brown color above with prominent black spots on its tail fin. It grows up to about twelve feet, weighs several hundred pounds, and inhabits the larger streams of the lower Mississippi Basin from above St. Louis, entering saltier water near the Gulf. Several related species are found in the Missouri River, Florida, and Louisiana.

Paddlefish and Sturgeon

The paddlefish and sturgeon are distinguished from the true fishes by the lack of a bony skeleton, their framework being cartilaginous. They have no scales, or at the best, the scales are vestigial. Their most prominent characteristic is the possession of a prominent snout.

AMERICAN PADDLEFISH *(Polyodon spathula)*. Length: 4 feet. Range: Mississippi Valley. Rare.
American Museum of Natural History

PADDLEFISH

SLUGGISH and clumsy, the paddlefish can be seized by the nose and tail and dragged into a fisherman's boat. In Moon Lake, Mississippi, these one-hundred-and-sixty-pound, six-foot fishes support a small local industry. Discarding the heads and fins, the fishermen boil them for oil. Also, a very good caviar is manufactured from their roe, from two to fifteen pounds of which can be taken from a single fish. The roe is rubbed on a coarse wire sieve until the eggs are separated from the membrane and then collected in a bucket. Raw paddlefish eggs bring about half a dollar a pound and account for the rapid decimation of the species which now faces extinction.

The upper half of this fish's mouth extends far out in a paddle-shaped protuberance. Besides its ornamental value, this member is used to rake up the mud and silt for the worms, leeches, insects, and minute organisms upon which it feeds. Delicate organs of touch in the paddle aid it in its search for food, its eyesight being very deficient.

Paddlefishes are found nowhere but in the lakes and rivers of the central States as far north as the Great Lakes, but they are most numerous and abundant in the lakes connected with the lower Mississippi. Their nearest relatives are found in the rivers of China.

One mystery concerning them is still unsolved—the location of their spawning grounds. The fry are never seen until they have grown to about six inches in length.

Paddlefishes are also called spoonbill cats, duckbill cats, and spadefishes—though they are not related to the marine fishes of the latter name.

STURGEON

LIKE a hog rooting for truffles, the sturgeon rowels its snout around in the muck of the ocean floor sometimes twenty-five fathoms down. The sensitive barbels on its chin feel out the succulent marine worms and mollusks buried in the slime and when the sturgeon engulfs its defenseless prey it swallows a good quantity of mud along with it. Occasionally its fare is varied by the addition of sand launces and other small fishes.

The sturgeon is formidable in appearance only. No other fish has its helm of bony plates on the head, united by sutures; its skin armored with a row of bony shields, twelve rows on each side along the back. Each of these shields has a spiny outgrowth extending longitudinally. But the mouth of the sturgeon, placed on the under side, is toothless except in the larval stage. Its tail, like a shark's, has a longer upper lobe along which the spinal column extends.

The long, slender body is colored an olive-green or bluish-gray above, lighter on the sides, and white on the belly. Record specimens in this country have attained eighteen feet in length and one white sturgeon taken at Astoria, Oregon, weighed nineteen hundred pounds; but today a length of more than ten feet is decidedly rare for this almost extinct species. The male usually grows no larger than six or seven feet.

Late in the spring the adult sturgeons begin their journey up the rivers in company with shads, alewives, and salmon to the spawning grounds in the upper reaches. During May, June, and July the fertile females lay as many as 2,400,000 eggs, each of which hatches about a week after fertilization. Two months later the small fry have reached a length of five and a half inches.

After spawning, the older fishes return to the sea. The number of annual spawning trips each fish makes is unknown.

The common sturgeon of the Atlantic coast ranges from the Gulf of St. Lawrence to the Carolinas, occasionally being found in the waters of the Gulf of Mexico. The largest of these fishes, however, comes from the Pacific coast region. Known as the Sacramento, Oregon, or white sturgeon, it once occurred abundantly between Monterey, California, and Alaska and was taken in the Columbia, Yakima, and Fraser Rivers, although now nearly extinct. The green sturgeon, inhabiting the same range, is smaller.

COMMON STURGEON (*Acipenser oxyrhynchus*). Length: 9 feet. Range: Atlantic coast and coastal rivers from Maine to South Carolina. Becoming rare.
S. C. Dunton, New York Aquarium

STURGEON

Rarely entering the sea, the lake sturgeon is a fresh-water species found in the lakes of the Mississippi Valley. It reaches a weight of one hundred pounds. The hackleback or switchtail sturgeon also occurs in these inland bodies of water. The short-nosed sturgeon ranges from Cape Cod to Florida, while the white shovelnose is a rare fish sometimes taken in the Mississippi River.

Sharks, Rays, and Chimeras

The ancestors of present-day sharks roamed the primeval seas of the Devonian period, millions of years ago. Sharks show this ancient heritage in the primitive state of their skeletons and vital organs. The bony structures of the higher vertebrates are replaced in the sharks by gristle and cartilage, strengthened with deposits of calcium compounds.

Sharks are legendary as the raiders of the deep, but not all sharks are predatory. The slow-moving nurse shark eats offal while the blunt-toothed Port Jackson shark of Australia crushes shellfishes. The whale shark and the basking shark have very large mouths which they use to entrap small marine animals, much in the manner of the whales. Only one shark, the man-eater or mackerel shark, reputedly attacks humans although at least one authority questions that it ever attacks man.

Lacking scales, the shark's body is covered with a tough hide studded with little toothlike formations called denticles. Shark skin is used for its abrasive qualities in polishing wood and ivory as well as for decorative purposes. A leather known as *galuchat* is also made of this tough hide or shagreen.

Sharks lay comparatively few eggs, and these are endowed with large yolks. The embryos draw nourishment from them for a long time so that they are able to take care of themselves directly after being hatched. In some species, however, the eggs hatch out within the mother shark and the young are nourished by means of growths extending from the region of the gills.

Despite their peculiar flattened bodies with large fins at either side, the rays and skates are closely allied to the sharks. They have the same cartilaginous internal structure and rough hide. The spreading pectoral fins are the principal means of locomotion while the long trailing tail acts as a rudder. In the rays and skates the gill slits are on the under side; water for them is pumped in and out of openings behind the eyes.

Between the sharks and the rays certain intermediate forms show the process of transformation clearly. The monkfish has enlarged pectoral fins, but these are separated from the head by gill slits which are placed at the side as in the sharks.

Down in the lower depths of the ocean, the chimeras or silver sharks lay their eggs in horny cases in the manner of most sharks. They have strong teeth and jaws.

In all, forty-seven species and subspecies of sharks inhabit our coastal waters. They include the bullhead sharks; the cow sharks; the cat sharks, whose ancestors go back to the Jurassic period; the sluggish nurse sharks; the gray sharks; the swift hammerheads; the enormous whale sharks, largest of all fishes; the powerful-tailed thresher sharks; the sand sharks; mackerel sharks; and basking sharks.

The dogfishes, sleeper sharks, and bramble sharks lack the anal fin. The angel sharks are small forms, like skates in structure and midway between the two forms.

Native rays and skates include the saw-snouted sawfish; the guitar fishes; the cow-nosed rays, the skates and rays; the electric rays, capable of giving a severe electric shock; the sting rays; the eagle rays; and the sea devils which include the devil fish, romantic in fact and fiction. This group comprises fifty-two species and subspecies.

Fifteen species of chimeras are found in deep water off both coasts.

BASKING SHARK

FROM the frozen seas of the Arctic where it is supposed to be born, the great gray-brown basking shark comes down to the warmer waters of the Atlantic and Pacific. Fishermen off the shores of Virginia and California, and on the other side of the Atlantic near Portugal, have seen its huge form lolling sluggishly at the surface, exposing first its white belly, then its sides to the warming rays of the sun.

Forty-five feet long, this great hulk of a fish is a quiet and inoffensive monster. Its small teeth would help it little if it were minded to lead a predatory existence, but they serve well enough to break up the tiny crustaceans, copepods, and similar small fare that it subsists on.

A single basking shark liver yields two hundred gallons of oil. So the basking shark, now rare in these waters, was once the object of many a harpooner's cast near New Bedford. The great fish is indifferent to the approach of a boat. It is still hunted extensively off Ireland and Iceland.

MACKEREL SHARK

COLORED a deep-sea blue that matches the Gulf Stream, the blue shark or porbeagle prefers the warm seas of the tropics but may be found as far north as Nova Scotia. It makes itself a nuisance by rolling up like a ball in fishermen's nets and by destroying or driving away schools of menhaden, mackerel, shad, hake, herring, and other edible fishes.

Stout and heavy-shouldered, the porbeagle attains a maximum length of twelve feet. This species gives birth to live young.

Largest of the mackerel sharks, the man-eater has large triangular teeth with nearly straight cutting edges. It grows to thirty feet in length, sometimes as much as forty. Occasionally moving as far north as eastern Nova Scotia, the man-eater or white shark is the only member of the shark family which reputedly attacks man, although one living authority, Dr. William Beebe, maintains that even the man-eater will not wilfully injure a human being.

Black or slaty gray, sometimes a leaden white, the man-eater is fortunately rare throughout its range which covers the warm temperate seas as far north as Nova Scotia. It feeds on large fishes and sea turtles and one thirty foot specimen was found to have swallowed whole a good-sized young sea lion.

The sharp-nosed mackerel shark is agile and swift in the water. This oceanic fish finds its way as far north as Maine. More than ten feet in length, it is somewhat slenderer than the common mackerel shark, but similar to it in habits.

THRESHER SHARK

WHILE the long scythe-shaped tail of the thresher shark is not employed in beating porpoises to death, it does serve a function when the fish is scouring about for food. These sharks often work in pairs, flailing their tails about to herd schools of herring, pilchard, and menhaden together so they can be devoured more conveniently. The thresher grows to fifteen feet, rarely to twenty, and has been found in all temperate seas. On the Atlantic coast it ranges as far north as Block Island and infrequently to the Gulf of St. Lawrence. An unwelcome visitor, it tangles and tears mackerel nets and drives away the fishes.

SHARKS PURSUING SEA TURTLE.
American Museum of Natural History

NURSE SHARK

NEAR the Florida Keys the sluggish nurse sharks come into shallow water to mate. As their bellies scrape along the sandy bottoms, their dorsal fins protrude high into the air. Boys will be boys, and the lads of the Keys are no exception. Seizing the flustered sharks by the pectoral fins they mount them for a breath-taking ride until they are dragged out into water too deep for safety.

Nurse sharks feed on squids and shrimps, and in captivity have accepted almost everything edible. A small barbel on each side of the mouth serves to distinguish this harmless species.

Large as goose eggs, the eggs of the nurse sharks are enclosed in a delicate horny wrapper. These are retained in the body during the entire period of their incubation and the free young are released. Thus, the nurse sharks occupy a position zoologically between the true dogfishes which lay eggs and the requiem sharks which produce live young.

The young at first bear a spattered marking of dark spots which disappear in the adult stage. Between six and ten feet long, the nurse sharks rarely are found above the Carolinas. They are also known along the west coast of Mexico.

TIGER SHARK

ROVING the high seas of the tropics the well-named tiger shark preys on the large sea turtles, fishes, other sharks, and occasionally engulfs a bit of carrion. Its head is large and massive and its convex snout overhangs wide jaws studded with strong sickle-shaped teeth.

Tiger sharks may reach thirty feet in length but twelve feet or so is more normal for this species. While no authentic record of their attacking humans exists, they are much feared in the West Indies. On the Atlantic coast they may straggle as far north as the waters of Maine.

HAMMERHEAD SHARK

THE strange head of the hammerhead is useful as a rudder as that fish makes sharp right-angle turns in pursuit of its prey. Hammerheads are denizens of the high seas where they swim with their dorsal and caudal fins above the surface. They are found in tropical seas all over the globe.

Fishes, squids, clams, and barnacles are the fare on which they generally subsist, and even pieces of sting rays have been found in them. Along the edge of the "hammer" run the elongated nostrils which may aid the shark in smelling out its food. At any rate, whenever blood has been spilt far out to sea, the hammerheads have been among the first to get wind of it. Their eyes bulge out at either side of the flattened head.

Large hammerheads achieve seventeen feet in length although twelve feet is more common. A big hammerhead will weigh more than three quarters of a ton. They bear large broods; thirty-seven embryos were taken from one female.

SANDSHARK AND SHARKSUCKERS *(Odontaspis littoralis* and *Echeneis naucrates).* Length: 9 feet. Range: Cape Cod to Cape Hatteras.
New York Zoological Society

DOGFISH

SWARMS of small sharks infest the New England coast every spring. Hunting in packs, these spiny dogfishes drive off the mackerel, cod, herring, and haddock, tear and foul fishermen's nets, appropriate bait, and even take fish off the hooks. The damage to gear and tackle each year off the Massachusetts coast alone from these predatory fishes is estimated to amount to $400,000. Rumors that they have attacked swimmers and torn them to pieces have never been proved, however.

Grabbing a spiny dogfish in the hand is a dangerous business. Their sharp spikes, one placed before each dorsal fin, are capable of inflicting nasty wounds as they wriggle about. Trawls of fifteen hundred hooks have been brought up with a wriggling dogfish, some of them six feet long, on every hook. In British waters 20,000 of them have been taken at one time.

The spiny dogfish is viviparous. Its young have a row of small white spots on each side which fade as the fish grows. The adults are slate-colored with rounded heads and flattened snouts.

The black dogfish is rare off our coasts but more plentiful in the region of Nova Scotia. Lacking spines, it is about the same size as the spiny dogfish.

The light-gray smooth dogfish comes into harbors and bays in the neighborhood of Cape Cod where it is especially abundant. Two to three feet long, they feed on crustaceans, fishes, squids, mollusks, and razor clams. They are the lobsters' greatest nemesis.

Four to twelve live young compose a litter. The pups are a foot long and resemble the parents in form when born.

SAND SHARK

WITH the exception of the dogfishes, the sand sharks are the commonest of the sharks. At Nantucket, fishing for these harmless six-footers has long been a popular sport. They range between the elbow of Cape Cod and the Bay of Fundy. During the warm months they come close to beaches and enter the mouths of rivers, progressing slowly with their tails and dorsal fins protruding. In winter they retreat from the New England coast to warmer waters.

Sluggish as sharks go, they are nevertheless able to surround and attack shoals of bluefish. They also destroy great numbers of smaller fishes like menhaden, cunner, mackerel, skate, flounder, alewife, silver hake, and butterfish.

Adults are gray spotted with brown, the fins sometimes being edged with black.

WHALE SHARK

THE whale shark is the largest living fish, and next to the mammalian whales it is the most colossal inhabitant of the sea. Specimens are reported to run sixty feet in length, according to Dr. Gudger who has made many detailed studies of this species.

STING RAY

Their distinctive pattern is a checkerboard formation of lines on the back dotted with white spots. Otherwise they might be mistaken for basking sharks which approach them in size.

Huge but harmless, the whale sharks have three thousand teeth in each jaw which are only one eighth of an inch long. They have no enemies but man and will put up a strenuous fight.

Whale sharks are found in all warm waters of the Atlantic and Pacific and have been seen in the Mediterranean, near the Cape of Good Hope, and in the vicinity of the West Indies.

STING RAY

FROM Cape Cod south along the Atlantic coast the sting rays lie half buried in the sand. Their tails are long like whips and are provided at the base with formidable pointed spines, barbed along the edges. The barbs prevent the spine from being withdrawn easily from a wound, and cause great suffering to anyone attacked.

WHALE SHARK *(Rhineodon typicus)*. Length: 35 feet. Range: Coasts of Florida and California and in all oceans.
American Museum of Natural History

AMERICAN WILD LIFE

COW-NOSED RAYS *(Rhinoptera bonasus)*. Length: 7 feet. Range: "Nantucket to Florida" (Breder).
S. C. Dunton, New York Aquarium

Sting rays as a rule, fortunately for bathers, are averse to cold water, and are seldom encountered as far north as Florida or southern California. The northern sting ray, known from Maine to Cape Hatteras, reaches a length of twelve feet, although individuals longer than six feet are rarely seen. It feeds on mollusks, crabs, annelids, and similar food. Much smaller, the round sting ray is common throughout the West Indies and the southern shores of the United States. Other species are found on the Pacific coast. It grows to a foot in length, and is brown in color, speckled with yellow spots.

TORPEDO

THE well-named torpedo is able to give a severe electric shock, enough to disable a man temporarily. Its "battery" consists of two large organs placed between the head and the pectoral fins which provide a center for the nervous activity of the fish. The

SKATE

strength of the discharge depends upon the health, size, and condition of the individual torpedo.

Torpedoes or crampfishes are found from Maine to Cuba and on the coast of California, but fortunately are not common around any particular locality. While individuals weighing more than thirty pounds are rare, some have been known to reach a weight of two hundred pounds. The young are born alive.

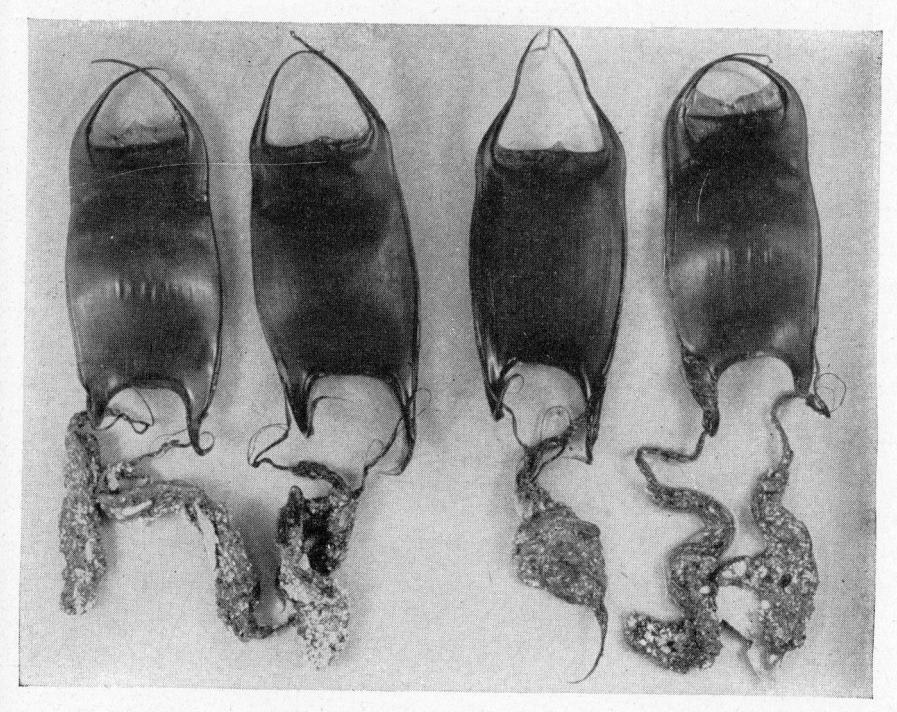

CLEAR-NOSED SKATE EGGS *(Raja eglanteria)*.
S. C. Dunton, New York Aquarium

SKATE

THE common skate comes into shoal water off Massachusetts in April and May, and returns during the winter to the deeper waters. It customarily dives thirty or more fathoms down, where it feeds along the bottom, flapping its graceful wings in pursuit of hermit and other crabs, as well as mollusks and small fishes.

Sixteen to twenty inches long, half of which length is tail, the common skate is colored gray to dark brown spotted with darker brown. It ranges from Halifax to Charleston. Other species are found on both coasts.

The eggs of the common skate are laid in the spring and hatch out in summer and autumn. They measure about two inches.

SAWFISH

SAWFISHES are rays that resemble sharks, with horizontally flattened snouts that extend far beyond the mouth. Teeth stud the edges of these members, making them most formidable weapons for defense and attack and placing much larger creatures such as whales at the mercy of their slashing onslaught. The teeth of the sawfish are small and it would be completely unfitted for a predatory existence were it not for the saw.

Found in warm seas, but straggling from the Gulf of Mexico and the tropical Atlantic to New Jersey occasionally, these picturesque fishes sometimes reach a length of eighteen feet. When very small, they are said to make good eating. The young hatch within the body of the mother. Their saws, while developed at birth, are covered with a fleshy sheath which they soon lose after leaving their mother's body.

Somewhat related to the sawfish is the guitarfish, named for its shape. One species is common around Florida and sometimes goes as far north as North Carolina. Two others are found off California.

MANTA

LARGEST of all the rays, the famed devilfish or manta reaches a width of twenty-two feet across its wings and a weight of more than a ton and a half. Harpooning these monsters is a thrilling and dangerous sport in tropical waters. They can pull a fishing boat through the water at a great rate of speed or turn and crush it with a flap of one of their enormous wings. They are said to be especially dangerous when accompanying their young.

CHIMERA

GLINTS of gold, copper, and brass flash from the skin of the silver sharks as they rise to the surface of the sea, balancing themselves delicately on their fin tips. Fluttering about, they thrust their oddly formed snouts into the air for a moment or two, and then disappear into the depths.

These strange fishes, rarely seen by fishermen, trace their ancestry back further than the sharks. Their remains have been found in earlier geological strata. They are the only vertebrates to retain traces of a third pair of legs.

Near Monterey, California, there is an area where chimeras may be taken by trawling with some degree of regularity. Experience has shown that they band together, taking advantage of certain fishing grounds on the ocean floor. The jaws and sharp teeth of the silver sharks fit closely together and can inflict a bad wound. They bite easily through the carapace of a crab. Their dorsal spines are good weapons too. Taken from the water, these delicate deep sea denizens die within fifteen minutes. They rarely last more than two days in aquariums, spending

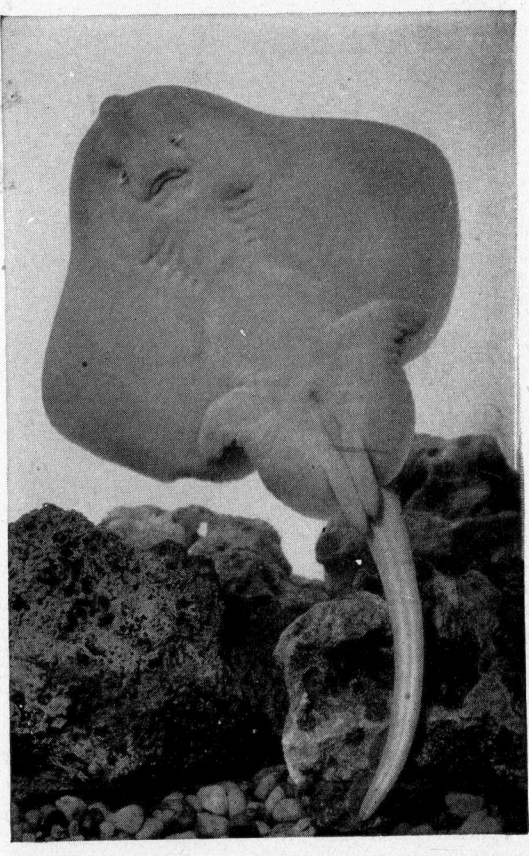

CLEAR-NOSED SKATE *(Raja eglanteria)*.
Length: 2 feet. Range: Cape Cod to Florida.
New York Zoological Society

CHIMERA (*Chimaera monstrosa*). Length: 3 feet. Range: Cape Cod northward in deep waters.
Ralph De Sola

the time in captivity swimming restlessly to and fro and avoiding the light.

Water is taken in through nostrils and released by means of a tiny slit valve, less than three-sixteenths of an inch in diameter. In addition to crabs, the three-foot-long chimera feeds on mussels, clams, prawns, and sand worms.

Its large eggs, laid in dart-shaped capsules, are found from June to December. The adult males are slightly smaller and darker than the females and trawls have caught five males for each female.

In the deep and open parts of the Atlantic from Cape Cod to Portugal range two species of chimeras, one the common and the other the deep-sea chimera. A lead-colored chimera closely related to the deep-sea chimera is found in the waters of the Gulf Stream. The so-called ratfish or elephant fish, also a chimera, is found in cold water off the Pacific coast from California to Alaska.

Lamprey, Borer, and Hagfish

The lampreys, borers, and hagfishes are fishlike vertebrates inhabiting inland lakes and streams, and coastal waters. There are about eleven native species: one hagfish found off the New England coast, two borers off the coast of California, eight lampreys of nation-wide distribution.

Resembling the eel in shape, and scaleless, they attach themselves to their prey by means of their jawless sucking mouths. Their harsh muscular tongues rasp off portions of the victim's flesh.

These marine vampires lack the bony skeleton of the true fishes; instead of backbones they have notochords. The nerve chord is buttressed with cartilage along either side, while the cartilaginous skull is open at the top. When forced to defend themselves, lampreys, hagfishes, and borers exude a slimy mucus which covers their bodies. They are popularly known as slime eels. A single nostril, centrally placed, and the absence of paired fins serve further to distinguish them from true fishes. Spherical sacs enclosed in pockets of muscle tissue expand and contract, drawing in and expelling water from which the oxygen has been extracted.

Of the eight species of lampreys found in the United States, the majority occur in the coastal waters; others are confined to the lakes and streams. The two borers are Pacific species, one being found along the coast and in the fresh-water bodies of California, while the other occurs only in deep waters of the Pacific. The single hagfish, or slimefish as it is also called, is seen along the North Atlantic coast from Cape Cod to Newfoundland.

LAMPREY

LIKE the salmon, adult lampreys make their way up fresh-water streams to lay their eggs. On the way they cross numerous obstacles, natural and man-made, until, when they have completed their reproductive functions, they die exhausted. Lacking limbs they use the sucking disk on their snouts to climb dam walls and even to move stones about on river beds in order to prepare a spawning nest.

The sea lamprey is a strong swimmer. It is able to attack such comparatively fast fishes as the mackerel, cod, and haddock. It seizes these by the side and cuts into their flesh with its sharp teeth. These teeth are not only present in the mouth but are on the rasping tongue itself.

Landlocked lake lampreys spend their entire lives in fresh water and lay their eggs there. They are abundant in the Great Lakes and their tributaries as well as in the small ponds and streams of the Middle Atlantic and New England States.

These lampreys make a shorter migration than the sea lampreys of the same species. In spring they travel from the lakes up the tributary streams until they come to the shallowest headwaters. The trip is made at night, the day being spent in resting. At the end of the journey a pair of lampreys will clear a nesting site, moving the pebbles away from the center until they form a low protecting wall. Here the eggs are laid and buried in the sand by the mating pair. The spawning continues through April, May, and June.

The young remain in the nest a few weeks after hatching. In this stage they are eyeless and toothless. Burrowing in the sand they live like worms in the stream bank. When about five inches long they begin to assume the appearance of adult lampreys.

SEA LAMPREY *(Petromyzon marinus)*.
Length: 2½ feet. Range: Atlantic coast as far south as Chesapeake Bay; ascends streams to spawn.
S. C. Dunton, New York Aquarium

Grown lampreys live wholly on fish blood except during the breeding season. Just before this period they grow ravenous and kill hundreds of fishes, leaving their drained, pierced bodies floating on the surface of the lakes.

Lampreys attain two to three feet in length and weigh somewhat more than two pounds. Formerly they achieved a certain popularity in New England as a dietary item, but today they are no longer eaten to any extent.

Female lampreys may lay more than two hundred thousand eggs apiece. While small in themselves, the eggs are heavy. The young have been found in the open sea when only six inches long.

Besides the sea lamprey, which is found around Chesapeake Bay and becomes more abundant northward when it ascends streams to spawn, there is the lake or mud lamprey, landlocked in Cayuga Lake and other lakes of western and central New York; the silver lamprey of the central States and Great Lakes; the small black lamprey or brook lamprey known from New York to Iowa; and about six other species inhabiting the Pacific and its coastal streams and rivers.

BORER

THE American borers are hagfishes from the coast of California. The California hagfish or lamperina is found along the streams of northern California and is quite common in Monterey Bay. A related species is found in deep water from Santa Barbara to Alaska.

HAGFISH

GROPING about on the soft sea bottom, the sightless hagfish or slime eel smells out its food. Captive fishes, snared in nets or on lines, are often attacked by this scavenger which otherwise would have to confine its raids to dead or injured fishes. The slime eel or hagfish is considerably less active than the lamprey.

Hagfishes inhabit the cold ocean depths from the Arctic down to Massachusetts. Possibly their most remarkable feature is their ability to exude a mucous secretion in enormous quantities. A slimefish of average size is easily able to fill a two-gallon bucket with its slime and when placed in a vessel of water soon converts it into a mass of jelly.

Some authorities believe that these eely creatures begin life as males and later develop into females. Unlike the lampreys, their eggs are large and few. Each spawning consists of about two dozen eggs, each four-fifths of an inch in size. These are covered with tough shells and have hooked protuberances which permit them to cling for support to objects on the sea floor.

EEL-POUT *(Macrozoarces americanus)*. Length: 1½ feet. Range: Labrador to Delaware.
John G. Shedd Aquarium

Lancelets

The lancelet is not a fish at all, but a member of the subphylum Cephalochordata, and interesting because they form a possible link between the lower marine animals and the higher fishes. Its feeding apparatus is interesting, consisting of cilia about the mouth which carry food particles into the alimentary tract where they are carried through to the intestine, all by ciliary action. This same mechanism occurs in larval lampreys, and provides one of the few well-marked evidences of relationship between the vertebrates and the lower non-vertebrate animals.

LANCELET

NO more than two inches long, the lancelet or amphioxus is easily mistaken for a worm as it wiggles in the sand. At the bottom of the vertebrate scale, the lancelet possesses a skeleton of the softest cartilage. It has no skull whatsoever. The functions of the higher fishes and vertebrates, however, operate in the lancelet if only in a rudimentary way.

Along the shoals and shallows of the Atlantic coast from New York to the Gulf of Mexico and in the Pacific, lancelets conceal themselves on the bottom, only the small tentacles along their mouths remaining visible. Occasionally they wiggle themselves to the surface of the water with undulating motions of their flesh-colored, tapering bodies and, when tired, wiggle their way back again to concealment in the sand. The young seem less fond of burrowing than the adults.

Sometimes as many as six lancelets will attach themselves together, head to tail, and in chain fashion weave about over the sandy floor of the sea.

When the lancelet feeds it lies on its back in quiet repose drawing water into its slitlike, jawless mouth. The water passes through the gill openings and out of the branchial pore. On the way numerous small plant and animal organisms are caught in the mucous lining of the pharynx which is separated from the mouth by a ring of cartilage. Then they enter the esophagus where the water is

CALIFORNIA LANCELET *(Branchiostoma californiense)*. Length: 2 inches. Range: Shallow waters from San Diego Bay southward to the Gulf of California.
American Museum of Natural History

squeezed out and the food is compressed into a compact stringy mass. An intestine leads to the anal vent which opens downward at the side of the fin.

The blood of the lancelet is colorless, containing only a few white corpuscles. Its heart is a mere expansion of the *vena cava* or principal vein from which smaller vessels carry the blood to the mouth and various organs. A thin spinal cord follows a canal along the notochord which is the forerunner of the backbone in higher vertebrates. Nerves branch out from it to all parts of the body.

Fertilization of the eggs takes place in the water. The young lancelets are quite transparent.

Three lancelets are found in American waters. The one Pacific species occurs from San Diego southward. The Atlantic species as described by Dr. Carl L. Hubbs are the Virginia lancelet, found from Chesapeake Bay to Florida; and the Florida lancelet, common along the shores of that State.

The lancelet retains the notochord in its maturity. Farther down in the evolutionary scale are the sea squirts which, during the larval stage, possess a notochord and a tubular nerve chord—specialized toward the front to form a brain and an eye. As larvae, the sea squirts move freely in their watery environment, but when

LANCELET

mature they fix themselves to the sea floor and the tail, brain, and bilaterally symmetrical form degenerate. Still farther downward in the scale are the wormlike marine animals, the hemichordata, lowest of the chordates. When these possess notochords they are short and confined to the front part of the body.

REPTILES

Copperhead Snake

Reptiles

At the headwaters of the celebrated Suwannee River, the Okefenokee Swamp of southeastern Georgia and northern Florida is covered with a film of shallow water, moss-choked during the summer months. Primeval and weird is the luxuriant subtropical vegetation which rises from the cypress bays, spreading over the smaller shallower lakes. Waterlilies and floating water-hyacinths creep over the damp surface and fuse with the slender, naked trunks of the cabbage palmettos which spread over the savannas in wild profusion, and at the water's edge tree trunks gape open at the roots. Here and there an island protrudes from the bogs, thickly wooded with pond cypresses whose branches droop long festoons of Spanish moss. Saw palmettos and evergreen live oaks line the higher ridges, forming an impenetrable wall into the wild "hammock" country beyond.

The entire region, recently set aside as a wildlife refuge, is returning to almost virgin state. Bears, cougars, raccoons, otters, rare birds, and tropical fishes swarm through the sedge grass, the orchid-bearing vegetation, the tall pitch pines, and the sluggish streams. But found in far more abundance than anywhere in the United States are the reptiles, which inhabit the Okefenokee, the Everglades of southern Florida, and the mangrove thickets of its coasts. Indeed, the crocodile is found nowhere else in our country but in the mangrove-fringed lakes and marshes of the coastal tip of southern Florida. Sink holes and swamps shelter alligators; snapping turtles and terrapins slip in and out of pools. Found in the shallow depressions of the flatwood country are multicolored terrapins, tortoises, legless lizards, and large snakes.

But this reptilian paradise holds no terrors for the natives who know that, contrary to popular misconception, these creatures are neither slimy nor clammy, and frequently are more meek than malicious. Both the alligator and the crocodile will almost invariably flee from man rather than face him in an encounter; most of the species of lizards are harmless and furtive; of the two hundred or more varieties of American snakes, only four types are deadly; and the tortoises, terrapins, and turtles are innocuous.

More truthful than dramatic are these facts about this maligned but extremely useful group of creatures. Playing an important part in maintaining the delicate balance of nature, their hides and even meat have been utilized by man. A few of the outstanding by-products are the alligator skins used in the manufacture of shoes, purses, and other leather accessories; tortoise shells converted into eyeglass frames, combs, and cigarette cases; and the green turtle, terrapin, and rattlesnake are utilized respectively for soups, stews, and cocktail relish.

Somewhat ludicrous and always ill-founded are some of the superstitions many people still harbor about reptiles. A common tale concerns the snakes that swallow their young; another myth credits them with rolling up in a hoop and chasing people; a milk snake supposedly milks cows; and most ridiculous of all is the belief that a frightened snake will put its tail in its mouth and swallow itself.

Reptiles are the descendants of a class of backboned animals which probably originated more than one hundred and fifty million years ago in Carboniferous times. They appear to have evolved from certain amphibians and in turn to have served as evolutionary springboards for such higher and more developed classes as the birds and mammals.

Reptiles are vertebrate animals breathing by means of lungs and possessing four-chambered hearts and a variable body temperature that generally corresponds to the temperature of the surrounding air or water. Hence the designation "coldblooded." Protected by a covering of scales and plates, they are also equipped with bony shells and some with poison and musk-dispensing glands. The rattle of the rattlesnake and the hisses emitted by many other species of snakes may also be considered a form of protection in that they probably serve to warn the enemy to retreat or suffer the consequences. It is possible, however, that the rattling, hissing, and emitting of nauseating odors are all mere manifestations of fear disguised as bravado.

With the exception of the tortoise, whose ribs are fused into a bony shell which covers most of its body and whose jaws are armed with horny sheaths, all reptiles have ribs and teeth, and most of them have long tails. The members of this class reproduce by means of internal fertilization and usually lay shell-covered eggs, although in a few species the young are brought forth alive.

It is sincerely hoped that the reader will reach the logical conclusion that the majority of reptiles are peaceful, inoffensive, and useful. He may likewise agree upon learning their true nature and habits, that they are as deserving of man's protection and conservation as are the birds, trees, flowers, and other forms of wildlife.

Crocodilians

In the Southeast, where temperate America succumbs to the domination of the Torrid Zone, dwell the only two representatives of the order of crocodilians in the United States. Of the world's twenty-five species of crocodilians, the United States contains but one of the two species of alligators, one of the fourteen species of tropicopolitan crocodiles, and is of course devoid of any of the seven South American caymans and the two gavials of India and Malaysia.

Although they divide their time between land and water, crocodilians are much more at home where they can swim than where they must walk or crawl. When they attack in the water, they often dive below their intended victim and come up, jaws open, directly under it. A valve separates the throat from the mouth, so that crocodilians can keep their jaws open under water. Much of their time is spent in idly floating about, only eyes and nostrils above the surface of the water.

These creatures have a four-chambered heart and their circulatory system is the most highly developed of all reptiles. Their backs are protected by rows of bony shields and their under surface, tail, and legs are covered with coarse, leathery scales. Superficially, all of them are quite similar, distinguished largely by the snouts which range from long and thin to short and blunt.

The once prolific American alligator has been gradually decimated as the ever-increasing number of alligator handbags, shoes, and pieces of luggage indicate. But it is still more numerous than the crocodile, which is confined to extreme southern Florida and is a more typical denizen of the larger West Indies, Central and South America. The American crocodilians, some of which have grown to twenty feet, are the largest reptiles in the United States.

ALLIGATOR

CRAWLING through the jungle-lined swamps of the subtropical southeastern States, the American alligator becomes fully alert when prodded on by hunger. Its lazy sluggishness is transformed into sharp attack if its prey is at hand. The alligator swiftly seizes the animal in its jaws, which are so powerful that they cannot be pried apart after closing, and slides back into the water.

ALLIGATOR

AMERICAN ALLIGATORS (*Alligator mississippiensis*). Length: 12 feet. Range: Southern United States. Becoming rare.
Ralph De Sola (PZG)

If small, the animal is swallowed whole without further effort. A larger beast, such as a pig, is held between the alligator's teeth and the sinewy reptile lashes about furiously in the water to tear it apart or dismembers it by twirling around on the long axis of its body and tail. Another method of dealing with a large animal—if the 'gator is not particularly hungry at the moment—is to carry it down to the underwater den and leave it there until the flesh decomposes and becomes quite soft. Muskrats and pigs, snakes and insects, are samples of this reptile's diet.

Hunger appeased, thirst slaked, the blackish colored alligator stretches out lazily on a warm rock or mud bank while the hot sun beats down upon it. Sometimes the 'gator lolls about in the water, with only eyes and tip of nose protruding above the surface. If alarmed, it sinks at once to the bottom. And, if need be, the scaly reptile swims with astonishing rapidity, propelling itself through the water by means of its powerfully muscled tail and body.

In less informed circles, the mention of alligators conjures up visions of a dreadful beast which waits impatiently for human beings whom it can devour. Despite its formidable reputation, the alligator will usually shy away from man. However, if cornered, the reptile is a dangerous antagonist and the wise intruder will keep his distance. The alligator uses that mighty tail to wreak havoc on anyone who dares approach. The whole body bends like a bow, since the thick neck does not turn, and is then snapped back with crashing impact. A two-hundred-pound man, who believed a nine-foot alligator to be dead, was given a shocking surprise. With one blow of its tail the alligator broke his leg, threw him several feet, and knocked him unconscious.

In the spring these usually stodgy creatures wax romantic in keeping with the more colorful wildlife of the region. Males leave a musky trail in the water, the fluid being emitted from chin glands during the mating season. Mating is a serious business with the male 'gators, and is preceded by fierce fights for females. The water is churned to a wild froth as the loudly bellowing contestants fight it out with tooth and tail. Flecks of red on the teeming surface testify to the gory conflict. The full fury of the struggle is manifested later when exhausted 'gators float about minus a toe, limb, or section of tail.

The female lays almost three dozen eggs in her damp, warm nest on the shore of the swamp. She guards them solicitously and two months later her patient vigil is rewarded by a squeaking inside the shelter. This is a signal of the young that they are almost ready to hatch, and the mother opens the nest to permit their debut into the world.

At birth the youngsters are only eight inches long, but they grow rapidly, attaining maturity at about the ninth year. Today the average size of adult alligators is approximately eight feet, though in past years, when their development was not hindered by man, specimens of twenty feet have been observed.

During the winter these reptiles, relatively inactive in summer heat, are completely torpid. Their dens are constructed in a mud bank and equipped with an underwater entrance. When winter sends its first mild advance warning, the alligators enter their dens to hibernate until spring. Sometimes they are away from home when winter overtakes them, for they may travel long distances in search of water. If they are not able to return to their dens in time, they will lie completely dormant wherever they happen to be until spring.

Before the Revolutionary War, Sir William Bartram paddled a canoe down the St. Johns River in Florida. He wrote that "the alligators were in such incredible numbers, and so close together from shore to shore, that it would have been easy to have walked across on their heads, had the animals been harmless." But during the nineteenth century it was discovered that alligator hide was excellent material for shoes, and the slaughter was on.

Hunters unearthed the reptiles by locating their dens and prodding them with long-hooked poles. When the annoyed creatures seized the poles, the hooks caught in their mouths and they were hauled up like fishes and shot. Nevertheless, as late as 1890, the

ALLIGATOR GUARDING NEST.
E. A. McIlhenny

supply was still great enough to keep the price down to ten cents apiece. Man, however, was the ultimate and undisputed conqueror, for millions of alligators were hunted and killed. Now these ancient reptiles, found only in America and China, are quite rare. They are theoretically protected by legislation although, without wardens for enforcement, the laws do little to deter alligator hunting.

Aside from their commercial value as raw material for bags and shoes, the alligators have aided man by destroying harmful insects and muskrats which undermine Mississippi levees. Dr. Murphy, noting the wanton extermination which goes on, and mentioning the example of one Florida tourist camp which sold several hundred baby 'gators in a year, wrote: "Aside from its zoological interest, the alligator eats enemies of game fish and, if protected, it could support a well-planned hide industry."

Alligator country is the district from the Carolinas through the Gulf region and including peninsular Florida. One of the features of the region is the "alligator farm." A number of these offer as a main attraction alligators which, they advertise, were born with half a tail, or with three legs instead of four. However, these freakish physiques are chiefly the results of battles among themselves.

The farms also ad-

ALLIGATOR AND CROCODILE COMPARED.
From Ditmars' "Reptiles of the World."

vertise wrestling bouts between a man and an alligator, which have all the earmarks of an extravagant spectacle, and seem second only to the long-awaited boxing match between a man and a gorilla. But the peaceable reptile doesn't want to fight, and is often far too slow-moving. Usually after much pushing and mauling, the daring wrestler can leave the ring an indisputed champion over the alligator.

"Alligator farms" do not raise alligators but merely exhibit captive specimens to tourists.

It is not strange that the alligator is considered ferocious, for it has that appearance. Its heavy head and lipless mouth, containing eighty teeth visible even when the jaws are closed, do not induce one to caress the creature. The muscled jaws snap shut as though pulled by steel springs, and though a man cannot open them against the alligator's wishes, he can easily hold them closed with one hand. It has a tough brown hide with diamond-shaped patterns and rows of bony scales which once were erroneously believed to be bulletproof. It also has a third transparent eyelid covering each eye, enabling it to keep its eyes open when under water.

The word alligator is derived from *el lagarto* (Sp., the lizard), for early Spanish explorers believed that these creatures were huge lizards.

CROCODILE

WHEN a hungry crocodile stuffs its mouth with the flesh of an animal it has just killed, it may begin to cry. That seems a most hypocritical thing to do, and consequently "crocodile tears" has become a descriptive term for hypocrisy. But the "tears" are shed neither in pretense of sorrow nor in actual contriteness for wrongdoing. The crocodile weeps only because the pressure of food against the top of its mouth loosens a flow of "tears" from its lachrymal glands.

The American crocodile is the only crocodile found in the United States, and is similar in habits to the alligator. However, it is distinguished by a less bulky physique and a longer, thinner head.

AMERICAN CROCODILE *(Crocodylus acutus)*. Length: 14 feet. Range: Extreme southeastern Florida, the Florida Keys, the Greater Antilles (except Puerto Rico), and tropical America. Almost extinct in the United States.
New York Zoological Society

The fourteen-foot crocodile is olive-colored while the shorter alligator is blackish.

According to Dr. Raymond L. Ditmars, the crocodile is much more vicious than the alligator. A number of captive crocodiles were "voracious in their feeding and anxious enough to take food from their keeper's hand; in fact, so greedy were the brutes that they were very dangerous. They would spring half their length out of the water by suddenly elevating the heavy tail, and as that member fell like the weighted end of a seesaw the body shot upward."

On one occasion a crocodile, looking peaceable enough and seeming to be at a safe distance, swung its heavy tail and sent the eminent naturalist flying. Only by rolling over and over, did he escape the reptile which was pursuing him with some speed, mouth ominously held open.

The crocodile is a tropical creature, more so than the alligator, and is found in this country only along the lower eastern and extreme southern strip of Florida. Its range extends as far south as Ecuador, and it is also an inhabitant of most of the larger islands of the West Indies. In Florida it may sometimes be observed in the salt or brackish water of marshes, creeks, estuaries, and bays. Its presence in this country was first brought to the attention of the scientific world by Dr. Hornaday who located it in Arch Creek at the head of Biscayne Bay, just a few miles north of where the city of Miami now stands. Its northern range in 1875 was Lake Worth and the Palm Beach area, but a survey of its range made in 1933 showed that it was seldom seen north of the Keys, was rare even in the Cape Sable region. Unprotected, the usually inoffensive American crocodile is faced with extinction. The hardier alligator can live much farther north and is able to withstand the slight frosts which would render the crocodile helpless.

If unmolested, the American crocodile in the wild state never makes threatening advances toward a man. It is quite definitely not a man-eater.

Lizards

Lizards are the most abundant of the living reptiles. They are coated with scaly folds of skin, have four legs and a tapering tail. Some, however, are legless and resemble snakes, but even these can be distinguished by their ear openings and movable eyelids.

They travel in many different ways. The primitive crawling type of walk is most common. The "glass snake," a legless lizard, glides along on its belly. Geckos have adhesive toe pads permitting them to run on smooth vertical surfaces and even on ceilings.

An interesting characteristic of lizards is the ease with which many of them can leave their tails behind. This gift is of some protective value, for frequently a pursuing animal is distracted by the detached tail, which continues to wriggle while the rest of the lizard escapes. New tails are soon grown, but they never regain either the full scalation or perfect form of the original.

Protective coloration is sometimes used as a defense. The chameleon or anole, however, changes its color according to its emotional state. Thus, unstable persons are frequently said to be "as changeable as chameleons."

Geckos are egg-laying, soft-skinned, small lizards. Included are the xantusids, inhabiting the western deserts of North America, and a few introduced forms.

Skinks are medium-sized lizards covered with overlapping scales, beneath each of which is a bony plate embedded in the skin.

Wormlike lizards are usually covered with mere vestiges of scales, lack visible eyes and ears, have pinkish bodies and bluntly rounded tails, which explains their name. The group is divided into three families: amphisbaenids; anniellids, found only in California; and anguidids.

Poisonous lizards include the Gila monster of our Southwest and the Mexican beaded lizard. Their bite is venomous and should be treated in the same way as a snake bite.

GECKO

GECKOS are most readily distinguished from other lizards by their flattened toes, which in many species have a spongy, adhesive surface, and by their skin, which appears to be soft and pliable like that of a toad. This effect is produced by the small size of the gecko's scales. The adhesive toe pads enable this lizard to run with great agility on ceilings and smooth vertical surfaces. The gecko's tail is short and stubby and is easily separated from the body. Most geckos are nocturnal in habits. Their diet consists of insects. The name gecko is supposed to approximate the sound of the harsh cry emitted by some species. Geckos lay two or three eggs at a time.

This group of lizards is widely distributed. There are three families and nearly fifty genera, with habitats including dense jungle and barren desert. Some of the tropical varieties are a foot in length.

There are only five species of geckos in the United States. They are all small in size and may be distinguished from other American lizards by their flat, pointed heads and swollen temples. They vary in length from three to five inches. All inhabit the southern portion of our country.

WARTY GECKO

WARTY geckos, also called tubercular or consumptive geckos, are sometimes seen racing across the walls and ceilings of the Indians' huts in Lower California and extreme southern California. Including their diminutive tail they are nearly five inches long. The ground color may be pale gray, yellowish white, or pale brown, spotted with dark brown or slate gray. Several rows of enlarged warty scales running down the back are the source of this lizard's name. The natives tend to fear these geckos, believing that contact with them will cause the hand to shed its skin.

Warty geckos are believed to flourish in rocky country; otherwise little is known of their habits.

BANDED GECKO

THE three-inch banded gecko hides by day in the rocky crevices of the Southwest. Toward dusk these gay-colored creatures emerge to pursue their insect food up and down the crags and boulders of their arid home. For this they have large feline eyes. Like other geckos they are slow and deliberate in their hunting methods. Quietly stalking their prey until almost on top of it, they then seize it with a rush and a dart of the tongue. These creatures are not exactly slow-moving when alarmed, but they are no match for such speed demons as the swifts and racerunners who depend upon their agility for protection.

The body of the banded gecko is encircled by broad brown bands and narrower, wavy white ones. The head is brown, or whitish with brown spots instead of bands. The species, in two color phases, inhabits the same localities. Perhaps because of its bright colors, some natives of the Southwest believe this harmless creature to be highly poisonous. It is, however, quite harmless, its bite not being at all toxic.

When captured the banded gecko emits a low squeal. In captivity the species is rather sluggish although it lives rather well if provided with the proper food.

BANDED GECKO *(Coleonyx variegatus)*. Length: 3 inches. Range: Texas, New Mexico, Arizona, Nevada, southwestern Utah, California, and northern Lower California.
New York Zoological Society

BLUNT-HEADED GECKO

THIS species, native to Texas, resembles the banded gecko, except that its snout is shorter and blunter. Little is known of its habits.

MEDITERRANEAN GECKO

THIS gecko is not indigenous to the United States. Native to the Mediterranean and Red Sea regions, it appears to have stowed away on cargo ships bound for the New World and to have remained aboard until the ships landed at a spot where it liked the climate. This turned out to be Key West, and its American range is restricted to the Florida Keys.

The color of these small creatures is brown or gray with darker spots or mottles. The scales are exceedingly fine, except for fourteen to sixteen lines of warty scales on the back and sides.

REEF GECKO

SMALLEST of all our reptiles is the reef gecko, only two and five-eighths inches long. It is brownish yellow with dark spots which sometimes merge into bands. The ridged scales are coarser than those of other American geckos.

Like the Mediterranean gecko, this species was brought to America in the holds of ships. It now inhabits the southern tip of the Florida mainland as well as the adjacent Keys.

CHAMELEON

MEMBERS of the family *Iguanidae*, the American chameleons are not related to the true chameleons of the African continent, but have been popularly classified as such because of similar color-changing characteristics. Two species occur in the United States—the American chameleon, also called alligator lizard, fence lizard, and green lizard; and Stejneger's chameleon. The former is found in the coastal regions of the southeastern United States and in the Neuse River area of North Carolina, south to Florida, and west to the Rio Grande of Texas.

The American chameleon or anole is lively and pugnacious. Taking on a glowing tint, emerald green, it plunges at a rival male, snapping its sharp teeth. The two opponents remain locked in battle until the weaker loses its mouselike five-inch tail. The victor marches off with the trophy dangling from its jaws while the vanquished retires quickly.

The anole can change its color with amazing rapidity. From its dull-brown everyday hue it sometimes goes through the stages of golden yellow, slaty gray, green, and emerald green within approximately three minutes. Color changes, however, are affected through temperature, light, and emotional state—anger, fear, and sleep—and not through the influence of the object upon which the chameleon happens to stand or rest. The commonest hues are brown and green, regardless of the background. In sleep it is usually pale green, the abdomen white; at the approach of the male rival the tint becomes bright green; when frightened the reptile turns green; and during emotional calm it is dark rich brown, turning slaty or yellowish in the afternoon.

In shape the chameleon somewhat resembles a diminutive dragon. The seven-and-one-quarter-inch body is covered with tiny scales. On top of the relatively large head is a ridged elevation or crest, tapering toward the snout. The loose body skin forms a fold or dewlap pouch at the throat, which remains useless in the female. The male, however, is capable of dilating this blood-red pouch during courtship and physical combat. The long limbs are sturdy and highly developed for jumping and climbing, and the four flattened toes possess adhesive qualities, which facilitate its excursions upon smooth and vertical surfaces.

The chameleon spends the night sleeping in the trees. During the day it hunts for flies, gnats, butterflies, beetles, spiders, wasps, and scorpions. It approaches its victim cautiously and slowly, keeping its body close to the bough. Finally it spreads its jaws and engulfs its prey.

CHAMELEON

The anole lays its eggs in the hollows of trees; the young when hatched remain in seclusion among the leaves until they are fully grown.

The American chameleon is a familiar and often entertaining sight at country fairs and circuses. Displayed in boxes and on tables

"CHAMELEON" or ANOLE *(Anolis carolinensis)*. Length: 7 inches. Range: Coastal region of the southeastern and Gulf States from Tennessee and North Carolina to Texas.
New York Zoological Society

as part of the side-show attractions, these color-changing lizards, chained or ribboned about the neck, are sold to the curious public as souvenirs and charms.

Stejneger's chameleon, which is somewhat smaller than the American chameleon (measuring six and one-half inches including the four-inch tail), is confined to southern Florida and the Keys. It is bright green during its lifetime, and the throat is somewhat tinged with a rim of darker green. The throat fan is carmine at the base and somewhat darker at the edges. The scales look like ashy-gray dots. Known from two specimens, a male found in 1931, and a female found forty years before, Stejneger's chameleon is a rare lizard and seen infrequently. Dr. Thomas Barbour, who described it, suspects that it will probably be found by collectors throughout the mangroves of extreme southwestern Florida and the Keys. It is named in honor of his colleague, Dr. Leonhard Stejneger, a well-known and distinguished American herpetologist.

IGUANA

ALTHOUGH it is equipped with suitable weapons for protection and attack, the thick-set, sinister-appearing black iguana prefers to escape from man whenever possible. Failing that, it turns quickly, stands ready and menacing, jaws wide open, lashing its spiked tail from side to side.

The black iguana is just that—black above and below. Measuring four feet, the greater part of its length is devoted to the tail, which is thirty-two inches long, ringed with jagged spines. This

DESERT IGUANAS (*Dipsosaurus d. dorsalis*). Length: 11 inches. Range: Deserts of the southwestern United States.
From Ditmars' "Reptiles of North America"

clublike weapon is capable of inflicting serious injuries on all assailants.

In spite of its belligerent characteristics, the black iguana spends its leisure basking in the sunshine. Usually this sun worshiper is found stretched upon a flat stone or fallen tree, lying motionless and apparently happy. So important are the ultraviolet rays to its well being, that when captured it must be given a large cage in which to roam and expose itself to the sun.

Its escape from danger is somewhat melodramatic, not at all in keeping with its pugnacious character. Disturbed while sun bathing, it hurtles to the ground, falling heavily and crashing through the vegetation. A great clatter usually accompanies this somewhat ignominious retreat from potential enemies.

Omnivorous in its diet, the black iguana in captivity is particularly fond of vegetables (lettuce and celery) and fruits (especially bananas). In the wild state it supplements this dainty menu with young birds and rodents which it catches easily and shakes well before swallowing.

In the United States the black iguana is confined to the most southerly part of Arizona. In Mexico, where this reptile is abundant, it is eaten as food, rated on a par with chicken.

A related but much smaller species is the desert iguana. Known also as the pygmy iguana, it measures eleven and one-half inches in length, including a seven and one-half inch tail. It is pale brown in color, marked with wavy dark-brown and black lines. The tail is yellowish spotted on top with dark circles.

Stout and well rounded in body, the desert iguana may be distinguished by a row of large keeled scales, resembling armor, covering the center of the back. The long and tapering tail is extremely brittle, and when a foe grasps this part of its body, the iguana turns quickly, snaps off a portion of the appendage, and thus manages to escape.

The desert iguana roams the arid regions of the southwestern United States and may be found in Colorado and the Mojave Desert east to the Colorado River. It feeds on birds, small flowers, tender leaves, and insects.

CHUCKWALLA *(Sauromalus obesus)*. Length: 1 foot. Range: Deserts of the southwestern United States.
New York Zoological Society

CHUCKWALLA

THE chuckwalla waddles lazily over the rocky precipices of its home, fat-bodied and complacent. Although it measures only a foot in length, it is (with the exception of the Gila monster) the largest lizard found in the southwestern desert region of the United States.

Little is known about the habits of this creature. In Nevada, Utah, and Arizona it inhabits crevices of mountains or rocky cliffs. While basking in the sun it sits on scorching hot rocks without any apparent discomfort, sluggish and uninterested in the events occurring outside of its somnolent, vegetative existence.

The coloration of the chuckwalla ranges from dull brown to olive and black above, while the abdomen is rusty red spotted with black. The top of the body and the broad head are covered with granular scalation; the tail, thick and sturdy, is five inches long.

In defending itself the chuckwalla uses the tail to advantage, swinging it from side to side and striking quickly when annoyed.

Laurence M. Klauber, who has had occasion to observe the species, writes: "The chuckwalla, when alarmed, seeks refuge in a crevice in which he inflates himself and defies removal. The Indians are said to deflate these lizards by puncturing them with sharp sticks. Others who have tried this say it will not work. A more sporting method is to take a soft iron wire and thread it through the crevice in back of the chuck; then by sawing and pulling on the two ends he can usually be brought out. Another scheme, if his head can be reached with a stick, is to tap him repeatedly on the nose, whereupon he will accommodatingly back out. Don't make the mistake of seizing his tail or a leg until he is fairly well out or he will quickly reverse his motion.

"In captivity chuckwallas have a varied diet; amongst other things they will eat radish tops, lettuce, bananas, watermelon, cantaloupe, and grass.

"The greatest concentration of chuckwallas I have seen was in the Black Mountains, between Oatman and Goldroad, Mohave County, Arizona. These were fine, large specimens, well suffused posteriorly with red.

"While chuckwallas are usually rather tame, in twisting about endeavoring to escape they will occasionally slash with their tails. When annoyed they open their mouths and will sometimes try to bite."

COLLARED LIZARD

THE collared lizard, measuring only a foot in length, is a fierce savage little creature. It turns upon a foe, its menacing jaws open, long tail poised to strike. But only when cornered does it become bold and pugnacious; at other times it runs and hides from danger.

Its favorite form of recreation is lying in a bed of soft dry sand, basking in the sunshine. In fact, the sun seems to stimulate its energy, for it is in the daytime, and especially during the hottest part of the afternoons, that this lizard is most active. Deprived of sunlight, it becomes sluggish and inert.

Perhaps the greediest of all lizards, this reptile has been known to swallow spiny horned lizards larger than its own head. Frequently

COLLARED LIZARD *(Crotaphytus c. collaris)*. Length: 1 foot. Range: Central and southwestern United States: Missouri, Kansas, Arkansas, western Texas, and eastern New Mexico.
American Museum of Natural History

its voracity also causes its destruction; with a brother lizard stuck in its throat, the collared lizard dies an ignoble death, unable either to swallow or dislodge the horny morsel. In tenderer moments it eats blossoms, leaves, and insects; also swifts and snakes.

The collared lizard, yellowish, pale gray, or bright green in color, blends remarkably well with the desert background of the regions it inhabits in Arkansas, Missouri, Texas, and eastern New Mexico. In northern Arizona it is slate-black when cold, a light green when hot. The back and sides are spotted with white or yellow patches. Its main distinguishing feature is the double collar behind the head of two black bands separated by a white or yellowish space. In the gray-colored female this collar is not so pronounced. The body of the collared lizard is short and stout, the head large, and the hind legs exceptionally long. When running and jumping it uses the hind legs only and moves in an upright position in a manner somewhat like the kangaroo.

Most frequently it is found in mountainous regions, two thousand to eight thousand feet above sea level.

There are four subspecies of the collared lizard, all practically alike in appearance, each one foot long. They are Bailey's collared lizard, reticulated lizard, leopard lizard, and blunt-nosed leopard lizard.

Bailey's collared lizard inhabits southwestern Texas, New Mexico, Arizona, Utah, Nevada, Idaho, and southwest California. Its head is narrower and the snout longer than that of the collared lizard.

The reticulated lizard inhabiting southwestern Texas is yellowish or grayish in color; its head, body, limbs, and tail are streaked with pale gray or yellow lines.

The yellowish-brown leopard lizard is a slender and elongated species. Its body is covered with black or brown blotches surrounding numerous red dots. The throat is barred with black lines. It occurs in the Great Basin from northern Idaho to New Mexico, especially in eastern California, Nevada, and Arizona.

Identical with the leopard lizard, distinguished only by its snout which is shorter, is the blunt-nosed leopard lizard which inhabits the San Joaquin Valley of California and parts of Washington.

SWIFT

APPROPRIATELY named is the swift, speediest and one of the most versatile of the reptiles. It is as elusive a quarry as the chicken hawk, as difficult to corner as the fastest fish. Even when by some freak of circumstance it has been caught, it will twist and squirm, breaking off a large portion of its tail. It does not fear or even regret the loss of this valuable appendage, for in time it is again adorned with a brand new tail, differing but slightly from the original.

AMERICAN WILD LIFE

The swift races about its arid homeland with dazzling bursts of speed, aided by slender-toed legs especially attenuated in the back. It is an extremely wary creature, watching with vigilant eye the progress of anything encroaching upon its domain, and the slightest motion or disturbance will send it flashing off in a blur of color. When pursued it frequently climbs a tall bayonet-spined yucca plant and remains there motionless but alert until danger has passed.

Two separate groups comprise the American swifts, the small-scaled swifts and the spiny swifts. Similar in shape and generally comforming in habits, they are easily distinguishable by the different shapes of scales which cover the bodies of both types of lizards.

DISTRIBUTED throughout the United States, but especially populous in the South and Southwest, the spiny swifts are a ferocious ruffled-appearing lot, their bodies encased in a coat of bristling spines which, except for their smooth bellies, cover the

PINE LIZARD AND SPINY SWIFTS *(Sceloporus u. undulatus and S. undulatus floridanus)*. Length: 5 inches and 9 inches. Ranges: Southeastern New York to Florida; extreme western Florida to Texas.
New York Zoological Society

SWIFT

SAND LIZARD *(Uma notata).* Length: 8 inches. Range: Colorado and Mojave Deserts in the southwestern United States.
From Ditmars' "Reptiles of North America"

lizards from head to foot like armor. The spines are large, keeled, and flecked with green or blue blotches, although in the more sedate members the prevalent hue is gray. The patches of rich blue about the throat and abdomen which differentiate the males from the females seem to depend for size and vividness on the relative activity of the particular lizard, with additional influence being brought to bear by climatic conditions. Generally, however, the predominant protective coloration is either gray, brown, or olive. The neck is adorned with a thick black collar, and the back is crossed with rows of dull wavy bands.

The diet of the swift consists of insects, worms, caterpillars, and grasshoppers—depending upon the type of food prevalent in the particular locality which each species inhabits.

Thirteen species of the spiny swift, varying in size from five to ten inches, are found within the borders of the United States. They are the desert swift of southeastern California, Arizona, Nevada, and Utah; Orcutt's swift of southern California; Yarrow's swift of Arizona; the Pacific swift inhabiting the West from central California to Washington; Couch's swift found in southern Texas; the yellow-banded swift roaming the Dakotas, south of Texas and west to California; the collared swift of Texas and Arizona; the sagebrush swift scattered throughout Oklahoma, Utah, Nevada, and California; the spiny swift inhabiting western Florida and extending west to New Mexico; the eastern swift found on the Atlantic coast from southeastern New York to Florida.

THE small-scaled swifts are strong, sharp-clawed reptiles, and although lacking the adhesive foot pads of the gecko, are still able to imitate to some degree that creature's ability to run along non-horizontal surfaces. Slenderer in body than the spiny swifts, less bristling in appearance and sporting longer tails, the coloration of the small-scaled swifts is generally brown or dull gray, frequently green—a color scheme which serves to camouflage them when viewed against the background of their native terrain. Their bodies are stout, somewhat depressed, and surmounted with a small pear-shaped head. Their total length varies from five to twenty inches. The backs and sides are overlain with minute scales, serving as the basis for their name.

Four species of small-scaled swifts inhabit the United States. Stanbury's swift is found in Utah, Nevada, and southern California; the ornate swift ranges in the southwestern United States from western Texas to California; the olive swift inhabits New Mexico and Utah; and the longtailed swift wanders through southeastern California, southwestern Arizona, and southern Nevada.

SPOTTED LIZARD

THE spotted lizards, a compact family group, have little difficulty in escaping their enemies—coyotes, hawks, and larger lizards. At the least sign of danger they dart across the sand, run as swiftly as a horse for short distances, and stop suddenly in their tracks. The human eye can barely perceive the fleet movements of these lizards for their bodies blend remarkably with the desert background.

When traveling at high speed, spotted lizards swing their long tails over their bodies. At other times they may scamper for short distances using only their hind legs.

All spotted lizards are approximately the same size, measuring four and one-half inches in length including the two-inch tail. They are extremely active creatures, able to climb rocks and other vertical surfaces with great ease. Mostly, however, they prefer to remain on flat land. Too noisy to apprehend flies, they gather about dry rocks and feed largely on beetles and grubs.

THE zebra-tailed lizard measures about five and one-half to six inches from snout to tip of tail. Its head is small in relation to the body and somewhat flattened. The limbs are extremely long and the two-inch tail is depressed like a spear head.

The coloring of this lizard is grayish, speckled with white. The abdomen is white, tapering into bluish patches on the sides. The male is distinguished by the bold markings on the tail, which is white striped with black bars.

The zebra-tailed lizard feeds on small blossoms, tender leaves, and insects, for which it hunts from morning till night. After sundown it buries itself in the sand and, thus hidden from the eyes of the enemy, spends the night. It inhabits the desert regions from southern California to Texas, and north to Utah and Kansas.

L. M. Klauber speaks of this lizard as follows: "This is the most frequently seen lizard in the sandy or gravelly areas of our southwestern deserts; it does not entirely shun rocky places, but is most common on flats where a few small boulders may be scattered round about. On these it likes to perch for observation, raised up on stiffened legs when it is hot, and often bobbing its head up and down as if to clear its vision. Occasionally the males display their throat fans.

"*Callisaurus* is an extremely speedy lizard, probably the fastest on the desert. It is practically impossible to follow it with the eye when it is alarmed and traveling across the line of sight. Usually it will stop just before taking refuge in a bush; sometimes, however, it will place a bush between itself and the pursuer before pausing to reconnoiter. When it stops it usually has the tail curled over the back and waving slowly from side to side; this renders the black bars on the underside particularly conspicuous. Then it is away again like a flash, the neutral gray streak of the disappearing lizard being so inconspicuous as to leave the eye anchored on the spot lately occupied by the swaying, brightly-marked tail. Whether the lizard actually runs at its highest speed with the tail curled over the back, and whether it uses only its hind legs, I am not sure, for this is very difficult to see. The statement, so often made, that it runs with the tail curled, may be the result of observations on lizards at rest or coming to a pause."

HORNED LIZARD

THE horned "toad" is not a toad but a lizard. Resembling a grotesque prehistoric monster in miniature, the horned lizard is an odd-looking reptile, its body covered with spines, the head equipped with conical horns. But in spite of its appearance it is a meek creature, never attacking an enemy and seldom biting a captor. When frightened it scampers out of sight with amazing speed.

One of its most peculiar traits is squirting thin jets of blood when frightened or annoyed. It ejects this fine blood stream through the corner of its eyes which become enlarged and seem to protrude from their sockets. The blood-squirting operation finished, the horned "toad" closes its eyes, flattens its body to pancake shape, or blows it up enormously (this trait varies with the individual species), plays 'possum, uninterested in anything taking place outside of its mysterious existence.

L. M. Klauber, who is well acquainted with the species, writes: "I have never been able to determine in advance when one of these horned toads will eject blood from its eyes, nor to correlate the result with sex, season, temperature, or any other factor. Sometimes they will; more often they won't, but I can't tell which it is to be. I think that horned toads are naturally so gentle and tame that, unless they will spit when first captured, they will seldom do it later. To get them to go into action we usually scratch the sides of their heads or the lateral edges of the body (not necessarily with roughness). Often this will cause the eyes to swell, but without the final ejecting of blood, which result is secured much less frequently.

"There is some evidence that a dog can precipitate a stream of blood when other means fail; at least this has worked on two recent

PACIFIC HORNED LIZARD *(Phrynosoma b. blainvillii)*. Length: 6 inches. Range: Southern California and northern Lower California. Non-poisonous.
George L. Dowden

occasions. Many years ago, when horned toads were much more common hereabouts than now, we owned a white bull terrier. Whenever he came home with his forehead spattered with blood we knew he had been nosing a horned toad. And although he would tackle anything on four legs (he had two bob-cats to his credit), if my memory serves me correctly, he let the horned toads go their ways. Maybe they were beneath his notice; maybe there is here indicated a partial protection against the coyote. At least, a sudden fine stream of blood in the eyes is rather disconcerting.

"Frank F. Gander tells me that his house cat slightly injured a horned toad of this species. The horned toad retaliated with a spray of blood in the cat's face. The cat showed signs of considerable discomfort; it rolled over and brushed its head violently with its paws and frothed at the mouth. This lasted but a short time; however, the cat was observed to avoid horned toads thereafter.

"I remember that some 50 years ago we children were amazed at the repeated rediscovery by scientists that the blood-spitting horned toad was no myth. This was old stuff to us, for the horned toad was our best-known reptile; it made the best pet, and there was a fairly good sale for them at 10 cents each. Maybe I only remember the times when the market wasn't glutted. At any rate in those days no eastern tourist was supposed to return without one of these creatures stuffed and fastened on a thin, diagonal section of an orange tree trunk. In the highly varnished results (they varnished both the wood and the animal) our early commercial taxidermists reached a new low in nature groups."

The body of the horned lizard is flattened and, to be sure, resembles superficially the compact warty body of the toad. The tail is short; the entire body is covered with spines and varies in length from three to six inches.

The horned "toad" differs from most lizards by producing six to twelve living young. At birth the smooth-skinned brood is covered with a transparent protective envelope. Immediately after breaking through this "cellophane wrapper," young horned lizards are active and able to care for themselves.

Heat and a dry habitat are essential to the existence of the horned "toad." It thrives and becomes most active during the hottest part of the day, under conditions which would be unbearable to most humans. It is while the sun is high and the heat most intense that the horned "toad" scurries about in search of ants, grubs, roaches, grasshoppers, and crickets. Having once located it the lizard stalks its prey slowly and stealthily. Within striking distance of the insect, the "toad" ejects its thick viscid tongue, capturing the victim forthwith. Long before the sun begins to set the horned lizard starts to prepare for the night. Using its head and the horny sides of the body, it digs a burrow two or three inches below the surface and buries itself almost completely for the duration of the cold night. The head horns alone remain above ground like periscopes.

Seventeen species of the horned lizard are found in western North America. Many of them vary only in size or the range in which they are found; all are similar in habits.

The Douglass horned lizard is four to five inches long. Blunt-nosed, its horns reduced to small tubercles, it inhabits parts of Oregon and Washington; two subspecies are found in the Southwest, the Rockies, and the Great Plains. The short-nosed horned lizard is found in North Dakota and Wyoming. The Mexican horned lizard, inhabiting the extreme southern portion of Arizona as well as Mexico, is five inches long, dark reddish-brown in color. The little horned lizard is a small species (three and three-quarters inches). Yellow-pink in color, it is found in western Texas, New Mexico, and Arizona as well as northern Mexico. The smooth horned lizard of the desert regions of Idaho, Nevada, Utah, western Arizona, and the Pacific States is pink or buff in color. Its five-inch body is marked with dark wavy crossbands.

The flat-tailed or MacCall's horned lizard has the longest head spines of any of the concealed-eardrum species. It is ashy gray in color, with a narrow brown line upon the back. It is three and three-quarters inches long and inhabits the Colorado desert. The widespread Texas horned lizard is the most common of the species. The six-inch broad body is striped by a yellow band from head to tail. Two prominent central horns rise from the spined head. Most frequently it is found in Texas, New Mexico, and Arizona, although occasionally specimens have been discovered as far north as Nebraska and eastward to Arkansas. This species has been introduced into Florida—probably by tourists or side-show operators. The Pacific horned lizard is the largest species (six and one-quarter inches) and the most bristling of the horned lizards. Its body is elongated, and a row of spiny marginal scales on the tail is its chief distinguishing characteristic. It inhabits California from the San Francisco region southward to Lower California. The regal horned lizard is a rare specimen, inhabiting southern Arizona and the overlapping Gila and Colorado deserts. Measuring five inches in length, it is pale brown in color, its temples and head adorned with six and four spines respectively.

TEXAS PLATED LIZARD *(Gerrhonotus infernalis)*. Length: 1¼ feet.
Range: Southern Texas and northern Mexico.
New York Zoological Society

PLATED LIZARD

AS THE plated lizard runs from its enemies, it can shed its tail without any outside help. The detached tail goes on wriggling violently for some time, serving to distract the attention of the pursuer. Thus the lizard often uses its tail as a decoy, and an adult of the family equipped with its original tail is rather a rarity. The first tail is about seven inches long, while the rest of the reptile measures less than five inches. Succeeding tails are progressively shorter.

The plated lizards are related to the "glass snake." Though they have well-developed legs, they progress by a combination of lateral undulations and leg movements. As they move, they get their bearings by feeling about them with their tongues. Though not exactly sluggish, they are not so swift as the more highly developed families of lizards and are therefore more easily captured.

Plated lizards bear living young, wrapped at birth in a membranous sac not unlike a glassine wrapper. Extremely agile, they are paler in color than their parents, and much smoother and shinier when they first emerge from their sac.

Captive plated lizards are at first pugnacious, but later grow tame enough to feed from their keeper's hand.

Several species of plated lizards inhabit the western United States, where they adapt themselves to a wide variety of country, including forests, sage desert, and mountain ranges up to eleven thousand feet. All the species are characterized by two soft fleshy stripes running from the ears to the base of the hind legs. The American species include the long-tailed plated lizard, found along the coast of northern California. This species is brown with light and dark blotches, the scales are keeled. The skink-tailed plated lizard inhabits western Washington, Oregon, and California. This lizard has nine or ten dark bands across its body. Webb's plated lizard of southern California is stouter than other plated lizards, its body thickly spotted. The northern plated lizard of western Oregon and Washington is brownish with faint blotches. The Texas plated lizard of southern Texas is brownish or olive with seven or eight faint crossbands. King's plated lizard has ten bars across the back and a mottled head. It is found in New Mexico and Arizona. Palmer's plated lizard, found on the mountain slopes of central California, is covered with small spots and its tail is short.

"GLASS SNAKE"

THE "glass snake" loses its tail with even greater ease than other tail-losing lizards; the severed tail does not grow back on the body, but a new and somewhat smaller appendage grows again in a short time. This fact has inspired the fantastic popular belief that a "glass snake," if broken into small pieces, will put itself together again. Actually a shattered "glass snake" reacts in exactly the same way as Humpty Dumpty.

The movements of this lizard are slow, lacking the agility of either a true snake or lizard. Since its larger enemies such as the king snake can easily overtake it, the "glass snake's" chief hope resides in its tail. The caudal appendage, making up nearly two-thirds of the reptile's length, struggles violently, so as to occupy all of the snake's attention. The king snake insists on swallowing its prey head first and tries to maneuver the lizard into a suitable position. At the crucial moment the lizard abandons its tail in its enemy's jaws. Profiting by the snake's momentary confusion, it then attempts to burrow underground.

"GLASS SNAKE" *(Ophisaurus ventralis)*. Length: 2¼ feet. Range: Southern and central United States from Virginia and Tennessee to Wisconsin, New Mexico, and northern Mexico. Harmless.
Ralph De Sola (SIZ)

The average length of this serpentine lizard is slightly more than two feet, its thickness about three-quarters of an inch. It has no visible legs whatever and progresses by lateral undulations. But the "glass snake" can easily be distinguished from a true snake by its well-developed eyelids and ear openings. Moreover, its belly is covered with smooth scales which do not help it in getting about, unlike the snake whose under-scutes provide traction.

"Glass snakes" divide their time above and below ground. Underground they pursue earthworms, slugs, and insect larvae; on the surface they prey on birds' eggs, breaking the shells with their strong jaws and lapping up the contents with their flat forked tongue.

"Glass snakes" are found in the southern States from North Carolina to Florida, though not directly on the Atlantic seaboard; and in the Middle West from Wisconsin, down through Illinois and Nebraska to Texas.

"WORM SNAKE"

THE silvery footless lizard is a seven-inch burrowing species of "worm snake" inhabiting Lower and southern California. It is a good example of adaptation to environment and need. It burrows so ardently because it dies almost immediately if exposed to the sun; and in burrowing, legs are of little value. Its color is a bright silvery gray. Three dark lines run down its back. It is found in seaside regions and in sandy desert. It subsists on insect larvae.

The "blind worm" is another burrowing species of the same genus, known only from specimens taken near Pacific Grove, California. It is found in the soil beneath pine forests and in sand dunes. It has a dark purple color.

GILA MONSTER

THE savage Gila [*] monster crawls about the cactus deserts of southern Texas, New Mexico, Arizona, southern Utah, and Nevada with sluggish but not awkward movements. Its heavy-set mottled body is usually not raised from the ground, but is dragged over the sands by the stubby, powerful legs. When excited, however, this 19-inch monster can raise itself up and break into a moderate run.

This is the most ill-tempered of American lizards. It will snap at any moving object on sight, twisting about with remarkable agility and hissing violently as it seeks an opening. A human being who comes too close may find it hard to evade its jaws, and once they have connected, they remain firmly embedded, even in death. The

[*] pronounced *heel-a*

human hand is not strong enough to pry them open and some sort of instrument such as a pair of pliers or a screw driver must be used to break their hold. The biting jaws grind from side to side, while the lizard's venom flows along its grooved rear-fang teeth. This poison is generally fatal to small animals. It is not believed to be always fatal to man, but a side-show performer who allowed himself to be bitten by a Gila for the delectation of a jaded public finally died of poisoning after carrying on his act for some years. It is best for strollers in the desert to give the angry heloderm the right of way and if bitten, to treat the wound as they would a snake bite.

The Gila monster is black, mottled, or banded with pink or yellow, in a design that is comparable with that of an Indian beaded bag.

This lizard is very fond of birds' eggs. Some authorities claim that it feeds on ants, but in captivity it shows a marked dislike for both insects and their eggs. The tail is used as a storehouse for fat. When food is plentiful, it grows thick and solid; in the dry season the Gila lives on the stored calories and the caudal appendage grows thin and flabby while the lizard continues in a state of torpor.

In July and August the Gila monster lays from six to thirteen smooth, tough-shelled eggs, which are placed in damp sand and exposed to the sun. A suitable spot is the bank of a stream, where the eggs are kept moist by infiltration. Incubation takes four weeks. The young are about four inches long, exceedingly lively, and brighter in color than the adults.

In captivity these creatures become docile and friendly and like to have their backs scratched. They eat birds' and reptiles' eggs, the former sometimes mixed with chopped meat.

If captive Gila monsters are placed in the sunlight, they resume their native savagery, but grow tame again as soon as they are restored to a shaded cage. This has nothing to do with the temperature, for it may be just as warm indoors; the wildness is apparently caused by the direct solar radiation and the absence of confining walls. "Harry the Gila"—a specimen kept in quiet surroundings

GILA MONSTER *(Heloderma suspectum)*. Length: 1½ feet. Range: Arizona, New Mexico, southern Utah, Nevada, and Sonora in northern Mexico. Only poisonous lizard in the United States.
Ralph De Sola (SIZ)

by the editor—proved to be a good pet, docile at all times, and ever ready to feed from his hands.

NIGHT LIZARD

BLOOD-RED and dazzling, the sun sinks suddenly over the wasteland of the southwestern corner of the United States. Momentarily the desert shimmers, seems to vibrate as if longing for union with the vanishing spears of light, then creeps back into receding shadows. The fading light falls on the tall Joshua trees standing in their loneliness, briefly outlining the great branches drooping to the ground. A strange stillness enfolds the rapidly cooling soil, hiding from view the teeming night life which will soon burst forth from every crevice and hole as if disgorged by the earth.

The night lizard now creeps out. A full day's napping under the branches of the Joshuas or in a bundle of dead leaves or even in an abandoned termite hole, has rested it and filled it with hunger pangs. Prowling in and out rock piles, up and down the stiff branches of the yuccas in tireless search of food to fill its empty stomach, the night lizard must work hard and diligently to procure its sustenance. Its taste is not too discriminating—any bug or beetle, weevil, or even ant will serve its needs.

All night long it roams the desert and the adjacent dry mountainous regions, its slender round body moving in and out of holes, around crags and broken rocks. In the morning, its appetite satiated, it crawls back to its refuge among the yuccas. In the mountains it squeezes its slim small form into crevices of rocks and it is here that collectors will often find it during the day.

When this creature is exposed to sunlight a peculiar chromatic phenomenon is likely to take place. While its ordinary color ranges from gray through yellow and brown, the fine granular scales of the back are speckled in variegated spots, producing the general effect of a piece of colored mosaic. But the moment it is put in the glare of burning sunlight, it assumes an extremely light tint. With

ARIZONA NIGHT LIZARD *(Xantusia arizonae)*. Length: 4 inches. Range: Arizona.
L. M. Klauber

the coming of sundown, it reverts to the darker shades which probably distinguish its waking and working hours. Thus thoughtful nature has equipped the night lizard with its own peculiar brand of wardrobe change, that its sensitive little body might the better fight off the hot rays of the southern California sun, direct exposure to which means instant death for many desert reptiles.

The night lizard reaches a maximum length of seven inches, although some of the species measure but three inches. Its flat little head is covered along the top with a patch of symmetrical scales, large but slightly bulbous in appearance. It has no protective eyelids and its large irises, vertical, like a cat's, remain open always. The head and body are depressed, and the fragile tail has a tendency to snap off, but soon regenerates. Its crowning indignity, however, if viewed from man's point of view, is a triple chin—three separate folds of skin about the throat.

Small as it is, the night lizard gives birth to living young, the one or two tiny creatures which make up the brood coming into their yucca-strewn world late in the summer.

Four American species of this diffident creature inhabit the desert plains and mountain regions of California, Arizona and Nevada. They are the Arizona, Xantus', Henshaw's, and Rivers' night lizards.

RACERUNNER

A FAMILIAR sight to the westerner is the lithe, whiplike form of the racerunner on the hot sandy plains and edges of dusty roads. But the slightest motion of man, the most imperceptible hostile sound, will send this reptile into feverish activity. Its first impulse is to race to its burrow, and it accomplishes this act as if by magic. It glides over the ground so rapidly that its form takes on the aspect of a hazy blurred image—something the spectator is not certain he saw at all. When it reaches the hide-away hole, it stops suddenly, then plunges out of sight.

The racerunner or striped lizard is a slender and agile creature, the pointed head and body tapering into a long tail. The black forked tongue serves both to catch insects and to detect irregularities in the ground. Colored olive or brown, it is easily identified by a series of four to six yellow stripes which run from head to tip of tail.

Most active of the North American reptiles, the racerunners inhabit the subarid plains of Texas and the desert regions of the far

SIX-LINED RACERUNNERS *(Cnemidophorus sexlineatus)*. Length: 9 inches. Range: Maryland through Florida, westward to Arizona, northward in Mississippi Valley to Lake Michigan.
From Ditmars' "Reptiles of North America"

West, although one species is found at an altitude of six thousand feet in the southern Appalachians. Their food supply consists of insects, termites, and ants. Adults, however, sometimes raid the nests of ground birds and devour the small eggs. The egg-draining operation is performed by cracking the shell and scooping out the contents by means of a flat forked tongue.

For protection against the collared lizard, its chief enemy, the racerunner digs a burrow, using it for a bedchamber as well as a fort. Eggs are laid by the female in a hole scooped out in the sand, then covered until they are hatched by the sun's rays.

RACERUNNER

The Cape striped lizard is eight inches long, exclusive of the five-inch tail. The scalation of the head and the single plate between the eyes (this plate is divided in other species) differentiate the Cape lizard from other species. It is light brown or olive above, black on the sides, and the abdomen is red. Large numbers are found from San Diego southward into Lower California.

The tessellated lizard, colored dark olive-green, with seven yellow wavy stripes on the back and sides, is eighteen inches long (tail twelve inches). It is found in the subarid regions and deserts of southwestern Texas, New Mexico, Arizona, Nevada, Utah, and eastern California.

Stejneger's tessellated lizard of southern California is distinguished by the nine longitudinal rows of irregular black spots. The sides of the head are spotted with black markings and the lower surface is pure white, spotted with black.

Cope's tessellated lizard has no stripes; instead it is covered with twelve to fourteen longitudinal rows of pale spots against an olive background. It inhabits the Colorado Desert and other parts of Arizona.

The spotted racerunner, with a pointed snout and six yellow stripes on its back, inhabits the southern United States from Arkansas to Arizona. One of the smaller species, it measures ten to twelve inches in length.

The banded racerunner is found in Texas and New Mexico. Its body is striped lengthwise, with a wide brown band covering the back of the neck.

The smallest of the racerunners found in the United States and the only eastern species, the six-lined lizard, is ten inches long, distinguished by its blunt muzzle and six bright-yellow stripes which originate at the head and end at the base of the tail. It roams along the Atlantic coast from Delaware south to Florida, and is also found as far west as Arizona.

Graham's lizard, also called the tiger lizard, is fourteen inches long and inhabits Texas.

All the species of racerunners exhibit the same characteristics of agility in escaping danger.

SKINK

THE skinks are a large family of moderate-size lizards with smooth and usually shiny scales. The body surface is hard, for there are bony plates beneath the skin.

These lizards are widely distributed, numerous species occurring in both hemispheres. Different species of this family represent different stages of evolutionary development. Most varieties are swift runners despite their short legs. Others have diminutive limbs with which they drag themselves along when not in a hurry; in time of emergency these species tuck up their limbs and glide away like snakes. In some species the forelegs are lacking; in others the hindlegs. Still others are limbless and serpentine.

Three genera and about fifteen species inhabit the United States. All the American varieties have well-developed limbs and are fast-moving. All are rather small, and all have shiny scales. The genus *Leiolopisma* has one hundred and sixty species scattered throughout the world, but only a single one of these ground lizards is found in the United States. All other American species belong to the genus *Eumeces*, with the exception of *Neoseps*—the wormlike skink of Florida. Most of the *Eumeces* tribe have stripes when young, but they fade with maturity.

LIKE many other skinks, the five-lined variety radically changes its appearance with age. For this reason it has two sets of popular names, and many persons regard the two color phases as distinct species.

The young lizard is jet black with a bright yellow line running down either side and three similar lines, joined at the head, running down the back. The tail of this creature is a brilliant blue, hence the youngster is properly called the blue-tailed lizard. The popular term "five-line" applies only to this phase, though its specific name *quinquelineatus*, having the same meaning, is applied to the creature throughout life.

As the skink grows older, the black turns to dull brown, and the stripes fade, beginning with the central ones. Females remain dully

SKINK

striped throughout life; the males turn a uniform olive-brown, except for the head, which becomes bright red. The popular name is now red-headed lizard or "scorpion."

Five-lined skinks are abundant throughout the South, especially in South Carolina, Georgia and Florida. They range westward to Texas and north to Massachusetts. They are fairly common in New Jersey.

These lizards flourish in deep forests, where they dash about in search of insects. The adult "scorpions," however, which attain a length of ten inches, also eat small birds' eggs and newborn mice. When not hunting they seek out small clearings to bask in the sun. Like all skinks, they are strictly diurnal—active only during the day.

Whether hunting or taking life easy, these lizards are exceedingly wary. They never venture far from a tree hole or a tangle of underbrush, and at the slightest alarm they dart to cover in a streak of uninterrupted motion. Most other lizards stop in midflight to see

BROWN SKINK *(Eumeces obsoletus)*. Length: 11 inches. Range: Utah and Kansas to northern Mexico.
W. Lincoln Highton, Work Projects Administration

FIVE-LINED SKINKS (*Eumeces fasciatus*).
Length: 8 inches. Range: Eastern and central United States westward to Arizona.
American Museum of Natural History

how their pursuer is getting along, but the skink keeps on running till it reaches safety. Consequently these creatures, even where most abundant, are hard to catch.

In early spring they burrow under the bark of dead trees in pursuit of ants. Large numbers of them are uncovered when the bark is peeled off. In the summer they prefer holes in tree trunks for their hiding place.

Captive blue-tails thrive best when provided with hiding places, such as a few strips of bark. On lifting up one of these strips Dr. Ditmars found a number of the lizards lying in a coiled position, unusual for lacertilians. They turned out to be females coiled round their three or four eggs. If they actually were guarding their eggs, the skink in this respect occupies a position almost unique among oviparous reptiles, the vast majority of which show no concern at all for their eggs once they are deposited.

These skinks possess powerful jaws. Adult males bite vigorously and tenaciously when handled. If seized by the tail, both young and old shed this appendage, which continues to wriggle violently.

The other species of this genus have similar habits. Those inhabiting the United States are the many-lined skink, found in the central States from the Mississippi to the Rockies. The limbs are small and far apart. The ground color is olive, bordered on each side with five dark-brown stripes interspersed with pale olive. Hayden's skink is six inches in length. The young have five stripes and a blue tail; adults are a uniform olive. They inhabit the central States from Nebraska to northern Texas. The Sonora skink attains a length of twelve inches. The limbs are short. The young are black with five faint stripes. The adults are yellow or olive, with a darker hue at the borders of the scales and have a reddish head. The range is a triangle taking in Kansas, central Texas, and Arizona. Skilton's skink is seven inches long and has short legs. The young are olive with two white lines on either side. Between the white lines is a dark band. In the adults the stripes are fainter. This species is abundant throughout the Pacific region and western Nevada. In Gilbert's skink the young are dark brown above, the scales having pale centers. Adults are brownish olive, tinged with red, no stripes, head bright red, sometimes with greenish dots. This eight-inch species inhabits the western slopes of the Sierra Nevada.

The black-banded skink, ranging from Minnesota to Kansas, has four black stripes on the back and two white stripes on each side with a black band between them. The Florida skink, only four inches long and extremely slender, almost like a worm, is the smallest American species. Olive to reddish brown in color with four white stripes bordered with faint dotted lines, it inhabits southern Florida and the Keys.

At least a half dozen other skinks are known and these are widely distributed over the United States.

THE brown-backed skink, or ground lizard, has well-developed legs, but they are too short to be of much use in running. This three-inch species, however, can move at a good speed by a combination of running and wriggling. It looks more like a salamander than a lizard.

The ground lizard is found in the eastern States from Florida to New Jersey and in the central States from southern Illinois to Texas. It is rarely seen by the casual observer, for it leads a retired, burrowing life. But large numbers are sometimes found by stripping the loose bark from dead and fallen trees. They are a bronze or olive color with lines of dots covering the body. When exposed, they wriggle swiftly away, or burrow into the soft wood. These skinks are preyed upon by a number of snakes.

The ground lizard thrives in captivity if sufficient ants and beetles are available. But since its chief activity is hiding, it is not the most diverting denizen of the reptile house.

WORMLIKE LIZARDS

WORMLIKE lizards neither look nor act like lizards. They possess no scales, but are covered with a skin made up of ringed segments. They do not run like other lizards, but push through the soil by movements of their segments, coupled with vertical undulations of the body. Spending most of their time beneath the ground, they are virtually blind; their eyes are hidden beneath heavy membranes. They have, however, a keen sense of smell, and both their tongue and skin possess a sharp tactile sense. Most of these degenerate lizards have heavy shields on head and chin, which serve as aids in burrowing.

The wormlike lizards fall into two families, the *Amphisbaenidae*, which are totally limbless, and the *Euchirotidae*, having one pair of rudimentary limbs. Each of these families is represented by the United States species.

THE worm lizard of northern and central Florida moves forward and backward with equal ease and can change direction without the necessity of turning around. Its two extremities are so much alike that they can scarcely be distinguished by the naked eye. When frightened, this legless creature raises not its head but its tail, and this habit may serve as a sort of protection, though actually in its native sod or manure pile, the worm lizard is king.

A good-sized Florida worm lizard may be nine inches long, with a uniform thickness of less than a quarter of an inch. The skin is a shiny lavender color and is deeply ringed. Both extremities are blunt.

Worm lizards rarely come to the surface except after a rain or when turned up by a plow. When they do, they merely squirm about for a short distance in search of a soft spot to burrow into. Their food consists of small earthworms and insect larvae.

THE nine-inch two-footed worm lizard looks like a large flat earthworm except for its small but well-developed forelimbs. Each limb has four well-developed toes equipped with sharp claws

TWO-FOOTED WORM LIZARD *(Bipes biporus)*. Length: 9 inches. Range: Lower and southern California.
Raymond L. Ditmars

and a fifth toe which is clawless. Though nothing is known of this reptile's habits, the claws are believed to aid in burrowing. This worm lizard's eyes are two minute dots which can be seen through the translucent head scales. They are of little or no use to the lizard, which spends all its time underground.

This species is found in Lower California and possibly in southeastern Arizona, according to Dr. Edward H. Taylor.

Snakes

About 136 kinds are recognized in North America. In the mind of the average person snakes are malign creatures that drop out of trees to strangle men in their coils, or creep into tents and houses to kill people with their poisonous fangs. There are tropical snakes that do these things occasionally, but the great majority of American snakes not only are harmless in their dealings with man but even assist him greatly in controlling rodent and insect pests.

The larger snakes, such as the exotic pythons and boas, are not the only kinds capable of swallowing prey many times their own girth. All snakes can perform this feat because their jaws readily spread both at the hinges and at the front where the two halves of the lower jaw are held together with an elastic ligament, unlike the fixed jaws of lizards. Legless lizards should not be confused with snakes.

SNAKE BITE

In the United States snake bites account for the death of only slightly more than one hundred and fifty persons each year, while estimates based on careful research have placed the yearly number of non-fatal snake bites as somewhere between 1,500 and 2,000. This is far less than the 30,000 persons killed each year by automobiles in the United States. Yet, strangely enough, most people are still much more afraid of snakes than they are of motor vehicles. From the figures it is clear that only some ten per cent of all snake-bites in this country prove fatal. This is not a very high figure, when one considers the toxic powers of some of our poisonous snakes. These figures could be lowered appreciably if persons frequenting snake-infested areas would exercise elementary caution.

TO AVOID BEING BITTEN

There are many who enjoy camping, hiking, and other outdoor activities which may lead them through wooded or brush areas where poisonous snakes are apt to be found. It is wise for such persons to take a few precautions.

A pair of thick canvas or leather leggings is an excellent protection against the poisonous reptiles found in the northern United States. High shoes should be worn with the leggings, for otherwise a portion of the ankle may be left exposed and thus become an excellent target for the snake. One should also be wary while pushing one's way through thick underbrush, particularly uphill, to see that the hands are not thoughtlessly thrust into the neighborhood of a snake crevice or den. Eyes should be on the alert continually as the best guarantee of safety. One can save time, trouble, and worry by finding out about the snakes of a region in some reliable book. Frequently, poisonous snakes are found only in restricted parts of their range and consequently many local areas are free of them. For example, Long Island, New York, is now clear of venomous snakes although at one time rattlers were known there.

Unfortunately *no hard and fast rule of thumb can be given to differentiate poisonous from harmless species.* In general, however, the pupils of poisonous serpents are elliptical while those of all but one or two harmless species are round. The relatively thick heads and tapering necks of rattlers and copperheads also help to distinguish them but are misleading diagnostic characters because they are also found in boas and pythons. Then, too, there is the hognosed snake, or puff adder, dangerous looking and acting, but harmless and beneficial.

In southerly areas of our country where weather conditions tend to reduce the resistance value of leggings, the best possible protection is a pair of leather puttees thick enough to be a defense against the fangs of any snake. In the southern States it is wise also to be wary of hollow tree trunks. They serve in many cases as the hiding places of venomous reptiles.

IF BITTEN

Don't give whisky or alcoholic drinks of any kind. Alcoholic stimulants will only quicken the circulation of the blood, thus hastening the distribution of the venom through the system.

Don't burn or cauterize the wound.

Don't use any of the so-called "folklore" remedies. They are useless, and in many cases downright harmful.

Don't apply any whole grains of potassium permanganate to the wound. However, a weak solution may be made with water and washed into incisions. This will neutralize any venom the solution reaches.

(1) The victim should be encouraged to remain as calm as possible. Excitement or physical exertion will only send the blood racing

to the heart, and speed the absorption of the venom. He should be reminded that the bites of American snakes are rarely fatal, especially with any kind of treatment. Get the patient to a hospital or a doctor as soon as possible. In the meantime—

(2) A tourniquet should be applied between the bite and the heart. Cord, rubber tubing, or even a necktie will do. Pressure *should not be so great as to stop blood circulation entirely. The idea is to halt the flow of lymph.* Loosen the tourniquet for a minute at fifteen minute intervals.

(3) Connect the two fang punctures with a single incision of a clean, sharp-bladed instrument, preferably a single edged safety razor blade. The cut should be approximately one-quarter of an inch deep, or in cases where an unusually large snake has been responsible for the bite, three-eighths of an inch deep. The blade should be sterilized before the operation with iodine, alcohol, or even the flame of a match.

(4) Apply suction by means of the suction bulb included in the snake-bite kit, or with the lips if necessary. The latter method should not be undertaken by anyone who has sores in his mouth or abscessed teeth. Suction should be continued for at least a half hour.

(5) If anti-venin serum is available, use according to the instructions on the package. But in any case the suction operation should also be performed, as either of these techniques alone does not constitute a complete treatment.

(6) If the swelling progresses up the limb, make additional incisions at the point of swelling, and repeat the suction treatment. The tourniquet, however, should always be kept above the swollen area. It is best to apply a second tourniquet in such cases, before removing the original one.

(7) If the victim is faint, he should be given some strong hot coffee or tea.

Treatment should be taken from an authority like the Red Cross Manual. Tourniquets are ineffective on some parts of the body.

Many people are bitten each year by harmless snakes, and much undue excitement ensues. However, the bite of a venomous snake is unmistakable since it causes a burning pain in the region of the bite within one to five minutes. After such an attack, a swelling develops within ten minutes. Without these symptoms there is nothing to fear, and the bite may be treated as any other wound or ignored if the snake is small.

It is interesting to note that snake venom has positive as well as negative values. Persons afflicted with epilepsy, arthritis, asthma, and cancer have responded to treatments employing snake venom in excessively minute doses.

HARMLESS SNAKES

WORMLIKE SNAKE

ONE of the smallest of all North American reptiles, the blind worm snake, is a meek and sluggish creature that spends most of its dark existence creeping slowly through the subterranean burrows and tunnels which serve as its permanent home, and searching perpetually for worms and insect larvae. Its movements are feeble and its vision so ineffectual that it can but barely discern the difference between day and night. Never happy when exposed to air or light, whenever it is forced out of its underground quarters it proceeds methodically to dig itself in again.

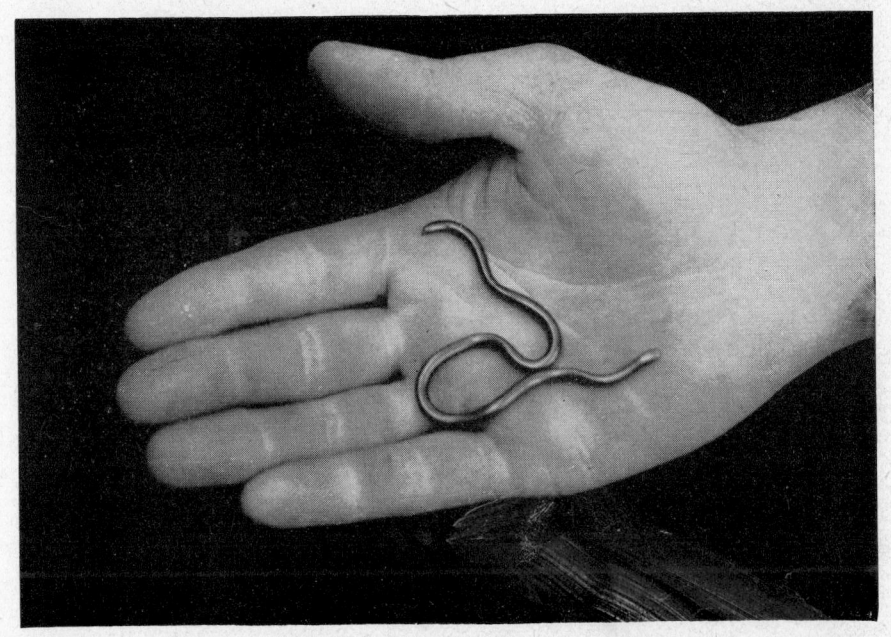

WORM SNAKE *(Leptotyphlops dulcis)*. Length: 10 inches. Range: Texas, Oklahoma, New Mexico, and northern Mexico. Harmless.
New York Zoological Society

The blind worm snake is a degenerate species of the wormlike snakes of which three species are found in the United States: the Texas worm snake inhabiting Texas north to Oklahoma, the Mexican worm snake of southern New Mexico, and the California worm snake of southern California (a subspecies of the California worm snake, the desert worm snake, is found in the Colorado and Yuma deserts of California and Arizona).

One of the smaller species, the worm snake (also known as the blind snake) measures a foot in length, varies in color from pinkish lavender to pale brown and is usually spotted with darker hues. The snout of the blunted head overlaps the mouth and pinhead black eyes are covered by a translucent shield.

DWARF BOA

THE dwarf boa is a diminutive copy of the giant-sized boa constrictor of South America, but unlike its fearsome cousin, it is harmless, docile, unhurried in its movements, and shies away at the approach of man. When frightened it will try to escape by burrowing into ground, or hide its head from danger by rolling into a tight ball. It may then be tossed about like any other ball without causing the snake to unwind itself.

Varying in color from pale yellow to brown, gray, or olive and banded with brown stripes, the body of the three-foot-long dwarf boa is thick-set. The head is long and easily distinguishable from the neck. The eyes are proportionately large, equipped with the elliptical pupils generally characteristic of poisonous snakes. Needless to say, perhaps, it is not poisonous. It feeds on birds and small mammals, and when in captivity will eat young mice and small birds. Some of the species have been observed to kill their prey by constriction.

Three species of the dwarf boa are found in the United States—the rosy boa, rubber boa and the desert rosy boa. The rosy boa is confined to the southeastern portion of California and western Arizona; the rubber boa (also called the silver snake and the two-headed snake, the latter because of the similarity of its head and tail) inhabits the Pacific coast from Washington to California, east to

RUBBER BOA *(Charina bottae)*. Length: 1¼ feet. Range: Western United States. Harmless.
New York Zoological Society

Montana, Idaho, and Wyoming (this species, somewhat smaller, measures fifteen inches in length); and the desert rosy boa found in southern California.

GARTER SNAKE

WHEN a garter snake is first handled, it will emit a foul odor, believed to emanate from a gland at the base of the tail, which is normally used to attract the opposite sex. Thereafter it will usually grow very tame—especially the common variety found nearly everywhere east of the Mississippi. All it needs is a little glass-fronted box with a gravel bottom placed in a dry atmosphere, a dish of water and a meal of earthworms every five to seven days. Some pet specimens have been known to live for ten years or more, although Dr. Ditmars found those reared in captivity from birth grew larger and died sooner. Children are especially fond of the species because of its smooth glistening scales, its beautiful markings, and its lack of resentment against being handled by them.

It is by far the most common type of serpent in the United States. The garter snake is also called the ribbon or striped snake. Though distributed over most of North and Central America, it is

GARTER SNAKE AND YOUNG *(Thamnophis s. sirtalis)*. Length: 3 feet. Range: Eastern United States and Canada as far west as Minnesota, as far south as Texas. Harmless.
From Ditmars' "Reptiles of the World"

chiefly limited to this country, swarming with bewildering profusion in every region—one variety even frequenting large city parks. This fact and the ease in taming it has brought the snake to nearly everyone's attention at some time, though the multiplicity of species has long defied scientific systematization.

Adaptability to different conditions and a prolific reproductive capacity are ascribed as the chief causes of the snake's abundance and wide distribution. Though nearly every variety is semiaquatic in habits, frequenting the vicinity of pools, creeks, and swamps, it is found in arid desert regions as well. There are plains and prairie garter snakes and mountain types taken at a height of 13,000 feet. The garter snake is found the farthest north of any serpent.

As many as seventy-eight young have been found in a brood of this viviparous genus although the average number is more likely to range between twenty and thirty. The young, moreover, are immediately able to take care of themselves, breaking through the fœtal membrane in which they are coiled at birth, to seek shelter and earthworms, and shed their first skin. After the winter hibernation they are themselves already mature enough to breed young.

In keeping with their hardiness, garter snakes are the first ones to emerge from hibernation nests in the spring and the last ones to disappear from the feeding haunts in the fall. The nests are usually rock crevices or mounds of vegetable trash on the southern side of slopes. Before the final retreat, their occupants will emerge during the middle of the day to bask in the sun.

Known also as striped snakes, the garter snake is popularly distinguishable by its longitudinally striped pattern, consisting usually of a stripe on each side and one in the center on top. As these are often a vivid yellow, green, or orange, contrasting with the darker body hue, the effect is very striking. In several varieties, however, one or all of the stripes may be lacking or cut by bold black or red spots alternately placed, giving a checkerboard effect. The vivid colors do not appear to have anything to do with sexual attraction, and as the genus is anatomically akin to the water snakes, they are also believed to be of little protective value. Dr. A. G. Ruthven, however, has shown that the lighter hues correlate with more arid surroundings and the darker with wet ones, while, of course, the linear pattern and whitish belly signify nature's concealment of body shape as in other forms of animal life.

Though exhibiting a wide diversity in form as well as in coloration and pattern, most varieties are less than thirty inches long and about an inch in diameter. The male is a little smaller than the female, but has a relatively longer and more tapering tail. Concealed in the base of the male's tail are paired sexual organs, one of which is used in copulation. The male woos the female by rubbing his bumpy chin over the latter's neck.

The breeding season is in the early spring—late March or early April—as soon as the snakes emerge from their winter sleep. Though they pair off in mating, large numbers have been noticed tightly intertwined, and, with heads protruding in all directions, apparently inseparable and oblivious of danger. In giving birth to young in the late summer or fall, the female raises her tail and ejects the newcomers one at a time from the cloacal vent. As each birth takes some minutes and may be separated by longer intervals from the next, the process may take several hours.

WESTERN RIBBON SNAKE *(Thamnophis sauritus proximus)*. Length: 2½ feet. Range: Louisiana, Texas, Mexico, and Central America. Harmless.
From Ditmars' "Reptiles of North America"

Wet years are especially good for garter snakes since they feed on tadpoles, frogs, small fishes, insect larvae, and earthworms primarily. This recalls the primitive worship of snakes in propitiation of the rain god or the power they were believed to possess over rain —especially that of the Hopi Indians in the Southwest in their snake dance. However, in dry or upland regions, this snake is known to feed on grasshoppers and small dead animals, such as field mice or birds. The greatest enemies of the garter snakes are hawks and bitterns, who hover over and wade about inland bogs in pursuit of their prey.

At the approach of humans, most varieties of garter and striped snakes will scurry for shelter in all directions or dive into the water from their perches along a bank or from overhanging foliage. It is this agility, together with large litters, that has probably given rise to the belief that the mother swallows her young at the approach of danger. As many herpetologists have pointed out, such an accomplishment has never been proved, and would be a physical impossibility and generally contrary to the habits of snakes. Like other snakes, however, the garter snakes have been observed to disgorge a meal of still living tadpoles when alarmed.

Some species have exhibited marked peculiarities, suggesting degenerative organs. Thus the slenderest and most active of all, the pretty ribbon snake, seems to see only moving objects well, and lashes the water with the end of its tail as though to distract attention from the fish it is eating when in company with others of its kind. Young of this species also swim about with their mouths open until they strike a minnow, and then carry it out of the water. On the other hand, the smallest, almost headless type, Butler's garter snake, moves slowly and awkwardly, while a subspecies of the western garter proceeds in sidewise loops of its body, its head turned in the opposite direction and now and then jumping in a straightened position over a distance of a foot.

Although the classification of the species and subspecies is probably the most controversial in the field, between ten and twenty distinct species are generally recognized. They are based on the general form, the scutellation, number of scale rows, and location of stripes, the color and pattern offering the least stable index.

Among those with lateral stripes on the second and third rows of scales and larger number of scale rows and lip plates are the western garter snake on the Pacific coast; Marcy's garter snake in central Texas and southeastern California; Hammond's garter snake in Arizona and California; the brown snake in western Texas, Arizona, and northern Mexico. Similar, with a smaller number of scale rows and lip plates, are the common garter snake found in eastern North America; the red-barred garter snake of western North America; and Pickering's garter snake confined to the northwestern United States. Among those with lateral stripes on the third and fourth rows and a stout body are the plains garter snake found from Indiana to the Rockies; the Arizona garter snake in Arizona, New Mexico, and northern Mexico; and Butler's garter snake found in Ohio, Illinois, and Indiana. Similar, with slender body, are the eastern ribbon snake, found east of the Mississippi; the southern or Florida ribbon snake in South Carolina, Georgia, and Florida; and the western ribbon snake in Indiana, Illinois, and southwestward through the desert regions to Mexico.

WATER SNAKE

THE water snake can be an ugly customer when cornered. His strong jaws are able to inflict a bad wound, but this heavy-bodied, dull-brown swimmer is not poisonous. His savage and sinister appearance, however, causes him to be widely mistaken for the venomous water moccasin of the southeastern States. Often he is erroneously called a moccasin.

All water snakes swim and dive easily, remaining at the bottom for considerable periods when danger threatens. They find their ideal habitat near the borders of streams, ponds, lakes, and marshes where they subsist on a diet of cold-blooded creatures—frogs, toads, and fishes.

Sportsmen have leveled the charge that the water snakes destroy quantities of game fish and thus are to be considered nuisances. But it seems hardly likely that many of the speedier fishes can fall prey to the comparatively slow-moving serpents.

Water snakes range from Canada to Florida through the central portion of the United States. In the Southeast they overlap the range of the poisonous cottonmouth moccasin which does not extend farther north than North Carolina. Water snakes bring forth live young in great numbers.

WATER SNAKE

The water snakes include the two-foot-long queen snake of the eastern half of the country, especially abundant in Ohio and Illinois; Graham's water snake of the Mississippi Valley, extending along the Missouri; the twenty-inch striped water snake found from Pennsylvania to Florida; the three-foot Clark's water snake of the Gulf coast; the flat-tailed water snake, almost two feet long, which is

WATER SNAKE *(Natrix s. sipedon).* Length: 4 feet. Range: Eastern North America. Non-poisonous.
From Ditmars' "Reptiles of the World"

found only in southern Florida; the northern and southern water snakes or "moccasins" which extend from the Atlantic coast to the Rockies and from Canada to the Gulf; the red-bellied water snake, Kirtland's, of the central and southeastern States, a mere twenty inches long, found in the north central States to the Atlantic coast. The largest of the species, which total twelve in number, is the brown water snake, five feet in length and found throughout the South. This snake, by reason of its size, is a particularly formidable opponent.

IN THE tangled underbrush of swamps throughout New England and the Central States the common water snake hangs lazily from a limb overlooking the near-by area for signs of something edible, and if a fish should pass, it drops into the water and swims off in hot pursuit.

Annoyed or intruded upon, the water snake flattens its head and strikes again and again, but being a discreet serpent, it will always attempt to escape if a way is left open.

These snakes have a well-developed sense of smell. A cage full of them can be thrown into a frenzy by rubbing a piece of fish along the floor or walls. The reptiles will bite each other in their anxiety to snatch a morsel of the bait. Water snakes have been caught with small fish suspended in the water on lines. The reptiles swallow the fish, line and all, and are hauled in. Probably because they are so greedy, it never seems to occur to them to disgorge the bait and escape.

A large litter of live young, sometimes more than forty in number, is brought forth by the female in August or September.

BROWN SNAKE AND SMALL SWAMP SNAKE

THE small swamp snakes and brown snakes are harmless and inoffensive creatures, spending the greater part of their existence in hiding from potential enemies. Once in a while, usually on a warm afternoon, one of the bolder members may peer from beneath its refuge, may even venture to the side of the road, playing with the idea of crossing in order to find what tempting morsel may lurk in the distance on the other side. But this interlude of communion with light is brief; alarmed over its rash escapade, it promptly wriggles to the protection of its hole.

Feeling at home as long as they are covered with an object which hides them from view, almost any enclosure, board, or rock serves as living quarters. Many of the swamp snakes and brown snakes are found under sod, boards, tar paper, cement building blocks, pieces of tile, in vacant lots, and even in city parks.

Abundant throughout the United States and especially in swampy or moist regions, swamp snakes and brown snakes manage to survive and multiply primarily because of their cautious, almost furtive habits, their ability to find hiding places under any object. Only during the spring mating season do they crawl out boldly. The result is a brood of thin stringy specimens, so insignificant in size that they are dwarfed by an ordinary worm. However, they grow rapidly, though never reaching great size.

The small swamp snake is fourteen inches long; the brown snakes vary in size from eight to twenty-five inches. Their coloration ranges from gray to deep brown, and the sides and back are usually spotted with black dots. The head is small and pointed, the eyes large. The diet of both types of snakes consists almost exclusively of earthworms, although some of the species have been known to eat slugs and the soft-bodied grubs of beetles.

GRAYISH brown in color, its back striped by a yellow band and bordered with black dots, the striped swamp snake in many respects resembles the garter snake. It is distinguished chiefly by its smaller head and the white or yellow dotted abdomen. It reaches a maximum length of fourteen inches and its living young number two to fourteen. An innocuous and friendly creature if not alarmed, it is abundant in the central States ranging as far west as South Dakota and southward to Texas.

DE KAY's snake is a brown snake inhabiting the central regions of the United States, east of the Rockies and south to Texas. Measuring twelve inches in length, it is chestnut in color, its sides spotted with black dots.

Young DeKay's snakes are diminutive in size and when born the twelve to twenty helpless creatures resemble a series of three-inch strings. Bolder and livelier during the mating season, members of this species may often be seen basking in the sun, but when alarmed they promptly glide out of sight. DeKay's snake is one of the most harmless and timid of the species, has never been known to bite even when captured.

SIMILAR in appearance to DeKay's snake, but somewhat smaller (ten inches long) Storer's snake is particularly abundant in the mountain regions of New York and New Jersey. It is also known locally as the red-bellied snake, brown snake, and ground snake.

FIVE other species of the brown snake are found in the eastern and central regions of the United States. They include the Florida brown snake; the ground snake or worm snake inhabiting the Atlantic coast from Virginia to Florida and extending west to Minnesota; Valeria's snake, smallest of the species, reaching a maximum length of eight inches and found from southern New Jersey south to Georgia and west to Ohio; Virginia's snake; the black swamp snake or mud snake, measuring seventeen inches in length (found in South Carolina, Georgia, and Florida); and Allen's swamp snake, largest of the species (twenty-five inches long) inhabiting Florida and the Okefenokee Swamp of south-eastern Georgia where it feeds chiefly on mud eels and other related amphibians.

RACERS

SPEEDY, slim, and graceful, the racers can travel almost as fast as a man runs. The indigo snake of the southeastern States and the "blue bull" of Texas, typical racers, are the largest snakes on the North American continent, attaining a length of nine feet. Large and agile though they are, the racers do not kill their prey by constriction; they press the victim to the ground by virtue of their superior weight, and then proceed to swallow it. With the exception of the indigo snake or gopher snake and its darker phase, the black gopher snake of southwestern Texas, the racers have dull satiny scales. Gopher snakes are marked by the lustrous metallic gloss of their scales.

The racers include the blacksnake of the eastern half of the continent; the eastern blue racer of the central States, and its near relative the western blue racer of the far western and Pacific coast States; the eastern and western coachwhip snakes found from the Carolinas to Florida and along the Gulf; the red-banded and pink-bellied racers of the Southwest; the striped racer which extends in range from Mexico north to Idaho; and the green-spotted racer, the ornate racer, the half-striped racer, Schott's racer, and Ruthven's racer, all ranging from Mexico into Texas.

WITH the sun glittering on its prismatic black scales, the gopher or indigo snake glides across the sandy wastes of the southeastern States. Any smaller snake, bird, frog, toad, or lizard encountered on the way is so much grist for the mill to this handsome fellow who sometimes attains a length of nine feet, thereby attaining the record length for American snakes. It flaps a heavy fold or two of its powerful body over the struggling victim and proceeds to swallow it.

Gopher snakes make excellent pets, for while they exhibit an ugly temper when first caught, this soon subsides and they become friendly. In anger they flatten their heads and compress their necks

GOPHER SNAKE *(Drymarchon corais couperi)*. Length: 7 feet. Range: Southeastern United States and west to southern Louisiana. Non-poisonous.
Raymond L. Ditmars, New York Zoological Society

vertically in a slight arch. Vibrating their tails, they will strike several times, making a considerable show of viciousness, although they are harmless to man.

In and around the small towns of the South, gopher snakes are often seen near dwellings and farm buildings where they are regarded as good ratters. Sometimes such a snake will frequent the same restricted area for several years and come to be regarded as a pet by the people who live there.

Indigo snakes are oviparous; their eggs are about the size of bantam's eggs. Specimens from Georgia and Florida are a uniform gloss-black except for traces of deep lustrous red along the neck and sides of the head. These snakes of the southeastern United States are an offshoot of a larger family of snakes inhabiting tropical South and Central America where they may be olive-brown or blackish on the forward portion of the body, becoming bright yellow rearwardly.

THE blacksnake will writhe up into branches of a tree until it comes upon a bird's nest secured to a strong crotch. Then it swiftly gorges itself upon the eggs and young.

Large blacksnakes reach six feet in length and crawl gracefully along stone fences or in and out of the bushes at the meadow's edge. These black racers aid the farmers considerably in keeping the rodent population in the fields at a safe level. Yet ignorant people kill them on sight because of the myths that surround them. Blacksnakes are alleged to hypnotize squirrels and birds, to attack human beings, and to be able to crush the blood from an arm or leg by constriction. As a matter of fact, the blacksnake does not constrict at all but, like the racers in general, it kills its prey by holding it to the ground and swallowing it. Blacksnakes will kill and eat other snakes smaller than themselves. As for hypnotic qualities—this nonsense about snakes has been the stock in trade of fiction writers and witch doctors since the beginning of literature and folklore. Confronted by a human being, the black racer puts its astonishing speed to such good advantage that it is almost impossible to catch it once it has gotten a good start.

RACERS

BLACKSNAKE *(Coluber c. constrictor)*. Length: 6 feet. Range: Eastern United States. Non-poisonous.
Raymond L. Ditmars, New York Zoological Society

Smooth and satiny, without being glossy like the gopher snake, the black racer is black above and beneath, with white chin.

ACTIVE and nervous, the slender coachwhip snake moves through open country of the South with the speed of a walking man. When pursued it often seeks shelter in the burrow of the gopher tortoise. The coachwhip snake eats small rodents, birds and their eggs, and requires more food than most snakes because it is very energetic.

Coachwhip snakes make poor captives. Their taut, nervous disposition seems to make it difficult to endure confinement.

Reaching a length of eight feet, coachwhip snakes are among the largest American serpents. The forward portion of the body is black or very dark brown which becomes paler toward the rear. The under side is white.

The western coachwhip snake found throughout the southwestern States is fully as large as the typical form, but varies in color from yellowish brown to dark olive. In addition to rodents, birds, and lizards, this snake consumes large quantities of plains grasshoppers.

FLAT-NOSED SNAKE

GLIDING swiftly over rock-strewn plains in the southwestern United States the flat-nosed snakes, distantly related to the racers, lead an unobtrusive existence. Secretive in their movements, they have been observed infrequently, and little is known about their habits.

The flat-nosed snake is relatively a small creature, measuring approximately two feet four inches in length. Its back is striped by a wide yellow band which in turn is flanked by two dark-brown or olive lines. The abdomen is yellow, the head light, and the lips bright yellow. A peculiar characteristic of the flat-nosed snake is the enlargement of the rostral shield, which is wedge-shaped, overlaps the mouth, and makes the snout seem blunt and square.

Three subspecies of flat-nosed snakes inhabit the United States and extend their range into Mexico. They feed on small mammals, birds, and lizards but do not constrict the prey; all are oviparous.

The banded flat-nosed snake (Graham's) inhabits parts of western Texas, New Mexico, Arizona, and Utah. The Arizona flat-nosed snake is confined to Arizona and southern and Lower California. The third subspecies has been seen in southern California.

LEAF-NOSED SNAKE

ONE of the rarest and most elusive of the snakes in the United States is the leaf-nosed snake. According to L. W. Klauber, only ten specimens were collected from 1868 to 1922, and since then, because of more improved and ingenious methods of collecting reptiles, one hundred and sixty-five.

Measuring a little more than a foot in length, this mysterious wormlike inhabitant of the arid wasteland of Nevada, Arizona, and California is nocturnal. Its coloration varies from white to pale yellow, spotted with dark brown blotches on the back. Its head is short and thick-set, the rostral plate of which is so enlarged that it resembles a leaf. The eyes are large and the pupils elliptical as in poisonous serpents.

Two species comprise the genus of the leaf-nosed snakes, Brown's flat-nosed snake and the peninsular flat-nosed snake. Similar in every respect except coloration, they are distinguished primarily by two rows of spots on the sides, apparent in the peninsular flat-nosed snake, non-existent in Brown's flat-nosed snake. The rarer of the species, Brown's flat-nosed snake, has been found only near Arizona.

A small but related genus of the Southwest is found in Arizona containing but two subspecies of smooth-scaled gopher snakes.

BULL SNAKE

ILL-TEMPERED and belligerent, the bull snake fears no opponent, striking the object of its enmity or displeasure upon the slightest provocation. In one of its predominantly ugly moods this eight-foot-long, stout-bodied reptile swings its tail in a rapid tattoo, opens its jaws wide, and whipping the head forward produces a startling hiss. Calculated to alarm and intimidate the intruder, this sinister prolonged sound may be heard more than fifty feet.

The angry voice of the bull snake, described by Dr. Ditmars as comparable with "the effect produced by plunging a piece of hot metal into water," is made by the tubular arrangement of the glottis which is covered by a membranous appendage functioning somewhat like the reed of a wind instrument. To hiss, the bull snake inhales deeply and emits its breath gradually, forcing the air to vibrate the "reed."

One of the largest of the eastern snakes, the bull snake is seldom silent in its movements and usually makes itself known by its noisy antics. In dry vegetation it is often mistaken for a rattlesnake, for when approached its tail makes a disturbance amid the leaves, that sounds like the dreaded rattle. If the enemy is still unimpressed by this display, the bull snake strikes boldly and rapidly, regardless of consequences.

In captivity, it remains sullen and seldom becomes resigned to its fate. Perhaps more than any other snake it resents familiarity, often refuses to take food, and starves rather than submit to confinement.

A virile constrictor, the bull snake eats rabbits, squirrels, and other similar-sized rodents. It is fond of birds and especially their eggs, consuming as many as a dozen at one meal. Swallowing the egg in its entirety, its breaks the shell when it is ten inches deep in its throat, swallows the contents of egg and shell.

The head of the bull snake is small, pointed at the snout; the scales of the back are ridged and the tail terminates in a hard spiny scale. The snake lays fifteen to twenty-four eggs.

THE eastern species of the bull snake is generally known as the pine snake or the white gopher snake. This species is dull white in color, spotted with black blotches, and inhabits the Atlantic coast

FLORIDA PINE SNAKE *(Pituophis mugitus)*. Length: 5 feet. Range: Peninsula Florida. Non-poisonous.
From Ditmars' "Reptiles of North America"

from southern New Jersey to South Carolina. The southern pine snake is found in Florida and Georgia; Ruthven's pine snake is confined to Louisiana; the black pine snake is found in southern Alabama.

The western species of the bull snake are the western gopher snake, the Arizona gopher snake, the Pacific bull snake, the San Lucan gopher snake, and the Mexican gopher snake.

The western gopher snake (bull snake) is the exhibitors' delight, for it is vividly colorful, vicious, and fearful to behold. At fairs and circuses it is sold to all those who are fascinated by its savage twisting about the cage and angry hisses. Its color is orange-yellow or reddish brown, the back prominently blotched with rows of reddish brown or black marks. The dark-yellow head is adorned from eye to eye with a brown or black band. The abdomen is yellow, spotted with black. This bull snake is found throughout much of the United States from Canada to Mexico but not east of Illinois.

The Arizona gopher snake is smaller than the eastern bull snake (four feet nine inches), and is found from New Mexico to southern California. The Pacific bull snake or yellow gopher snake inhabits the Pacific coast west of the Sierra Nevada. Dull yellowish brown in color, spotted with reddish brown or black blotches on the back, it is less formidable and smaller than the bull snake and gets along quite nicely in captivity if kept warm and dry.

The San Lucan gopher snake is straw-colored, measures five feet four inches in length, and is found in the southernmost part of southern California and in Lower California. The Mexican gopher snake roams along the Mexican border from Texas to California. Both like the hot dry desert.

RAT SNAKES

THE eleven species and subspecies of rat snakes found in this country come by their name because of an apparent fondness for small rodents. All rat snakes, or chicken snakes as they are sometimes called, prefer warm-blooded prey; few of them are averse to eating an occasional chicken, a wild bird, or eggs.

The slaughter of these generally useful reptiles, however, is not to be justified on that score. The harm they may do pales into insignificance compared with the inestimable service they perform in keeping field rats and mice at a safe minimum.

The abdomens of rat snakes are flattened at almost right angles with the sides. Stout-bodied and square-headed, these powerful serpents kill their victims by constriction. The rat snakes include the gray-brown box snake of the central United States; Emory's rat snake which ranges from Kansas to Mexico; Baird's rat snake of Texas; the corn snake of the Atlantic coast States, which ranges westward to the Mississippi; the gray rat snake or gray chicken snake of the South; the pilot blacksnake or black chicken snake of the Atlantic coast States ranging westward to Texas and Michigan; the yellow-brown banded rat snake of the deep South; Deckert's chicken snake of the upper Florida Keys; the pink rat snake of the lower Florida Keys; and the green rat snake which crosses the Mexican border into Arizona.

LARGE, strong, and agile, the chicken snake climbs about in the branches of the high trees and penetrates the soggy recesses of swamps with equal facility. The largest specimens of the yellow rat snake, as this constrictor is also called, are found in Florida where they attain a length of seven feet. Chicken snakes are also quite numerous in South Carolina and Georgia.

Lurking in the rafters of barns and henhouses, the chicken snake drops down upon the young chickens, swallowing them whole. A half dozen or more eggs at a time also comprise a satisfactory meal for this ophidian. The eggs are swallowed, shell and all, until they pass down the snake's throat to a distance of about fourteen inches, when the shells are broken by a spasmodic contraction of the muscles. Even the fragments of shell are digested. Only the pilot blacksnake rivals this reptile as a predator of poultry.

When angered, the chicken snake will vibrate its tail so violently that it appears blurred at the tip and produces a whirring sound. This characteristic of the rattlesnake is matched by the S-shaped loop into which the snake's neck is flung as it prepares to strike.

Older captive chicken snakes continue to kill their food by constriction and prefer live food adding to the cares of their keepers, as much nourishment is required. Younger captives will accept frogs, grubs, and even young garter snakes. When first taken, the chicken snake emits a powerful scent from glands situated near the base of the tail. The musk is white in color and resembles the odor of a fox.

Chicken snakes lay their eggs during June and July. One clutch may number as many as two dozen. These are laid in burrows tunneled in loose earth or gravel and begin to hatch out in about nine weeks. When first laid, the eggs contain a tiny embryo with threadlike body and a comparatively enormous head. Within three weeks the embryo is well along in its development; it has a large, lumpy head and white body showing the beginning of scale development. The heartbeats and the unborn snake may be seen occasionally twitching, if the shell is opened.

When first born the chicken snake has a vivid pattern of brown blotches on a pale-gray background. Through successive stages it gradually transforms itself into a handsome yellow snake with four dark brown or black longitudinal stripes—two on the back and one on each side.

ALONG the Atlantic coast from Massachusetts to Florida, and westward to Michigan and Texas, the pilot blacksnake is found along river bottoms, abandoned canal beds, hillsides, ledges, and ravines. This comparatively slow-moving six-foot reptile gets its name from a mistaken notion that it leads venomous serpents like copperheads and rattlesnakes to safety when danger threatens. Perhaps this is proof that even the appearance of evil should be avoided, because the pilot blacksnake is often seen in association with those reptiles.

The small mammals of the woods and fields constitute a great portion of the pilot blacksnake's diet. Squirrels, chipmunks, shrews, weasels, and opossums as well as field and meadow mice fall victim to it. Wild birds, poultry, and eggs too are quite acceptable as food when they are obtainable.

The pilot blacksnake is a constrictor, like all the rat snakes. It throws its heavy coils about the prey the instant that its victim is firmly seized in the mouth. The bones of the prey are crushed, but death probably comes through suffocation.

One of the numerous myths concerning the black racer or blacksnake, a snake of a genus different from the pilot blacksnake, has it that the black racer can crush an arm into numbness by coiling around it. While racers do not constrict and therefore are incapable of crushing arms, the pilot blacksnake does constrict and is quite capable of retarding the circulation in a human limb to an uncomfortable degree.

Pilot blacksnakes are killed in great numbers along the highways by automobiles. They are slow enough to be caught in the hand unless there is shelter for them close by. They will fight when first caught, drawing the neck backward in a graceful curve, the mouth open and prepared to strike. An additional protection which avails the snake but little is the scent released from musk glands at the base of the tail.

During July the female lays from twelve to twenty or more eggs covered with thin leathery shells and coated with a moist adhesive substance which binds the eggs together as it dries. Upon hardening, the eggs turn slightly yellow. Manure piles, damp earth, and sawdust provide excellent hatching places for the young pilot blacksnakes. When first born, these have a pattern of brown blotches on a gray background. Later they will become nearly uniform black or brownish black.

THE corn snake is one of this country's most beautiful serpents. On a pale red or reddish-brown ground color appears a pattern of crimson saddles bordered with black. Lower, toward the abdomen, the red verges into orange. Reaching a length of six feet, this snake is an agile climber, often ascending into the branches to kill young birds. Most abundant in the southeastern States, the corn snake is found from New Jersey southward to Florida and westward to Louisiana, thence up the Mississippi Valley to Missouri where it becomes rather rare.

Strong and unafraid, the corn snake, so named for its habit of frequenting fields of grain where it preys upon rodents, will put up a strenuous fight when cornered. In captivity, however, it becomes fairly tame. The corn snake is oviparous, laying from one to two dozen eggs.

KING SNAKE

THE king snake is not the sworn enemy of poisonous or even harmless snakes. It neither prefers them to other sources of food, nor does it keep a constant vigil intent on their destruction. But even though it does not discriminate between snakes and small rodents, when hunger pangs beset it the king snake becomes the terror of the reptile world, fears and respects no snake whether it be the poisonous rattler or the most powerful constrictor. It coils its powerful frame tightly about the opponent and begins a systematic application of pressure against every portion of the victim's writhing body. Briefly the rattlesnake struggles, injecting its venomous fangs into the king snake—but to no avail—for the clutch of the master remains steady and unyielding. When life finally has ebbed from the victim, the king relaxes its grip and swallows its dead relative. Immune to snake poison, the bite of the venomous snake only tends to irritate the king snake, making its attack more vicious and methodical.

The king snake is as beneficial to man as it is deadly to its brethren. To the agriculturist it is a valuable friend, perhaps unwittingly helping about the farm and doing its share of useful work. That its good work—the destruction of rodents and venomous snakes—is not appreciated, is evident from the widespread destruction of this species, perhaps because of an inherent fear of snakes.

Unaware of this hostility toward its kind, the king snake is as tame and good-natured as a puppy, shows no disposition to attack man. When handled it coils itself about the captor's hand, snuggles closely as if seeking protection and warmth. Some of the species, notably the milk snake, at first attempt to bite, choosing what they consider a tender portion of man's body. The break in the skin thus produced is no larger than a pin prick, the effect more felt than seen.

KING SNAKE (*Lampropeltis g. getulus*). Length: 5 feet. Range: Southern New Jersey to northern Florida and southeastern Alabama. Non-poisonous.
Raymond L. Ditmars, New York Zoological Society

One of the commonest snakes in the United States, the king snake varies in length from one to six feet. All the species are equally pugnacious and cannibalistic. All are powerful constrictors and feed on small rodents and other snakes. They deposit ten to twenty-four eggs, and six weeks later hatch a brood of lithe specimens. In captivity they are mild-mannered, seem easy to please, and will eat rodents, dead or alive, sparrows, and even pieces of beef.

Eight species of the king snake are found in the United States. The largest and best known is the common king snake, known also as the chain snake and thunder snake. It is six feet long, colored black and striped with narrow yellow or white crossbands. The common king snake is found throughout the United States south of latitude forty.

Blanchard's red king snake inhabits North Carolina and Virginia east of the Allegheny Mountains.

The four-foot yellow-bellied king snake is colored pale grayish brown spotted with dark brown, and inhabits the central States.

KING SNAKE

The brown king snake (three feet long) is light brown, blotched with red, and is found in Maryland, south to Florida and west to Alabama.

Holbrook's king snake inhabits Alabama, west to Texas and north to Illinois.

Boyle's king snake, colored black or brown, with white or yellow crossbands, is found in Arizona, Nevada, and California.

The striped king is dark brown or black, striped with a yellow band, found exclusively in southern California.

The Davis Mountain king was observed on Davis Mountain, Texas.

TWO species of the king snake closely resemble the poisonous coral snake and are falsely designated with the coral name. The true coral snake is ringed with broad red and black bands, bordered with narrow rings of yellow. The scarlet king snake or false "coral" snake has similar red and yellow rings, except that the black stripes which border the yellow are narrower. The head of the coral snake is rounded and the snout is black; that of the king snake is sharp and conical, the snout red.

The "coral" king snake is a gentle creature that spends most of its time burrowing under decaying trees and hiding under vegetation. It feeds primarily upon smaller snakes, lizards, and young mice.

The scarlet king snake or false "coral" snake is found in North Carolina and Kentucky, south to Florida and Louisiana. The California "coral" snake is one of the most colorful of the species.

A WIDESPREAD myth credits the milk snake with the ac-

KING SNAKE EGGS.
Hans L. Stecher

complishment of abstracting milk from cows. Because of this ill-founded superstition the harmless milk snake has been subjected to much abuse by the farmer, who does not hesitate to destroy one of his most valuable friends.

Fond of mice and young rats, the milk snake consumes innumerable rodents which plague the agriculturist and endanger his crops. It is, however, none too eager to drink milk, couldn't do so even if it wanted to, for it is rarely thirsty and when it is, its liquid capacity is two teaspoonfuls of water.

Because of widespread decimation, the milk snake is a secretive creature, making its home under flat stones or in debris, and in dairies and cellars. In the late afternoon or at twilight it ventures from its haunt in search of rats, mice, slugs, and young lizards. In the summer, usually in July, it deposits six to eighteen leathery-skinned eggs, hiding them under logs, boards, or in rubbish piles. For a period of six weeks to two months the female hatches her brood, coiling itself about the eggs.

Five species of the milk snake are found in the United States. The common milk snake is three feet long, gray in color and spotted with brown or black patches. It inhabits the eastern United States, from New York to South Carolina, west to Iowa. The red milk snake is found in the Central States; the western milk snake is familiar from South Dakota to Texas; the Arizona milk snake is found in Utah and Arizona. Another species is Cope's milk snake, found in the lower Mississippi Valley from Mississippi to Texas.

SHARP-NOSED SNAKES

THE sharp-nosed snake spends most of its waking hours burrowing in search of food. Extremely cautious, it glides noiselessly toward its prey and, twisting its head rapidly, seizes the victim and winds its coils tightly about the struggling body. To ground lizards, brown snakes, young ring-necked snakes, and young wild mice, the sharp-nosed snake is a dangerous and merciless constrictor. Its hunger pangs gone, however, it is a docile and friendly creature.

SHARP-NOSED SNAKES

The length of the sharp-nosed snakes varies from eight to twenty-four inches, depending on the particular species. Their stout bodies are covered with smooth shiny scales, and are generally brilliantly colored. Oviparous, they deposit small elongated eggs, and at least one of the species, the scarlet snake, has been observed swallowing its own potential brood—this it did in captivity, however.

Sharp-nosed snakes are found throughout the United States. Of the ten species only the scarlet snake and the worm snake have been studied sufficiently to warrant description of their peculiar habits.

LeConte's snake, the largest of the sharp-nosed snakes, measures two feet in length. Its body is spotted with black and red blotches. The rostral plate of the head is sharp and extends over the mouth. This species is found in western Texas, and from western Kansas to California.

The sixteen-inch, slender scarlet or "coral" snake is extremely colorful, and is sometimes mistaken for the smaller of the scarlet king snakes, which it often imitates, as well as the poisonous coral snake. The cylindrical body is covered with wide scarlet blotches, the abdomen is white, and the top of the head is orange with a black bar extending from eye to eye. Against the background of decaying trees, in its habitat in the southeastern United States, the vivid coloring of the scarlet snake is sharp and outstanding. Unlike the coral snake that it superficially resembles, it is non-poisonous and entirely harmless.

The worm snake is colored chestnut-brown above, salmon-pink below. Measuring only ten inches in length, its coloration blending with the damp leaves, the worm snake is furtive, extremely difficult to observe. Most of its days are spent in subterranean passages, where it hunts for earthworms and the soft-bodied grubs of insects. In July or August it deposits a few elongated soft-shelled eggs and five weeks later hatches out a brood of tiny specimens which are smaller than earthworms. It is found along the Atlantic coast from southern Massachusetts to the Gulf, and west to Kansas, but is especially numerous in the Black Mountains of western North Carolina.

Other species are the pale-brown Taylor's snake of Texas; the yellow ground snake found in Oklahoma, Texas, and west to

California; the red and black ground snake of Arizona and southern California; Strecker's hook-nosed snake—a recently discovered species, twelve inches long, ashy gray in color, described by Dr. Taylor.

The banded ground snake is red or orange above, striped with black crossbands. The head of this snake is black, the snout red or orange, and the abdomen is white. It inhabits the arid plains of the central United States.

The snout of the ringed ground snake is more pointed than in any of the other species. Colored milk-white or yellow, with a narrow black band circling the body, it is found in Colorado, Utah, Arizona, and southern California.

Cope's hook-nosed snake, reddish or orange-yellow on top, striped with reddish brown crossbands, inhabits western Texas and Arizona, and is the smallest of the sharp-nosed snakes, measuring eight inches in length.

GREEN SNAKE

DEEP in the recesses of vegetation at the edge of the forest the myriad forms of wildlife are pleasantly astir. There are the chirping of crickets, the drone of bees, the hopping of grasshoppers and frogs, the flitting of rabbits, and the busy burrowing of moles and mice. Suddenly there is the sound of dogs barking and twigs cracking as footsteps approach. The wildlife is still—gone in hasty flight for the nearest shelter. That is, all but the green snake. Entwined on a leafy branch, the green snake drowses on apparently unconscious of any danger. And why not? Who can see its slim body against that natural backdrop of vegetation in which it appears like a moss-covered creeper on a stem?

In the leaf-green color of the green snake, nature has devised one of her almost perfect camouflages. Surprised in the open, the green snake will speed for the nearest foliage, and then subside to a slow crawl no matter how closely pursued, as if aware of its protection. So difficult is it to distinguish in its green background that collectors have found it easier to shake the bushes on the edge of fields where it is found rather than hunt for the body of each individual snake. Green snakes appear to come by their color naturally, as, of the two varieties in this country, one is strictly arboreal and the other shows arboreal tendencies. This is rare among snakes, though common with lizards.

Strange as it may seem, the very coloring of the snake that protects it in the animal world, makes it especially feared in the case of humans. It is believed that the color is the sign of a poisonous secretion. There are, however, no poisonous green snakes in the United States and Canada, and in the case of those in the tropics, the color has nothing to do with poisonous qualities. As a matter of fact, green snakes are known to herpetologists as among the gentlest of all snakes. Even rough handling on the first contact with humans elicits no sign of anger on the part of the snake. It cannot even be induced to bite, the minute teeth being quite ineffective except for use on such small prey as spiders, grasshoppers, crickets, and smooth green caterpillars which they swallow whole. As insect eaters, moreover, they are especially useful to man, so their destruction is doubly unfortunate.

The smaller smooth-scaled variety of green snake is one of the few types of snakes found as far north as Canada. More earthbound than the other type, it is also known as the grass snake. The larger keel-scaled variety is also known as the green whip snake, because, like the whip snakes of the tropics, it sticks its tongue out straight without spreading the black forked tips or waving them as most snakes do. The tongue is a pale flesh color and very noticeable as it protrudes from the green head. This organ probably serves as an aid in hearing.

RING-NECKED SNAKE

WONDER and admiration of its striking color pattern often overcomes fear in the case of the ring-necked snake, another species seldom two feet long, a quarter of an inch in diameter, and quite harmless. The bright-yellow, orange, or pinkish band around the neck contrasts sharply with the solid dark-gray or brown body color; the abdomen is also bright, usually conforming to the collar, though often spotted. Dr. Ditmars has received many specimens of this species sent in containers through the mail from individuals who believed they had found a new and rare type of serpent. In reality ring-necked snakes are not at all rare, being spread generally over the country and adapted to diverse conditions.

An interesting feature of both the eastern ring-necked and smooth-scaled green snakes is that both apparently exemplify the transition between egg-laying and live-bearing types. Both, like most small snakes, are classed among the oviparous or egg-laying species which they resemble structurally, but both have been known to bear live young. The comparatively short incubation period, and large size of the newborn, also indicate a close approach to the viviparous or live-bearing forms. Heat and other environmental factors account for the great variability of four to twenty-three days in this period observed in the case of the green snake, and make understandable the several recorded cases of the birth of live young in favorable conditions of captivity.

The elongate eggs of these varieties tend to become twisted into irregular shapes. The thin shell dents to the touch and discloses the dark embryo inside. Upon breaking the shell with its teeth, the young will poke its head through tentatively and withdraw inside many times before finally emerging. If nothing seriously alarms it, the hatching may take from a half to a full day; if there is any disturbance it will be indefinitely postponed. The eggs, usually laid in a well-protected spot under a sun-warmed rock, are quite devoid of a mother's care. After the youngsters shed their birth skin within the first hour, they become very lively.

The eastern ring-necked snake has a special liking for the anthills found under loose logs and rocks of mountainous regions, suggesting some sort of mutual aid, though yet unexplained. It is omnivorous and nocturnal in its habits. Also nocturnal probably is the rock snake, a small gray or yellow type with dark-brown blotches on back and sides, which, because of the elliptical pupil of its eye and large rear teeth of its upper jaw, has led some to associate it with the rear-fanged poisonous snakes. However, it is harmless—not even mildly poisonous.

The coral-bellied ring-necked snake has the curious habit of lifting and twisting its tail in a way suggesting the entwining propensities of the larger constrictors such as the snake-eating king snake. It also appears to live on small burrowing snakes as well as small salamanders and earthworms. That it actually uses constriction on its prey, however, is somewhat doubtful, as the tail movement may merely be imitation or use of flash colors in turning up its red abdomen to frighten enemies—maneuvers well known in the serpent kingdom.

In the case of the silver-gray short-tailed snake, one of the small burrowing varieties with a two-inch tail, it is definitely known that the snake constricts its prey. Also partly cannibalistic, it is believed to be a small, degenerate descendant of the king snake group although this fact is not well established.

The smooth-scaled green snake, which is fifteen inches long and white underneath, is found from southern Canada through the eastern United States to Florida, in the Central States west to North Dakota and Colorado, and south to Texas and New Mexico. The ridge-scaled variety, which is about thirty inches long and yellow underneath, roams from Connecticut to Florida, west to New Mexico, and up the Mississippi Valley as far north as Illinois. Ring-necked snakes, comprising about a dozen varieties ranging in length from fourteen inches to two feet, are scattered all over the country. The other types of miscellaneous small snakes, most of which are about a foot long, are limited to certain localities in the South.

RAINBOW SNAKE

GLIDING out of the slime of southern swamps, the rainbow snake, the handsomest of all North American snakes, exhibits a flash of colors just as startling as the dazzling chromatic display in the sky after a storm. Three rich red or orange stripes on the back and a broad yellow one on the sides are set off by the dark-purple body color. The gloss of the smooth scales adds a luster that is all the more effective because of the drab surroundings in which the snake is usually found.

Gentle and harmless, there is only one drawback to the proper appreciation of this handsome serpent; it is seldom seen. A degenerate burrower, it seldom comes to the surface. Its minute tongue and eyes in the forward part of its head are out of all proportion to its five-foot body length. All the force of its vitality seems to have found expression in its vivid color pattern.

In captivity the snake also hides itself at once in the sand or moss of its cage, or, lacking a burrowing element, it soon dies. Until recently, adult specimens refused food, although the young took earthworms. This was apparently due more to the type of food offered, however, than to any sullenness on the part of the snake, since it is now reported to feed voraciously if given mud eels or sirens. It attacks these tailed amphibian salamanders hungrily.

Both species of rainbow snake, each representing a different genera, have a red abdomen. One, however, lacks the black abdominal spots, and is known as the red-bellied snake, red points penetrating up the sides. It is also known as the stinging, horn, or hoop snake. This is because it has a small spiny scale at the end of its tail which it sometimes uses as a kind of flail, and because it often forms itself into a circle. Although without a real sting or any venomous secretion, the startling rapidity of its tail maneuver and spur have led to a widespread but erroneous belief among the uninitiate that it is dangerous. Herpetologists believe it to be merely an instrument for use in subduing and puncturing the soft, slippery bodies of the mud eels on which the snake feeds. But many people in the South still cling to the notion that the snake rolls swiftly after humans in a hoop, and then attacks with its "sting."

The female of both species lays between twenty-four and fifty smooth white eggs, usually in July or August, which hatch in September or October. The only instance of breeding habits observed and reported, however, is that of a pair of red-bellied snakes. Mating early in the morning of July 11, the much smaller male lay rigid at right angles across the tail of the female, most of whose body remained loosely coiled. During the day they emerged from the water to the concrete floor of the cage, and at night returned to the pool, remaining coupled all the time. The next morning they had separated, and displayed as little interest in each other as they had before their mating. Twenty-eight smooth, elongate, white eggs were deposited by the female on September 5. Placed in warm boxes with sugarcane residue, they enlarged to the size of small hen's eggs, two and a half times their original bulk. Nineteen hatched on October 30 or shortly after; the young were exact miniatures of the adults, ranging from six to nine inches long. They burrowed at once and shed their skins in a week, it is reported in *Copeia* by George P. Mead.

The rainbow snake is found along the swampy coasts of South Carolina, Georgia, and Florida; also from Virginia to the Gulf of Mexico and Alabama. The red-bellied snake is found from North Carolina, south through Florida, and west to Louisiana; also north in the Mississippi Basin to Indiana.

A subspecies is recognized and ranges from extreme western Florida northward in the lowlands to southern Indiana and southeastern Missouri; westward along the coast to about the 97th meridian.

HOG-NOSED SNAKE

THE hog-nosed snake is the chief exponent of the art of acting among snakes. Although without fangs, poison, or a constricting capacity, and comparatively small, it can by flattening its head and neck, and hissing, make itself appear almost as ferocious as the most dreaded cobras of the Old World. When molested, it will coil its tail, raise its head, and, taking a deep breath in perfect imitation of a venomous species, spread its hood to almost three times the normal size. Hissing loudly, it begins to strike, though it cannot be induced to bite.

Nor is this all. If pugnacious tactics fail to ward off danger, it will resort to the opposite course, and simulate death as though suddenly struck down by the mere threat of danger before it. It opens its mouth, goes into convulsions until exhausted, then it rolls over on its back as though dead. Vigorous handling, moreover, while in this state will produce no sign of life in the snake. The only flaw in the show is that the snake has learned its lesson too well, for when placed on its abdomen it will immediately roll over on its back again as though this were the only position suitable to the dead, assuming it even when it has been surprised trying to run off, after believing itself alone.

Why doesn't it run off in the first place? Perhaps because it is too stout to move rapidly, and then, too, its stubby form and flat head give it a pugnacious look. Thus there are good reasons for this creature's tantrums.

Known variously as spreading adder, puff adder, blow snake, and blowing viper in localities where it is erroneously believed to be poisonous, it would better be termed the star bluffer. Its only potency is in the large fangs in its rear jaw. These, however, are invisible, and used only to puncture the bodies of frogs which resist being swallowed by inhaling deeply and puffing up. The sharp shield-protected snout is used to root out toads buried in soft soil near the surface.

The most common of the four or five varieties is yellow-brown in color, crossed by brown or black bands. The female lays about

HOG-NOSED SNAKE *(Heterodon contortrix)*. Length: 3 feet. Range: Southeastern Canada, eastern and southern United States. Harmless.
New York Zoological Society

REAR-FANGED SNAKE

HOG-NOSED SNAKE PLAYING DEAD.
Joe Hall

two dozen eggs during the latter part of July. They adhere in a cluster, and gradually grow till a third larger and irregularly shaped, before hatching in the early fall.

The common and black varieties of hog-nosed snakes roam from Massachusetts to central Florida, and west to Minnesota, Kansas, and central Texas. The stouter, smaller southern type is limited to South Carolina, Florida, and the intervening area to the Mississippi. The western variety inhabits the western States.

POISONOUS SNAKES

REAR-FANGED SNAKE

WHEN night falls on the mesas and canyons of the Southwest, many creatures begin their "day." Out of fissures of rock so narrow as to be unnoticeable, from under slabs of stone no man can move, out of holes in the desert sand or fertile valley glide an army of slim little creatures. The shadows hold no terror for them, for they can see in them and remain unseen themselves. And should they get their tiny jaws well up on the sides of a stray lizard, frog, or young snake, all they need do is hold on and wait till the poison from their rear fangs takes effect. But in the morning they are all gone again to doze in the sheltering rocks and sand. For the magic of their movements disappears in daylight. The light is too blinding and the heat too suffocating.

These are the nocturnal rear-fanged snakes, which well illustrate the first development in the large group of harmless snakes of that dread power of poison and cunning that has made the serpent the most feared of creatures. Virtually harmless to man, they yet represent the link to the most specialized types. They are quite small —thirty inches or less—and their half-inch rear fangs are grooved on the sides to catch poison from the glands above instead of being perforated and emitting it from the tip as in the dangerous types. The poison, too, is mild, experiments showing it ineffective on mice or rats. But the fangs and poison are there for the first time in the evolutionary series. So too are the broad, flat heads, and the bulging eyes with their elliptical pupils for night vision.

The poisonous glands, which automatically release their contents when the fangs are imbedded, appear to be a development of the chemical resource of snakes, shown in their ability to dissolve and digest all sorts of prey swallowed whole. In this elementary group the jaws, after gripping a victim, advance in a chewing motion till the fangs come into play. Having imbedded these, the snake waits a minute or two for the victim to stop struggling and grow perfectly limp, which takes two or three minutes more. After that it starts engulfing the prize, head foremost, keeping the limbs folded against the body.

Although only one branch of the subfamily to which these rear-fanged serpents belong is found in this country, it contains many types, exemplifying the diversity found in the largest and most harmless group of snakes. Only the two largest and flat-headed genera, however, are truly nocturnal and potentially dangerous. These are popularly known as the lyre snake, for the marking on top of its head, and the bush or annulated snakes. Both are very similar, with broad, distinct heads and broad black or brown blotches, but the latter lack the lyre mark and minor technical details of the former.

An arboreal type is the Arizona vine or long-headed snake. Much more slender but just as long as the foregoing, its tail comprises two-

LYRE SNAKE *(Trimorphodon vandenburghi)*. Length: 2½ feet. Range: Southern California and Clark County, Nevada. Mildly poisonous.
L. M. Klauber

thirds of the body length and the reptile weighs only an ounce or two. It is closely related to a tropical variety of green snake, which has the art of waving its neck and head like a leaf in the breeze, making it virtually impossible of detection, even at close quarters.

The black-banded snake is also slender but only about fourteen inches long. Unlike the other mentioned, its head is rather indistinct. It is pale brown in color with a black band on the back and either side. It is also the slowest-moving of the entire group. The slender black-headed snake, just as small, is, on the other hand, the most agile of the group. According to L. M. Klauber, who has studied all these snakes, it may often be found in groups of half a dozen, but few are ever caught because of their quickness.

Since they are all secretive or nocturnal in habits, little is known of the breeding habits of rear-fanged snakes. All are egg-laying, however, and females of the bush snake deposit as many as two dozen eggs at a time. Because of timidity or viciousness, none of the group makes a good pet. The lyre snake has a habit of vibrating its tail very rapidly when annoyed, much like a rattlesnake, and has also been observed to burrow in pursuit of prey and constrict in subduing it.

Three varieties of lyre snake have been recognized. The Arizona lyre snake is light gray in color and found in Arizona, Utah, and Lower California; Vandenburgh's lyre snake is darker, browner, and more spotted, and found in southern California and in Clarke County, Nevada; Wilkinson's lyre snake, marked with narrow black crossbands, is found in western Texas and northern Mexico.

The bush snake inhabits southern Texas and northeastern Mexico; the reddish Arizona vine snake, Arizona; and the black-banded snake, Mexico to southern Texas. The half dozen varieties of black-headed snake, equally divided between those having a collar band and those lacking it, are most widespread, ranging in nearly all the southern States from Virginia and Florida to California.

CORAL SNAKE

RELATED to the deadly front-fanged poisonous serpents of Australasia and Africa—cobras, tiger snakes, and death adders—the American coral snakes, although outwardly passive and sluggish, are among the world's deadliest serpents. What small evidence there is seems to indicate that their bites are fatal fifty per cent of the time. The venom injected by coral snakes attacks the nervous system and will cause death within twenty-four hours.

Coral snakes are so named because of the bright coral red pattern of rings arranged alternately with rings of black and red over their bodies. These brilliant serpents never grow to great size, rarely reaching three feet in length in the United States. An additional source

CORAL SNAKE

of danger from coral snakes is the resemblance they bear to several species of harmless snakes similarly colored. Most frequently confused with the coral snakes are LeConte's snake, the Arizona king snake, and the western milk snake of the southwestern States; and the scarlet king snake and scarlet snake of the South. Closer examination, however, reveals that with the coral snakes, the black rings are bordered on each side by yellow ones; the harmless snakes have yellow rings bordered with black. Another point to remember is that the coral snakes have rings that completely encircle the body; the harmless snakes have abdomens that are either a uniform white or blotched. Finally and easiest to remember, perhaps, is the fact that the true coral snake alone has a black-tipped head.

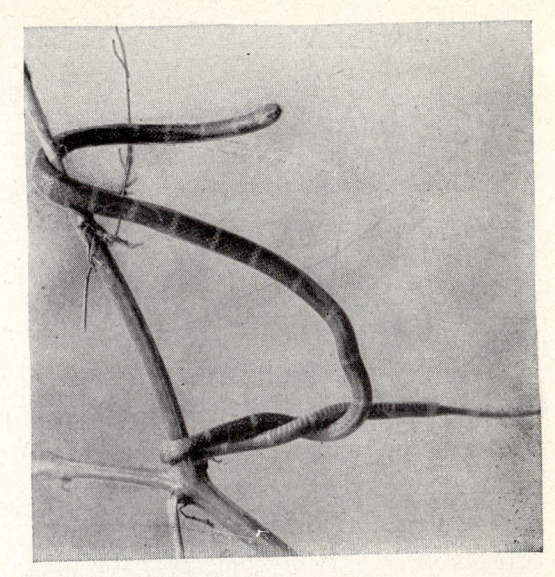

CORAL SNAKE *(Micrurus fulvius)*. Length: 3 feet. Range: Southern and mid-western United States. Dangerously poisonous but rarely encountered by man.
New York Zoological Society

The two coral snakes of this country are the harlequin snake of the Southeast and the Gulf States extending to southern Ohio up the Mississippi Valley, its subspecies, Barbour's coral snake of extreme southern Florida, and the Sonora coral snake of southern New Mexico and Arizona extending into Mexico.

The Sonora coral snake may be distinguished from the harlequin coral snake by the fact that its red and black rings are of equal breadth. These red and black rings are narrower than those of the harlequin snake, while the yellow rings that separate them are broader. The Sonora snake, considerably smaller than its southeastern relative, attains an average length of fifteen inches.

The angry coral snake gives no warning. Unlike other snakes which strike at the source of annoyance, the coral snake shifts uneasily about, as if to disarm the offender, and then with lightning rapidity seizes upon the hand with its jaws, chewing savagely until it has injected venom in several places with its short teeth.

These degenerate reptiles spend much of their time burrowing beneath bark, loose earth, and decayed stumps where they pursue the blue-tailed lizard of which they are fond. They eat their prey with savage gusto which belies a generally torpid appearance. If the victim puts up any resistance, the coral snake will bite it repeatedly, meanwhile working its jaws to the point where it may swallow the lizard or snake head first. Eventually the venom ends the creature's struggles and it is swallowed whole.

Coral snakes fare poorly in captivity as they require a temperature above seventy-five degrees Fahrenheit and several inches of moss in which to burrow. When so provided for they spend most of their time hiding from the light.

Coral snakes lay seven or more eggs during the summer months. The young when first hatched are immediately belligerent and will attempt to defend themselves with their tiny fangs.

COTTONMOUTH MOCCASIN

A SINISTER appearance is lent the cottonmouth moccasin by the sullen droop to its mouth and the overhanging shields which give the impression of beetle-browed, glowering eyes. Appearances in this case are not very deceiving; the heavy-bodied cottonmouth is inclined to have an irritable temperament.

The snake's fighting spirit is demonstrated at an early age. Even before it is completely out of its embryonic membrane, it will bite fiercely at a moving object. At birth it is already equipped with enough venom to inject a strong dose. A full-grown specimen, which may reach a length of six feet, is a magnified example of infantile bad temper. A cottonmouth one night entered the cage of a South American anaconda, three times its size, and in the morning the larger serpent was dead, reports Dr. Ditmars.

COTTONMOUTH MOCCASIN

The cottonmouth inhabits southeastern swamplands and the Mississippi River region. Sometimes it lolls about on branches overhanging the water and, if frightened, may drop off and swim away underwater. When it is surprised, it throws back its head and opens its mouth wide, revealing the cause of its name. If the cottonmouth can flee after this display, it does so. If it is cornered, it beats a rhythmic tattoo with its tail and lunges forward to drive home its poison-bearing fangs.

When a hungry cottonmouth attacks a small creature, it begins to swallow almost as soon as its fangs strike and before the venom's work is done. A larger creature receives more deliberate handling. The cottonmouth's jaws are clamped about the victim and held securely until resistance succumbs to the spreading poison. The snake's prey includes almost any of the smaller vertebrate creatures, whether they be mammals, birds, reptiles, amphibians, or fishes. It is not finicky about its food and even eats harmless snakes which live in the neighborhood, though it will not eat other cottonmouths.

COTTONMOUTH MOCCASIN *(Agkistrodon piscivorus)*. Length: 5 feet. Range: Southeastern United States, Gulf states. Dangerously poisonous.
From Ditmars' "Reptiles of North America"

This snake is olive or brownish in color. Its abdomen is yellow and is marked by blobs of a darker hue.

In captivity it grows sluggish and comparatively amiable. A specimen lived more or less happily in confinement for twenty-one years. It may even catch a cold, as did one whose nose and mouth ran as it sneezed heartily. The cottonmouth sometimes emits an evil-smelling glandular fluid when it is handled.

COPPERHEAD

THE brown and copper pattern of the copperhead's skin melts indiscernibly into a background of dry leaves. Safely concealed, the poisonous snake is well content in its solitude and rarely evinces a desire to seek trouble, especially in the form of an encounter with human beings.

It gives active proof of its retiring disposition. A man coming upon a copperhead may not even see the reptile, which ignores all tradition and glides discreetly away. Of course when stepped on—and the snake cannot be expected to know that it was done unintentionally—or when attacked, it casts aside the cloak of shyness and steps forth a valorous and dangerous warrior.

For example, should a copperhead be pinned down under a stick wielded by an enterprising hunter, it throws itself wholeheartedly, desperately, into the struggle to free itself. It lashes about with such rage that part of its body may be hurled against its own bared fangs. This is the nearest approach in actuality to the tales of snakes swallowing themselves, for the copperhead's fangs may inflict a nasty wound. Like all poisonous snakes, however, it is immune to its own venom.

If a copperhead is cornered as it lolls about in the open, it creates a buzzing sound by the vibration of its tail in the dry grass or leaves. Its triangular head lunges forward, fangs extended, to ward off the enemy. Meanwhile, however, its body may execute a series of sinuous loops and, though striking forward with its head, the snake may really be retreating. It prefers withdrawal into the security of a crevice to the risk of battle.

COPPERHEAD

This beautifully colored brownish reptile, named for its coppery tint, is the most common poisonous snake found near eastern cities, though its range extends into the Central States. Most cases of snake bite in the East are therefore attributed to the copperhead. Its bite is rarely fatal, however, since its venom is not as virulent as a rattle-

COPPERHEAD SNAKE *(Agkistrodon mokasen)*. Length: 2½ feet. Range: Eastern United States. Poisonous.
Ralph De Sola (SIZ)

snake's and the amount injected is smaller. It cannot, as a general rule, kill a healthy adult; nevertheless, the danger of a copperhead bite should not be underestimated. The prevalence of this snake around populous sections is shown by the recent discovery of a record specimen, almost four and a half feet long, near White Plains, only a few miles from New York City.

The copperhead glides about rocky ledges, woods, and marshy terrain in search of insects, rodents, frogs, birds, and smaller snakes. Its victims need not be pursued, for they will virtually walk into the mouth of the copperhead as it lays concealed by its protective coloring. The young are perhaps more ingeniously equipped for hunting. During the first few years of their life they have a bright yellow tail whose wiggling attracts inquisitive creatures. As soon as they approach the copperhead's jaws spring open to seize the unwary interloper. The Texas variety of copperhead retains a greenish-yellow tail throughout life. Two other subspecies are also known.

Often the copperhead sinks its fangs into a large animal and then permits it to go free while the venom does its fatal work. After a while the snake searches for the carcass, which it tests cautiously with its tongue. Assured that all is well, the copperhead swallows the prey head first. A smaller victim may be bitten and then held between the jaws until *rigor mortis* sets in. And tiny creatures, like baby mice, may simply be gulped down.

Copperheads mate soon after emerging from the crevices in which they hibernate. The females gather in secluded spots to give birth to their young, usually six to nine in a litter. Within an hour after birth, the ten-inch infant copperhead has enough venom to kill a mouse, although it may not demonstrate its prowess at once.

RATTLESNAKE

RATTLESNAKE bites recorded in this country have been fatal in only fifteen per cent of all cases not properly treated. The smaller rattlers do not secrete enough venom to kill a man. The larger ones like the great diamondbacks have such capacious poison glands that if they were loaded with the venom of the Australian tiger snake, one load could kill four hundred men, Clifford H. Pope calculates in his book *Snakes Alive*.

It is hard for the average person to think of the rattlesnake as a shrinking violet, yet this notorious serpentine killer is shy and retiring. Rattlers do not strike when unprovoked, and even when encroached upon, they lie quiet, hoping to escape detection. Finally, when there is no alternative, the frightened reptiles make a stand, their warning rattles sounding like the hiss of escaping steam punctuated with sudden buzzes. The body is thrown into an S-shaped posture which will permit the snake to strike for a distance sometimes exceeding half its length. The striking motion is so swift

RATTLESNAKE

as to be invisible; only the momentary blur of the open mouth is seen as the snake prepares to withdraw its head. The mouth is closed until just before the fangs actually make contact with the victim. These hypodermic organs lie folded against the roof of the mouth and spring erect just in time to inject poison into the victim from ducts leading to the poison sacs.

Extracting the fangs is no guaranty against snake bite, as snake charmers have discovered through painful experience, because reserve teeth quickly grow in. Deeper operations, like taking out the

EASTERN DIAMOND-BACK RATTLESNAKE *(Crotalus adamanteus)*.
Length: 8 feet. Range: Southeastern United States west to Louisiana and Arkansas.
Dangerously poisonous.
L. M. *Klauber*

PRAIRIE RATTLESNAKES *(Crotalus v. viridis)*. Length: 3 feet. Range: Great Plains of southern Canada and the United States. Poisonous.

Ralph De Sola (SIZ)

reserve teeth or the poison sacs themselves usually have resulted in the death of the snake. A technique recently developed now successfully removes the venom glands. Oddly enough, the fangs continue to grow even after the glands have been removed.

Rattlers live everywhere. While the greater number prefer arid or semiarid brushland, rattlers may climb mountains as high as 14,500 feet, or pick their way through forests and swamps. They have been seen swimming in lakes and rivers—even in the ocean. According to L. M. Klauber, there are about forty species and subspecies of rattlers. The largest of these, the eastern diamond-backed rattlesnake, grows to an average of seven and one-half feet in length; Willard's pigmy, a diminutive pest local to Arizona and New Mexico, achieves all of fifteen inches. Of the whole fearsome tribe the western diamond-backed rattlesnake has been awarded the palm as killer-in-chief.

Sometimes the skins of enormous rattlers are exhibited in circuses and side shows. These "colossal" trophies are achieved by stretching the hides of ordinary large snakes to twice their size. Often extra segments of rattle are added. Real and unimproved record specimens of the great eastern diamond-backed rattler reach about nine feet in length.

During the spring and autumn, rattlers forage for their food by day, but during the hot season appear only after sunset. The direct heat of the southern sun will kill a rattler in less than a quarter of an hour. With the first frost, these delicate reptiles retire underground to snake dens or fissures in the rocks extending sometimes as much as thirty feet below the surface. There, intertwined in a state of torpor, they spend the cold months. Large numbers of them collect in these favorable retreats and it is at such times that the problem of rattlesnake eradication is most successfully coped with. Poison gases and liquids have been employed against the rattlers with varying success. It is unfortunate that this snake is dangerous to humans, for economically it is an asset. The service it renders to farmers by killing field rats and mice is inestimable. Conversely, the best method of ridding a vicinity of rattlers is to diminish the rodent population to the point where it will no longer support snakes. In August and September rattlers bear from eight to ten young.

Other economic uses of the rattlesnake are the yielding of its skin for the manufacture of fancy leather goods, and its flesh, which is canned in Florida for the delectation of epicures. A rattlesnake oil sold in the Orient and at American side shows is alleged to relieve the twinges of rheumatism, cure gout, and grow hair on "billiard balls."

In addition, rattlers create an economic demand which they supply themselves. Their venom is extracted and manufactured into anti-venin used in the treatment of rattlesnake bite. Experimentation is proceeding in the use of venom to cure epilepsy and other disorders.

Beginning as a single button, the rattle makes its appearance after the first skin has been shed. With each shedding an additional segment appears. Most specimens have rattles composed of five or six segments. Occasionally, in snakes like the sidewinder rattler which inhabits sandy locations, the rattles may be longer because there is little in the terrain to break them off. As many as fifteen segments have been noted. But the number of segments, except when the button is still present, is a poor way to tell the age of the snake, because of breakage.

Rattlers have two types of toxin in their venom. One toxin breaks down the walls of small blood vessels, dissolves cells, and paralyzes nerve centers, making breathing difficult and causing congestion. The other type prevents the clotting of blood, thus causing hemorrhage.

When first captured, rattlers can be kept alive only through forced feeding with eggs and viosterol or some similar highly vitaminized preparation. Nervous and intolerant of handling, they fly into defensive tantrums. Later they will eat live rodents, but if annoyed during the kill will regurgitate them.

Rattlers play an important part in the religious life of the Hopi Indians. During the ceremonial snake dance, live rattlers

SIDEWINDER or HORNED RATTLER *(Crotalus cerastes)*. Length: 2½ feet. Range: Southwestern United States. Poisonous.
L. M. Klauber

are handled by priests and young boys without apparent harm. Large numbers of the snakes are caught before the great festival in summer and stored in earthenware jars. Attendants wash and dry them, passing them easily through their hands in the process. During the dances the priests even put the snakes in their mouths. The fangs are not withdrawn, yet for some unknown reason the snakes inflict no injuries on their handlers.

The rattlesnake was so familiar in early American settlements that it was used as a revolutionary emblem on a colonial flag with the warning: "Don't tread on me." Found all over the United States, rattlers reach their greatest abundance in the Southwest, Arizona harboring the greatest number of subspecies, fifteen. Mr. Klauber says that rattlers are probably more numerous now in certain localities than they were in primitive times because of the destruction of competing predators which shared the available rodent population with them.

Turtles

Nature has bestowed upon the order of turtles one of its most ingenious protective devices, the two shells which, joined at the sides by bony bridges, encircle these reptiles. The development of this armor doubtless accounts for their venerable history; turtles plodded about in the days when dinosaurs reigned supreme and since then many kinds of animals have come and gone but the turtles are still here.

Turtles are in general the most gentle of American reptiles and few of them are equipped to carry on a serious offensive battle. Their mainstay lies in defense, which is usually an almost invulnerable carapace, or upper shell, and a plastron, or lower shell. The shell is formed by flat ribs, fused together, with a horny covering. But the armor varies from that of the box turtle, which can completely encase itself in its hard shells, to the soft-shelled turtle, whose flabby cartilaginous carapace is little more protection than a pancake, which it resembles.

There are many other divergences in the physical attributes and habits of these four-legged creatures. Some of the turtles, it is true,

SNAPPING TURTLES HATCHING.
American Museum of Natural History

are of nasty disposition and dangerous, while others cannot inflict any injury and seem too mild to harm anyone if they could. Turtles do just about everything but fly, for among them are sea dwellers, pond dwellers, those dividing time between land and water, land-lubbers of the first order, and even turtles which live underground. Land dwellers, or tortoises, have domical top shells and elephantine legs; turtles, whose realm is the ocean, have flippers instead of legs; and terrapins, equally at home in land or water, have feet which are webbed between the nails.

They range in size from the four-inch mud turtle to the huge trunkback turtle sometimes more than eight feet long and weighing three-quarters of a ton. They have different dietary habits, too, some being meat eaters, others vegetarians, and others not fussy enough to give any type of food a second thought. But it is probably just these differences which permitted them to fit into an environment and survive, while many kindred reptiles have passed from the scene forever.

SNAPPING TURTLES

COMMON SNAPPING TURTLE

THE snapping turtle plods along on land in a quiet unassuming manner, its shell held clear of the ground. It seems meek enough ordinarily but if its ire is roused the snapper becomes a dangerous creature. Should a finger then be within striking distance, the turtle elevates its hind parts and shoots its beaked head forward with such impetus that the whole body skids ahead. The snapper clamps down on its target with a beak as sharp and powerful as a pair of heavy shears with ragged, keen blades. A well-directed snap can completely amputate a man's finger and the turtle's proclivity for indulging in such exercise (even when a finger is not available) accounts for its name.

The brown-shelled snapper has the deceptive appearance of a mud-encrusted, algae-coated rock as it lurks motionlessly on the bottom of a shallow pond or stream. Consequently it is able with little effort to gobble up unsuspecting fishes as they swim directly over its head. Like most turtles, the snapper, whose shell is fourteen inches long and whose average weight is twenty pounds, is as inactive as possible. But when food is at hand it moves with dexterous speed, as it surely must, to seize fast-moving insects and fishes.

Should the snapper sense a small waterfowl floating about overhead, it brings all its skill and acumen into play. It speeds upward through the placid water and, when it is just beneath its prey, relentlessly clamps its mighty beak on the bird's limbs. The snapper swerves back and the ruffled waters quickly close over its captive's head. The bird is held at the bottom until drowned and then the snapper tears it apart with its claws, eating it morsel by morsel. Many wild ducks are killed yearly in this way. This turtle, however, can go for months without food and its varied diet includes crawfishes, snails, amphibians, fishes, and insects.

Sometimes the snapper clambers ashore to catch a reptile or chicken, but it always drags its find back into the water. It is believed to be able to eat only when underwater; at any rate, it has never been seen feeding without its head submerged.

Despite her aquatic existence, the female snapper marches out on land to find a site for her two dozen eggs. A sandbank is often used, though Dr. Harold L. Babcock once observed a female who unwisely chose the middle of a road. She scoops out a hole and after the eggs have been laid she spreads dirt over them. Forthwith her maternal cares are ended, for she then leaves without even a backward glance at her handiwork.

As soon as the young snappers emerge from the eggs they must begin shifting for themselves. They head instinctively for the water and find their way even if picked up and faced in the opposite direction over and over again. They are so drawn to the water that even death does not deter them. On one occasion, a snapper's head was cut off but the decapitated creature plodded several hundred feet toward its pool before giving up the ghost.

Snapper eggs are preyed upon by raccoons and skunks and similar creatures. As it grows, the snapper is confronted by such enemies as the otter, a ruthless opponent whose nature is demonstrated by its habit of killing a far greater number of fishes than it can eat. When the two clash, the snapper seems to know that its back is to the wall, for it discards every vestige of sluggishness and fights with desperation. But the outcome is foreordained; the otter invariably emerges the undisputed victor, often by biting off the snapper's head.

SNAPPING TURTLE *(Chelydra serpentina)*. Length: 1½ feet. Range: Southern Canada to Ecuador. Dangerous.
New York Zoological Society

Man, too, is probably more of a foe than a friend. Snappers' flesh is considered a delicacy by many persons, especially Chinese-Americans. Farmers used to catch young snappers, throw them in a swill barrel to feast until they fattened up and lost their musky odor, and then killed them for dinner. The swill barrel so agreed with one snapper that it attained a weight of eighty-six pounds. Philadelphia snapper soup is still regarded as a delicacy by many, and in some sections of the country the eggs are eaten fried.

But the snappers harass man by slaughtering fish and fowl, and therefore these turtles are killed to prevent further depredations. A snapping turtle sometimes innocently annoys fishermen by grabbing the hook under water and tugging away with a strength that gives an angler visions of realizing a fish story—only to have the dream dispelled when he sees the clawing snapper.

Authorities suggest that a snapper be picked up—if at all—only by its tail and held at arm's length. If it is held incorrectly, it can swing its beak around with such rapidity and range that it may seize a part of the body or clothing of its captor. Its long neck which makes this feat possible, plus its long tail, give the snapper a total length of three feet.

Any pond, lake, or stream east of the Rockies is a possible haven of the snapping turtle. This was well known to a number of Indian tribes which once inhabited the vast region. The Indians made a rattle by trimming the snapper of virtually everything save its neck and shells, which were loaded with stones and sewn together. A handle was made by inserting a piece of wood through the neck and the finished product was used as a musical instrument during festivals.

ALLIGATOR SNAPPING TURTLE

THE giant of American fresh-water turtledom, the alligator snapping turtle, is reckoned the ugliest and most dangerous by anyone who has encountered it in the rivers of the Gulf coast, the Mississippi Valley region, and in the southeastern States. Four feet long from head to tail, weighing almost one hundred and fifty pounds, it strides ponderously about in slow, stiff-legged fashion. Its massive head contains a pair of jaws which, given the opportunity, can bite off a man's arm or a foot with little difficulty.

It is a magnified edition of the common snapper, and acquired its name because early settlers believed it to be the offspring of an alligator and a common snapper. It has the latter's long, knobby tail but in most other respects it resembles its relative. Three rows of keels jut prominently out on its yellowish top shell. In captivity one specimen lived fifty years.

When it is underwater, it waves the two filaments extending from its tongue. Fishes take the moving objects to be worms and do not recognize the rocklike shell of the snapper. As they come

ALLIGATOR SNAPPING TURTLE

down to swallow the "worms," the turtle's cavernous jaws open to swallow them instead. These great water reptiles also eat snakes, amphibians, and waterfowl, and are in turn eaten by natives of their region.

ALLIGATOR SNAPPING TURTLE *(Macrochelys temminckii)*. Length: 3 feet. Range: Mississippi River region and southern states from Texas to southern Georgia. Dangerous.
Raymond L. Ditmars, New York Zoological Society

Like the common snapper, the female alligator snapper goes ashore to lay her round white-shelled eggs. As she walks, her heavy tail is used to help support her ponderous frame. Not far from the water, frequently in a sandbank, she deposits her twenty to forty eggs—each of them the size of a golf ball. Like the common snapper, too, she digs the hole with her flippers, deposits her eggs, and returns to the water. The eggs are left to hatch in the heat of the sun, and the small turtles, immediately they are hatched, head for the water.

The strength of a full-grown alligator turtle is revealed by its ability to break an oar into small bits by crunching it in its jaws.

MUSK AND MUD TURTLES

MUSK TURTLE

THE puny six-inch musk turtle is an expert at the skunk's defensive game, as it can waft a pall of obnoxious odors over its immediate surroundings. Consequently this four-legged chemistry laboratory has been given such graphic local nicknames as stinkpot and Stinkin' Jenny.

At first glance this turtle seems far too innocuous a creature to be worthy of its formidable reputation. But it is an individual of grouchy temperament, easily annoyed—and whenever it is annoyed it is apt to discharge a musky, yellowish fluid from two glands on each side of its body. That evil-smelling fluid not only sends passers-by scurrying away, but is also believed to be a device by which the musk turtle attracts a mate.

In addition to its frontal attack on the olfactory senses, an angry musk turtle snaps at the source of annoyance in the snapper's best style. Here, however, its small size prevents it from being too dangerous, although it is able to inflict a painful wound.

Protected by its ever-replenished arsenal of musk, the turtle is able to lead an easy life in quiet, slow-moving bodies of water. It crawls about on the bottom where it acquires a coat of mud and green slime which hides the natural dark brown of its top shell as well as such features as the yellow stripes on its large hook-jawed head. It eats, voraciously and indiscriminately, tiny fishes, insects, snails, tadpoles, fish eggs, and bits of vegetation. It also serves as the neighborhood's sanitation department, disposing of dead fishes and waterfowl. These, however, are often too large to be swallowed in one gulp; in that case the turtle grabs hold of the object with its beak and pushes away with its feet until a mouthful is torn off.

It is another of the turtles that would rate high were fishermen to cast their vote in an unpopularity contest. Aside from its depredations among young fishes, it covets the bits of food with which anglers optimistically bait their hooks. When a musk turtle is hooked —to the sorrow of all concerned—it swims off quite fast and puts up a merry tussle. The fisherman needs no persuasion to set his catch free once he sees and smells it.

Most of the musk turtle's time is spent in water, and it has been shown to exist in deeper water than other pond turtles. During the winter the musk turtle digs into the mud on the bottom to hibernate. Late in the spring the female goes ashore to lay from three to seven eggs in rotting tree stumps, reeds, or mud. Females, segregated from males, have continued to lay eggs for four years. The young are but a half-inch long at birth, attaining maturity in a year.

The common musk turtle inhabits the eastern and central States. Other species are the southern musk turtle, whose shell is more elongated, found in the Southeast, and the keeled musk turtle of the Southeast and Gulf regions, whose wedge-shaped carapace is ridged at the posterior portion. It is found from the Mississippi Valley to Texas.

MUSK TURTLES *(Sternotherus odoratus)*. Length: 3½ inches. Range: eastern United States and Canada; westward to Texas.
From Ditmars' "Reptiles of North America"

MUD TURTLE

THE mud turtle is similar to the musk turtle in its habits and choice of habitat, and also possesses the same skunkish attributes. It is known as mud box terrapin, since it has a hinged plastron and is able to withdraw into the shells which close around it like a box.

MUD TURTLE *(Kinosternon s. subrubrum)*. Length: 5 inches. Range: Eastern and southern United States.
New York Zoological Society

The mud turtle is a bit larger than the musk. Unlike its relative, the mud turtle leaves the water to hibernate in an underground burrow. The male "talks" by rubbing together the horny scales on its calf and leg, an action which produces a sound like a cricket's chirp. Some observers claim that this noise is used to attract the smaller female during the mating season. The long thick tail of the male ends in a blunt nail while the short thin one of the female terminates in a thin nail, Major Chapman Grant has noted although it is not known to what use these are put.

TERRAPINS

DIAMONDBACK TERRAPIN

EPICURES concede that the diamondback is the most popular terrapin in the country, although it meets with little or no favor as it paddles about the salt marshes and muddy tide flats of the Atlantic and Gulf coasts. In its native haunts it has no more admirers than any of its relatives. But once this creature, whose top shell is criss-crossed with characteristic diamond-shaped patterns, is transferred to the kitchen, it wins wide acclaim. For the unbounded praise of gourmets is showered not upon the animal but upon the delicious concoction to which the turtle is indispensable—diamondback terrapin stew.

The desire for this delectable dish was actually so great at one time that diamondbacks were hunted out and killed until there was

DIAMONDBACK TERRAPIN *(Malaclemys centrata concentrica).*
Length: 8 inches. Range: Marshes from Massachusetts to North Carolina. Extinct in many parts of its range. Deserves protection.
New York Zoological Society

danger that they might vanish completely. A large terrapin has brought a price of ten dollars; the usual price for average specimens with a shell length of eight inches and a weight of three pounds has been about sixty dollars a dozen.

Further evidence of the diamondback's value is seen in the farms which breed and raise them for market. One such farm near Savannah, Georgia, even puts on a side show in which a terrapin appears to play a player-piano by sitting on the instrument and moving its toes. Some of the States, too, have acted to stop the decimation of these creatures; North Carolina, in cooperation with the U. S. Bureau of Fisheries, in 1923 placed a five-year closed season during which the killing of diamondbacks was prohibited.

The turtle, a dark olive color above and yellow below, floats about the water eating shellfish, snails, mollusks, and grass, which it swallows only below the surface. Its sharp-edged mouth is equipped with a grinding plate that enables it easily to devour creatures with shells.

The female is the larger sex, attaining a shell length of eight to twelve inches while the male is only half that size. She lays her five to twelve eggs in a hole which she has scooped out in a mud bank. The young are hatched out in the summer but they remain secluded in the nest until the following spring.

In captivity diamondbacks must be kept in salty, brackish water, since fresh water permits a fungus to form on their bodies and infect them.

The two Atlantic subspecies of diamondbacks range along the east coast from Cape Cod to Cape Hatteras and from that area to Florida, while the two Gulf coast subspecies are found from the west coast of Florida to Texas.

OTHER TERRAPINS

OTHER somewhat related terrapins are the ten-inch Troost's terrapin, ranging chiefly along the Mississippi Valley; the twelve-inch hieroglyphic terrapin, whose shell is decorated by peculiar yellow lines and circles, ranging in Georgia, Alabama,

TROOST'S TERRAPIN *(Pseudemys t. troostii).* Length: 8 inches. Range: "upper reaches of Cumberland and Tennessee Rivers" (Stejneger and Barbour).
New York Zoological Society

and Tennessee; the southeastern cooter, or red-necked terrapin, whose name is derived from *kouta,* African for terrapin; the Florida terrapin whose brown shell is decorated with yellow; the Mobile terrapin of the Southeast whose carapace is highly arched; the Alabama terrapin whose plastron is yellow in color; the red-bellied terrapin of the East which scoops out a hole for its eggs with its tail rather than legs; the southeastern yellow-bellied terrapin; the Cumberland terrapin of the eastern and central States, whose head is marked by a crimson band and yellowish lines; and the Texas terrapin. The slider terrapins include the map turtles and LeSueur's terrapin, both of the Mississippi Valley district. Virtually all of these species, like the diamondbacks, are sold commercially in eastern fish markets, as well as the snake-necked chicken terrapin, a species inhabiting the Mississippi region and the southeastern States. A more detailed account of the foregoing and all other American species is contained in Clifford H. Pope's *Turtles of the United States.*

POND AND BOX TURTLES

PAINTED TURTLE

ON sunny days groups of pond turtles like to clamber on a floating log and, lined up in a row like soldiers, bask in the sun. Their gay colors are responsible for the name; they have a six-inch shell of black or olive, yellow borders on the front margin of each plate, yellow stripes on the throat, and a plastron of yellow. Their limbs, tail, and marginal plates between the shells are a brilliant red.

PAINTED TURTLES (*Chrysemys p. picta*). Length: 6 inches. Range: North America from New Brunswick to Florida.
Raymond L. Ditmars, New York Zoological Society

If they sense danger, these gaudy-hued but timid creatures quickly slip off their log and seek safety at the bottom of the pond. After a while their heads protrude from the water. They cautiously survey the scene and, if the coast appears clear, resume their interrupted sun bath.

Unfortunately the painted turtle's habits are not conducive to showing off its flashy clothes. It plods about the shore and generally picks up an overcoat of mud which hides its raiment.

This turtle eats insects, small fishes, tadpoles, and moss, and is in turn eaten by skunks, weasels, crows, and birds of prey. Man has not bothered it much because, while the painted turtle's flesh may be eaten, there is too little of it to be of commercial value.

Four subspecies of the painted turtle are recognized by Mr. Pope and comprise the eastern, and the western whose range extends beyond the Rockies, the central, and the southern.

SPOTTED TURTLE

LIKE the painted turtles, spotted turtles clamber up on logs to sun themselves. But they are less orderly and sometimes so many of them scramble about a log that by the time they have settled down they are sitting on one another. Usually found in eastern fresh-water ponds, they are occasionally observed in areas of brackish water.

The spotted turtle has a four-inch top shell, and in the center of each black shield is the yellow-orange spot for which it is named. In captivity it can learn to make its way through a maze if food is the reward.

It hibernates in mud under the water. Like other turtles, it sometimes makes the fatal mistake of believing a warm winter day to be the inception of spring. It swims to the surface and goes ashore for a walk. After the sun sets, however, chill winter regains its sway and the slow-moving turtle is trapped in the freezing mud. When spring does arrive, the turtle will be dead, its shell cracked and broken.

The range of the spotted turtle extends from Maine south to Florida and west to Wisconsin. Related species are Muhlenberg's turtle of the Northeast; the western pond turtle of the Pacific coast; the wood or sculptured turtle, whose shell is a bright brown and body an orange-red, ranges south from Maine to Virginia and west to Wisconsin and Iowa; and Blanding's turtle, known as the

BLANDING'S TURTLE *(Emys blandingii)*. Length: 7 inches. Range: Eastern Canada; north, central, and northeastern United States.
New York Zoological Society

semi-box turtle, which is found chiefly in the Midwest, though also as far east as New England.

BOX TURTLE

WHEN alarmed, the peaceable little box turtle stops its peregrinations in search of insects, worms, and berries and takes shelter within itself. It pulls in its legs, head, and tail and draws its hinged lower shell tightly against the upper shell. This operation complete, the body of the turtle is encased in its sturdy armor. The shells are so perfectly formed that the creature seems to be almost hermetically sealed; it is impossible to insert even a sliver of wood between the two shells.

After a while, from the inconspicuous sphere resembling a stone, the legs, head, and tail emerge. The journey is continued and though the box turtle seems to wander far and wide it does not get lost.

Observers have carried a box turtle miles from its home grounds, attached a long string to it, and set it loose. By following the trail of string, the observers found that the turtle headed with unerring accuracy straight back whence it had been abducted. Dr. Babcock mentions a report of a "specimen found by a man within a quarter of a mile of the spot where it had been marked by his father sixty years before." Frequently in their journeys they take to man's smooth roads, and consequently many thousands of them are killed annually by autos. Careless drivers run them down and some even find it "funny" to drive down the road squashing box turtles into the tar.

Instead of digging a hole as a shelter, this turtle either hides under bushes or relies on protective coloration. In the latter case, it burrows its legs into the ground, and then draws down its top shell until that is imbedded in the earth like a protruding stone. Its shells are brown or black and the spots of yellow, orange, or red are usually dulled by dirt, so that to all intents and purposes the turtle is invisible.

Although box turtles never seek a quarrel with a human they sometimes fight with each other. Miss Marion Bush recorded a battle between two males wherein one simply encased himself in his armor while the other pecked futilely away at the shell until, his nose torn and bleeding, he managed to overturn his wiser foe and like a victor place his feet on the closed plastron of his uninjured antagonist.

Not only do the shells protect battling box turtles from each other, but they also insure safety from other animals. However, young members of this group, whose shells have not hardened, are subject to attack. Immature specimens have been found in crows' stomachs. Mr. H. A. Allard, reporting on the mating of box turtles in *Copeia*, writes of the difficulty sometimes encountered by males in righting themselves if they have lost their balance after mating. "To right itself, the turtle extends its head as far outward and downward as possible to pivot its snout upon the earth. Then with a twisting movement, using its head as a lever, it throws itself over to the normal position, using the legs to assist this movement. But in loose and soft leafage and ground debris its head may fail to function as a fulcrum and lifting agent and the legs can get no grip upon anything solid, so that the poor creature is doomed to die a lingering death from starvation while the female moves away with no further concern regarding its unfortunate mate."

Box turtles live from thirty to sixty years; Major S. S. Flower records a specimen one hundred and twenty-three years old. Scientists establish the age by marking the plastrons of the turtles when first observed and by counting the annual growth rings of the shields. Less scholarly people sometimes carve their initials or other inscriptions in the shell for personal reasons. A story is told of a visiting European professor who found a box turtle on which was inscribed, "G. W. 1732." The naïve professor rushed to his host, a Pennsylvania German farmer, with the startling discovery of a two-century-old turtle marked by the first President. The farmer, to show his guest the improbability of it all, simply went into his yard and soon returned with a better find—a box turtle marked "Adam, 1."

EASTERN BOX TURTLE *(Terrapene carolina)*. Length: 5 inches. Range: Eastern United States except Florida. Frequently a victim of careless motorists.
New York Zoological Society

In captivity this turtle becomes very tame and feeds out of one's hand. As it grows used to the safety of its environment, it becomes so much at ease that it cannot be tempted to close its protective shells. Older specimens may put on so much weight that their fat bodies cannot fit between the armor, grotesquely sticking out in several places if the creatures do try to close their shells. A tame box turtle can be taught such tricks as coming to a water faucet and begging for a drink.

The box turtles of the United States are classified with the water and pond turtles though they are more like tortoises than terrapins. As a matter of fact, the box turtle appears to avoid water, entering a pond only to cool off, escape a foe, or get to the other side.

At birth the box turtle is the diameter of a half-dollar; fully grown, its shell is usually less than six inches long. The females are a bit larger than the males, who may be distinguished by a reddish eye. The Gulf coast box turtle, attaining a shell length of more than seven inches, is the largest of the species in the United States. The best known species, the eastern or common box turtle, ranges from Maine to Georgia and west to Michigan.

Subspecies include the three-toed box turtle, ranging from northeastern Texas to western Georgia; the Gulf coast box turtle, ranging from southeastern Georgia into Texas; the Florida box turtle; and the western or ornate box turtle, ranging between the Mississippi and the Rockies. In Colorado the ornate box turtle has been found living at an elevation of six thousand feet.

TORTOISE

TORTOISES are as thoroughly terrestrial as sea turtles are aquatic. They are such landlubbers that when thrown into the water they are almost as helpless as babes. If they were to develop a philosophy about such things, no doubt it would be similar to that accredited to the cat—water is for the internal consumption of the thirsty, not for bathing. The gopher tortoise illustrates this group's mode of life to the extreme, for it not only lives on terra firma but under it.

The gopher tortoise's lower shell is extended in front into a heart-shaped projection which serves as an all-important shovel. With this tool it burrows out its deep underground home, sometimes constructing a passageway more than a dozen feet long. The entrance is marked by a mound of scooped-out earth.

In this cool sanctuary peacefully dwell the married couple, whiling away the hot hours of the day in their lonely home. Although gopher tortoises settle in colonies, usually in arid, sandy regions, the neighbors are not a bit neighborly, one never entering the other's domicile. However, such visitors as the burrowing owl, raccoon, blacksnake and gopher frog drop in to use the subterranean channel as a hide-out when danger threatens above. Investigators discovered that the gopher tortoise had other neighbors too, among them a species of tumblebug formerly unknown to science. This beetle lives on the gopher's excrement and has been observed only among a colony of gopher tortoises. Fourteen other invertebrates are found in close association with the gopher tortoise in the capacity of parasites and messmates.

Day after day, patient spiders tirelessly weave their strands across the entrance to the burrow, and daily the tortoise breaks the web as it emerges. When the gopher leaves its hole at dusk, it is hungry. Grass, clover, lettuce, and berries make its meal, but the gopher unfortunately makes no distinction between wild growths and gardens. Consequently it is considered a pest and killed by farmers. Inclined to be a vegetarian, it will deign to accept a snack of raw meat in captivity. It also learns to feed out of one's hand, and one kept around the editor's house as a pet never failed to be at the table for meals.

The breeding season is marked by the male's mating call, a rasping utterance. In June his wife lays five eggs which are secreted under the mound at the front door. Persons in the Southeast, where these tortoises dwell, eat the eggs which are the size of pigeon's, and the flesh of the tortoise itself is not scorned. When fully grown, the tortoise has a twelve-inch brown shell and weighs nine pounds.

One difference between youth and old age among gophers is that an elderly specimen, beset by danger, withdraws into its shell

DESERT TORTOISE *(Testudo berlandieri)*. Length: 1 foot. Range: Southwestern corner of Texas and northeastern Mexico.
American Museum of Natural History

and sinks to earth with forlorn fatalism, but a young buck heads for home with all the speed that a tortoise could possibly muster. If picked up, the energetic youth will try to beat its way to safety by pummeling with clubbed feet. An old tortoise is really old, since it may live for more than a century.

Two related species, Agassiz's desert tortoise of the Southwest and Berlandier's tortoise, confined in this country to southwestern Texas, are the only other land tortoises in the United States. Major Grant witnessed a race between some children, each of them supported and carried by two desert tortoises. The proverbial speed of the tortoise was measured and found to be about twenty feet a minute or four miles a day.

Dr. Ditmars wrote that, from his experience with reptiles of all the orders, he considers the various species of tortoises that have come under his observation to have displayed the most marked indications of intelligence. Among all reptiles they are the most docile, and even with the huge species from the Galapagos Islands and their allies from the Aldabra Islands, which have power enough in their jaws to sever a man's hand at the wrist, there is the same docility, combined with an intellect that approaches the mental capacity of warm-blooded creatures.

SEA TURTLES

TRUNKBACK TURTLE

THE trunkback or leathery turtle is the heavyweight not only of the turtles but of all living reptiles as well. Record specimens have attained a weight of fifteen hundred pounds and a length of eight feet. The bulky body is encased in an armor of seven longitudinal keels covered by a hard leathery skin.

In spite of its ponderous size, this seagoing fortress moves swiftly through the water. Long flippers, which have a spread of nine feet, propel the trunkback through the ocean depths. As it cruises about the bottom it cranes its massive head armed with hooked jaws, searching for fishes, shellfishes, mollusks, and seaweeds. It probably consumes large quantities of food to attain its elephantine size, but scientists have been unable to garner much information about the habits of this ocean resident.

True to sea turtle form, the female takes to land after mating. She clambers above the tide line and scoops out a two-foot hole with her hind flippers. There she deposits seven dozen to a gross of eggs, takes great pains in covering the surface of the nest to conceal her handiwork, and hies herself back to the water. When the young are ready to hatch, without any help from either parent, they break the shells with their egg teeth and march directly into the sea.

The trunkback's flesh was not designed for food, but its blubbery coating yields a pint of oil per cubic foot. One species inhabits the warm waters of the Atlantic and another those of the Pacific. The former ventures as far north as Maine and Nova Scotia in warm weather; the latter is sometimes found off the coast of southern and Lower California.

TRUNKBACK TURTLE *(Dermochelys coriacea)*. Length: 6 feet. Range: Found on the coasts of the United States and in all temperate and tropical oceans. Rare.
American Museum of Natural History

GREEN TURTLE

THE gentle arch of the green turtle's shell bobs slowly with the waves as the creature sleeps peacefully on the ocean's surface. Gulls and terns stop to rest on the shell which protrudes from the water like an unsteady buoy. But the scene's aimless serenity is exploded by the approach of men armed with nets, harpoons, and poles, hunting for green turtles along the coast. If the reptile is trapped while sleeping at sea, its slumber may pass swiftly into death; if ambushed on the beach, where it sometimes takes a nap, the green turtle is turned helplessly on its back by a quick stroke of a long pole.

Economically valuable as a food, green turtles are shipped alive to markets, either lying on their backs or in huge water tanks. Occasionally one is so heavy that it must be loaded and unloaded with derricks. However, they have been hunted so systematically that specimens of large size are becoming increasingly rare. The day of six-foot green turtles weighing five hundred pounds is gone. The usual catch now ranges from seventy-five to one hundred and fifty pounds.

This denizen of all warm seas is the source of green turtle soup, an expensive dish acclaimed by epicures. The soup is made of the shell with the dense green fat clinging to it. This delicious concoction is also believed to have medicinal value because of the iodine and phosphates contained in the seaweed eaten by the turtle.

The green turtle's shell is olive or brown marked with yellow; its under side is all yellow. Its shell may be coated with barnacles

KEMP'S LOGGERHEAD (1), HAWKSBILL (2), AND GREEN (3) SEA TURTLES *(Caretta kempii* (1), *Eretmochelys imbricata* (2), *and Chelonia mydas* (3)). Length: 2 feet (1 and 2) and 3 feet (3). Ranges: Atlantic and Gulf coasts of the United States (1 and 2); all coasts (3). Found respectively in tropical waters.
New York Zoological Society

or bits of seaweed, for its life is spent in the ocean, though it must come up for air and go ashore to lay its eggs. This habit of living in the sea and coming ashore only to deposit their eggs is peculiar to the aquatic turtles.

Related species, the brownish Atlantic loggerhead turtle and Kemp's bastard turtle, a diminutive loggerhead, range throughout the warm Atlantic, the Gulf, and the Caribbean, but are not prized as food. The olive-green loggerhead of the tropical Pacific is sometimes taken off the coast of California.

KEMP'S LOGGERHEAD TURTLE RISING.
Ralph De Sola (NYA)

HAWKSBILL TURTLE

COMPARED with the trunkback, the hawksbill turtle is a pygmy. It is the smallest of sea turtles, a large specimen attaining a length of but two and a half feet.

The hawksbill is valued for the clear, horny shields of its shell which is black or brown and splotched with yellow. This is the tortoise shell used for expensive cigarette cases, Spanish combs, and inlaid furniture. The high cost of genuine tortoise shell has resulted in the manufacture of a cheap but more durable plastic imitation which has practically replaced the genuine.

In Cuba the hawksbill is captured with the aid of a remora, or sucking fish. The hunter throws the fish into the ocean at the end of a line, and when the adhesive disk on the fish's head is fastened to the turtle, the line—and the turtle—is drawn in. The turtle is killed and left on the beach to rot, thus loosening the plates. Then the plates are placed in boiling water until pliable. A large hawksbill will provide eight pounds of tortoise shell.

Its flesh is not usually considered edible, though Singhalese fishermen of Ceylon eat it when assured that it is not poisonous. Their decision is made by feeding the turtle's liver to the crows. If the crows refuse the morsel, the flesh is believed to be poisonous.

The American range of the hawksbill is the Gulf of Mexico, the Caribbean Sea, and the Atlantic Ocean off the coast of Florida. Stray specimens, however, sometimes wander into New England waters in summer but usually perish with the cold of winter.

SOFT-SHELLED TURTLE

THE leathery shell of these turtles so resembles a flapjack that they have been dubbed flapjack turtles. Nor are appearances in this case deceiving, since the flat exterior is of no more protective value than a flapjack. Even the lower shell is so soft and pliable that the creatures cannot long move on a rough surface lest their under parts become torn and bruised. Nevertheless soft-shells, in the best turtle tradition, are likely to withdraw into their shells to avoid trouble.

Their lack of defensive strength is somewhat offset, though, by an ability to use their sharp mandibles, deceptively concealed by soft lips, effectively. The force of the bite is enhanced by the long serpentine neck which shoots out in a manner that would do credit to an attacking snake. Not without cause have soft-shells been compared with snappers, both in temperament and in the seriousness of their well-directed bites. And they have sharp claws, too, capable of administering painful scratches. All in all, considering these trappings, the flabby soft-shelled turtles are no mean antagonists when their anger is aroused.

SOFT-SHELLED TURTLE

Peculiarly fitted by their physical construction to an aquatic life, soft-shelled turtles pass their days on river bottoms. Sometimes they disappear into the muck by gently worming their way into the soft bed, only to poke their heads out inquisitively a little later. They usually bury themselves in water shallow enough for their heads to

SPINY SOFT-SHELLED TURTLE *(Amyda spinifera)*. Length: 1 foot. Range: Eastern United States and westward to Montana and Colorado.
New York Zoological Society

protrude above the surface since they must breathe air from time to time, although like other water turtles they exercise anal respiration—discharging wastes and carbon dioxide and taking in oxygen through their cloacal vents. In such a situation the long neck is indeed a handy instrument, since it serves as a breathing tube for the submerged turtles.

They swim about, their heads held above water. Their food consists of mollusks, small fowl, fishes, frogs, and fishermen's bait which is dangling in the water. With a reptile's delight for warmth, softshells like to climb on a floating log or on the river bank to bask in the sun. They often rest on the sloping shore with their heads pointed toward the water; when frightened, they immediately slide headfirst under the surface.

Perhaps the only other occasion on which these water-loving animals leave their native haunts is when the females lay their eggs. They scoop out a hole in the bank above the water line and bury themselves save for the protruding head. They may remain in that position for days until all of their several dozen eggs are deposited. The brittle, hard-shelled eggs, according to Mr. Roger Conant, "remind one of a ping-pong ball and they even bounce somewhat similarly when they are dropped on a hard surface."

With proper care, soft-shelled turtles can thrive in captivity. They are, however, hard to capture, for their round, soft shells are not easy to grasp. And while one essays this feat, the turtles use their claws and sharp beaks to inflict scratches and bites that are severe enough to make the enterprising captor wonder whether it is really worth his while.

The largest species in the United States, the southern soft-shelled turtle, is eighteen inches long and weighs forty pounds. The upper shell is brownish, with dark spots which disappear as the turtle grows older, and the lower shell white. In the Southeast, where they abound, they are regarded as a tasty dish. Another species, the spiny soft-shelled turtle of the Mississippi, St. Lawrence, and Great Lakes, is a foot long and is marked with spines extending from the front edge of its shell. The other species in this country include the brown soft-shelled turtle of some central and western States, which is less than ten inches in length, having a spineless front edge to its carapace; and Emory's soft-shelled turtle of the south central and southwestern States.

AMPHIBIANS

AMERICAN TOAD

Amphibians

Buried deep in the Adirondacks, Lake George seems suspended between the undulating wooded ranges which frame its glassy, listless surface. Broad alluvial terraces and soft sandstone valleys dip to the water's edge, fusing in color with the blue-green vegetation framing the winding bank. Standing like sentries in majestic rows, pitch pine, hemlock, silver birch, and spruce form an angular arboreal pattern.

The lake is pure and clear, almost transparent, mirroring sky and gnarled twigs of the dogwood and the uniformly swaying tips of the pines, blending them into hazy, grotesque images. The surface of the water is calm and the rays of the sun magnify the slightest motion. Occasionally a water bug furrows the surface.

The air is full of sounds—the chirping of birds and high-pitched tones of the crickets. Even the water seems to possess a peculiar, muffled sound, as it laps the reeds and lily pads near shore.

But suddenly a booming call breaks in upon the other sounds. It is deep and prolonged, emerging as a series of basso profundo croakings and grunts. No one can fail to recognize this symphonic performer of the swamps and lakes who easily drowns out the cry of any competitor—for it is the self-assertive voice of the master musician, the king of the lily pad, the greatest fly killer in the universe—Maestro Bullfrog, himself.

A typical amphibian, the bull frog represents the class of animals whose place in the evolutionary scale forms a fusion of the characteristics of the fishes and reptiles. But though amphibians are the evolutionary descendants of fishes and the ancestors of reptiles, their eggs are devoured by the former, and when mature are eaten by the latter.

The life history of the amphibians parallels the slow evolution of their fossil ancestors. Like most fishes, amphibians are hatched from eggs which are generally deposited in water and surrounded by a protective gelatinous envelope. The ensuing tadpoles breathe through gills and propel themselves by means of their large tails.

It is at this stage that a remarkable change occurs in the growth and development of the amphibians, bridging the gulf which separates creatures of land and water. In many species, such as the frog and toad, the gills are greatly reduced, the tail fin is absorbed into the body, the larval skin is shed, the lungs begin to form, legs sprout, and eyelids emerge and partly cover the eyes. Recent discoveries indicate that these changes are to a great extent controlled by the action of the glandular secretions, particularly those of the thyroid.

But here the evolutionary parallel ends, for though the amphibians live partly on land and partly in water, they are equipped to live entirely in neither, and are consequently incapable of breaking completely with their aquatic mode of life. Since reproduction can be accomplished only in a watery medium, amphibians must inevitably return to the ponds and streams to lay their eggs, which in turn pass through an aquatic larval existence before changing into gill-less adults. Thus is the cycle completed.

Amphibians include the salamanders and newts, frogs and toads. All are backboned animals and respire chiefly through the skin which may be either rough or smooth, depending upon the particular species. They have three-chambered hearts and, like reptiles, a variable body temperature which corresponds to the temperature of the surrounding air and water. Because of these characteristics, the amphibians, like reptiles, are referred to as cold-blooded creatures. All species hibernate through the winter months, coming out in the spring to destroy countless insects and to reproduce.

Amphibians are enmeshed in incredible myths and superstitions. The warty toad has long been held in contempt because it supposedly transmits its lumpy blemishes to anyone handling it; the salamander, because of its cold, slimy skin, supposedly is able to live through fire; "showers of frogs" have been described by many "reliable" observers. The frog shower story might be explained by the fact that during the rainy season many terrestrial species come forth in great numbers and in some localities are very thick.

From the scientific standpoint, amphibians have proved to be the most valuable of creatures. Some of our most fundamental discoveries in general psychology, endocrinology, and embryology have been made through the observation of amphibians, especially frogs which make ideal laboratory tools.

Tailless Amphibians

Frogs and toads are not readily distinguishable from each other, but generally frogs are smooth and wet-skinned whereas toads are rough and dry. The intelligence quotient of the toad is conceded to be higher than that of the frog. In general the terrestrial species of amphibians seem brighter than the aquatic. Toads usually tend more to a life on land but, as will be seen, some are almost totally aquatic. Though there are not many age records of these amphibians, some European toads are known to have lived thirty-six years in captivity.

Both toads and frogs are renowned for their leaping ability, a fact well established in Mark Twain's tale of the jumping frog. They have the exceptional advantage of being able to breathe with their lungs while above water and through the scaleless skin when submerged.

Frogs and toads not only aid man by eliminating noxious, crop-destroying insects, but also serve as food. Advertisements of canned frogs' legs, the "technique of frog farming in ten easy lessons" and "mating frogs for sale" more than indicate the extent to which some Americans are addicted to frog flesh.

The frogs and toads of the United States are classified in seven families: narrow-mouthed toads, true frogs (here are included bull frogs and most of the common pond frogs), robber frogs, tree toads, true toads, spadefoot toads, and bell toads.

Because of the great number of species of toads and frogs, it would be manifestly undesirable to recount the life histories and habits of each. Only the most representative and interesting will be treated in the pages that follow. However, these have so many closely related species with similar characteristics that the necessary limits are not as severe as they might at first seem.

Warts, it should be repeated, are not the result of handling frogs and toads. The toad is warty but keeps its own "warts" and does not pass them on to its captors.

NARROW-MOUTHED TOAD

HERE is a toad that might well be called the turtle-necked toad. Its head is small and its snout pointed. Directly above the eyes the skin creases in a fold that resembles the "collar" of a turtle's neck.

TAYLOR'S NARROW-MOUTHED TOAD (*Hypopachus cuneus*). Length:
1½ inches. Range: Southern Texas.
From Wright's "Handbook of Frogs and Toads"

Only an inch and a quarter long at their largest, the common narrow-mouthed toads bleat *baa* as they sit in the water half submerged. They may utter as many as twenty calls in thirty seconds. The forefeet rest on the bank of the pond or on fairly solid floating vegetable trash. As they utter their calls their throats swell out in a bubble several times the diameter of their heads. Because they croak most frequently during rainy spells when they breed, narrow-mouths have also been termed rainy-day toads or simply rain toads.

Their eggs are laid in packets, each sometimes containing more than a hundred. Because the repository is a water-filled ditch or pond, they are often eaten by water insects. Narrow-mouthed toads, of which there are four kinds, range throughout the South from Virginia to Florida and Texas, and northward to Indiana. They are nocturnal and frequent moist places where they can take cover under decayed stumps and other natural shelters for they prefer safety to staying in sight.

Smooth-skinned, their backs may be black, brown, or gray. The under parts are dusky gray or speckled with brown.

TEXAS NARROW-MOUTHED TOAD

THROUGH central and southern Texas this toad breeds in ponds, roadside ditches, and temporary rain puddles. Its bleat is similar to that of the narrow-mouthed toad but it begins with a pleasant *whee*.

Also nocturnal, it hides beneath dead logs or stumps and in the southernmost portion of its range under the fallen stumps of Spanish bayonet. Its head is even more pointed than the narrow-mouthed toad's.

The Texas toad breeds from March to September during periods of heavy rain. The small grayish-olive tadpoles, less than an inch in length, transform into toads in thirty to fifty days. Grown Texas narrow-mouths are barely more than an inch in length. A related form, known as Mitchell's toad, occurs only in two counties of southeastern Texas. There are no published records concerning its voice or its breeding. It is also called the toothless frog.

TAYLOR'S TOAD

LARGEST of the narrow-mouths, this toad of southern Texas reaches an inch and five-eighths in length. Its skin, loose and leathery, folds across the back of the neck. The neck may be withdrawn or extended within this loose covering. Its back is a greenish-brown or olive color marked with a distinguishing stripe or thread of light yellow or orange running vertically down the center. A broad white stripe extends downward from the angle of the mouth to the shoulder.

These toads have slender fingers and toes with very short webs. Their bulging eyes have a beady quality. They are preyed upon by the western ribbon snake.

Frogs

Frogs are so inseparable from their association with our native landscape, that it is difficult to imagine a pond or brook without including them in the picture. The females do not sing, but the males' orchestral accomplishments, consisting of a repertoire which ranges from birdlike chirpings to plain guttural croakings, have pleased and entertained many a naturalist, and have annoyed many city-bred "summer folk" to distraction. Hopping about the countryside in almost every section of the United States, they serve humanity by destroying many millions of beetles, plant lice, caterpillars, and other insect pests. Unchecked by the frogs, these pests would literally devour all available plant life.

Unwittingly frogs also serve man in the laboratory, for they have proved to be ideal research material. And to the delight of the gourmet, since Roman times at least, their hind legs have frequently found their way into the kitchen, to be boiled, broiled, or stewed and served as one of the greatest delicacies yet discovered.

The average ignominious victim of man's appetite is a five-inch frog, greenish in hue, and adorned with a pair of sparkling, cherry-shaped bulging eyes. Every summer it goes about its business of mating and spawning, usually laying the eggs in a large gelatinous mass. These eggs grow into tadpoles or pollywogs and in about two months they complete their metamorphosis and become frogs. The bullfrog, however, remains in the tadpole stage for about two years.

Frogs protect themselves against enemies in the same fashion as do toads, ejecting a milky poisonous secretion, so potent that it leaves an exceedingly unpleasant astringent taste in the mouth of the would-be attacker. The sticky tongue of the frog is fastened to the front of the mouth. When the frog sees its prey (usually some insect), it throws out its tongue, snares the insect, and flips it back so rapidly that it is almost impossible to follow the swift movement with the naked eye.

Frogs have leaped their way into literature via Mark Twain's *The Celebrated Jumping Frog of Calaveras County*. In commemoration of the famous story, Calaveras County, California, holds yearly jumping events for frogs. "Zip," the titleholder in 1938, leaped for a new record of fifteen feet ten inches, while in the same year "Gas House Gus" of Sarasota, Florida, broad-jumped nineteen feet.

There are twenty-four species and subspecies of the frog in the United States. The smallest is the northern wood frog, measuring but one and three-eighths inches in length; the largest, the common bullfrog, reaches eight inches in length and attains a weight of seven pounds.

BULLFROG

MASTER of American frogdom in voice as well as size, the bullfrog emerges from hibernation in May, and stretching its limbs in the warm fragrant air, begins to croak vociferously. Although it is easily induced to song, the bullfrog disdains membership in any ordinary chorus of pond frogs, prefers to sing solo in a booming assertive voice. According to some, he seems to say, *jug-o-rum, jug-o-rum.*

Inhabiting pools, ponds, and weed-choked creeks, the bullfrog spends its leisure hours floating among the pond lilies or perching on logs, always on the lookout for insects, water beetles, crawfishes, and other choice bits. When beset by hunger pangs, it will even eat an

BULLFROG (*Rana catesbiana*). Length: 7 inches. Range: Eastern United States, Canada, and northern Mexico. Introduced in the west but not native to the extreme southeast or Gulf Coastal Plain.
Hans L. Stecher

occasional duckling or water rat and often consumes tadpoles and smaller frogs. Its greatest natural enemies are water snakes and cottonmouth moccasins, to whom its poisonous milky secretion is no deterrent.

Generally green or greenish-brown, the color of the bullfrog varies according to age and locality. In some regions the male has a yellow throat, in others the throat is drab and brownish; the under parts are either white or spotted. Bullfrogs have been introduced into the West.

During spawning season in May or June the female bullfrog lays approximately twenty thousand eggs which hatch in two months. The tadpoles are extremely large, measuring seven inches in length. Bulbous eyes, fleshy lips, and muddy marbled markings emphasize their puffy aspect. Ranged along each side of the throat are three sets of internal gills which are the sole breathing apparatus of the tadpoles. At a later stage the gills disappear and are replaced by lungs. During the metamorphosis the tadpole is entirely dependent for locomotion on its long tail, which quickly reappears if amputated. Gradually the tail is absorbed into the body and is replaced by powerful hind legs.

The southern bullfrog, ranging from Louisiana to Florida and southern Georgia, scarcely deserves its name, for its voice most closely resembles the grunt of a pig. It reaches a maximum length of six inches, and is colored yellow-green and brown.

LEOPARD FROG

THE leopard frog is the most common of the American species and is found everywhere except in the Pacific coast area. Its name comes not from any ferocious traits, but from the hue of its back which is green and striped with two bronze folds of skin, traversing the back from the eyes to the posterior. Between the folds, the body is spotted with brown or olive-green dots, each encircled by a fine yellow or white line.

Infrequently the leopard frog ventures from its pond for an overland trip. If apprehended on these occasions, it ejects an offensive

LEOPARD FROG

SOUTHERN BULLFROG *(Rana grylio)*. Length: 6 inches. Range: Louisiana to Florida and southern Georgia.
John G. Shedd Aquarium

liquid and stages a determined fight for freedom. When captured, however, it soon grows resigned, sometimes almost chipper. Its voice is pleasant and is produced by vocal pouches which swell up behind and under the ears. It utters a musical purr when water is poured on it.

Like other frogs, the leopard frog changes its skin frequently. When the skin begins to open on the back of the head, the frog pushes it down over its eyes, using the front feet for the operation; then pulling the skin over the back, it kicks it off with its hind legs. This feat is accomplished by stretching the legs arduously back and forth until the skin is worked loose and finally pulled off.

The southern leopard frog is the most colorful of the species as well as being aristocratic, for it refuses to mate with the ordinary leopard frog, which often shares its habitat. Easily distinguished from the leopard frog by its intense metallic green and brown mixtures, the southern leopard frog of the Southeast can also be recognized by its long, gracefully pointed head, and the circular white spots at the center of each ear. Dark green or brown spots cover the bullet-shaped body.

PICKEREL FROG

THE agile pickerel frog of eastern North America does not resemble its piscatorial namesake, but is used extensively as bait to capture the pickerel. An unpleasant skin secretion renders the pickerel frog unfit for human consumption, and naturalists believe that its secretion is injurious even to frogs, for when other species are confined with it, they usually die. Spending most of its time on dry land, it is often confused with the leopard frog because of its spotted coloration. The young pickerel frog sheds its skin even before it is out of the tadpole stage. In the sunlight it appears lustrous bronze in color, but when emerging from the water, it can scarcely be distinguished from mud.

WOOD FROG

THE eastern wood frog is unique in its ability to turn in midair, so that on landing from its long leap, it faces the enemy. Most terrestrial of all the species, the wood frog possesses excellent protective coloration, but once detected it can easily be identified by its dark-brown cheek patches and the yellow-gold line which runs along the sides from the jaw to the shoulder.

GREEN FROG

THE green frog seems to jump out of nowhere, landing in the water nimbly and uttering a deep *jurg* sound before submerging. Its voice may resemble a dog's bark or the sound of paper being torn. This familiar, metallic-green creature of the East is almost entirely aquatic, seldom venturing on shore. It sheds its skin four or five times a year, and if shedding takes place on land, the frog usually eats its skin.

GOPHER FROG

THE Florida gopher frog eats toads and does not seem to be affected by the poisonous secretions of its fellow amphibians, ejecting the fluid as soon as the prey is swallowed. Most frequently it squats at the top edge of the gopher tortoise's tunnel. If danger threatens it disappears deep into its ready-made refuge. The color scheme of the gopher frog ranges from grayish brown to yellowish purple. Gopher frogs inhabit the Southeast.

NORTHERN FROG

LITTLE is known about the habits of the northern frog, which is considered to be the probable link between the genus *Rana* to which belong all of the foregoing species and some of the lower forms. It prefers rivers to ponds and sometimes is called the mink frog, probably because of its mink-like odor. It is found in the Northeast.

WESTERN FROG

FROM California and the far West come some of the most brilliantly colored frogs in the United States. The red-legged frog is one of these. Colored red on bottom, it matures, according to Dr. Mary Cynthia Dickerson, in eight years. On land its gait is awkward, and when captured it becomes extremely clamorous and angry. Another California species, the two-inch yellow-legged frog, is warty and resembles the toad.

ROBBER FROG

WHEN a Texan cliff frog is seized, its body becomes bloated and it emits an irritating secretion. The fluid is too mild to affect the hands, but stings if it enters the eyes or an open wound.

The frog is three and one-half inches long and largest of the robber frogs in the United States. It is of strong physique and has powerful forearms and long fingers, well adapted for climbing about the limestone ledges where it lives. This amphibian, brownish in color and marked with dark spots, is also known as the barking frog. Its call has been described as a throaty whir, and it seems to be some-

ROBBER FROG *(Eleutherodactylus latrans).* Length: 2 inches. Range: Texas.
From Wright's "Handbook of Frogs and Toads"

thing of a ventriloquist. Cliff frogs are often so close to Texas ranch houses at night that their loud, insistent barking may awaken from sound slumber anyone within earshot.

The Texan species is believed to breed from February to May. The eggs are deposited during a rainy period in some such moist sanctuary as a crevice in the cliffs. The embryo probably passes through the tadpole stage within the egg.

All of the six species of robber frogs in this country inhabit extreme southern stretches, for the group is most prevalent in Mexico and the West Indies. The Mexican cliff frog, which comes into southern Arizona, is another hearty barker. It is a nocturnal animal and is therefore seldom seen but frequently heard after dark. In summer it has been observed attached to the trunks of smooth-barked trees. The frog's color blends so well with this background that it is not easily discerned.

The smallest members of this group are Ricord's frog, which is from three-fifths of an inch to an inch or more in size, and Camp's frog, five-eighths of an inch to an inch long. Ricord's frog, inhabiting southern Florida, mates in secluded places. The members of this species, unlike most frogs and toads, do not congregate at the water during mating time. Camp's frog, of the Rio Grande Valley, utters a quiet whistle which is sometimes blended with a chirp resembling that of a cricket. This petite, olive-colored frog is found even in the heart of Texas cities, where it may be heard after sundown as it calls out from yards and gardens.

The only other robber frogs in the United States are the two-inch white-lipped frog and the greenish Marnock's frog, usually an inch or more in size. Both are found in Texas.

Tree Frogs

Perching precariously on trees, the tree frogs are barely distinguishable from the bark and foliage. Their protective coloration is so remarkable that they can be detected only by chance, or because of their tremulous voices which in summer evenings, especially before a thunderstorm, rise in crescendos loud enough to be heard half a mile.

The tree frog is a tiny creature, usually measuring about two inches in length. Its color varies from fawn to dark brown and is changeable. The white under-parts are smudged with bright orange and yellow patches, particularly in the folds of the hind legs. The toes are equipped with adhesive pads which enable it to climb vertical surfaces easily.

The tree frog ends its winter hibernation in May, and immediately proceeds to a pond or pool. It is at this time that it joins its mate in a complacent, highly resonant chorus, which begins in the early afternoon and continues until late at night. Sitting on a lily pad, the undersized male, with translucent vocal sacs blown out to resemble a balloon, croaks and sings, undaunted even if confronted with a glaring searchlight.

Mating is carried on at night, and a month later the female begins to lay a mass of brownish eggs. These are usually attached to vegetation near the surface of the water. Two months later the new, half-inch tree frog is fully matured and ready to climb ashore.

The diet of tree frogs consists of insects and worms. The frogs are common throughout their range in the eastern and central United States.

Twenty-eight species and subspecies of tree frogs are found in the United States. The tiniest member is the chorus frog, measuring only seven-sixteenths of an inch in length. Incidentally, the chorus frog is also the smallest vertebrate in the United States. The largest tree frog is the Key West tree frog, which is five inches long.

CRICKET FROG

THE cricket frog or the Savannah cricket, measuring an inch in length, varies in color, black to dark brown, reddish brown, light brown, green, and gray. The Savannah cricket is terrestrial and sits in the shade of a leaf, or hides under the flower box on a veranda, rarely permitting itself to be seen.

GREEN TREE FROG *(Hyla c. cinerea)*. Length: 2 inches. Range: Eastern United States from Virginia to Texas and up to the Mississippi to southern Illinois.
New York Zoological Society

Between February and October it breeds in pond shallows, laying about two hundred and fifty brownish eggs, which are attached to stems of grass or other vegetation. The resultant dark-olive pollywogs are an inch long.

The range of the cricket frog extends from New York south to Florida and west to Ohio and Texas. It is typical of the genus *Acris*.

CHORUS FROG

FOUND throughout the Midwestern States, the chorus frog, the smallest of the species, is gray or brown in color. It breeds from March to May, laying its eggs in masses and attaching them to vegetation or trash. The males usually arrive at the ponds before the females and seem to be more numerous.

The body of the chorus frog is soft, delicately translucent, and slightly warty. Its voice resembles a creaking chirp, yet is somewhat melodious. There are nine other species of the genus *Pseudacris* in the United States.

TREE FROG

THE most widespread of the tree frogs is the common tree frog or the common tree toad, found throughout the United States. Its coloration varies from pale brown to ashy-gray to green, and its skin is granular and warty. Its protective coloration makes it almost invisible and often it is mistaken for a stone or a piece of bark.

The peculiar call of the tree frog is a long and vibrant trill, which starts and stops abruptly. It is especially vociferous after thundershowers, voicing its contentment approximately twenty-two times a minute.

Breeding in April or May, the tree frog lays thirty to forty eggs. Fifteen other species of the genus *Hyla* are found in the United States.

Toads

On a summer evening the mist rises from the lake and spreads rapidly over the countryside. But it is a soft and hazy mist, gently caressing the foliage which absorbs its moisture, and which weighted with dew, rustles quietly. A soft melodious sound penetrates the stillness, seems to be carried closer and closer by the mist. Suddenly there is another call, and another, starting and stopping abruptly, until the entire countryside becomes alive with these chirping croaking sounds which seem to originate right under your feet.

This is the song of the toad. It is a tremulous plaintive cry, melodious and haunting. Sometimes in large bodies of water where many of these creatures congregate, this incessant croaking becomes almost a deafening roar, and only with the dawn comes the finale of this symphony of the swamps.

Fat-bodied and warty, the toad is not a particularly attractive animal. Because of its somewhat grotesque appearance it has been mistreated and attacked—this in spite of the fact that it is undoubtedly one of the farmer's most beneficent friends, each toad doing approximately twenty dollars worth of work a year. Unfounded legends have credited it with producing warts when handled by man, of poisoning infants, of causing cows to go dry. Actually, the only magic of which it is capable is destroying countless spiders, ants, potato bugs, beetles, and plant lice, consuming such vast quantities of these insects that its sides begin to bulge. In one summer the toad consumes no less than ten thousand garden pests.

The toad is a short, thick-set amphibian, usually about four inches in length. Its back is covered with warts of various sizes, and the arms and legs are also warty. The eyes are prominent and luminous, giving the toad a somewhat wistful expression. The predominant color is olive.

The commonest type of toad in the United States is the hoptoad, a species of which can be found in every State. Inhabiting gardens, cultivated fields, and lakes, it spends the day sleeping under piazzas, boardwalks, flat stones, boards and woodpiles. At night it comes out of hiding to hunt for food. Since only moving objects are capable of making an impression on the toad's sensory nerves, it hunts only for live insects and worms. Throwing out its long, flat, sticky tongue, the base of which is attached to the front of the mouth, it ensnares an insect and flips it back into its mouth.

The breeding season begins in April, lasts until June. During these months the female deposits in water from four thousand to fifteen thousand eggs which hatch in twelve days. The pollywogs are small and black, but not helpless. Gradually the legs appear, the tail is absorbed into the body, and in two months the tadpole is transformed into a full-fledged hoptoad. In the winter the toad hibernates, digging a burrow with its hind legs and always creeping in backward.

The hoptoad has innumerable enemies. Its eggs are eaten by water beetles; ducks, chickens, and guinea-fowl eat the young; and young snakes find the smaller toads a delicacy worth hunting. It has one means of protection—the secretion of a milky, mildly poisonous fluid which produces a bitter astringent taste in the mouth of the attacker. If it can outwit all its enemies, however, the hoptoad has quite a long life span ahead of it and has been known to reach the ripe old age of thirty-six years.

There are at least eighteen species and subspecies of the toad in the United States. The smallest is the oak toad which is three-quarters of an inch long (found in the southeastern United States); the largest is the giant toad, seven inches long, inhabiting southern Arizona and southern California.

AMERICAN TOAD (*Bufo a. americanus*). Length: 3 inches. Range: Eastern North America.
Hans L. Stecher

SPADEFOOT TOAD

One species native to the West acts like an ostrich when frightened. It jumps head-first into the mud, with its posterior sticking out in ludicrous fashion. Another species, the southern or Carolina toad, is also called the charming toad because folklore throughout the Southeast insists that looking at this toad causes one's eyes to turn green.

SPADEFOOT TOAD

DUG out of its burrow the spadefoot toad resembles a brown clod of earth. Suddenly it expels the air from its lungs and collapses like a punctured balloon. It lifts its awkward forefeet, one at a time, to rub its round, brilliant golden eyes. By this time the uninitiated captor will find his hands befouled with a secretion suggestive of garlic, emitted from the skin of the toad.

If left alone it will disappear into the ground sometimes to a depth of three feet, its spadelike hind legs working furiously. For living quarters, the spadefoot digs a six-inch hole where it remains until the breeding season, which for the different species occurs between March and September.

No sooner has the young toad ceased being a tadpole than it begins burrowing into the ground. If unable for any reason to get out of the water at this stage it is likely to drown.

Hermit toads, as the spadefoots are also called, are green, yellow, or ashy brown. Their under sides are whitish, turning to purple toward the rear. A curved yellow line may extend backward from each eye.

THROUGHOUT the Southwest the cries of these hermit toads are heard after a heavy rain. *Wow, wow,* they call, like someone in pain. This toad, which goes by the additional name of Couch's spadefoot, is short and fat, attaining a length of but three and one-fifth inches. It has a rough greenish marbled skin.

These spadefoots are nocturnal, spending the day in the subterranean burrows. They breed from April to August throughout their arid range, laying their eggs in gelatinous bands a quarter of an inch wide.

AMERICAN WILD LIFE

SPADEFOOT TOADS *(Scaphiopus h. holbrookii)*. Length: 2½ inches. Range: Eastern and southern United States.
New York Zoological Society

FROM Texas through North Dakota the western Hammond's spadefoot breeds in temporary rain pools. When the rainfall is heavy enough, generally from April to August, the females attach their cylindrical masses of eggs to grass stalks or plant stems. In about two days the large greenish-black tadpoles are flailing their tails about, looking for food. The tadpoles are carnivorous and may even eat their own kind in addition to large quantities of mosquito larvae.

The adult Hammond's spadefoot is stout and resembles the common toad. Its skin is comparatively smooth, greenish on back, and yellow to mineral gray along the sides. It attains a length of almost two inches, and has a broad head and a short muzzle overhanging the lower jaw.

Lying on the surface of the water, the males croak with a rolling or bubbling call. Various descriptions of these sounds have com-

SPADEFOOT TOAD

pared them with a cat's purr, and the grinding of auto gears. There is a ventriloquial quality to their call.

MAKING shallow burrows in the ground, Holbrook's spadefoot is active only at night. Along the Atlantic coast from Massachusetts to Florida and westward to Texas and Oregon this toad almost three inches long, utters its hoarse *wank, wank,* similar to the croak of young crows.

In their *Handbook of Frogs and Toads,* Drs. Anna Allen Wright and Albert Hazen Wright describe the egg laying of Holbrook's toad as follows: "The pond was filled with pairs. When ready to lay, they went to the bottom of the pond, often the male with his eyes closed, and the female with hers partly closed. When she found a stem to suit her, she seized it with her front feet and pushed it with her hind feet. She walked or climbed up the stem or along it if it fell to a horizontal position as she laid the eggs, the male clinging close to

FOWLER'S TOAD *(Bufo fowleri).* Length: 3 inches. Range: Generally in the United States east of the Rockies.
Ralph De Sola (SIM)

her back. There was a strong chorus that night and by the next morning the ponds were all churned up and muddy. Many egg masses were there, but no toads."

DOWN in the Florida Keys and on the extreme tip of Florida, the Key West spadefoot, slightly more than two inches long, makes its home. Similar to Holbrook's spadefoot, its pattern is lighter than that of the toad's. Its color characteristic is a great amount of white on the back, flanks and upper surface of the limbs.

THE solitary Hurter's spadefoot is confined to the eastern half of Texas. More than three inches long, it is pale greenish above with yellow-white under surfaces. Its dimensions are similar to those of Holbrook's spadefoot and it is still debated among taxonomists whether or not it is a separate species.

BELL TOAD

IN THE forests of the Northwest, high on the mountain sides, the bell toad may be seen on the wet ground after heavy rains. Usually it makes its home under rocks on the brinks of swiftly flowing icy streams.

Adult bell toads reach two inches in length. They may be pink or gray and sometimes brown to almost black. In the male black spots accentuate a generally olive-drab or russet ground color. A pale green or yellow bar crosses the head. The females are usually lighter than the males.

Bell toads lack even the slightest community instinct; rarely are two seen together. Their reactions seem to be slow, and when placed on land they are awkward and clumsy, making little effort to escape.

From May to September they lay their eggs in beaded strings attached to the under side of stones in creeks. These eggs are quite large, reaching a third of an inch in diameter.

After their metamorphosis has been completed, the young toads are little more than half an inch long. Male bell toads are the only toads possessing an extension of the cloaca, which, used as an

MALE AMERICAN BELL TOADS *(Ascaphus truei)*. Length: 2 inches. Range: Western Montana, Oregon, and northern California.
From Wright's "Handbook of Frogs and Toads"

intromittent organ, permits an internal fertilization of the female's eggs.

Outside of the United States, where there is but one species, the only other bell toads known to science are found in New Zealand.

Tailed Amphibians

Salamanders and newts are frequently confused with lizards because of their similar appearance. They are, however, immediately distinguished from those reptilians by the complete absence of scales. Newts, generally considered, are the smaller members of the salamander family. None of the salamanders can be considered dangerously venomous, but the skin of some species secretes fluids which are mildly toxic.

Salamanders have often fallen prey to human superstition. Because of their cold shiny skin and seeming indifference to injury, these amphibians were believed in medieval times to be immune to fire, and the belief has persisted to this day in some backward rural regions. In order to prove or disprove this theory, countless salamanders have been flung to the flames, whence of course they never emerged. The chief victim of this practice of superstitious man was the spotted yellow-on-black European fire salamander, which in fact owes its common name to human credulity. In olden times, when wood was gathered from the forest and brought indoors to dry by the heat of the hearth, fire salamanders would emerge from the bark and crawl about the house. The inhabitants always believed they had emerged from the fire, however. Hence their name and the superstition surrounding them.

Virtually all salamanders, regardless of their mode of life, lay their eggs in water. The larvae have three pairs of gills at each side of the neck; in some salamanders these gills disappear at later stages and in others they remain through life. One species, in fact, may under certain conditions never leave its larval form. This is the axolotl, long considered an unclassified aquatic species, found in the Southwest and Mexico. They are now known to be the larvae of the tiger salamander, an American species so named because of its blotchy yellow stripes on a brown or black body.

SIREN

THERE is nothing alluring about this siren, for it is an ungainly creature and is one of the least attractive of the none-too-beautiful tailed amphibians. Except for a pair of undeveloped forelegs, it looks very much like a thick-bodied eel. The absence of hind legs distinguishes it from other salamanders. And claws, seldom seen

SIREN

among amphibians, are present in the form of clawlike caps covering the siren's fingertips.

Little is known of this esoteric creature's habits. It has been ascertained, however, that it feeds on great quantities of algae or green

SIREN *(Siren lacertina)*. Length: 2½ feet. Range: South Atlantic, Mississippi, and Gulf regions of the United States.
New York Zoological Society

pond scum, and is itself the favorite food of rainbow snakes. When handled it emits a milky, mucous substance through its skin, a nuisance, perhaps, but not poisonous. Males are said to whistle when courting. These amphibians, popularly and more descriptively known as mud eels, have lived in captivity for twenty-five years and longer.

The siren, or mud eel, and a rather similar and related genus, the *Pseudobranchus*, constitute the family Sirenidae. Both are swamp-living salamanders which never completely develop in adult life but retain larval characteristics.

The siren attains a length of two feet, but the *Pseudobranchus* is only ten inches long and has a slimmer form. The blackish siren can also be differentiated from the brownish striped *Pseudobranchus* by its three open gill clefts, for the *Pseudobranchus* has only one. The blunt-headed *Pseudobranchus* is an adept burrower, but the closest approach of the siren to burrowing is its manner of slipping through the dense vegetation bordering its watery home in the swamps and abandoned rice fields of South Carolina and Georgia.

MUD PUPPY

THE only dog that a mud puppy could possibly resemble is a dachshund, for this amphibian has a long torso supported by very short legs. Its flattened head has a certain canine quality, enhanced by the bushy gills which may be likened to the dachshund's flapping ears. Here, however, the highly fanciful comparison ends. The mud puppy has a long, flattened tail of a kind that a dachshund would never call its own, and observers have yet to hear the faintest trace of a growl or a bark come from this mute creature.

Its completely aquatic life has also given the mud puppy the name of water dog, both appellations having descriptive value since it not only lives in the water but spends a great amount of time nosing about the muck on the bottom. Its dark-brown body, adorned with mottled patches and spots, is usually so covered with a coating of slime that it is as slippery as an eel's. Its inconspicuous coloration blends so well with its surroundings that the amphibian is perpetually concealed. It does have one distinctive feature, however, in the velvety red gills which stand out clearly when expanded.

Swimming easily by means of its long, flat tail, the mud puppy gobbles up all kinds of food which it encounters. Water insects, snails, little fishes and their eggs are on its bill of fare. This diet is believed to be governed not by taste but by availability, and it is unfortunate for such organisms as crawfishes and insects that they are fated to be the mud puppy's neighbors.

The twelve-inch mud puppy is a denizen of clear streams and ponds in eastern and central States. It is a nocturnal creature and

MUD PUPPY (*Necturus maculosus*). Length: 1 foot. Range: Eastern United States.
New York Zoological Society

often conceals itself beneath flat rocks on the bottom. Related species of the genus *Necturus* are believed to be burrowers, either tunneling into soft stream beds, or taking over the burrows of such of its neighbors as crawfishes. Some species may spend the summer in the seclusion of these tunnels.

In the fall the mud puppies mate and the females lay their eggs during the following spring or summer. These are attached to stones and the females stand guard over the improvised nest until the young are hatched.

LUNGLESS SALAMANDERS

THOUSANDS of feet up in the Appalachians and the Sierra Nevada, where the air is very light and pure and brooks and springs gurgle invitingly in the cool ravines, live the little lungless salamanders. So far away from others of their kind, they look odd among the assortment of tiny creatures that come to life each spring after the winter hibernation. And many million years ago, when these mountain ranges were being formed by the cooling and crumpling of the earth, they were part of the primitive group of salamanders in the lowland marshes and rivers near the sea. But as the rivers and lakes dwindled to brooks and pools, this little group found itself suddenly isolated. As a result, they grew smaller and weaker. This in turn made the lungs, which tended to fill with water in the swift current, unnecessary; so they lost them and became more fishlike, breathed through throat membranes and the skin instead.

Indeed, so well did this little family adapt itself to the new conditions that today it is by far the largest family of salamanders, comprising more than half of all in existence. Among its numerous genera are some that have gone back again to the lowland, supplanting less vigorous ancestors that have passed away. One type even inhabits deep artesian wells far under the earth's surface, as though to make its versatility complete. They are agile, darting under rocks more cleverly than any frog, and squirming into holes in the earth or logs more adroitly than a mole. Some never leave the water, others never enter it. All, however, remain near it, and are more or less striped with yellow, orange, and brown, and well spotted. All, too, eat insects, worms, snails, and crustaceans.

They mate usually in spring. On land the male impregnates the female directly. In water the female absorbs the pinlike clusters of spermatozoa deposited by the male on the lips of her cloacal vent at the base of her tail. The eggs are usually found in the summer months, suspended like clusters of grapes from the under surface of rocks in or out of water. Two or three levels of eggs may be distinguished in a cluster, each egg being connected with a separate stalk which merges at the top. This is due to the fact that the female first deposits a supply of mucus on the rock, and then lays her eggs, one after the other, so that the sticky shell adheres to the mucus on the rock or other eggs and becomes suspended. The method seems to be well adapted to aquatic conditions, keeping the eggs firm and safe in the current, as well as moist in case the mother cannot do so by coiling about them.

LUNGLESS SALAMANDER

The young larvae hatch in the late fall or early winter as a rule. All but those of the most advanced terrestrial forms go through a gill-bearing stage. The length of time this transformation takes varies greatly, indicating the wide range between primitive and advanced types. One, indeed—the blind, artesian-well salamander living two hundred feet below the earth's surface—never loses the gills, remaining a permanent larva with long slim legs of no use on land. It lacks the thyroid gland which has been found to control this transformation in all vertebrates. It is marked by red gills and spindly legs. The primitive types are also free-tongued.

MOST common and one of the best adapted salamanders to mountain-brook life is the nocturnal variety of the dusky genus. It is seldom seen, however. The best time to catch it is during the summer when clusters of fifteen to twenty eggs fill the drying banks of streams. The eggs may appear unguarded, but the adults will be found only two or three feet away hiding under rocks. At

LONG-TAILED CAVE SALAMANDERS (*Eurycea i. longicauda*). Length: 4½ inches. Range: Eastern United States in the Appalachians.
Charles E. Mohr

this they are very adept because of their rigid lower jaw, a natural wedge possessed also by the fin-tailed, purely aquatic, black-bellied variety.

Duskies are also so-called because of their red-brown backs and gray bellies. The male is about five and a half inches long—slightly larger than the female. This is the only case in the entire family in which the male is larger, not conforming to the usual rule of greater female vitality in all lower forms. The eggs are usually deposited during one night and hatch in eight weeks. The young live on land for fifteen or sixteen days, at which time they are about three-quarters of an inch long and enter water. Here they remain for eight or nine more months before becoming fully grown and emerging in the spring to breed.

ANOTHER very common type is the slimy salamander, noted for the thick mucous substance it secretes and, when annoyed, is capable of excreting from the pores of the skin, so that it cannot easily be grasped. As many salamanders give off noxious or toxic mucus, this is undoubtedly a similar protective device. One of the largest of the family—seven inches long—it is a forest dweller like the other ten species in the genus, and makes long burrows. It is black with white spots on the back.

A SMALLER, red-backed variety is the forest salamander which inhabits only pine woods and has the peculiar habit of jumping the length of its body when excited. It jumps immediately, whether near the ground or not. The tail appears to play a part in jumping, since it pushes into the support; moreover, it appears somewhat prehensile, entwining about the hand when handled. It can be disconnected, too, when the animal is suddenly surprised under a log. As though relying on the movement of the disjointed tail to distract attention, it will crawl away stealthily. About ten per cent of those caught show a tail stump in process of regeneration.

The eggs of most of these forest varieties are hung from the inside of logs or from patches of moss covering them. The mother rests below, her back in contact with them. This and the moisture of the log prevents their hardening and decay. As the outer ring of eggs gets more moisture and heat, they usually hatch a little earlier and with larger larvae. Many of those hatching out of the center group die. This, however, shows the general tendency to decrease the size and number of eggs in the center and concentrate on a fewer large ones on the outside. In this way survival is assured, since these small, slender forms of salamanders cannot lay many eggs, while the larvae need considerable yolk and require care.

There is no aquatic stage in these forest types. The gills are already gone when they are born. The young remain close to the mother till early in October. Thereafter they forage for themselves. Despite their smallness, they appear to stand the winter as well as adults. Much the same is the life history of the burrowing types, whose wormlike bodies are still more adapted to life beneath the surface. They have non-nucleated red blood cells, providing a greater reserve of oxygen. They disappear during the dry summer but return with the rains in November.

ONE of the most highly evolved types is the tree salamander. It is black or brown or mottled and rather long and slender, the tail being sometimes longer than the body. Tree salamanders have Y-shaped terminal phalanges on their toes, which facilitate climbing. Their nests are found in holes at the base of trees or at varying distances up inside cavities in the trunk. So small are the entrances to these that they are ordinarily unnoticed. Within, however, there are often what appears to be true family groups, two adults with a litter and an intermediate flock, representing the previous year's litter. They eat damp fungus and wood as well as the usual insects and worms. Two varieties are nocturnal and one possesses a prehensile tail. All are great wanderers, disappearing in the dry season.

MORE primitive is the aquatic mud salamander, a small brown type found in the Coastal Plain marshes, and the two types of white, blind cave dwellers. The latter detect their food by the sense of touch on cave and well walls. One of them has normal legs and is gill-less in the adult, while the other is a permanent larva that never leaves the water of the deep wells in which it is found. The Yosemite salamander from Yosemite National Park, another primitive type, lives near glacial streams at an altitude of more than 10,000 feet. It is chocolate-colored with yellow back stripes and gray spotted sides.

LONG-TAILED CAVE SALAMANDERS.
C. L. Baker, Reelfoot Lake Biological Station

THE red salamander is by far the most beautiful. Against the gravelly bottom of cold springs, the coral-red young adults, with fine irregular black spots and white bellies, are an attractive sight. They are also the most prolific and hardy in captivity, producing as many as fifty eggs in a cluster and eating earthworms and fresh meat. The young grow to almost adult size—four inches—in the two and a half years they take to lose their gills and mature. In adults the red color changes to a purple-brown.

THE numerous varieties of two-lined salamanders have a brownish body with a dark line running from eye to tail on either side with black spots underneath. The larvae take two years to develop, losing their gills when two inches long. After hatching they lie for two weeks in the hollow at the bottom of the stream where they were born, living on their store of egg yolk while waiting for their digestive tracts to form. The purple type, the most primitive of all, numbers among its two varieties one of the rare ones which in self-defence will snap and contort itself to inspire terror. It is about six inches long; light red in color with purple blotches. It inhabits small streams and at times will even prey on the two-lined and four-toed salamanders.

There are altogether fifteen genera of lungless salamanders, with some seventy-one full species, fifty-four of which are found in the United States, according to Dr. E. R. Dunn. The dusky types range from Canada to Florida, and west to Illinois and Texas. The forest types range from Canada to Florida and west to Missouri, Texas, and Wisconsin. The burrowing and tree types occupy the Pacific coast mountainous regions from Canada to Lower California. The four-toed salamander ranges from Massachusetts to Michigan, Georgia, and Texas, and the mud salamander the east coast from Liberty County, Georgia, to the Dismal Swamp of Virginia. The blind cave salamanders are found in Missouri and Arkansas and the artesian wells of Hays, Kendall, and Crockett counties, Texas. Their skin lacks pigment and appears pink only because of the blood in its veins. But two species are found in the United States and they are among the rarest of cave dwellers. The red and two-lined types range from New England and New York to northern Florida, and the purple types from Maine to Georgia, all reaching westward to Ohio. The black-bellied variety is found only in the southern Blue Ridge of North Carolina.

CONGO EEL

LARGEST North American salamander, the Congo eel is neither an eel nor from the Congo. Black and slippery, this three-foot-long amphibian bears a certain resemblance to the eel, but four hardly discernible feet serve to differentiate it from the fishes, if they serve no other purpose.

The Congo eel inhabits muddy streams, ditches, and swamps from the Mississippi River to South Carolina. The erroneous notion that it was brought to this region with the first importations of African slaves is responsible for the "Congo" part of its name.

This sightless creature is a burrower. With the largest red-blood corpuscles of any animal, it is sure of a great reserve of oxygen whether under water or on land. The overhanging upper lip of its blunt snout and the fold on its chin separating the lower lip from the throat both have sharp edges for scooping. Slimy rows of mucus pores along the slaty-gray or black cylindrical body and grooves along the sides also aid it in its progress through the mud.

The peculiar physical traits of the Congo eel clearly show the evolutionary development of living creatures from water to land dwellers. When first born, it is to all purposes a fish, still breathing through gills. It never quite becomes adapted to the land as do other amphibians. Its eggs are numerous and small, fishlike, and do not have the gelatinous covering characteristic of other amphibian eggs.

CONGO EEL *(Amphiuma means)*. Length: 3 feet. Range: Southeastern United States and westward to Louisiana along the Gulf plain.
New York Zoological Society

Its legs show the transition from fins to arms and feet. The fore pair are about half an inch long; the hind pair nearly an inch, each limb having from one to three digits.

The mating season is in early July. About one hundred and fifty eggs are deposited at one time by the female. Globular in shape, they are connected by one continuous cord, like a string of large beads intertwined. If unwound, the entire strand would stretch to about eight feet. Under the thin transparent cover of the egg, which is made of the same material as the cord, the dark embryos are clearly discernible curled up in spiral positions.

The eggs are laid in hollows under logs in August and September. The mother, a good brooder, coils about them to keep them warm and wet; but once the young are hatched she shows no more interest in them.

Although unsatisfactory pets, like all burrowers, the Congo eel has been reported to have lived twenty-six years in captivity. When disturbed they often give a shrill peep, which may be due to air escaping from the branchial slit on either side of the neck—all that remains in the adult of the three external gills with which they are born. Crawfish, clams, and earthworms are their food, but when quite hungry they will eat their own kind. Sometimes in attacking they become really vicious, twisting about their prey like a constricting snake and biting. They are, however, usually no match for the larger red-bellied swamp snake or the mud snake.

Of the two species generally recognized, one is somewhat smaller and browner. It has only two digits on its limbs; the larger, blacker one usually has three. The smaller one is found from Virginia to Florida and west to Louisiana; the larger, from northern Florida to southern Louisiana, and up the Mississippi to Missouri.

NEWT

THROUGHOUT the eastern United States the crimson-colored spotted newt lives in quiet streams and ponds. When fully grown these small salamanders are about three inches long, colored an olive- or yellow-green with black-bordered crimson spots lining

SPOTTED NEWTS *(Triturus viridescens)*. Length: 3 inches. Range: Eastern North America.
New York Zoological Society

each side. They are better known, however, in their larval stage. These red efts, as they are then called, are a brilliant coral color and are often seen after rains or on foggy mornings crossing paths or leaf-strewn glades. At this stage, nests are almost entirely terrestrial. Later, when mature, they return to the water.

In April and May newts breed in the water. The male may be recognized by the swollen base of his tail and his stocky hind legs which are stouter than the forelegs. Thick black ridges of skin cover the inner surfaces of the hind legs during the breeding season, while the tail fin and cloaca become larger.

Gripping the female with his hind legs the male touches his cheek to the snout of the female. The secretions from his cheek glands serve to quiet the female. Later, when he deposits the spermatophores on submerged leaves, these secretions even compel her to follow him. Then she lays her eggs on submerged vegetation or stones. The female will wrap the single eggs in leaves where available. Spherical in shape, each egg is enclosed in an oval mass of jelly.

When the larvae hatch out they have branching gills and fishlike tails. Changing from green to red in the fall, the little newts lose their gills which are replaced by lungs and then they are ready for the terrestrial existence of their next few years. They frequently migrate from their ponds to winter on land. A migration of spotted newts was recorded on October 3, 1937, in Massachusetts. Apparently thousands of these small creatures were attempting to scale a dam to reach a small pond. In some regions they do not leave the water at all.

In all, there are four species of newts in this country, two in the eastern States, one in the South, and one in the West. The western newt is known as the water dog. The skin of the male western newt is much smoother and thicker than that of the female.

TIGER SALAMANDER

FROM head to tip of its long tail, the grotesque blackish body of the tiger salamander is marked with irregular yellow stripes. Hence, by a considerable stretch of the imagination, one may recognize a certain similarity between the eight-inch salamander and a real feline tiger. The undersurface of this mild amphibian "tiger" is gray in color, and its chin is yellow.

Throughout the United States it dwells in the neighborhood of ponds, concealing itself beneath stones or logs. Sometimes it burrows a hole in the sandy shore, just deep enough so that its head protrudes when it stands upright. The burrow is placed so that the water overflows it regularly and keeps it full. This is an ideal home for an amphibian as it changes from dependence upon gills to lungs.

A tiger salamander was kept in a fernery in the study of Prof. Edward Drinker Cope, who described it as "nocturnal in its habits." During the day it remained in the burrow which it had constructed in the fernery. The burrow had three outlets, and from one of them, as evening approached, it projected its head and watched with attention what was going on in the room.

This burrowing creature generally passes through its larval stage in a manner prosaic to most amphibians. The change, however, can be retarded by keeping the larva in water. For example, in the Southwest, perhaps owing to the arid surroundings, it never leaves its watery haunts and retains a larval form throughout its life. For a long time it was believed to be a distinct species. This axolotl, as it is called, grows to maturity and begins to reproduce just like full-grown tiger salamanders.

The eggs laid by the female may develop into axolotls, rather than tiger salamanders, if the conditions remain the same. Consequently, it is impossible to tell whether the larva is the child of a land-living tiger salamander or water-confined axolotl. In this way, generation after generation of axolotls may reproduce without ever setting foot on land or using lungs. Yet a sudden change in environmental factors may snap the chain and send the axolotl ashore where the normal development takes place. This can be achieved by reducing the water supply and forcing it to breath through its lungs. The axolotl is eaten by Mexican Indians who evince little concern about its genealogy.

SPOTTED SALAMANDERS *(Ambystoma maculatum)*. Length: 3 inches.
Range: Eastern North America.
New York Zoological Society

SPOTTED SALAMANDER

SOMEWHAT similar to the tiger salamander, the spotted species is daubed with yellow spots rather than stripes on its shiny black body. It, too, is a secretive, nocturnal creature which conceals itself in damp, dark places. When annoyed or otherwise excited it sometimes emits a transparent liquid as do some toads.

In the spring the male deposits sperm globules in the water. The female gathers these in and keeps them until they are needed to fertilize her eggs. At night she lays clumps of eggs which may be attached to floating leaves, according to Dr. Ann Haven Morgan in her *Field Book of Ponds and Streams*. In two or three weeks the larvae are hatched, and they already have the flat heads which characterize adult spotted salamanders. Fully grown, this amphibian of eastern and central States measures about six inches.

OTHER MOLE SALAMANDERS

MOLE salamanders are so called because of their zest for night life and their burrowing proclivities. There are eleven species in North America.

One of their characteristics is the habit of "playing 'possum" when handled. They usually pretend to be dead for a minute or two, but occasionally the pose may be maintained for as long as an hour.

They feed on insects and worms, although a mole salamander has no compunction about including a smaller salamander in its diet. There is even a record of an eight-inch mole salamander conquering a two-foot garter snake. The mole salamanders, however, have their enemies in fishes, water insects, small crustaceans, and even other salamanders, all of which feed on their eggs.

The largest land salamander in the world is a mole salamander of the Pacific coast. This is the blackish-brown *Dicamptodon* which grows to more than ten inches.

Indigenous to eastern and central States, the five-inch marbled salamander has a grayish body with white markings. Unlike other mole salamanders, this one lays its eggs on land and solicitously curls about them. The eggs, whose covering is comparatively tough, are laid in the fall. The young hatch with the coming of rain and then enter the water.

MARBLED SALAMANDER *(Ambystoma opacum)*. Length: 5 inches.
Range: Eastern and central United States.
John S. Robas and Charles Ellis

Jefferson's salamander, dark brown and decorated with blue markings, inhabits approximately the same range. It was named in honor of Thomas Jefferson, as well regarded in his day as a naturalist as he still is as a statesman. His political adversaries accused him of mixing affairs of state with fossils, salamanders, and snakes—insisting that he kept such odd things in the White House. Whatever the justification for such an accusation, it is a fact that Jefferson was one of the best-informed men of his time on all the natural sciences.

HELLBENDER

THE hellbender, as its name implies, is a tough and ugly-looking customer. This eighteen-inch denizen of the Mississippi and other rivers in central and eastern States has the added distinction of being the largest American river salamander.

The hellbender's warty head is flattened horizontally, its tail flattened vertically like a rudder. It has tiny, lidless eyes. Its body is brown and covered with irregular dark markings, and its four short legs do little to raise the animal's aesthetic value. The thick slimy

HELLBENDER GUARDING EGGS (*Cryptobranchus alleganiensis*). Length: 1½ feet. Range: Western New York and central Pennsylvania southward to Georgia and Louisiana; westward to Iowa.
American Museum of Natural History

skin of its body is so loose that it forms a parallel series of fleshy ruffles on each side which extend from the front to the hind legs. All in all, the hellbender is so lacking in the essentials of beauty that it has been favorably compared only with such unattractive objects as dried-up cucumbers.

It is a nocturnal creature, skulking about the water after dark in search of worms and small fishes. It has earned a reputation as a fisherman's pest because of its fondness for stealing the bait from the hooks of hopeful anglers.

Unlike most amphibians, the hellbender is completely aquatic. It makes no use of its lungs, breathing instead through the skin. However, it sometimes rises to the surface for air. So tough is it, though, that some specimens have lived on land for twenty-four hours. Scientists have also placed hellbenders in alcohol for a day, expecting to take them out dead after that period. Instead, the alcohol-soaked hellbenders displayed their hardiness by not only emerging alive but moving about with unexpected activity.

These odd animals live among underwater rocks and vegetation. Their life is more like that of a fish than might be expected. This is especially noticeable in their breeding habits. In true fish style the male hellbender prepares a small cavity on the river floor in autumn. The female comes to this nest to deposit her eggs. Then the male fertilizes the eggs and sends the female about her business. Alone he dutifully watches over eggs, which string out like two ropes of dried garlic, until they are hatched. It is reported, however, that his parental solicitude sometimes falls below par, and on such occasions he may eat a few of the eggs.

BIRDS

AMERICAN EAGLE

Birds

In a peaceful California valley, a chicken farmer looks out over his village of henhouses. The large barred-rock roosters chase each other around a pile of rusting agricultural machinery, squawking murderously. Scattered over the range, the hens industriously peck at the remnants of the morning's corn. Suddenly, over the rim of surrounding hills, a great bird appears, moving swiftly forward with each flap of its strong wings. The barnyard fowls are strangely quiet except for the low clucks of the mother hens as they herd the chicks against the shadowed sides of the henhouses. The great bird circles closer and closer.

"What a hawk!" the farmer's boy exclaims admiringly.

"That's no hawk," the older man replies, "that's an eagle." And as the bird swoops lower, the taloned feet come into view.

They grab sticks and run out into the chicken range shouting and waving threateningly at the bird.

"Shoot him, shoot him," the excited boy cries. The farmer shakes his head.

"You can go to jail for that." The feathered raider swoops once or twice more over the menacing figures on the ground, examines them coolly, unhurriedly. Then it is off, with slow dignified wing strokes, into the wind.

There is no such fierce grace and nobility in an eagle's glassy-eyed stare from atop the hunter's mantelpiece. A favorite sporting trophy, the eagle has been shot in great numbers. Now under Government protection, it seems to be surviving except in Alaska where a bounty is placed on its head.

Early in our country's history, the eagle survived an attack of another sort. Branding the eagle a coward and a bully, Benjamin Franklin waged a vigorous but losing campaign to have the turkey designated as the national emblem instead. No doubt, the Pilgrims would have concurred.

Turkey or eagle, birds in general have played a memorable role in America's past. Faced with a despairing and mutinous crew, Columbus saw a flock of migrating birds and followed them to the dis-

covery of the New World. Had it been spring instead of autumn the birds would have led him to what is now the United States instead of to Watling Island in the Bahamas, where he eventually landed.

This continent was so richly blessed with wildlife that it must have seemed at the beginning of the nineteenth century that the birds could be shot, trapped, and molested without end—their natural multiplication would save them. But the latter half of the nineteenth century was a bad period for birds. Probably the greatest factor in the extermination of some species and the great depletion of others was the advance of civilization along the growing network of highways. Forest regions set to the plow, streams polluted and despoiled of the small marine life which many birds depended on for food, the invasion of once secluded breeding spots by tourists and hunters, all played their part. In addition, birds like the now extinct passenger pigeon were shot to fill squab pies by the thousands, and others, the egrets, herons, spoonbills, and terns, were subjected to a systematic massacre for their plumage.

Great as the destruction has been, much still remains to us. Some species like the immense California condor and many game and fish-eating birds have greatly diminished in numbers. But the common everyday varieties, the crow, the starling, the jay, the robin, and many songbirds, still are plentiful. In the harbors the gulls play about wharves and ferryboats. The northern lakes resound to the call of the loon. From the fierce hawk to the domestic pigeon strutting about under the feet of pedestrians on New York City's Fifth Avenue and Forty-second Street, many species still respond to the call.

Many birds must be seen from a certain vantage point if their beautiful colors are to be appreciated. Red, yellow, and black are the only pigment colors to be found on any bird, so that other colors and combinations are the result of harmonized refractions of light striking the surface of the feathers. Layers of color cells or microscopic pits on the feathers act as tiny prisms which break up the light into the component colors of the spectrum. For the best effects, the observer should stand between the bird and the light shining on it.

Some of these color combinations produce startling effects. The rose-breasted grosbeak, for instance, a bird found in the eastern

United States, has black, white, and red coloring so arranged that it resembles a man in evening clothes who has splotched wine over his glistening shirt front.

Birds, with their unique covering of feathers, are so markedly different from all other classes of animals that with the possible exception of the dolphin-shaped penguins no one is likely ever to mistake a bird for anything other than a bird. These feathered vertebrates are egg-laying, warm-blooded creatures seen on land, at sea, and in the air. They are descendants of reptiles and still possess some resemblances to their forerunners in the evolutionary scale. Their egg-laying, as well as the scaly skin on their feet and legs, are reptilian characteristics. Even their feathers appear to be nothing more than modified scales useful not only in flying but also in providing insulation against heat and cold, and their periodic moulting is analogous to the shedding of snakes and lizards. It required millions of years for birds to evolve from reptiles—to acquire skill in running, climbing, leaping, gliding, and finally flying; but most important of all it required fundamental changes in their structures as new functions made new organs necessary.

Light, hollow bones are the framework for the streamlined bodies of flying birds which cut down air resistance and so facilitate their flight. While it is true that some birds such as the ostrich, the penguin, and their allies are flightless, all American birds can fly.

Connected with flight is the presence of a keel to which the flying muscles are attached—these sometimes weigh about half the entire body.

The body cavities of these winged aerialists are equipped with air sacs, providing both buoyancy and a breathing system to dispose of the heat generated in flight and rapid motion. Even the heavy teeth common to most animals are dispensed with in birds and replaced by a light horny beak whose form varies with the food eaten. The small muscular gizzard, another avian attribute and one that insures perfect digestion, is aided not only by the high temperature of the blood but also by its rapid circulation. The temperature of birds is the highest of all vertebrates, being two to fourteen degrees higher than that of mammals.

Despite such general features, the twelve hundred species and subspecies of American birds vary among themselves as much as do mammals. They range from the aquatic, fish-eating cormorant to the diminutive hummingbird which lives on the nectar of flowers. There are swift and poor flyers, swimmers and non-swimmers, melodious vocalists and birds that can't sing a note. There are monogamous birds like the dove, polygamous birds like the turkey, and philanderers like the wren. Although their average age is seventeen years, the big wild turkey lives to be only five; but the herring gull has been known to live forty years.

Only a few, however, like Cooper's hawk which eats chickens, and sparrows which eat fruit and grain, are harmful to man. The majority are beneficial since they eat crop-destroying and disease-bearing insects.

Too many such friends of man have been shot for no other crime than alighting in a cornfield. Knowledge of a bird's diet cannot be obtained simply by watching it, because a bird in a field of grain actually may be eating insects and not the grain at all. A few naturalists anxious to protect birds have helped to clear up many misunderstandings by analyzing the contents of their stomachs. Analysis alone reveals the average percentage of the different types of food consumed and alone can prove conclusively whether a bird is friend or foe.

In any case, birds cannot be diminished beyond a certain number, which varies with the different species, if extermination is to be avoided. Theoretically, as long as there is one male and one female of any species left, the groups may yet prosper in numbers. This widespread fallacy is ably refuted by Prof. W. C. Allee of the University of Chicago in discussing the fate of the heath hen in his book, The Social Life of Animals.

The heath hen was once abundant in Massachusetts, but by 1850 it had been killed off until it was to be found only on Martha's Vineyard and nearby islands and among the pine barrens of New Jersey. By 1890 to 1892 the birds had diminished to a scant two hundred at most, restricted to Martha's Vineyard. As soon as the "bird stuffers" heard how rare they had become, prices went up and museum collectors rushed in to get specimens before they disappeared like the dodo. By 1907 the count had been reduced to seventy-seven. The Heath Hen Association was formed. The society arranged for almost three thousand acres of protected range for the birds. By 1916 their numbers had increased to two thousand.

"Then came a fire, a gale, and a hard winter, with an unprecedented flight of goshawks, and in April, 1917, there were fewer than fifty breeding pairs. The next year, when there was an estimated total population of one hundred and fifty, the heath hen range was invaded by several expert photographers who took motion pictures of mating behavior. In the face of this disturbance at a critical time, still a good year allowed the birds to increase and again spread over Martha's Vineyard. In 1920 three hundred and fourteen were counted; but thereafter a decline in numbers set in which was never stopped," wrote Prof. Allee.

Although game wardens killed more cats, crows, rats, hawks, and owls, the heath hen census for the next six years were 117, 100, 28, 54, 25, and 35.

In the 1928 census of these birds, one male was found. It was banded and released and was last seen alive in February, 1932. That was the end of the heath hen.

No doubt, many conclusions may be drawn from the above and similar episodes. The lesson of greatest importance, however, one that should be stressed constantly by conservationists to careless bird lovers—and who is not a bird lover?—is:

"The time to save a species is while it is still abundant!"

Perching Birds

High up in forest branches, skimming over plowed fields, or clustered under the eaves of city apartments, perching birds twitter cheerily and sometimes break into melodious song. The perchers are the best known and most appreciated of the songster species, although some perching birds do not sing. The most popular songster is the imported house canary.

It is sometimes argued that such typical vocalists as the nightingale, skylark, thrush, and cardinal have nothing musical in their voices, but that human sentiment ascribes the art of music to them. It must at least be agreed that the sounds are charmingly sweet and, moreover, there is often controversy over whether human musicians really play or sing "music."

Perching birds are the largest avian order, including half of all the bird species. There are almost six thousand species of these sharp-sensed, graceful, little creatures found in all parts of the country.

Their long and speedy flights and vast energy are due to their high body temperature, highest of all vertebrate animals. Their feet are equipped with three front toes and one long hind toe which enable them easily to grasp the branches on which they perch. Four or more pairs of muscles control the vocal system of the songster species and aid them in producing their sweet tones.

Perching birds are helped in their search for food and their avoidance of enemies by unusual keenness of hearing, sight, and smell. They feed almost exclusively on insects and are hailed as friends of the farmers. However, perchers do eat seeds also, but apologists claim that these are mostly the seeds of weeds. And Dr. Hornaday adds that when birds eat fruit it is "more as a dessert than as a staff of life."

ROBIN

THE robin is a member of the thrush family which includes the bluebird, most familiar of American birds, as well as the hermit thrush, wood thrush, and veery, the finest of our song birds. In this family, brown and gray are the chief colors, while the breasts tend to be contrasting or spotted. The narrow wings are usually longer than the tail; the feet are slender, and the bill so short that it measures only about half the length of the head. The eyes are far apart.

ROBIN

ROBINS *(Turdus migratorius)*. Length: 10 inches. Range: Eastern and northern North America.
American Museum of Natural History

The robin is often seen hopping about on lawns, searching for worms or carrying grass to its nest. It perches on a limb, repeating its cheerful song and puffing out its cinnamon-red breast. The head is black, with a white spot beneath the chin. The back feathers are a fresh gray, the wings slightly brownish. In winter the male acquires an olive tinge on his back, while the colors of the female become a trifle duller.

Robins sometimes nest under the eaves of houses, though their usual choice is the crotch of a tree. The thick round nests are composed of mud, twigs, leaves, bits of paper and string, and a lining of grass. Two or three times a year the female lays four or five eggs. After the young have been hatched, both parents diligently bring worms and insects to them. So devoted are the adult birds that they will even fight a cat. Emitting a low cry of alarm, the birds fly back and forth above the marauder and peck desperately at him with their beaks.

There is one species with four subspecies widely distributed in this country which fly south in winter, but since those which breed in the far North usually stop in our northern States, many sections of the country have these birds throughout the year. Until 1913 they were viewed as game birds in some southern States, but now are protected by Federal law. With the growing scarcity of wild fruit and berries they have acquired a taste for cultivated berries and cherries, but they more than repay for this by devouring immense quantities of harmful insects. Orchards can be protected by planting mulberry trees near them, for when the robin sights a mulberry, it has eyes for no other food.

BLUEBIRD

A MOST conspicuous sign of spring is the arrival of the bluebird, as it flies northward after wintering in subtropical regions. The wings and upper parts of the male are bright blue, while the under side is reddish brown and white. Females show a duller blue except on the rump. The legs are short, the wings long and pointed, the tail notched.

Bluebirds naturally nest in hollow trees, fence rails, or holes in rocks, but readily adopt bird houses for their homes. Their food consists of worms, insects, weeds, and grasses, including practically no cultivated fruits. Fruit growers regard their presence in orchards as a sign of good luck. Other varieties besides the aforementioned eastern species are the azure, western, chestnut-backed, and mountain bluebirds. All of these, however, vary but little in their habits.

HERMIT THRUSH

BECAUSE of its delightful song the hermit thrush of the East has been given the surnames of swamp angel and American nightingale. A single phrase appears to be repeated in countless variations, each one higher in the scale than the last. Having reached the top of its range, the inventive bird turns to a new theme. The tone resembles that of a fine flute.

BLUEBIRD *(Sialia sialis)*. Length: 7 inches. Range: United States and southern Canada east of the Rockies.
American Museum of Natural History

It is difficult to sight the singing bird because its russet-brown feathers and spotted breast blend with the forest shadows. The hermit thrush sings in ventriloquist fashion with its bill almost closed; one must look closely to detect the pulsing of its throat. This bird neither benefits nor injures man economically, for it lives in deep forests where it eats only wild seeds, fruits, and insects. In the West there are six subspecies of hermit thrushes closely related to the eastern species and in this number is included the dwarf hermit thrushes.

WOOD THRUSH

THE note of the wood thrush, found in temperate parts of eastern North America, is fully as sweet as that of the hermit, but its melody is less varied. Since these birds often live near dwelling houses they are frequently seen. The wood thrush, also called the song thrush, bellbird, wood or swamp robin, has a light-brown head, a cinnamon-brown back, and an olive-gray tail; its breast and sides are light tan, spotted with dark brown. The nest, made of leaves and twigs, is placed from six to twelve feet from the ground in a young tree. Wood thrushes destroy beetles, cutworms, and grasshoppers.

WOOD THRUSH AND YOUNG *(Hylocichla mustelina)*. Length: 7 inches.
Range: Eastern North America.
American Museum of Natural History

Related to the wood thrush is the mountain-dwelling Townsend's solitaire. Found along the steepest slopes of western North America, this thrush is the loftiest dweller of its family. In Yellowstone National Park it may often be seen running along the ground in the manner of a robin.

VEERY

SO retiring is the veery, or Wilson's thrush, that as late as 1885 it was unknown to many naturalists including the one for whom it was named. It is most easily distinguished by its peculiarly resonant song, which fades into silence in a graceful diminuendo.

Its brown and black spotted breast reminds one of other thrushes in the East. The veery flies from its home in the bushes to hunt for beetles, snails, and wild vegetation. Its tawny-brown back is sometimes seen as high as five thousand feet in the Pine Ridge of North Carolina. In the West the veery is replaced by the somewhat duller and less tawny willow thrush. It breeds, according to Dr. T. Gilbert Pearson, in central Oregon, Nevada, Utah, northern New Mexico, and central Iowa and winters as far south as Brazil. Closely related to the veery is this widely distributed willow thrush which, however, does not appear in the East.

Other thrushes found in our country are Alice's thrush, better known as the gray-cheeked thrush, whose range extends from Alaska to Peru; the somewhat smaller but no less talented songster of the Catskills and northern New England, Bicknell's thrush; the russet-backed thrush of the Pacific coast; the widely distributed olive-backed thrush; the varied thrush of the West, which sometimes during migration straggles as far east as Massachusetts.

KINGLET

SMALLEST of all American birds with the exception of the hummingbird, the kinglet is aptly named. Its generic title, *Regulus*, means petty king, and the patch of yellow, orange, or scarlet, noticeable on the top of the bird's head when it is angry or excited, is its badge of office.

Four and one-half inches long, the fragile-appearing, delicately clothed, ruby-crowned kinglet survives and even seems to enjoy the blustering winter storms of New England. Its nest is sturdy, the soft thick walls being made of moss, fine strips of bark, grasses, and cocoons, and lined with hair and feathers. The eggs are generally five to nine in number, dull white or pale buff in color with a patch of speckled brown.

Sometimes it would seem that the bird knew it possessed a spot of color atop its head that could be made more striking at will. Especially during the mating season, kinglets flash their diadems at each other in a competitive display, piping shrilly and chasing in and out of the branches. The tails and the side feathers below the wings are spread out. Females lack the colored crown.

While the head ornament of the ruby-crowned kinglet is partly hidden, that of the golden-crowned kinglet is always plainly visible. These two birds also sing differently; the golden-crowned one emits a succession of five or six short shrill notes and ends with a sudden vociferous warble, while the ruby-crowned bird's song is much more musical and elaborate and has been compared in mellowness with a flute or the trained voice of an adult soprano.

Kinglets are found in North America as far north as Alaska to the limit of tree growth; they breed southward to Quebec, northern Michigan, and in the high mountains of New Mexico, Arizona, and northern California. In winter they may fly as far south as Guatemala.

Besides the brilliant head patch, the birds are colored an olive-yellow above, verging to a dull white at the tips of the greater covert feathers.

GOLDEN-CROWNED KINGLETS (*Regulus satrapa*). Length: 4 inches.
Range: North America east of the Rockies.
Ralph De Sola (SIM)

The five species include the western golden-crown kinglet and the Sitka or Grinnell's ruby-crowned kinglet, also of the West.

GNATCATCHER

THE sweetly singing blue-gray gnatcatcher can be heard only for short distances. In spring these birds are plentiful throughout the eastern United States. In form they resemble mockingbirds, but since they are only four and a half inches long they are rarely confused with that bird.

Gnatcatchers, as their name implies, are insectivorous and therefore are forced to migrate in quest of food. Their migratory flights take them as far south as Guatemala and Yucatan, but it has been shown that some remain through the winter as far north as South Carolina where they live in swamps.

In the early spring, male and female gnatcatchers begin the building of their nest which is so placed that when the leaves come out on the tree they will hide the nest. The interior of the nest is lined with such dainty materials as milkweed, cattail down, and withered blossoms, and these are bound together with horsehairs.

But delicate or not, this little bird will attack intruders many times its size when its four or five greenish or bluish white eggs are in the nest.

Also called the little bluish-gray wren and the flycatcher, the gnatcatcher is predominantly a bluish gray in color, but the front portion of the forehead and the sides of the forehead and crown are black in a conspicuous U-shaped design.

WREN-TIT

THE joyous call of the wren-tit may be heard for a quarter of a mile. The uplands of California and Oregon resound to the sharp whistling note, increasing in rapidity until at the end it almost trills. The feathered virtuoso gives voice to an extensive repertory of calls, signifying at times excitement, disappointment, anxiety, or pure joy of living.

Of all the many varieties of perching birds, these fluffy-feathered, long-tailed songsters are the only ones peculiar to North America. Fearless and inquisitive, wren-tits may be approached quite closely for observation. When they fly, hop, or balance themselves on a twig, their long tails waggle up and down. Head cocked, they will approach to investigate an unexpected sound; they are frequently led by curiosity to enter gardens near their brush country homes.

While the scientific name of the wren-tits connotes "on the ground," due no doubt to their unhurried and dignified demeanor, wren-tits spend much of their time in the air or amid the branches of trees seeking caterpillars, spiders, elderberries, and wild fruits. They like the seeds of the poison oak.

Twigs, strips of bark, and feathers are combined with a lining of grass or horsehair to form the nest. This is placed in a bush from one to four feet above the ground. In the early spring, three to five bright-green eggs are laid which take fifteen to eighteen days to hatch, both parents tending to the incubation. When the fledglings emerge from the shells they remain in the nest for another seventeen days while the devoted parents scurry around to find food for them.

Soon a second brood of youngsters arrives and when these are old enough to fly and seek their own food, adults and young may migrate to higher ground in June or July.

Wren-tits are especially careful in protecting their young. The nests are difficult to find as they are well hidden in the brush. The parents always approach them silently, and, should an intruder come, the brooding bird will not cry out or move, even if the bush is shaken. If finally driven from the nest, the bird halts a few feet away to watch and will even flutter about, pretending to be lame to draw away an attacker.

Both sexes are identical in appearance, call notes, and habits. Their soft straggly feathers, grayish brown above and somewhat lighter beneath, form a vague, mottled pattern. The forehead is short and the eyes pale, sometimes light yellow or whitish and glassy looking. In winter the plumage is duller.

CHICKADEE

Five subspecies of wren-tits are recognized, the distinguishing characteristic being the lightness or darkness of the feathers; there is no difference in their behavior. Resembling wrens in color, length of tail, and certain habits, wren-tits are closer to bush-tits in the shape of the head and shortness of the bill. In other characteristics they bear no resemblance to any bird on this continent, although likenesses have been noted to certain bird families of the Orient.

ACADIAN CHICKADEE *(Penthestes hudsonicus littoralis)*. Length: 5 inches. Range: Northeastern United States and Canada and southeastern British Provinces.
American Museum of Natural History

CHICKADEE

FLITTING nervously from twig to twig, the eastern chickadee seems never to stop eating. Hopping, twisting, and turning, the ever-hungry little bird snares a weevil here, a plant there, and is ever in quest of larvae, moth eggs, and seeds. It will even hang upside down, the better to locate an insect hidden in the bark.

Its black-topped head and white breast could, by a stretch of the imagination, be likened to the white shirt and top hat of full dress. But the spry little chickadee is rarely formal. As it dances about, it calls out a *chicka-dee-dee-dee-dee*, but may start weakly and end strongly so that only the last three *dee*'s are audible. In spring and fall the musical repertoire is enlarged by the addition of a whistled song of two or three dulcet notes. Henry David Thoreau described its song as "faint lisping notes like the tinkling of icicles on the grass."

The deserted nest of a woodpecker may be occupied by the chickadee which thereafter exercises squatter's rights. If a ready-made home is not at hand, the perching bird must go to work. A hole is excavated in rotting posts or stumps and a carpet of leaves and grass is laid. Feathers and the downy hair of rabbits comfortably line the nest.

In such a sanctum the female chickadee sits on her four to eight eggs. When an intruder appears, the diminutive lady can do little in defense of her home and family. Virtually her only stratagem is to take a deep breath, so deep that her body swells, and then exhale suddenly with a popping sound. This is calculated to frighten intruders away, and sometimes does if they are small enough. Subspecies of the chickadee number eighteen.

BUSH-TIT

ANOTHER titmouse, the bush-tit, seems to have real community spirit, traveling about as it does in groups of twenty which are increased to a hundred in winter. As it goes about its work, it gossips with its fellows by chattering softly. When one scents trouble brewing, its hushed tones rise to a shrill crescendo of warning, and all scatter.

Its most dangerous enemy is the blue jay, which rips open the nest and eats the bush-tit's eggs. The only recourse of the helpless victim is to repair its home and proceed to raise another family. It is reported that the older children in the bush-tit family help their parents to take care of the new brood and assist in providing food.

This four-inch bird of the far West is noted for its home building. Its nest is pouch-shaped, about ten inches long, though sometimes as large as twenty inches. It begins to build from the top, constructing the roof first and leaving an opening for the door. The nest may be suspended inside of, or around, a dangling mass of moss or mistletoe; sometimes it is woven of leaves, moss, and cobwebs, and the sides are anchored to branches. Not only does the bush-tit line the hallway and chamber as comfortably as possible, but it is concerned with appearances. Its flair for decoration results in a house fully ornamented with moth wings and acacia blossoms. There are five subspecies of bush-tits.

VERDIN

IN the arid, cactus country of the Southwest lives the four-inch verdin, a gray-and-white titmouse with head and shoulders coated deep yellow. The verdin does not appear to drink water. It is so well adapted to the dryness of its home that it subsists on the moisture extracted in eating insects and berries and the succulent cactus in which it often builds its nest.

When the female is brooding, the male sleeps in a private nest, but in winter both occupy the family dwelling. The nest is exposed to view since there is no heavy foliage where it can be concealed. Many other birds leave their home after raising a family; the little verdin, however, requires shelter constantly and must therefore keep its nest in repair the year around.

Verdins apparently dislike crowds and are found in pairs or small family groups. Their utterances vary from a single plaintive note to a repeated cheeping. Like all of their relatives, they are very friendly.

William L. Finley, observing a verdin's nest in Arizona, saw the mother enter it with food for her young. Father came along with a mouthful of worms, too, but stopped short when he saw strangers about. Instead of bringing the worms into the nest he swallowed them and then went hunting in nearby bushes as if to show "that he was merely skirmishing to appease his own appetite and that he had neither nest nor children." Only one verdin occurs within our borders.

TUFTED TITMOUSE

THE six-inch, tufted titmouse of the East, one of the largest of the thirty North American species and subspecies of titmice, is a friendly, unafraid bird. Olive Thorne Miller tells of one female who casually flew into a house, built a nest in a hanging basket, laid her eggs, and went about the rooms picking up bits of food. She left only when the people became so enthralled by her domestic life that they began to intrude upon her privacy.

Another titmouse, described by the same naturalist, pulled out a beakful of a man's hair as nesting material and liked it well enough to come back for more. The man was a bird lover and was therefore pleased to spare a few locks for the titmouse, of which there are some nine varieties in this country.

NUTHATCH

THE white-breasted nuthatch and its four American subspecies are rarely seen in summer when they reside in the forest. But in winter, when wild food is scarce, numerous pairs of these sharp-billed birds visit orchards and fields in search of nuts and grains. They derive their name of nuthatch from the habit of wedging a nut in the crotch of a tree and hammering it open with their powerful beaks. These foraging parties are often exceedingly noisy, disputes sometimes occurring between different groups of birds.

The color of this bird is a bluish ash above; the top of its head and neck are black, while the wings are black, blue, and white. The under parts are white, except for the tail, which is reddish brown.

In the spring the nuthatch returns to the woods, where it subsists on insects. The female makes her nest of leaves and feathers in a hollow tree or fence rail, and the male remains nearby to supply her with food. His mode of hunting is to spiral round a tree limb, burrowing and peeling off the bark as he goes. So firm is his grip that he is equally at home on the upper and the under side of the limb. As he burrows, he keeps up a constant chattering, as if to divert his nesting mate.

NUTHATCH

The female lays four to eight pinkish white eggs, spotted with reddish brown and lilac. After they have been hatched, she helps her mate on the insect hunt, often revolving round the same limb in the opposite direction. They do immeasurable good in the destruction of harmful insects.

The smaller red-breasted nuthatch has similar habits, except that it dwells mostly in evergreen forests, feeding on pine kernels. Here they are usually found foraging in parties with chickadees and small woodpeckers, all making a terrific din. Another nuthatch of like habits is the brown-headed species found in the southeastern pine forests.

The four-inch pygmy nuthatch of our western forests and mountains is distinguished by its soft, liquid song. Slightly larger is the white-naped nuthatch of southern and Lower California. A related Rocky Mountain subspecies of pygmy nuthatch is the black-eared variety.

WHITE-BREASTED NUTHATCH *(Sitta c. carolinensis)*. Length: 6 inches.
Range: Eastern North America.
American Museum of Natural History

BROWN CREEPER *(Certhia familiaris americana).* Length: 5 inches. Range: Eastern North America.
Ralph De Sola (SIM)

BROWN CREEPER

IN its search for food the grayish-brown creeper, also called the common creeper, begins at the base of a tree and works its way up, using its tail as a prop. Its bill is too weak for it to pierce the bark like the woodpeckers and nuthatches, so the creeper simply pokes into holes and crevices. As it climbs, usually in a spiral, it utters a soft, lisping call. After arriving at a point about halfway up the tree, the creeper flutters downward and begins again at the base of a new tree. So strong is its urge to climb that, where no trees are available, it may climb up telegraph poles, rocks, sandbanks, or on very rare occasions a man's leg or a cow's tail. One bird was observed to climb forty-three trees in an hour.

The creeper nests in deep woods of eastern North America under a sliver of loose bark on a decayed tree. The nest, woven of bark and moss, is set on a platform of twigs; sometimes it is lined with feathers. Four to eight cream-colored eggs are laid, sometimes spotted with reddish brown.

In its Canadian mating grounds the creeper sings a sweet four-noted song, which is rarely heard in the United States. Like the nuthatches, it approaches human habitations only in the winter. At this season it will eat the suet provided by thoughtful bird lovers.

Four other creepers, subspecies of the brown creeper, are the Mexican creeper which occasionally comes into southern Arizona; the Rocky Mountain creeper; the Sierra creeper of Washington, Oregon, Idaho, and California; and the California or tawny creeper whose range extends from Monterey County to Sitka, Alaska.

WREN

SEEKING a home site is the task of the female wren. She chatters and scolds, fluttering about, and with a good deal of show settles all the domestic problems. But if the home does not suit Mr. Wren, he will leave it while the female homemaker seeks a new husband. Although the male's song is more familiar, he is usually called "Jenny Wren."

For all the chattering and effort, the pair seemingly are indifferent to the external appearance of their residence. Utility comes before the picturesque, so that most wrens will nest in any shelter large enough to admit them. While they are partial to hollow trees in apple orchards, they will frequently pick an old shoe, a tin can, a straw hat, or a glove to which to bring twigs, grass, bark, spider webs, feathers, and other nesting materials. The Latin name for this family, Trogloditidae, means cave dwellers; the house wren, the long- and short-billed marsh wrens, as well as the winter wren, build their homes in cavities or make cave-shaped nests.

In the desert regions of the western United States the cactus wren makes a gourd-shaped bundle of grasses in the interior of the cholla cactus plant. The barbs at the end of the thorns on this plant serve to protect not only the white pulp at the center but also the bird's nest with the eggs in it.

Like the winter wren, the cactus wren often builds nests that are never used. These are called cock nests and it is believed that they are occupied by the male while the female is incubating the eggs. Many nests are found which give no evidence of occupation, and it is a moot point whether these alternative homes are built out of subtle caution as dummies or merely because of stupidity or whether they are found unsatisfactory on completion.

The cactus wren lacks the full-throated song of the house wren. It is larger in size than the English sparrow or bluebird and may be recognized by its white throat and breast.

From the point of view of diet it seems that wrens are more beneficial than otherwise. The house wren subsists on an almost entirely insectivorous diet, while the cactus wren eats less than twenty per cent of vegetable matter in its day's total food. The insect food on examination of one specimen contained the remains of harmful insects almost exclusively, while the vegetable food consisted only of the seeds of wild plants.

EASTERN HOUSE WREN *(Troglodytes a. aedon)*. Length: 5 inches. Range: Eastern United States and Canada.
American Museum of Natural History

Wrens are prolific, the broods of young ranging in number from six to eleven. The eggs are usually white or pink, speckled with reddish brown, although sometimes they are pure white, brown, or greenish blue.

Usually small birds, varying in length between eight and one-half inches for the cactus wren to four inches for the winter wren, they have fairly long bills which are slender and curved downwards at the end. The tail feathers are soft and rounded at the tips while the length of this member varies with the species.

As a family, wrens are noted for their musical, ecstatic calls, the best singers being the Carolina, the cactus, and the winter wrens. The Carolina wren, a formidable enemy of the boll weevil in the South, sings nearly the whole year around. Its notes sometimes show a great similarity to the calls of other birds, particularly the tufted titmouse and the cardinal, causing it to be called the mocking wren. The Carolina wren is not nearly so fond of the proximity of humans as the house wren, but it seems to be acquiring more and more confidence. Normally it seeks out a hollow tree in the woods, but in recent years it has been known to take advantage of bird houses set out for birds less afraid of man.

Besides the house, cactus, Carolina, winter, and the two marsh wrens, other familiar American wrens are the rock wren which breeds up and down the Pacific coast between Canada and Mexico, eastward to North Dakota; and Bewick's wren, a five-inch songster similar in habits to the house wren. Bewick's wren breeds from Nebraska east to Pennsylvania and south to central Arkansas and Alabama. The Florida wren, somewhat larger and darker than the Carolina wren, is found only in Florida south of the Suwannee River and the Okefenokee Swamp.

MOCKINGBIRD

MOST versatile American songster, the mockingbird not only carols its own sweet melodies, but even mimics the thrilling of other birds. In a ten-minute period it may imitate the songs of fifty of its neighbors, mockingly stealing their tunes and adding the polish and range of a master. For good measure it also can encore with imitations of a cackling hen, a creaking wagon, and a broken down phonograph.

Romantically inspired with the return of spring, the male mockingbird perches on a branch in the moonlight and serenades the female of his choice. His ardent operatic offerings seem to come from

BROWN THRASHER *(Toxostoma rufum)*. Length: 11 inches. Range: Eastern United States and southeastern Canada.
American Museum of Natural History

the depths of his soul. He throws himself so rapturously into the performance that he tires, becomes limp, and falls to the ground. But when his spell of weakness has passed he rises again, flutters to his moonlit balcony, and resumes his musical improvisation with a lover's ardor.

During this season he holds forth from dusk till dawn. His voice rises and falls in volume as his strength increases and diminishes. He is sometimes assisted by other birds in the vicinity, which join in to provide a chorus for his aria of love.

An elaborate ceremony precedes the marriage. Male and female stand face to face, heads held proudly high, tails stiffly erect. They hop up and down, solemnly circling about each other with a display of excessive formality. When the dignified nuptial dance is over, the two are man and wife.

The honeymooners build a nest in a thornbush or thicket more than ten feet above ground. The husband sings while the wife collects twigs and stalks, and fashions the nest. Occasionally he assists her, but never enough to be a bother to the industrious lady.

From four to six children are born in the nest. Men hunt them because they can be sold as cage birds. Sometimes a ten-day-old mockingbird tires of confinement and attempts flight. Untrained, it falls helplessly to the ground and becomes easy prey for a cat or blacksnake. The blacksnake is the mockingbird's perennial foe and the gray-and-white songster has been known to fight and kill a blacksnake in defense of its nest.

BROWN THRASHER

THE eastern brown thrasher which, like the mockingbird, is one of the mimic thrushes, is even more of a warrior. It will furiously, and with bitter vengeance, attack either beast or man if its nest is threatened. The thrasher inflicts severe bites with its long bill and savagely thrashes its tail about. It also moves its tail in time to its song, as well as when enraged. The tail-thrashing accounts for its name. Despite its pugnacity it is good-natured enough to sing beautifully in the early morning. It is also known as the sandy mocker. Thrashers in this country total eleven varieties.

CATBIRD

AN outcast bird, the black-and-gray catbird of temperate America is often attacked by gangs of its neighbors during the mating season. Apparently the reason for assault and battery is that the catbird has an element of cat in it and makes forays on the nests of robins, bluebirds, and sparrows.

This songster has a vocal expression described by some authorities as a snarl, and also possesses the feline habit of slinking through bushes in which there are nests.

The catbird does not quite rate with the top-notch singers of its family, the mockingbird and the thrasher. Its chief defect is a harsh note which sometimes enters its music, although it frequently utilizes this grating tone to imitate something it has heard. The catbird does have the distinction of mimicking such guttural creatures as the frog, a mimetic feat probably beyond the mockingbird's power. However, it can also render a wide range of sweet melodies and some insist it is an orchestra within itself, emulating the flute, piccolo, clarinet, and 'cello.

All mimic thrushes, of which there are about fifty species and subspecies, have the ability to sing melodiously and imitate others.

CATBIRD *(Dumetella carolinensis)*. Length: 8 inches. Range: "Temperate North America in general, but wanting in most of the region south of the Columbia River and west of Rocky Mountains" (Pearson).
American Museum of Natural History

Among them are the sage thrush, inhabiting arid regions in the West; Bendire's thrasher in the arid Southwest; the California thrasher which has the fighting spirit of the brown thrasher; the shy Crissal thrasher in the Southwest; and Leconte's thrasher, also in the Southwest, which has the added prowess of being a speedy and elusive runner on foot, second in this respect only to the roadrunner.

DIPPER

THE slate-gray dipper, or water ouzel, makes its home by streams and waterfalls, and lives by eating the minute insects that swim beneath the water's surface. The plumage of this fat little bird is so dense and oily that it can stay under water without getting wet. It propels itself below the surface by the same wing movements that are used in flying and even walks along the bottom of

DIPPER *(Cinclus mexicanus unicolor)*. Length: 8 inches. Range: Mountains of western North America.
William L. Finley, Nature Magazine

swift streams. In flight it never departs far from the water but carefully follows the stream's most tortuous meanderings.

The ouzel always nests near water, but its favorite spot is a waterfall. Frequently the nest is located beneath the falls, so that the bird must fly through the spray whenever it enters or leaves its home.

The nest itself is shaped like a small hut, with a round opening in the side. It is made of moss which the bird keeps fresh and green by constant sprinkling. This the bird accomplishes by diving into the stream and then rising above the nest and shaking its plumage. Sometimes the spray from the waterfall does the job for it.

The ouzel's eggs, numbering from three to five, are a pure white color. The young ouzel's plumage differs from that of its parents in that the chick's feathers are tipped with white and usually its throat is white. When the young bird wishes to be fed, it stands on a rock and "dips." This motion consists of bending its knees, dropping to the ground, and then standing straight again.

Ouzels are great singers. Even in winter, when most other birds have migrated, the dippers hop about in the snow, merrily singing. So inured to cold weather are they that they sometimes dive beneath the ice covering a stream, swim about underneath, and emerge from a water hole. What they live on in the winter is still something of a mystery.

PIPIT

THE pipit's head nods and its tail jerks unsteadily as the larklike bird wanders about in search of insects for dinner. It does not hop like most birds but walks, now and then breaking into a trot. When someone approaches, the pipit does not noisily flutter away, but crouches motionlessly. If its white tail is not flaunted, the pipit's brownish or grayish body makes it well-nigh invisible against the earth.

As it takes off for a flight, the pipit begins to sing a cheery *che-wee, che-wee* or call *pip-it, pip-it*. It flies erratically, since it gains altitude by reversing its course in a continual zigzag. Zoom-

AMERICAN PIPIT *(Anthus spinoletta rubescens)*. Length: 6 inches. Range: All North America.
American Museum of Natural History

ing higher and higher, it continues to sing in a clear tone and, as it disappears from view, its voice is still heard. When the pipit descends, it shoots earthward like an airplane in a power dive. Before striking, however, it suddenly slows down and lands on its feet with graceful ease.

In the summer the pipit takes to its home in Labrador, the Arctic, or the Rocky Mountain regions. There it breeds, sometimes at an altitude of fourteen thousand feet. Its nest may be secreted in a rocky crevice or in a scratched-out hole in the barren earth. Usually the nest is well hidden, for the pipit constructs it of moss, grass, and feathers which do not stand out against the background. Both mother and father take turns sitting on the four to six eggs.

With the coming of autumn, the family sets out for winter quarters throughout the United States. In the South the pipit does cotton growers a big favor by feeding on the boll weevil. In the Midwest it destroys locusts.

It likes the seashore, streams, and marshes. Sometimes a pipit flutters over to an isolated rock in the middle of a pond and nibbles water grasses. It also relishes mollusks and crustaceans.

Two species inhabit the United States. One is the olive-colored American pipit scattered throughout the country. The other is Sprague's pipit, which is brownish and dusky-streaked, ranging south and east of Montana. These thin-billed birds are members of the songster family of wagtails and pipits, but only one wagtail is found on this continent, in Alaska, and only these two of the eight species of pipits are encountered north of the Rio Grande.

WARBLER

SIX hundred miles across the Gulf of Mexico, buffeted and torn by winds, drenched by tropical rains, their indomitable wings ceaselessly beating, migrating warblers fly from South to North America in a single night. They might go through Central America and Mexico or follow the chainlike islands of the West Indies and keep in sight of land at all times. But the tireless coursers prefer the shorter route over the open ocean. Their reserve strength is so great that they can fly far inland before alighting. Many of them die during the long journey, their loose feathers torn by gales and tropical hurricanes.

Prodigious insect-eaters, warblers are among mankind's greatest natural benefactors. Their thin, sharp bills are constantly pecking and probing for young tent caterpillars and gypsy moths. These crawlers are very destructive to trees and when older are covered with bristles so that most other birds will not eat them. One warbler was observed to eat seven thousand plant lice in forty minutes, this staggering total being compressed in the stomach of the bird to almost one-third their normal bulk.

The hungry birds have trouble enough satisfying their own appetites, so that when their clamorous brood of youngsters arrives they are doubly busy. In most species it is the female that builds the nest and keeps the young warm during the eleven-day incubation period. The young, of warblers, born with a slight down, remain in the nest for ten days during which time they grow a complete nestling plumage. There is rarely more than one brood a year.

The more sober-colored, but usually among the best songsters of the eighty kinds of warblers, are those that nest close to the ground. Some build on the floor of the forest itself while others pick a bush three or four feet high as a home site. Snakes, squirrels, skunks, and other small animals take advantage of the accessibility of the nest to raid it and eat the eggs. The fact that the more numerous species of warblers are those that nest higher in the trees is therefore understandable. Often the warbler's nest is taken over by the female cowbird for laying purposes. The cowbird seems not to care whether the nest is on or above the ground.

Male and female birds of certain species are much alike in plumage. Even when the spring attire of the male is brighter than that of his spouse, his winter cloak will closely resemble hers. The young get their first breeding plumage after the first spring molt and thereafter look like their elders.

EASTERN YELLOW WARBLER *(Dendroica a. aestiva)*. Length: 4 inches.
Range: North and South America.
Frank L. Bird

OVEN BIRD

ONE warbler, the oven bird ranging east of the Rockies, builds a kiln-shaped nest with a flat arched roof and even a little door at the side. The grass-lined interior is protected by a framework of twigs lined with leaves and moss. The four or five white eggs are flecked with reddish-brown and lilac-gray.

During courtship the male oven bird sings while he wheels and circles in flight. On the ground he preens himself and struts like a miniature turkey. His bobbing orange-brown head and outspread olive-brown tail and wings are offset by the fluffy white breast feathers marked with characteristic parallel black streaks.

Teacher, teacher, teacher, the oven bird seems to be calling. A profuse outpouring of mellifluous notes ascends into the summer night, especially if the moon is shining.

REDSTART

LIKE a flickering flame through the brush, the constant motion of the six-inch redstart flaunts the salmon-orange of the wings and tail. Cubans call it "little torch." The male has a black back and head, and a white breast, while the female's back is greenish-gray and the breast a grayish-white.

The voice of the redstart is usually full and clear. But its repeated call *zee, zee, zee,* or *we see, we see,* is sometimes shrill and even rasping so that the call is hard to distinguish. These energetic, feather-covered bits of perpetual motion may be so engrossed in their busy search for food that they will even seize an insect near a person's feet. Two species inhabit the United States.

MARYLAND YELLOW-THROAT

AN impish little creature, the Maryland yellow-throat seems to observe and be interested in human beings to a much greater extent than other warblers. It mocks the song of the swamp sparrow and other birds living near it. It also has many calls of its own, including a swift-flowing flight song resembling that of the oven bird. The male has a black mask set off by yellow and buff lower parts and an olive-green back; the female lacks the mask but otherwise resembles the male.

Hidden under a clump of briars or an overhanging bush is the mass of leaves, grass, and rootlets in which the Maryland yellow-throat has its nest. The female is timid when incubating and quickly makes off if disturbed, leaving exposed the four white eggs with their characteristic red-brown and purple-black markings.

The Maryland yellow-throat has five related subspecies.

PROTHONOTARY WARBLER

PROTHONOTARY warblers fly north over the Mississippi Valley during April, seeking their homes in the damp woods near the waters of the great river and its tributaries. Their coming is heralded by the strong notes of their call, repeated all through the day and in any sort of weather. As they flash by, the yellow-green of their backs and their orange-colored heads are seen against the background of the gray wings and tails.

The male has a special soft trilling love song for its mate, which it sings as it slowly flutters back and forth. The pair seek an old woodpecker hole for their nest or some other hole in a tree not more than fifteen feet above the ground. Often a bird house is selected and the prothonotary warblers carry in bark strips and grass with moss for a lining. The female lays from five to seven eggs which are more vividly colored than those of other North American warblers. They are shiny white with purple and brownish red spots.

CERULEAN WARBLER

ORIGINALLY restricted to the Mississippi Valley, cerulean warblers are now found throughout New York State. Old habits die hard, so that when these birds migrate south they take the old path down the valley of the great river instead of traveling directly down the east coast.

YELLOW-THROATED WARBLER *(Dendroica d. dominica)*. Length: 5 inches. Range: Atlantic coast district from Massachusetts to Florida.
American Museum of Natural History

Male ceruleans are very beautifully marked with blue backs and black tail and wings trimmed with blue. The snowy breast is ornamented with a blue-black necklace. The young and the females have little blue coloring except on the tail, their back feathers being tinged with green. Their carefully woven nests, placed high in the largest trees, are composed of the usual grass and bark bound together with cobwebs. The eggs, three to four in number, are usually bluish or greenish white flecked with lavender or red-brown.

OTHER WARBLERS

BECAUSE it almost always sings while perching, the yellow-throated warbler is difficult to locate although its song is loud and clear. This sedate and dignified bird hops or flies slowly from tree to tree. Its head, tail, and wings are black, the wings being edged with gray. The belly is white, the throat vivid yellow.

High on a horizontal limb, where the branches fork, the nest is built. Lined with plant down, it will contain four or five greenish gray-white eggs. Early in July the birds leave for the tropics.

The black-and-white warbler of eastern North America constructs a partly roofed home somewhat resembling the oven bird's. Its brown-flecked eggs are normally five in number.

The worm-eating warbler of the eastern United States was said by John Burroughs to have a flight song which is "nearly as brilliant as that of the oven bird." Both sexes have a crown embellished with two lateral stripes of black and a center one of olive-buff. Inhabiting much the same region, the blue-winged warbler nests on the ground near the edge of the woods.

Other warblers found in eastern North America are the golden winged, Nashville, Tennessee, Cape May, black-throated blue, magnolia, chestnut-sided, bay-breasted, Blackburnian, Kirtlands, pine, palm, prairie, Kentucky, Connecticut, mourning, hooded, Wilson's, and Canada warblers, and the yellow-breasted chat, the water thrush, and the Louisiana water thrush.

In the western and southern States the following warblers occur: the prothonotary, Swainson's, Lucy's, orange-crowned, parula, yellow, myrtle, Audubon's, Grace's, black-throated gray, black-throated green, Townsend's, hermit, MacGillivray's warblers, and the painted redstart.

Typical perhaps of the method by which names of birds are coined is the case of the Blackburnian warbler. Writes Burroughs: "The orange-throated warbler would seem to be his right name, his characteristic cognomen, but no, he is doomed to wear the name of some discoverer, perhaps the first who robbed his nest or rifled him of his mate—Blackburn; hence Blackburnian warbler. The *burn* seems appropriate enough, for in these dark evergreens his throat and breast show like flame."

The yellow wings of the prothonotary warbler bring to mind the prothonotary of the Middle Ages, recorder of ecclesiastical matters, who wore a characteristic yellow cloak of office. This bird, again, is a good example of the varying means by which animals, and particularly birds, come by their names.

RED-EYED VIREO

IN spring before other birds have begun singing, and in fall when most songsters have left the northern latitudes, the red-eyed vireo is busy warbling. Often on hot summer days, when all other birds are resting in the shade, the vireo's note is heard.

RED-EYED VIREO *(Vireo olivaceus)*. Length: 6 inches. Range: "Temperate North America in general, except arid districts" (Pearson).
American Museum of Natural History

Yet this olive-green warbler, so difficult to sight amid the tree-tops, is no self-conscious artist. Even while singing, it does not neglect to procure a livelihood, but hops about from twig to twig in search of insects, occasionally interrupting its song just long enough to poke its beak into a crevice for a grub or to swallow a caterpillar or fly.

Some bird lovers have understood the vireo to cry *whip-tom-kelly*. Others call the same bird the preacher, maintaining that it seems to make a point in a few words, then to pause for its point to sink in. One writer records the sermon in the following phrases:

"You see it—you know it—you hear me—do you believe it?" Occasionally the red-eyed vireo may be heard in city parks. The warbler is easily recognized by its slate-gray head and a white line over its eye. In the fall, when insects are scarce, it feeds on berries.

The vireo makes its nest in a tree at the edge of an open field. Composed of grass and vegetable fibers, it is suspended from an upper branch. The three to five eggs are white with a few dull brown spots around the larger end. Since this warbler is a most solicitous parent, the cowbird often smuggles its eggs into the vireo's nest. The vireo hatches them with the same care as its own eggs, but when the young are born, the nest is often so overcrowded that most of the brood dies of suffocation.

YELLOW-THROATED VIREO

THE yellow-throated vireo builds a hanging nest about three inches deep and two in diameter, making use of such materials as strips of cedar bark, parts of spider webs, the cocoons of large moths, root fibers, and dry grass. The strands are stuck together by the bird's glutinous saliva. The outside of the nest is often covered over with moss, to make it resemble a moss-covered bump on a tree.

Somewhat smaller than the red-eyed variety, this vireo can be recognized by its rich yellow throat and breast, and the yellow line across the forehead and around the eyes. Its general color is olive in front, shading to ashy gray on the rump.

There are about twenty kinds of vireos.

OTHER VIREOS

ONE vireo, the greenlet, spends the greater part of its time in the tops of oak and elm trees. Its song is a light, rippling phrase repeated over and over. Others are the Philadelphia vireo, whose habit and song resemble those of the red-eyed variety; the blue-headed vireo, found east of the Great Plains and famous as an insect-killer; the black-capped vireo, found from Kansas to Oklahoma and Texas;

Bell's vireo of the Mississippi Valley prairies; and the white-eyed vireo, known as the politician, probably because it often lines its nest with bits of old newspaper. The song of this last bird has been characterized as "fluent, loud, and sarcastic." One listener understood its song as "Get out! Beat it!" This white-eyed vireo has two regional varieties, the Key West vireo and the small white-eyed vireo of the Rio Grande Valley.

SHRIKE

AFTER the bluish-gray northern shrike has killed a bird or large insect, it impales its victim on a thorn or fence barb prior to eating. Then, having devoured its fill, it leaves the remains of its victim for future attention. Often, however, this food reserve is completely forgotten and rots away until only the bleached skeleton remains. It is this habit that has earned the shrike the nickname of butcherbird. Because of the large numbers of grasshoppers found impaled in the bushes of some regions, the shrike was formerly given the name of nine-killer by countryfolk who believed that the butcherbird always slaughtered its prey in batches of nine. This, of course, had no basis in fact.

So voracious is the shrike that it will rush at the cages of domestic birds, often killing or injuring itself in the process. A canary whose cage was attacked by a shrike stuck its head through the bars in fright. In an instant the shrike had torn off the head, leaving the lifeless body inside. Starlings are frequent victims of the shrike. Often a bevy of these garrulous birds attempts to mob their enemy, though very rarely with success.

The usual note of the shrike is an unpleasant squeak like the sound of a rusty hinge, but in spring the male, and according to some authorities the female, too, are pleasant singers. A great mimic, the shrike has been known to imitate the quacking of ducks, the singing of songbirds and sparrows, and the raucous note of the catbird. In some cases the mimicry appears to serve as a decoy to bring small birds within striking distance; in others it appears to arise from caprice.

SHRIKE

The shrike's nest, situated in a tree or bush, is large and well built, consisting of sticks and grass lined with leaves and feathers. Four to six greenish-gray eggs, spotted with brown, are laid. The parent birds move about with their brood for the entire summer. At this time the male even attacks a hawk or eagle in defense of his young, and so great is his fury that the larger bird often declines combat.

The northern shrike frequently winters in the forests of Pennsylvania and New England and in severe winters may be found as far south as Virginia and Kentucky. In the West it is found in central California, Arizona, New Mexico, and Texas. Despite its voracious habits, it is valued by farmers as an insect-killer. A related subspecies inhabits the Northwest and winters as far south as Texas.

The loggerhead or southern shrike, ranging from Florida to South Carolina and sometimes seen in low-lying sections of Louisiana, is similar in appearance and habits, except that its diet is extended to include mice and gophers, which are impaled like its other prey. It rarely attacks birds except when wounded or cornered. In the mating season the loggerhead shrike becomes vocal.

NORTHERN SHRIKE (*Lanius borealis*).
Length: 10 inches. Range: Northeastern North America; south in winter to North Carolina.
American Museum of Natural History

WAXWING

FLYING in compact formation with military precision, a small group of cedar waxwings suddenly plunges down into an orchard. The birds perch on the branches of a tree in rows, billing affectionately. One waxwing plucks a cherry, nibbles it, passes it to the next bird, and it thus goes down the line like a peace pipe at an Indian gathering. Occasionally a berry or caterpillar is gravely handed from one to the other without being eaten at all. No one knows why waxwings indulge in this charming practice, instead of simply dropping the berry if they do not want to eat it.

Waxwings feast upon cedar berries in autumn and winter. However, one bird may destroy several thousand canker worms in a month, as well as beetles. They also eat bark, seeds, and snails.

These seven-inch songless birds are so called because of the red-tipped flight feathers which look as if they had been dipped in red sealing wax. Colorful markings extend from the glossy black of their bill and eye patch to the deep yellow tip of their tail. Their striking appearance is heightened by a pointed crest which stands erect when the bird is startled and droops when it is frightened.

The cedar waxwing inhabits most of temperate America. The Bohemian waxwing is found throughout the northern belt of the United States. This fawn-colored bird sometimes flies over the frozen Canadian Rockies in midwinter at a height of eight thousand feet. Only one other species of waxwing is known. It is indigenous to Japan.

SILKY FLYCATCHER

THE male half of a silky flycatcher family is a strange bird because he likes to work. With his wife placidly looking on, he flutters about gathering twigs and blossoms for their home.

He apparently does not regard it as an unpleasant chore. If his wife, in a helpful mood, so much as carries over a twig, he angrily orders her away. A strange male, indeed, is this, who so loves his

SILKY FLYCATCHER

home-building that he chases his wife away as if her very presence were annoying.

The nest is built in an oak or elder tree in the Southwest. And after the residence has been occupied by the couple, and the female has laid two or three eggs, the male again insists upon doing part of the housework. He spends considerable time sitting on the eggs, a practice seemingly scorned by most male birds.

This lover of domestic labor looks not at all like a meek creature. He is stern and dignified in demeanor. His glistening, silky, blue-black plumage and pointed crest befit the bold, hard-fighting knight more than the peaceable family man. In bearing, too, he is stiffly erect, sitting on a limb with a soldier's posture. However, he does have a shyness which makes it difficult to observe him, and he sings sweetly or in a hushed whisper.

When the flycatcher begins zigzagging after a fly, its meal is assured. When not chasing flies, it eats such things as berries, and will come into cities to feed on clusters which it may find on bushes surrounding houses.

CEDAR WAXWING (*Bombycilla cedrorum*).
Length: 7 inches. Range: Most temperate parts of North America.
American Museum of Natural History

AMERICAN WILD LIFE

The single species of silky flycatcher found in the United States from central California, southern Utah, and central western Texas south is also known as phainopepla, shining crested or black-crested flycatcher. Other species inhabit Mexico, Central and South America.

SWALLOW

AS the swallow circles gracefully in its swift flight, it easily plucks a meal of insects out of the air. The swallow spends the whole day aloft, borne along on powerful wings which, when folded back, are longer than its tail. Its tiny weak feet are unfitted for hopping about on the ground and are useful only for perching.

Twittering pleasantly, for it is not much of a singer, the swallow sets out on its long migrations. It soars along at such speed that it need fear no predatory hawk. High above the earth, it unflag-

PURPLE MARTIN (*Progne s. subis*). Length: 8 inches. Range: Temperate North America and tropical South America.
American Museum of Natural History

gingly carries on throughout the day and stops to rest at night, contrary to the habit of most migrating birds which fly by night and feed by day. During these seasonal peregrinations, the swallow always stops over at the same roosts, and certain of these wayside stations have become known as permanent camps for these transients.

Unlike the bold and daring warbler, the swallow prefers to be discreet and not risk a flight over large bodies of water. It generally skirts a large lake or bay, keeping the ground beneath it at all times. However, it likes to swoop into the mist overhanging waterfalls, even at Niagara, and snap up the mayflies. Its stay in the South is appreciated since it is a constant foe of the boll weevil and, in fact, rates high among the bird kingdom's insect killers.

PROBABLY the noisiest of the nine kinds of swallows in the United States is the eight-inch purple martin. At dusk a number of them will gather in an orchard and upset the peaceful calm of the neighborhood with a din of chattering. This bird is richly colored, its purplish coat tinged with violet, and its tail and wings a brownish black. When purple martins migrate, they travel in immense flocks numbering into the tens of thousands.

A subspecies of the purple martin, called the western martin, inhabits Lower California.

THE dark-colored cliff swallow labors long and hard in the construction of its home. The site of its nest may be a cliff or, much more likely nowadays, the side of a barn or house. The swallow uses mud as the building material and must scout about until it locates a suitable patch of ooze. Bit by bit the mud is carried in the bird's beak to the selected spot. The tiny particles are plastered together until the framework of the nest takes shape. Finally, grass and feathers are used for a comfortable lining.

THE bank swallow performs an equally amazing piece of home construction, excavating a hole in a sandbank. The burrow in which it lives may be four feet long. Sometimes a great number of

BARN SWALLOW (*Hirundo erythrogaster*). Length: 7 inches. Range: North and South America.
Ralph De Sola (SIM)

such holes will puncture a sandbank, for the birds seem to be friendly and companionable creatures.

The most brilliantly colored of the swallows is the violet-green swallow. It has a bronze-green head and back, purple wings and tail, white under parts, and black eyes. This swallow is most often seen among oak trees on a mountain side.

The nine species of swallows include the barn swallow, considered one of the tamest of wild birds; the northern violet-green swallow of the West; the rough-winged swallow, another sandbank inhabitant.

TANAGER

IN SPRING, when the scarlet tanager arrives in the northeastern United States after wintering in the tropics, the male bears his brilliant scarlet plumage, all the more striking against the black of his wings and tail. At this season he engages in an elaborate courtship ritual, parading about in front of his olive-colored mate-to-be, drooping his wings in dejection, though puffing up his scarlet breast with pride.

The female of the species is made for utility rather than beauty; it is she who gathers the weed stalks and twigs for the nest, which

SCARLET TANAGERS *(Piranga erythromelas)*. Length: 7 inches. Range: Eastern United States, Nova Scotia, and New Brunswick in summer.
Ralph De Sola (SIM)

is lined with flower stems and vine tendrils. The home is usually situated at the end of an oak limb ten to twenty feet from the ground in open woods, though occasionally the tanager may nest in an orchard. As she builds, and later as she sits on her three or four bluish white eggs, her handsome mate perches on a near-by limb, chirping away. When danger threatens, however, he too has his uses. He quickly leaps to her defense, eager to repel any invader. When the young are born, the male helps his mate in providing them with their insect food.

In spring the tanagers are frequently seen near the ground, pecking away at insects and making occasional sorties after berries, flowers, cherries, and other delicacies. Though the tanager is a rather inactive bird, it has a special knack of juggling berries. If a berry slips from its mouth, the bird leaps rapidly downward and, more often than not, succeeds in catching the morsel before it has fallen more than a foot.

It does not appear to accomplish much in the fruit and blossom eating line, for even the surliest farmer does not regard the tanager as an enemy, but praises it for its remarkable insect-destroying qualities. As the summer advances, the birds restrict their diet to caterpillars and insects. The female, apparently conscious of her protective coloring, moves about more freely than the male, who seems to know how conspicuous he is and sticks to the treetops. The female is often exceedingly tame, allowing humans to stroke her even when she is sitting on her eggs. The note of the female is a sort of chirp, but the male, though he too is a doughty chirper, has a more musical note, somewhat resembling the robin's.

The scarlet tanager, if approached closely enough, sometimes displays a rather remarkable habit. Cocking its head on one side, it peers out of one eye for a few moments; then, turning its head to the other side, it stares out of the other eye. Scientists believe this habit, often shared by other birds, is related to vision. It seems that at close quarters some birds are unable to see with both eyes and for this reason cock their heads and use only one eye.

In late summer, before leaving for the southland with its brood, the male bird begins to shed his splendid plumage. In the tropics it assumes the same olive-drab color as the female.

The summer tanager, slightly larger than the scarlet variety, is a brilliant vermilion color; in summer it frequents the eastern States as far north as the sandy regions of southern New Jersey. The western tanager inhabits the Rocky Mountains, but is sometimes found in the North Atlantic States. Other species include the hepatic tanager of the southwestern mountains and Mexico, and Cooper's tanager which breeds from southeastern California, southern Nevada, central Arizona, and New Mexico southward into Mexico. Sometimes it is seen in Colorado. It generally resembles the summer tanager.

PURPLE FINCH

OFTEN in the northern midwest, winter sends the thermometer tumbling far below the freezing point and the fields become icy, snow-white, silent fastnesses in the whip of the wind. Through the crisp sunlit air the chirping and caroling of the finches float down from the bare branches of the trees—they are still with us, long after their myriad brethren have gone "rolling down to Rio." Their bodies fat as suet balls, they flutter about as comfortably as in summer, looking for the seeds that keep them alive.

The family of finches, largest known in birddom and containing more than twelve hundred species and subspecies, is found all over the world except Australia. In the United States this family numbers two hundred members, counting species and subspecies. The general term, finch, is applied not only to those birds that bear the name, but to the grosbeaks, buntings, and sparrows as well. Their strong beaks permit these birds to eat seeds of many kinds, but mainly those of weeds. They also eat insects, so that with their varied diet they are not forced to migrate as extensively as other birds. Their destruction of weed seeds has been calculated to be worth millions yearly to the Nation, although some allege that they disperse these seeds over a wider range after digestion.

The purple finch sends its rollicking song bouncing through the tall aisles of the evergreen forests of the northeastern States. Alone or in bands these birds are especially musical during the spring mating season when they go through their courtship capers. The male picks up a straw with his bill and handles it like a drum major in intricate maneuvers, all calculated to impress the chick of his choice. With the conclusion of his dance he falls as dead as a 'possum in what is probably a bid for sympathy. At this point the female pecks at her recumbent suitor, arousing him. Forthwith, the two merrymakers indulge in a few osculatory acrobatics, after which they chase through the trees at high speed, the male in pursuit of his mate.

A related bird is the house finch which is particularly abundant throughout the West.

GROSBEAKS

THE robinlike pine grosbeak may be seen in the eastern United States eating berries, buds, and seeds. It nests among the pines very early in the spring, in some cases when the snow is still on the ground. It is liked best for its sweet, amiable whistle.

The evening grosbeak is a rare visitor to the East. Its home is usually in the bleak foothills of the Canadian Rockies whence it drifts east during occasional food shortages. Observed during one of these migrations, in 1916, it was described as being so fearless that it could be approached quite closely. The evening grosbeak is strikingly colored in yellow and black, arranged in such a manner as to afford it excellent protective coloration.

ROSE-BREASTED GROSBEAK

THE rose-breasted grosbeak helps the farmer by preying upon the potato bug which comprises a tenth of its diet. It is found in the Atlantic coast region and west to the edge of the Great Plains.

The male of this species pays much attention to his mate. He will carol to her and even bring her a potato bug. The black-headed grosbeak of the West is a handsome bird with a disproportionately large beak. The blue grosbeak, ranging the southern States near the Atlantic and Gulf coasts, preys upon weevils, grasshoppers, and other harmful insects.

CROSSBILL

THE dull red crossbill looks cross, but not because it is angry. Nature has endowed it with a bill that is almost X-shaped, a specialized tool that enables it to wrench its meal of seeds from the heart of the pine cones. When the food of other birds is buried beneath the snow, the crossbills use the limitless reserves of the evergreen trees. These northerly birds often go to work on the pine trees in groups and when so occupied their chatter, sounding like the clucking of chickens, resounds through the woods. Because of the never-failing food supply this pinkish-red bird has increased throughout the years.

ROSY FINCH

HIGH above the timber line among the mountain tops and glaciers of the Northwest, the gray-crowned rosy finch is occasionally seen. These lonely birds feed upon frozen insects and weed seeds. In the spring they nest in a cup-shaped affair of grasses placed in some rocky hideaway.

REDPOLL

THE male redpoll is one of the most considerate of birds. Not only does he nourish his young by regurgitation, but he also feeds his mate while she is employed in incubating the eggs. During the winter migration the common redpoll reaches the northern United States from its breeding range in Alaska and Canada.

GOLDFINCH

A COAT of bright yellow, cap of black, and wings of black and white adorn the American goldfinch, also appropriately known as the wild canary or eastern goldfinch. This pastel-tinted songster nests late in July and August when a plentiful supply of seeds assures the young of regular meals. The goldfinch eats many noxious insects, but its young eat seeds from the beginning of their lives instead of waiting until they are partly grown, as other birds do. Goldfinches are fairly abundant in all parts of the United States. A closely related bird limited to the West is the Arkansas goldfinch. Strangely enough this bird breeds while still attired in the plumage of adolescence. In all some six kinds of goldfinches are native to this country. The European goldfinch, an introduced species, appeared to be well acclimated to parts of the northeastern United States, although it is no longer seen in New York City where it was once well established. No longer common, today it ranges from New

Jersey to southern New England but in recent years its only recorded nesting sites have been on Long Island, according to John T. Nichols. In Europe it is prized as a cage bird and for centuries has ranked high as a pet.

PINE SISKIN

AFTER the breeding season siskins congregate in large flocks. Startled, the little striped brown birds rise as one from the ground and wheel off to safer areas. Feeding on white cedar seeds and those of the various pines and spruces as well as the fallen seeds of maple and elm, the pine siskins are distributed through the tall timber in the high mountains of Colorado and in many other States. Sometimes they are found at altitudes of seven thousand feet. In the winter they occur over most of the United States.

ENGLISH SPARROW

IN 1850 eight pairs of English sparrows were brought over from England to the United States, and ever since Americans have had cause to regret this tariff-free importation. Aggressive, omnivorous, and fertile, the sparrow is free from persecution by natural enemies while it attacks and drives away other birds like robins and tanagers. A winter resident, it gets a head start on other birds returning from the South and often usurps the bird shelters prepared for these wayfarers. It defiles walls, windows, and statuary; it raids fruit trees and flower and vegetable gardens. Finally, it destroys the eggs and young of such useful native birds as wrens and swallows. To offset this bill of particulars the English sparrow has a certain value as a scavenger in that it eats seeds, and in the cities is helpful in removing equine refuse from the streets. Its diet also includes harmful weevil larvae, cutworms, and other agricultural pests which it has learned to eat more recently.

Despite the activities of small boys armed with pea shooters and air rifles, the English sparrow's two broods a year enable the species to increase.

ENGLISH SPARROW *(Passer domesticus)*. Length: 5 inches. Range: Introduced from Europe in 1850 and today common in almost all settled parts of the United States and Canada except southern Florida.
American Museum of Natural History

VESPER SPARROW

THE song of the vesper sparrow sounds through the pastures like the descending notes of a violin. This shy bird of the northeastern and Atlantic coast States runs along the road ahead of the pedestrian for some distance before taking flight. By elevating the feathers on its head it can form a temporary crown, although it has no true crest. Also called the bay-winged bunting, the grass finch, the grass sparrow, and the bay-winged finch, the vesper sparrow lays four to six eggs in a nest of weed stalks, bark strips, and dried grass.

In the western United States except for the Pacific coast, a bird with slightly paler chest markings and more slender bill is called the western vesper sparrow. The Oregon vesper, smaller than the eastern vesper, replaces that bird on the Pacific coast.

OTHER SPECIES

THE Ipswich sparrow is a rare bird that lives in the grass of the sand dunes scattered along the Atlantic coast. Almost mute, its call is but a faint *tzip* uttered in one note. It eats berries, insects, and snails.

The Savannah sparrow of the northeastern States migrates south to the Gulf States in winter. It is a valuable destroyer of the boll weevil. Related sparrows are Bryant's sparrow of California, Belding's sparrow found on the Lower California peninsula, and the large-billed sparrow of the same region.

Also called the quail sparrow and the yellow-winged sparrow, the grasshopper sparrow of the northeastern States builds a nest of grasses to blend with the background. These nests are really hard to locate. The western grasshopper sparrow inhabits the plains of Mexico and the southwestern United States.

Found in the eastern half of the United States and wintering in the South is Henslow's sparrow, a plain striped bird with an undistinguished song. In South Dakota a paler bird is called the western Henslow's sparrow. Another similar species found in the Mississippi Valley goes by the name of Leconte's sparrow.

The sharp-tailed sparrow and the seaside sparrow, Atlantic coast birds, seem to be attracted by the salt-water smell of the coastal marshes and swamps. Two birds closely related to the sharp-tailed sparrow are Nelson's sharp-tailed sparrow of the Mississippi Valley and the Acadian sharp-tailed sparrow. A form of the seaside sparrow is the dusky sparrow of the Indian River region of Florida. The food of this seaside sparrow is similar to that of the sharp-tailed sparrow.

West of the Alleghenies the lark sparrow is one of the best-known and best-loved birds. In the city as well as the country, on farm, field, or desert, its chestnut and white head, its white breast with one black spot, and its white-edged tail make it a welcome sight. Its song is vigorous and musical. The western lark sparrow is a more lightly colored subspecies. The lark sparrow destroys great quantities of grasshoppers.

A little-known bird of the Missouri River Basin is called Harris's sparrow. Its breeding grounds in the Hudson Bay region were not discovered until 1900. It has a black hood extending from the crown of the head to the breast.

The white-crowned sparrow of eastern North America is matched in the West by Gambel's sparrow and Nutall's sparrow. These birds are seed eaters although they also consume a quantity of insects.

The golden-crowned sparrow breeds in Alaska and wanders south to the southern Pacific coast. This bird, oddly enough, sings better during the rain than in the sun as most other songbirds do. The raw climate reminds it, probably, of its Alaskan home.

The white-throated sparrow, said to be the sweetest singer of all sparrows, breeds in the United States in the northern portions of New England. Hay-fever sufferers have cause to be thankful for this bird's destruction of the seeds of ragweed.

The tree sparrow, also known as the snow chippy, winter chippy, chip bird, tree bunting, Arctic chipper, winter sparrow, and Canada sparrow is often heard in the winter in the eastern United States. The western species winters in the Southwest and like its eastern relative is five and three-quarter inches long. Tree sparrows in Iowa in one year fed on eight hundred and seventy-five tons of weed seed. Other species of native sparrows are estimated to save farmers $35,-000,000 every year.

The chipping sparrow, sometimes called the hairbird because of its fondness for horsehairs which it uses for its nest, is probably trying to the good nature of horses since these hairs are selected from the mane and tail. Related to this inhabitant of the eastern United States are several species in the West. A bird quite similar in appearance, although of a different species, is the field sparrow of the eastern United States.

The black-chinned sparrow, a bird of the Southwest, has a song that resembles that of the field sparrow, but its black-patched throat betrays it as a separate species.

Ornithologists recognize three subspecies of the black-throated sparrow, two of which are found in the western United States and the third in Lower California. Their cheery song is a delight to hear in the arid, monotonous wastelands where they are found.

Juncos are deserving of better protection for they destroy many harmful insects and baneful weed seeds. They rarely migrate far in the winter, and then only when the food supply has dwindled. Thirteen varieties of this bird are found throughout various parts of the country.

Amid the sand dunes of the Southwest, Bell's sparrow, a brownish bird, lives with its related subspecies, the gray sage sparrow.

The pine-woods sparrow breeds and winters in Florida and southeastern Georgia. The nest of this sparrow is cylindrical and almost eight inches long.

The song sparrow is identified by its strongly marked breast, stubby bill, and the slightly forked tail noticeable when the bird is in flight. Fifteen varieties are known to the United States with the exception of the southern Atlantic and Gulf States.

Lincoln's sparrow is distinguished for the timidity with which it steals along the floor of the woods, taking care to avoid observation. While it breeds in Canada it is known all over North America.

Swamp sparrows like the vicinity of swamps and marshes because they eat the seeds of water plants. Their range is from eastern North America to the Great Plains.

The fox sparrow, a handsome bird, belongs to one of the largest families of sparrows. Fifteen kinds are known in the United States. They breed chiefly in Canada.

The Texas sparrow prefers the thickets and bushes to open ground and is seen only in a restricted area of the United States, southern Texas. Male and female, and even the immature young, are alike in appearance.

BUNTING

ALTHOUGH its name gives poor indication of its surpassing beauty, the indigo bunting is a welcome inhabitant of the eastern United States. The male is much less self-conscious than the female who is inclined to be secretive. One of the more valuable birds, the indigo bunting enlivens the landscape and saves the farmer much trouble by feeding upon insects in addition to seeds and berries. Its favorite perch is a telephone wire. The bunting's nest of weed stems and grasses may have a floor of dead leaves. It is usually placed in a bush not far from the ground. Here the eggs are laid, and though the male does not help with the incubation, he feeds the newly hatched chicks and often the mother too.

Other buntings include the brilliantly plumed bunting of the West and the tropically daubed painted bunting significantly called nonpareil, of the South; the lark bunting of the prairies, which looks like a blackbird with white wings.

The snow bunting, which breeds on the barren tundra of Labrador and Alaska, visits the northern United States in the winter. Another winter visitor from the Arctic is the Lapland longspur.

DICKCISSEL

HEARING the name *Spiza americana*, few would realize that lurking beneath this scientific cognomen is one of the most representative of American birds, the dickcissel. The bird has named itself by its inveterate habit of calling *dickcissel*. Usually found in the grain fields and open areas east of the Rockies, dickcissels are particularly plentiful in the Mississippi Valley. In August they may frequently be seen in large groups, often fraternizing with other birds, until the mating season in April when they break up into pairs. For some unknown reason they may be missing one season from a particular locality where they have been abundant the year before. Only in recent years have dickcissels spread from their ancestral home, the Mississippi Valley, to the prairies of the West.

TOWHEE

THE towhee's name is a phonetic spelling imitative of its call. It is also known as the swamp robin. Resident of the eastern United States, it is a sleek eight-inch creature, nicely marked with black over its head, wings, and tail as if it were wearing a cassock.

The lower bosom is brownish or yellowish. Its well-hidden nest, usually containing four eggs, is situated on the ground behind a barrier of grasses or bushes, and is constructed of compactly arranged twigs, grasses, and fibers.

A ventriloquist of great skill, the towhee will be looked for everywhere but the place where it actually is. Its melody consists of three notes, the first two heavily accented. Like the hen, this bird scratches on the ground for its food, which consists of seeds and insects as well as wild berries and fruits. It is often duped by the cowbird who leaves her eggs in the towhee's nest for that bird to hatch with its own.

Some seventeen varieties of towhees are encountered in the United States.

CARDINAL

THE swift flash of red, visible for the fleetest of instants, heralds the presence of the cardinal, inhabitant of the eastern portion of the United States. This beautifully red, black-hatted bird builds its loose nest among the thickets where it believes its two to four eggs will be safe. The cardinals are a family of exceedingly cheerful, active, and industrious disposition. Their charm and enthusiasm and their melodious call make them welcome visitors wherever they show their pretty heads. A relentless foe of numerous insect pests, they also eat harmful weed seeds. Four subspecies are found in the United States.

PYRRHULOXIA

SIMILAR to the cardinal in many of its habits is a gray bird with red crest known only by the forbidding title of Arizona pyrrhuloxia. Naturally enough this bird is known popularly as the gray cardinal. It expresses its various moods by means of movements of the red cap which looks like a monk's cowl. It destroys weevils, grasshoppers, and caterpillars as well as weeds. A related subspecies is the Texas pyrrhuloxia.

EASTERN CARDINAL *(Richmondena c. cardinalis)*. Length: 8 inches.
Range: Eastern United States and southern Ontario.
American Museum of Natural History

BLACKBIRDS

A SQUADRON of blackbirds whirs to a quick landing in an open field. The birds spread out and begin foraging. Soon, however, those in the rear ranks have covered their ground so completely that they have difficulty in finding more food. They take wing, fly over the heads of their companions, and alight farther down the field, ahead of their former leaders. Shortly afterward, those left in the rear do the same, and this game of leapfrog is continued until the entire area has been scoured. All then soar in precise formation to the next field.

Blackbirds undoubtedly consume large armies of insects and are a formidable opponent of the boll weevil. But they are also known to eat grain, so that they are both acclaimed for their services and damned for their damages.

Their nests may be in the grass or a bush, sometimes at the edge of a marsh. A hundred nests may be placed in a small area, the occupants living more amicably than city neighbors. Even when one male keeps two or three females, there is apparently no discord in the harem. After hatching, the chicks crawl about, sometimes falling into the marsh, but they usually manage to struggle to safety. A blackbird father is a good parent. He keeps his eye on his brood, calling out a *king-quer-kee,* and will valiantly fight a hawk or other large bird to defend his offspring.

American blackbirds include the yellow-headed species, a blackbird with yellow head and chest and white shoulders, found breeding in the western and central United States; the red-winged blackbird of the East; the bicolored redwing of California; the tricolored redwing of California and Oregon; the rusty blackbird of the North and East; the handsome Brewer's blackbird which inhabits the West and whose color scheme ranges from deep black to bluish green and violet. In all some fifteen varieties of redwings are found in the United States in almost all sections of the country.

RED-WINGED BLACKBIRD *(Agelaius p. phoeniceus).* Length: 8 inches. Range: "Breeds from Ontario, Nova Scotia, and Quebec south to the northern parts of the Gulf States" (A.O.U. Check List, IV ed.).
American Museum of Natural History

COWBIRD

THROUGH the vast ranges of the West, the brownish cowbird flutters about in serene companionship with the roaming cattle. It follows the herd, seizing the insects which leap about. In the course of its prowling, the cowbird will hop almost under the heavy hoofs of the animal and crawl under the beast's belly. It even mounts the back of a cow and rides along, meanwhile picking insects from the hide. In past times, when the bison roamed the plains where domestic cattle now graze, the little bird was also associated with the mighty herds.

The cowbird leads an easy, happy-go-lucky life. It seems never to grow up and settle down like other birds. The males and females mate promiscuously, never establishing a home.

When the female lays her eggs, she has no nest of her own in which to place them. She therefore does the next best thing and places them in the nest of some other bird. Since the eggs are usually larger than the other eggs in the nest, those of the cowbird receive the most warmth when sat upon. Consequently the young cowbird hatches before the chicks which really belong in the nest.

Almost with its first free breath, the bad habits of this bird become apparent. The young ruffian will puncture the eggs of its foster mother so that they never hatch, or throw them out of the nest. Even if the eggs do hatch, the cowbird may drive the young birds out as though they had no business there. Another trick practiced by this creature is to gobble up all the food brought into the home by its adopted parents, leaving none at all for the other chicks which may therefore starve.

In spite of all this, the young cowbird expects its foster parents to feed it. A small sparrow may be followed about by a cowbird, twice as big, which entreats it for food—and usually gets it.

Most birds do not reject the eggs left by a female cowbird. This is lucky for future generations of cowbirds, because a mother cowbird would never care for them. She would, at best, deposit the eggs in a field and merrily depart. Besides the eastern cowbird there are five varieties found in the West.

PURPLE GRACKLE

IF "handsome is as handsome does," the twelve-inch purple grackle, despite its splendid plumage, is an ugly duckling. Not only does half of its food consist of grain, but it preys upon the eggs of other birds in most unfriendly fashion, and also eats salamanders and mice.

The grackle makes a feeble attempt at singing but most listeners agree that it is better silent. When a group of angry robins or thrushes is not chasing it, the richly colored grackle struts about pompously. It ranges throughout the eastern United States. Its relatives, the boat-tailed and great-tailed grackles, inhabit the South Atlantic and Gulf States and southern Texas respectively. Two subspecies of the purple grackle are the Florida grackle of the South Atlantic and Gulf coasts and the bronzed grackle of eastern North America.

BALTIMORE ORIOLE

WHEN the courtly oriole bows a greeting to his belle, his black, white, and orange plumage glistens brightly in the sun. Perched on a limb, he displays his hues to the lady he is courting, and tells of his love with a sweet chattering sound. If she accepts his suit, the two begin homemaking, and it is believed that they mate for life.

The male whistles while the female works. The nest is a pendulous structure suspended from a limb. As she fashions it, the industrious lady is sometimes forced to hang in an upside-down position. So much do they appreciate this swinging castle which Mrs. Baltimore builds that the pair are believed to use it year after year.

Although their feeding habits are quite beneficial to man, the Baltimore oriole has unfortunately developed a craving for grape juice. It sticks its beak into grapes on the vine and sucks them dry, much to the annoyance of grape growers.

Other American orioles include Audubon's oriole of Texas; Scott's, the Arizona oriole, and Sennett's oriole, all of the Southwest;

the orchard oriole, also known as the bastard Baltimore, of the East; and Bullock's oriole, an orange and black bird, inhabiting the West and Middle West.

Other members of this family include the bobolink of the eastern and central United States, which becomes so fat on its southern migration that it is then known as the butterbird; the meadowlarks of the East, South, Rio Grande, and the West. The widespread and well-known meadowlark has more than once been proposed as a substitute for the eagle as the national emblem, a distinction it shares with the wild turkey.

STARLING

IN 1890 sixty starlings were introduced from Europe into Central Park in New York City. They multiplied and spread so rapidly that now these birds are common throughout the eastern United States. Mountains seemed to restrict their spread for a few years, but at length a few hardy birds trickled through the passes and rapidly multiplied in new areas. It is believed, however, that starlings will not reach the Pacific coast for some years to come.

In the North Atlantic States they breed early in spring, nesting either in a hole in a tree or in a cranny in some city building. By mid-May the harsh food cries of the young can be heard. In late summer the young birds band together in immense flocks, which perform splendid mass flight maneuvers and complex gyrations above the streets and fields. Sometimes the parent birds raise a second brood in late spring.

Starlings do not migrate but show a certain tendency to move southward in winter. They also tend to leave the country for the cities in cold weather. By day they forage for berries in the parks and surrounding country; by night they return to the city comforts, lodging about business buildings, church towers, libraries, and museums. Recently the Metropolitan Museum of Art in New York City served as a night shelter for large numbers of starlings. As many as 35,000 birds lodged there in a single cold night, the birds huddling together to keep warm.

The note of the male starling is a clear, long-drawn-out whistle, but in addition starlings imitate the songs of other birds. In large flocks they scream and chatter. Starlings do not hop when on the ground—they walk.

Like another foreigner, the English sparrow, the starling has aroused the prejudice of the American farmer, who accuses it of

STARLING *(Sturnus vulgaris).* Length: 8 inches. Range: Introduced from Europe in 1890 and today common as far north as southern Canada, westward to Kansas, and southward to Texas, Mississippi, and Florida.
Ralph De Sola (AMNH)

destroying corn, garden crops, and fruit. It is true that the starling eats a certain amount of ripening corn, but far less than the native blackbirds and grackles with which it often associates. Farmers, however, do not often see who is doing the damage, and many, moreover, still confuse the starling with the blackbird.

Starlings also do a certain amount of damage to small truck gardens and cultivated fruit, chiefly cherries and apples, which they devour or seriously scar. Sometimes a flock of starlings will descend on a cherry tree and strip it of fruit, while leaving other trees in the same orchard unmolested. They are easily frightened, and a little shooting into the air two or three times a day while the fruit is ripening will keep the starlings away. They eat a considerable amount of wild fruit, such as black cherries and persimmons, but scarcely affect the general supply. To complete the list of their sins, they also eat poison-ivy berries and aid in spreading this plant nuisance, since the seeds are not affected by digestion. Some farmers assert that the starling by eating large amounts of wild fruit limits the food supply of beneficial domestic birds, but in view of the immense supply of wild fruit throughout most of its range, it is doubtful that any true shortage occurs.

Actually this bird does much more good than harm. Forty-two per cent of its diet consists of insects, including many harmful varieties. Among the most noxious of the pests it destroys are the Japanese beetle, the clover-leaf weevil, grasshoppers, crickets, and millipeds. These destructive pests it attacks with even greater vigor than many of our native birds. For such reasons the Department of Agriculture advocates that the birds be allowed to live and that they be controlled in local situations where they really become more of a nuisance than a benefit. The average life of starlings in captivity is nine years, although one lived seventeen.

COMMON CROW

ALTHOUGH they destroy large quantities of insects and their larvae, crows, because of their hearty and indiscriminate appetites, are popularly regarded as among man's chief avian enemies. Sometimes in great black swarms they descend on the fields to devour grain, fruits, vegetables, birds' eggs, as well as any carrion that they may find. They may even attack young chickens, ducks, pigeons, and game birds that farmers may have caught in their snares. They pluck nuts and break them by dropping them from a great height upon the rocks below. Like gulls, they dispose of shellfish in the same manner.

On the other hand, crows are also beneficial to man. They eat great quantities of grasshoppers, locusts, caterpillars, and other insects harmful to crops. Therefore the Biological Survey advocates their protection; suggests that where bothersome they be controlled by careful supervision lest they become rare. A farmer on the island of Martha's Vineyard offered a bounty of fifty cents apiece for crows, with the result that his grass stopped growing, its roots eaten by an insect grub which the crows had previously destroyed.

Crows, however, are difficult to hunt, because they have an uncanny instinct regarding guns. Though they may come quite close to an unarmed man, they avoid the same individual if he carries a gun. As for scarecrows, they are believed to frighten sparrows, but they have little effect upon crows. Aside from their exaggerated destructiveness, the countryfolk dislike crows because their black plumage has led them to be called birds of evil omen. Edgar Allan Poe's raven is believed by many authorities to have been a crow, because crows are better talkers than are ravens.

In the breeding season, which extends from March to May, crows retire to the forest, where they usually nest high up in evergreen trees, sometimes as much as sixty feet from the ground. Many pairs often occupy the same tree, roosting not far from their nest. The birds quarrel noisily among themselves and set up a vigorous cawing at the sight of any intruder.

The nest is built of small twigs woven together, plastered over with earth, moss, and hair. The inside is lined with hair, wool, and vegetable fibers. Three to eight greenish eggs are laid; the young are born naked and helpless, requiring a good deal of care.

Apparently crows mate for life but occasionally three birds are found in a single nest. It has not been ascertained whether the extra party is a male or female, but at all events the three live together in peace and harmony. When eight eggs are laid, two females are believed to have shared the work.

The parents show great valor in defending their young against owls, eagles, and raccoons, which are the crow's chief enemies. In these battles the crow is usually the loser.

If taken young, crows make mischievous and amusing pets. They talk almost as well as parrots and can be taught a number of tricks which they will perform easily.

YOUNG CROWS (*Corvus b. brachyrhynchos*). Length: 1½ feet (adults). Range: Temperate parts of eastern North America.
Allan D. Cruickshank, National Wildlife Federation

Because of their remarkable social instinct, crows are considered the most intelligent of birds. A bird which once fell into the sea and was unable to rise was helped to the shore first by one comrade, then by others. Crows easily learn where they are safe from guns.

Another fact, however, shows that their intelligence is limited. Large numbers of crows frequently roost in swamps among the rushes. Storms and rising tides appear to be beyond their understanding. When the wind stirs up the waters, multitudes of somnolent crows are often drowned.

FISH CROW

THE related fish crow is about half the size of the common crow. It is usually found by the shores of oceans, rivers, and lakes, where it subsists chiefly upon dead fishes cast ashore or floating on the water's surface. Fish crows also prey upon the eggs of such birds as herons and ibises. They are found along the Atlantic and Gulf coasts from southern Massachusetts to eastern Texas.

BLUE JAY

THE handsome crested blue jay has a bad reputation for robbing the eggs of other birds, for attacking small poultry and, occasionally, for eating its own eggs. Moreover, blue jays seem constantly to be quarreling with each other and with other birds. Wherever these saucy little fellows may be, their presence can be detected by a querulous screaming and chattering.

Yet they are not without social graces. They are most attentive to their young, and they take good care of their blind, aged, and infirm.

They have courage tempered by prudence. A flock of blue jays does not hesitate to attack a screech owl or even a hawk, often with success; but if the larger bird seems to be getting the better of them, they dive into a dense thicket where their enemy cannot follow.

In summer blue jays inhabit the woods of the eastern States, where they live on insects, fruits, and nuts. They store up large quantities for winter use, but by the time cold weather has set in, often forget the hiding place and move closer to human habitation, where food is more plentiful. They have a decided taste for corn and other grains.

Jays are remarkable mimics. They can imitate the cry of a hawk, the buzz of a saw, and even the human voice. One bird caused great confusion on a farm by "sicking" the dog on the cow.

The blue jay usually nests in an evergreen tree, building a new nest each year from five to fifty feet above the ground. The nest is built of sticks and twigs and lined with bark and feathers. The sticks are never taken from the ground but always from the trees. Four to five pale-green eggs are laid. Jays defending their nest are well able to drive away a cat or a tree squirrel. Two subspecies related to the northern blue jay are the Florida blue jay of the South Atlantic and Gulf States and Semple's blue jay of southern and central Florida.

STELLER'S JAY

NORTHERN BLUE JAY FAMILY *(Cyanocitta c. cristata)*. Length: 11 inches. Range: Temperate parts of eastern North America.
Claude W. Leister, New York Zoological Society

STELLER'S JAY

STELLER'S jay, inhabiting the coastal pine forests of the North Pacific States, is handsome, noisy, and rapacious like its eastern cousin. As it dashes through the woods it flips its tail like the blue jay and often utters a scream resembling that of the red-shouldered hawk. Some observers believe this mimicry is intentional, its purpose being to frighten other birds. When this bird calls, its crest is most prominent.

OTHER JAYS

THE Florida jay, restricted in range to the peninsula of Florida, is without a crest. Its favored habitat is scrub-oak country. This variety is celebrated for its noisiness, which is said even to exceed that of other jays.

Woodhouse's jay, also crestless, inhabits the Rocky Mountain region. Its characteristic cry is a hair-raising scream, but when numbers of these birds are together they produce an assortment of chuckles and gurgles. The male in the mating season coos like a dove. Similar to Woodhouse's jay is the blue-checked jay of southwestern Texas, and the somewhat paler Texas jay.

In coloration the California jay resembles the eastern blue jay, except that it lacks the crest. These birds are exceedingly noisy in the fall, but in the nesting season they do not call above a whisper. The California jay is a great fruit stealer, its favorites being cherries, apricots, and plums.

The Arizona jay is said to be even more quarrelsome and even more of a busybody than other jays. These birds like particularly to molest hawks, owls, foxes, and even snakes with their abusive chatter, always, however, keeping at a safe distance. They are found in southwestern New Mexico as well as in Arizona and Mexico.

The green jay of the lower Rio Grande Valley is a copious meat-eater and is much addicted to picking over garbage heaps.

The Canada jay, also known as the camp robber because of its audacity in stealing the camper's bacon or potatoes while his back is turned, is found along the northern border as far west as Minnesota, in the New England States, New York, and Pennsylvania. The color of this bird is black, white, and gray, with none of the bright blue which is characteristic of most jays.

The pinon jay or blue crow resembles a crow in shape, while its slate blue color and sociable habits are those of a jay. It inhabits the pine and juniper woods of the West.

The plumage of Clark's twelve-inch nutcracker is white, except for the black wings and tail, but it resembles a crow in habits. Inhabiting the conifer forests of the West, it was first discovered in 1805 by Lt. William Clark, of the Lewis and Clark expedition, near what is now Salmon City, Idaho. As might be expected, it feeds largely on the seeds of conifers in winter. During other seasons insects and berries make up its menu.

Though the various jays are apparently dissimilar in appearance and habits, they may easily be recognized as a family.

MAGPIE

IN arid or sparsely wooded sections of the western United States the magpie is seen in slow graceful flight. The white breast, and the white spots on its wings, offer a striking contrast to its general coal black color. The black tail is much longer than its dusky wings.

The magpie is a mischievous bird. Having a strong taste for blood, it torments cattle on the western ranges by pecking at any open sores they may have. The birds are also expert at stealing the bait from traps and devouring small animals that have been caught. Trappers in the sagebrush country often mark their traps by strewing cotton on the bushes. Magpies seem to understand these signs.

YOUNG MAGPIE *(Pica p. hudsonia)*. Length: 1½ feet (adults). Range: Western North America in treeless and sparsely wooded areas.
J. W. Jackson

The magpie's diet is nearly as varied as that of its relative, the crow, and includes numerous insects, fruits, berries, young mammals such as mice, small birds and birds' eggs.

The magpie makes a bulky nest of mud, lined with fine grasses and rootlets. The entrance is on the side, and the whole is covered over with an astonishing number of twigs arranged so as to bristle in all directions. This small fortress, often attaining the size of a small barrel, is frequently situated in a thorn bush but is sometimes found in trees at a height of fifty feet. The six to nine eggs are a pale gray or green, blotched with brown or purple.

In New Mexico magpies nest at altitudes of seven thousand to twelve thousand feet. In northern California, in the Sacramento and San Joaquin Valleys, lives the yellow-billed magpie, smaller than its cousin but like it in most respects except for its bright-yellow bill and the skin patch just behind its eye.

RAVEN

A GOOD-SIZED raven is more than two feet long, about twice the size of the crow, which it closely resembles. The raven's note is a coarse scream or grunt, tending to be deeper and louder than the crow's familiar caw.

These birds usually nest at the edge of high cliffs. The nest is built of large sticks, well interlaced, and lined with grasses and bark; seaweed is used when it is available. Ravens return each year to the same nesting place. In some localities a site may be shared by half a dozen pairs of birds; in others the ravens are most exclusive. Off the coast of northern Maine, for example, each small island is inhabited by no more than a single pair of nesting ravens. The five to seven eggs are an olive-green color, spotted and blotched with brown, green, and lavender.

Ravens are great scavengers. Though they may prey on small live birds and mammals, their usual food is carrion. In the desert they subsist mainly on dead rabbits; in our great national parks, large numbers of ravens assemble to devour refuse from the hotels and tourist camps. In some cities ravens perform valuable services as supplementary garbage removers. Where no offal is available, ravens will eat grain.

A captive raven exhibited in the National Zoological Park at Washington, D. C., lived there for more than twenty-four years.

Ravens found in this country comprise the white-necked raven of the deserts of the West, the American raven of the West and Northwest, and the northern raven of Alaska, Canada, and the eastern United States, which even breeds in the higher Alleghenies of the South.

LARK

THE horned lark runs gaily along the rim of a road or through a freshly plowed field, its two tiny black tufts of feathers, or "horns," sprouting upward from its head. Larks are found mainly in Europe, but the American countryside, mountain slopes, deserts, and marshes are fortunate in the presence of at least one member of this lovely family.

Traveling in flocks, these pretty birds, rich brown above with whitish under parts, give vent to a joyous flight song. They may take to the air suddenly and fly with speed and directness toward the horizon. An observer might expect them to continue on their way to some distant spot, but they may alter their course and, swerving back, alight almost in the same spot from which they took off. Their flight has been clocked at fifty-four miles an hour.

During the mating season, these birds fly so high that at times they go beyond the range of the human eye, only to plummet downward to bathe in the dust of the desert. At night the horned larks rest on the earth in nests made of leaves and grass. Usually the nests are placed beside a stone or beneath a clump of grass or other plant life.

The nuptial attire of the horned lark is not obtained by molting but by the wearing away of the tips of the winter feathers. The birds molt once a year. Two or three broods are raised each year and the young are soon running over the surface of the ground near their elders, roosting in small groups near upturned rocks or clods of earth.

Also known as the shore lark, prairie bird, roadtrotter, wheat bird, spring bird, and life bird, the horned lark breeds in the eastern portion of Canada whence it migrates to the Mississippi Valley and sometimes as far south as Louisiana.

Although there is but one species of horned lark, its range extends virtually all over North America; some fifteen subspecies have been recognized. The hind claws of the lark are very long and these spurs leave their marks in a great variety of terrain, thus indicating the presence of the bird to a sharp observer.

WESTERN MEADOWLARK *(Sturnella neglecta).* Length: 9 inches. Range: Central and western North America.
J. W. Jackson

SCISSOR-TAILED FLYCATCHER

PERCHED on a branch in lazy relaxation, the scissor-tailed flycatcher jumps to attention as suddenly as a sleeping sentry aroused by a gunshot under its nose. The fourteen-inch bird hurtles crazily into the air, snaps its wide hooked bill, wheels in mid air with a twist of its body, and returns to its station. This maneuver has as its objective the capture of an insect passer-by. It is repeated again and again, and it is this which earned the flycatcher its name.

Sometimes this grayish bird, which is marked with black, white, and pink, seems to execute a series of aerial stunts for sheer sport. Its seven-inch tail feathers gracefully open and close like a pair of long, thin scissors as the bird soars upward. At the apex of its climb it cries out deliriously, and then suddenly nose-dives.

The flycatcher may be flying along at an even pace, then, suddenly screaming, it shoots headlong toward the heavens. Perhaps it is such nervous antics which have caused Mexican peons to assert that the scissor-tail devours the brains of other birds. The implication is that either it has no brains of its own, or it acquires such a weird mixture of gray matter that it acts erratically.

Despite its seeming instability, the scissor-tail is a tenacious fighter and bravely chases predatory birds. It will land on the back of a caracara as steadily as an autogiro settles to earth. As it is carried along, its bill viciously stabs through its opponent's feathers successfully frightening off the larger bird.

The scissor-tailed flycatcher nests in locust trees, chaparral, or mesquite throughout the Southwest; it is occasionally observed in eastern and southern States. Cowbirds often drop their eggs into the nests of flycatchers.

Flycatchers usually loll about near water, since the insect pickings are most abundant there. Unlike most of its relatives, the scissor-tail also gobbles such land-living insects as grasshoppers, crickets, beetles and stink bugs as well as spiders.

KINGBIRD

THE pugnacious kingbird, screeching with rage, chases large hawks, jabbing at them with its bill. The Arkansas kingbird thinks so little of the hawk's prowess that it builds its nest in a tree occupied by its enemy.

Although they do not molest harmless birds, kingbirds fight among themselves during the mating season. These battles are as much vocal contests as they are physical; the noise is terrific. When not fighting, the kingbird eats, and it is believed to be able to sight a small insect flying at a distance of fifty yards.

Sometimes kingbirds leave the backwoods and go to the suburbs and towns where telephone poles, rather than trees, become the nesting sites. And instead of grass and twigs, the material for homebuilding consists of rags, paper, and string. The male kingbird does not sit on the eggs, but he likes to watch them for long periods as if he felt a paternal pride.

EASTERN KINGBIRD *(Tyrannus tyrannus)*. Length: 8 inches. Range: North and South America.
Ralph De Sola (SIM)

Most of the thirty species and subspecies of flycatchers in the United States are noisy, clamorous birds. They are of value to man because of their insect-eating proclivities, though some species destroy honey bees. Some kinds of flycatchers, like the hawks and owls, form the indigestible portions of their food into small pellets which are ejected from the mouth.

Among the flycatchers are the vermilion flycatcher, the male of which has a flaming red body; the phoebe flycatcher, which calls *phoebe, phoebe,* and is one of the first birds to fly north in the spring; the olive-sided flycatcher, a voracious bee-eater, which catches insects only on the wing; the wood peewee whose call is like *dear me, dear me;* the crested flycatcher, sometimes called the snakeskin bird because it has the odd habit of building its nest with the transparent skins shed by snakes; and the least flycatcher whose head and tail bob nervously. Other members of the family include the western flycatcher, Acadian flycatcher, Traill's flycatcher, Coues's flycatcher, and the yellow-bellied flycatcher.

Hummingbirds, Swifts, and Goatsuckers

The hummingbirds, swifts, and goatsuckers comprise three suborders. Each of these suborders has but one family and each of these families differs from the others in many respects. All, however, have weak feet unfitted for perching and spend most of their waking hours on the wing, even taking their food while flying.

Smallest of all American birds are the insect-eating and nectar-feeding hummingbirds. They are also perhaps the most brilliantly colored and certainly their aerial feats are beyond compare. Because of their inability to progress with any degree of ease on the ground, nature has adapted them for unusual flying.

Another group of insect eaters are the swifts. They also take their prey while flying—sometimes at speeds of two hundred miles an hour—the fastest recorded speed for all higher animals, but are chiefly remarkable for the nests they cement to the inner sides of hollow tree trunks and chimneys.

The third suborder is that of the goatsuckers, so named because of a European legend that the members of the group subsisted by milking goats. However, while the Old World belief is certainly untrue, it is true that these birds sometimes fly near grazing goats in search of insects. The nighthawk, or bull-bat, as misnamed as it is abused, is closely related to the poor-will, whip-poor-will, and chuck-will's-widow and looks very much like them.

HUMMINGBIRD

THE tiny hummingbird is the only bird known to fly backward as well as forward. It hovers motionless, poised in mid air before a flower, its wings vibrating so rapidly as to be almost invisible. The tiny bird, looking for all the world like an overgrown bumblebee, gently inserts its long needlelike bill into the heart of the bloom. This smallest of all birds, less than four inches long, has a coat of bronze-green and a red-stained gray breast.

The ruby-throated hummingbird follows the sapsucker as that bird punctures holes in the trunks of maple trees. Then the hummingbird inserts his tubular tongue and draws out the sap. While the hummingbird is well known for its diet of dainty flower and vegetable juices, it also feeds on small insects which it traps in the cup of a flower or under a leaf. Sometimes the swiftly moving birdlet will snare a bug on the wing. Toward the end of the summer, the hummingbird sucks the juices from bruised or imperfect fruits but does not damage fruit in good condition. In its wanderings it aids in the fertilization of flowers, but this may be offset by its spreading of a plant disease known as the pear blight.

For its size the hummingbird has more strength than any other bird. Its finely developed wings and apparently inexhaustible motive power give it a handicap on any pursuer. Perhaps that is why it is foolhardy enough to attack even the greatest birds of prey, hawks and eagles. Males attack each other, especially during the mating season, if there is a sufficient abundance of food in any locality to bring numbers of them together. The speeding birds are transformed into angrily buzzing bill-pointed projectiles as they lunge and maneuver in the air. The scene resembles a wartime aerial "dogfight."

The nest is so built as to conform to the general contour of the surroundings. It is camouflaged with moss and cobwebs and saddled to a horizontal tree limb. Silk spider strands are the cables that hold the

RUBY-THROATED HUMMINGBIRD *(Archilochus colubris).* Length: 3 inches. Range: Eastern North America.
Frank Pagan

one and one-half inch fortress together against wind and rain.

In the spring the nest contains two almost microscopic white eggs. The presence of the young is frequently betrayed by the father who will dash angrily at an intruder in the vicinity.

The ruby-throated hummingbird is the one member of the family that comes to the eastern States.

Rivoli's hummingbird, seen in the southwestern States, has a slightly forked tail. In the same region the largest hummingbird of them all, the blue-throated hummingbird, two inches longer than the ruby-throat, makes its home. A characteristic of the black-chinned hummingbird of the western States is the pendulum motion which he uses in courtship. The object of his affection is seated quietly on a limb while the male black-chin swings in an arc, a yard long, backward and forward before her.

Anna's hummingbird of California stuffs her young with insects, plunging her long bill like a dagger down their throats. The rufous hummingbird is found from the Rocky Mountains to the Pacific coast.

The broad-tailed hummingbird of the western mountain States preens itself sedately like any of the larger birds.

SWIFT

ASCENDING into the heavens in a great cloud, chimney swifts form into a funnel-like flock above a disused chimney and, whirling downward head first, the stream of birds descends into the opening. Arranging themselves in tiers within the structure, the birds may remain all night and leave the following morning.

They spend the day in gay aerial frolicking and scouting for food, and sometimes cover a thousand air miles in a single day's flight, rarely touching foot to ground. The bird is able to do this since it catches all its insect food on the wing, the fare consisting mainly of two-winged flies. In this, however, lies a great weakness of the bird, since storms frequently clear the air of insect life for a long time, starving great numbers of swifts.

SWIFT

Arriving in the South, the five-inch speedsters set to work building their nests. Sometimes the site is in a chimney, or they may choose a barn, a hollow tree, or even a well. The twigs used are held together and to the wall of the shelter by means of a mucilaginous saliva. There is a natural platform or flooring which is just large enough to support the five or six long white eggs. Later the platform is enlarged and provided with raised lips like a saucer. In this haven the young loll about for two weeks until they leave the nursery and cling to the adjacent wall. Their peculiar tail feathers aid them in getting a grip in the manner of a lineman's spurs although occasionally the birds fall into a fireplace below.

CHIMNEY SWIFTS *(Chaetura pelagica).*
Length: 5 inches. Range: Eastern North America.
American Museum of Natural History

Even their wooing takes place out in the open. They are very frolicsome birds, indulging in all sorts of gyrations in mid-air. Because of the weakness of their bills they are not aggressive after the fashion of the English sparrow and the blue jay. After the mating season is over, the salivary glands dry up and the birds put the sacs to use as shopping bags, in which they bring food to the nestlings. The allegation that they carry bedbugs from house to house seems to be without foundation. Another tale, that they hibernate in mud or in water, cannot be disproved, for oddly enough the whereabouts of these birds during the winter is a mystery as yet unsolved.

Also called the chimney swallow, this bird breeds in eastern North America and finds its way to the western border of the Great Plains. The related white-throated swift and the black swift inhabit the almost inaccessible mountain peaks of the western States. A fourth species, Vaux's swift, breeds from Alaska to California and extends eastward to Montana.

POOR-WILL

IN the high arid regions of the Southwest, the poor-will's song floats plaintively through the thin air. This eight-inch-long, rusty-colored, black-barred bird breeds west of the Mississippi to southern California.

Apparently blinded by the sunlight, the poor-will mopes during the day beneath a low-hanging tree or bush and may be approached quite closely in the open before it takes flight.

It lays two white unspotted eggs on the ground without the protection of a nest. Two subspecies of Nuttall's poor-will inhabit western deserts and resemble it in laying their eggs in the open and on the ground.

WHIP-POOR-WILL

UNDER cover of darkness the whip-poor-will approaches human habitations and parks, and it is then that its characteristic call is most frequently heard. More people have heard the call, by far, than have seen the bird.

Unceasingly the bird will utter one call after the other and as many as three hundred and ninety consecutive calls were recorded by John Burroughs. The bird's plumage blends so well with the background that it is almost invisible on the ground and, when flushed, will silently fly a short distance and take to cover again. If the bird is driven from its eggs it will go through a highly talented performance of fluttering, gasping, and limping as if mortally hurt,

CHUCK-WILL'S-WIDOW

hoping to draw off the intruder. The eggs are laid in the underbrush on a matting of dead leaves.

The typical whip-poor-will ranges the eastern States to the edge of the Great Plains. Stephen's whip-poor-will, a subspecies somewhat larger in size (about eleven inches), is found in the Southwest.

EASTERN WHIP-POOR-WILL *(Antrostomus v. vociferus)*. Length: 9 inches. Range: Eastern United States and southern Canada.
American Museum of Natural History

CHUCK-WILL'S-WIDOW

SO LARGE is the chuck-will's-widow's mouth that it swallows hummingbirds and sparrows whole. This foot-long bird is the largest of the American goatsuckers.

Dull brown, with splashes of black, the chuck-will's-widow makes its home in the eastern and central sections of the United States where it blends successfully with wooded backgrounds. Like other goatsuckers it lays its eggs on the ground.

The "widow" struts proudly during courtship and is devoted afterward. It is rarely seen until after dusk as its vision is best at night.

NIGHTHAWK

DESPITE its name, the nighthawk is not a hawk at all. In fact, it has a pleasant disposition far different from that of a bird of prey. It has the typical soft bill of the goatsucker and feeds upon insects.

After sundown the white-barred wings of this bird are seen in erratic flight and the unmelodic notes of its call strike the ear. It soars upward and upward, until from a height of several hundred feet it begins its spectacular dive. When only a few feet from the earth, it pulls its plummeting body gracefully out of the power dive, turning aside with great poise and deliberation. The rush of air against the wings during the descent causes a dull "boom" to be sounded. The rapid dive is the main similarity this bird shares with the hawks. Perhaps because it is nocturnal, the bird is also called the bull-bat.

The nighthawk's body is covered with a mass of complex markings of sooty black, gray, brown, and buff. It inhabits the central States to the edge of the Great Plains.

Building no nest, as is the way with goatsuckers, these birds lay their eggs in a rocky spot in the woods or fields. The eggs, two in number, blend with the forest floor so well that even oölogists have difficulty in finding them.

Seven related varieties of native nighthawks differ from the common variety chiefly in geographical location.

Woodpeckers

Woodpeckers drill holes in trees in order to reach the insects and larvae upon which they feed. Their strong, pointed beak, which easily penetrates bark and decayed wood, makes them well equipped for such knotty problems. Woodpeckers' legs, which have two strong claws pointing backward and two forward, are invaluable. They grasp the bark of a tree with their claws and, using their barbed tail as a gripper and a prop, are able to hold on to a vertical surface with ease.

As the woodpeckers peck away, they use their long, barbed tongue, moistened with a sticky substance, to catch insects. Although accused of destroying the trees from which they obtain their "bread and butter," woodpeckers are actually helpful. They dig out of the bark and decayed wood precisely those wood-boring insects which are the true culprits.

A cavity chipped out by a woodpecker may serve a double purpose. The woodpecker not only eats as it works, but may enlarge the hole and there make its home. Within the tree it lays its eggs.

This order is found throughout the entire world with the exception of Australia, Madagascar, and some other islands. It is represented in the United States by almost fifty species and subspecies.

WOODPECKER

ONE of the pleasanter percussions in the rustic symphony of nature is the drumming of the woodpecker. With its four-clawed feet firmly gripping the tree and its pointed tail feathers countersunk for added support, the woodpecker "whups" the tree with the cadence and persistence of a power drill.

When the sharp bill has pierced the rotten trunk, the long cylindrical tongue flicks through the gap, and ants, caterpillars, beetles, bark lice, cockroach eggs, soldier bugs, and many other larvae and insects are drawn into the avid mouth. Sometimes this meal is garnished with fruits, seeds, and other vegetable matter.

Chipping away the heart of a decayed stump, the woodpecker makes a home. It lets the chips fall where they may, and many of these fall to the floor of the excavation forming a soft cushion upon which are placed the shiny white eggs, four to nine in number. Where there are few trees, the woodpecker may dig a pocket in the side of a clay bank.

IVORY-BILLED WOODPECKER

THE scarlet-crested ivory-bill lives among the cypress trees of the South. This largest of the eastern woodpeckers, increasingly rare, utters a loud *yap-yap-yap* as it flies. It does not remain long in one place, ranging over an extended territory during the day. In Florida, where it is found chiefly in the western part of the peninsula, it occurs in greatest numbers between the Suwannee River and the Gulf.

Alexander Wilson, an early ornithologist, records in his *American Ornithology* the capture of one of these birds as far north as Wilmington, North Carolina. He drew its picture and was moved to observe that the bird "displayed such a noble and unconquerable spirit that I was frequently tempted to restore him to his native wilderness."

HAIRY WOODPECKER AND DOWNY WOODPECKER

THE large black-and-white hairy woodpecker, nine and one-half inches long, is found from Colorado eastward to the New England States. Its crown is a glossy blue-black. Its upper parts are black except for two outside tail feathers on each side, which are entirely white. Two and a half inches shorter, the downy woodpecker is found throughout the same region. Strangely enough, the downy woodpecker is not downy nor is the hairy woodpecker hairy. They spend the winter nights in holes excavated by their strong beaks.

Up in the forests along the Canadian border, the northern hairy woodpecker flits from tree to tree in search of succulent grubs and larvae. A much smaller species, the southern hairy woodpecker, also goes by the name of Audubon's hairy woodpecker. In the western United States three related varieties of this bird are Harris's woodpecker, of the north Pacific coast, found from British Columbia to northern California; Cabanis's woodpecker in California; and the Rocky Mountain hairy woodpecker, as large a bird as the northern hairy woodpecker. Nine varieties are encountered in the United States.

The ratio of vegetable food to grubs and larvae eaten by hairy woodpeckers is quite low, which makes the bird a valuable ally of the orchardist.

Related forms of the northern downy woodpecker are the southern downy woodpecker; Gairdner's woodpecker of the Pacific coast; Batchelder's woodpecker of the western States; and the willow woodpecker, found in California except on the northwest coast and desert ranges.

Like the hairy woodpecker, the downy is a valuable destroyer of insects. Unfortunately, the downy woodpecker spreads the seeds of poison-ivy which sprout after the bird has voided them, but he is not the only offender on this score.

RED-COCKADED WOODPECKER

SMALL troops of red-cockaded woodpeckers scurry through the southern pine forests. Not only the trunks of the trees but the cones also are subjected to close scrutiny, since the birds eat conifer seeds as well as bayberry, poison-ivy, and magnolia seeds in addition to the insects they may find.

The logger never brings to earth the tree in which the red-cockaded woodpecker has its nest. For this specialist is not deceived by what appears to be a healthy exterior. When the tree is rotten at the heart, the woodpecker will discover it and drill right through the healthy wood to the decayed portion. Year after year he returns to the find and drills right down the diseased core. Sometimes the red-bellied woodpecker drives him away.

In the spring the bark is perforated with holes above and below the nest, forming a sticky matting of pitch. This creates a natural flypaper across which marauding squirrels and ants dare not venture, no matter how appetizing the eggs and young may appear to them.

PILEATED WOODPECKER

THE day is never long enough for the pileated woodpecker. In search of a home site, it climbs hastily up the trunks of dead trees. It strips off the bark and pecks into the dead wood, and in the process of digging out may come across a succulent grub or two. Down to the ground it hops, always in a hurry, looking for an ant hill or flitting about in search of wild fruit or berries. The flight of this shy, solitary, untameable bird is direct but rather slow.

A loud nasal *kuk-kuk* is the pileated woodpecker's call. When two birds meet they make a sound like *wichew*. Mating from April to June, pileated woodpeckers nest in secluded swamps, digging an apartment out of a dead tree usually at a great height. Often a pair will return to the same nest year after year, cleaning out and sometimes enlarging the old one.

The eggs are three to five in number. While the female sits on them, the male entertains her by drumming. The young are fed by regurgitation and remain in the nest until fullfledged. Four subspecies of the pileated woodpecker are distributed over the country.

PILEATED WOODPECKER *(Ceophloeus pileatus).* Length: 1½ feet. Range: "Wooded regions of North America, mainly east of the Rocky Mountains" (Pearson).
American Museum of Natural History

THREE-TOED WOODPECKER

TWO main types of three-toed woodpeckers visit the United States: the Arctic, which breeds from Alaska southward to our more northerly States; and the American, also known as the ladder-backed woodpecker, rarer than its Arctic cousin, found in northern Minnesota, New York, Maine, and New Hampshire, as well as casually in Massachusetts.

The Arctic bird seems to like best the burned-over tracts of spruce where the charred stumps sometimes rise as high as thirty feet from the ground. Either fearless or ignorant of man's ways, the Arctic woodpecker is easy to approach and observe. On green land it is found either singly or in pairs; on burned-over ground, frequently in scores.

Somewhat smaller, the American three-toed woodpecker is known in three forms, the American, the Alaskan, and the Alpine. The Alaskan variety is not common even in Alaska and decidedly rare in the United States. It reaches the Northwest occasionally. The Alpine variety is a Rocky Mountain denizen ranging from Arizona and New Mexico to northern Montana.

Three-toed woodpeckers are non-migratory. Even during the coldest weeks of midwinter they somehow manage to find their food, insects, and their eggs, buried beneath the frozen bark of the conifers.

OTHER WOODPECKERS

WEAVING through the trees on the timbered slopes of the Guadalupe Range in western Texas, the Texas woodpecker is often seen in the company of the red-shafted flicker and the ant-eating woodpecker. Closely related, the San Lucan woodpecker inhabits southern and Lower California.

Similar in appearance to these birds, Nuttall's woodpecker, found west of the Sierra Nevada, seems to prefer the branches of the sturdy oak to those of other trees. The Arizona woodpecker, another "oak treader," has a dash of red along the nape of the neck.

The coloration of the white-headed woodpecker of the Northwest serves it as an excellent disguise. When the sun is shining, the bird may appear to be but a bright knot of wood protruding from a limb. More than half its food is garnered among the seeds of pine trees.

Known as the flag bird and the patriotic bird, the redheaded woodpecker sports the colors of the German flag—red, white, and black. Sometimes, however, the black seems to have a bluish or American cast. This bird is more often seen in the open than any other woodpecker.

So energetic is the ant-eating woodpecker that it attacks fences and telephone poles where trees are not available. It fills the resultant holes with acorns. The birds seem to realize how big a hole must be made if it is to receive acorns.

Named in honor of Capt. Meriwether Lewis of the Lewis and Clark expedition, Lewis's woodpecker flies with the regular and heavy wing beats of the crow. Like starlings, these woodpeckers gather in large flocks, especially during the mating season. Lewis's woodpecker is found throughout the western United States.

In the eastern States, the red-bellied woodpeckers frequently take over the uncompleted nests of other woodpeckers. The charge has been raised against them that they eat oranges in the Florida groves, but it seems unlikely that they do any considerable damage to the citrus crops.

In the deserts of the West, the Gila woodpecker is hard put to answer tourists who query: "How can this bird be a woodpecker when there is no wood for him to peck?" The bird does the best it can by boring its nest into the stalk of the giant cactus.

FLICKER

WHEN the flicker family sets to work building the nest, male and female usually aid each other in chipping away at the decayed wood. But sometimes the representative of the sturdier sex tires or becomes bored and lets the female carry on alone, which she does faithfully.

One each day, light and glossy, the eggs are laid in the hollow until the set is complete—five is the usual number. Now the cooperative pair set about hatching out the brood, and when the chicks have emerged, the parents leave the nest on long foraging expeditions, flying far afield for trips which may last almost an hour. They return with succulent tidbits for the always famished fledglings —grubs, pupae, larvae, and juicy berries.

For the first ten days after hatching, one parent stays with the brood all night.

SOUTHERN FLICKERS FEEDING (*Colaptes a. auratus*). Length: 11 inches. Range: South Atlantic, Gulf, and South Central States.
R. A. Romanes

Cleanly householders, flickers do not permit trash to collect in their dugout. Following every meal they carry the refuse out of the nest for some distance, first making sure that no enemies are near by. When the young have reached their third week, however, the nest is so crowded that cleaning is an impossibility, but the birds are soon ready to leave.

In about sixteen days the youngsters climb to the sill of the hole and peer forth. But eager though they may be to test their brave young wings in a new world, they must wait for the parental command, a terse *yee-up*.

The popularity of the flicker is attested by the fact that it is well known in this country by about one hundred and twenty other names. Some call it clape, others high-hole, wick-up, walk-up, yawker bird, yarrup, hairy wicket, and heigh-ho. Perhaps the most appropriate name for the bird is the yellow-shafted or golden-shafted woodpecker, because of the bright yellow under side of the wings. The eleven-inch bird gets slightly larger in the northern part of its range, which is the eastern United States to the Gulf coast and there is known as the northern flicker. In the western portion of its range the yellow of the under side tends toward red, and the bird becomes known as the red flicker. Like several other birds, the flicker has the habit of spreading the seeds of poison-ivy. Five kinds of flickers are found in this country.

SAPSUCKERS

MIGRATING sapsuckers lose all taste for insects and develop a liking for sap. Punching holes in trees, which are damaged in the process, the sapsucker inserts its tongue and licks up the fluid. This seems to send it on a jag as it chases other birds from tree to tree, squealing angrily. This bird's diet is largely vegetable, consisting of fruits, berries, seeds, and barks.

The yellow-bellied sapsucker has a black back irregularly barred with white. The bird is pale yellow beneath. During the mating season it raps a terrific staccato against the dry branches with its beak. The red-breasted sapsucker of the Pacific coast is particularly injurious to prune, apple, apricot, and evergreen trees. A subspecies lives in southern and Lower California.

The male and female Williamson's sapsucker were believed at one time to be two separate species. The male was called the brown-headed woodpecker. Today some authorities doubt that this woodpecker of the western mountain forests is a sapsucker at all. The male has absolutely no red on its head, while every other four-toed woodpecker in the United States has at least some. Natalie's sapsucker, a subspecies of the foregoing, lives in the forests of the American Rockies and winters from southern New Mexico and western Texas to Talisco, Mexico.

Kingfishers, Trogons, and Cuckoos

These varied orders embrace three separate groups of birds which seem to have little in common. Although most of them fly about and nest in trees, some are ground dwellers.

The cuckoos are found in most parts of the world, but the American species do not have the parasitic habits of their European relatives. They include the roadrunners, anis, as well as the several varieties of cuckoos. None of them is very brightly colored.

In sharp contrast are the trogons, to which order belongs the famous quetzal of Central America, one of the world's most beautiful birds. Most trogons live in the tropical parts of the world, and only one species inhabits the United States.

Two species of the large and widespread family of kingfishers dwell in North America—the Texas kingfisher found along the Rio Grande in that State and in southern Arizona, and the two subspecies of belted kingfishers hereafter described.

KINGFISHER

FLUTTERING a few feet above the water, the kingfisher searches for food with eyes as sharp as if aided by telescopic sights. When a tiny fish comes into focus, the bird zips downward, its headlong dive carrying it below the surface. Sometimes it dives from a perch forty or more feet above the water. All wet, but triumphant, the kingfisher emerges with its prey in its long powerful beak, which is sharp enough to be used to spear fishes.

The bird flies back to its perch and kills the fish by smashing it against a limb. Then the fish is swallowed, head first. The bird is not actually as harmful as is often believed, since it feeds mainly on such small fish as minnows and chubs, as well as on frogs and insects.

The kingfisher acts with the proprietary instincts which traditionally govern anglers who locate a hidden trout-filled stream. When the bird settles down, it will tolerate no neighbors. Should another kingfisher venture near, it will be noisily driven away.

The bluish back and rusty-colored breast of the kingfisher is explained by an old legend. It seems that when the kingfisher left

Noah's ark, it flew toward the setting sun, so that the blue sky was reflected on its back and its breast was scorched by the sun. Another legend explains the expression "halcyon days." In early times the bird was known as the halcyon, and when it laid its eggs in midwinter, the sea was always calm or so, at least, goes the story which has been repeated for generations.

BELTED KINGFISHER *(Megaceryle alcyon)*. Length: 1 foot. Range: North America and tropical South America.
American Museum of Natural History

Usually the bank of a stream is the site of the kingfisher's nest, and both male and female dig out the loose soil with their strong sharp beaks. The four-inch tunneled burrow may be twenty feet long, ending in a small chamber. A kingfisher's nest can usually be located by the presence of fish scales and bones which have been swallowed by the bird and then regurgitated after the more digestible parts of the fish have been assimilated.

The two varieties of belted kingfisher are the eastern and the western.

TROGON

THE male trogon is one of America's most dazzlingly colored birds. It has a black crown surmounting a bronze-green body and vivid red breast. Perched on a limb, its exceptionally long tail dangling down, the trogon utters a contented clucking call. Only one species, the coppery-tailed trogon, is found north of Mexico in the mountains of southern Arizona and along the lower Rio Grande Valley of Texas. It is rare in the United States.

ROADRUNNER

DANCING with agile feet around and around a rattlesnake, the roadrunner, or chaparral cock, fearlessly engages in a death struggle with this poison-fanged terror of the desert from whom most other creatures flee. Spotted crest flicking bolt upright, shoe-button eyes gleaming with the excitement of the fight, and long strong tail feathers cocked stiffly, the roadrunner swiftly darts in and out or jumps deftly into the air, always just an inch beyond the reach of those needle-sharp fangs.

Angered by the nips of the roadrunner's sharp beak, the rattler takes the aggressive at first, desperately slithering about as it seeks a position to strike into that thickly feathered body. Coiling and uncoiling, its rattles whirring, the snake wastes its energy in tactics that usually frighten its victims. But the courageous bird perfectly times each blow with beak and claw, lunging at the snake just when, not being coiled, it cannot strike back. Its energy flagging, the rattler tries to escape and the roadrunner takes the offensive. Pouncing upon the snake's back, the bird seizes it behind the diamond-shaped head, shakes it ferociously, waves it in the air, throws it down, and then dances away from the ever-weakening, slowing stab of the wicked fangs. No longer deadly, America's largest, most poisonous snake succumbs; the killer is killed. It goes head first down the gullet of the plucky bird, disappearing as digested. This exciting spectacle was recently recorded in motion pictures in *The Adventures of Chico* by Stacy and Horace Woodard.

ROADRUNNER *(Geococcyx californianus).* Length: 2 feet. Range: Parts of California, Utah, Colorado, Kansas, Texas, and Mexico.
S. and H. Woodard's "Adventures of Chico"

The dingy white and olive of this land-dwelling bird, though not very beautiful, serve as protective coloration against the drab desert lands of the Southwest. Sometimes the bird springs forward suddenly from a clump of chaparral to race along the road before a horse. Uttering a rasping squeak, it will set the pace for miles. However, it dislikes the machine age, since it has discovered that autos travel far too swiftly to permit a mere roadrunner to set the pace.

Much of the roadrunner's time is spent darting after lizards, which are its chief food. Even the young are nourished on these reptiles. Almost from the moment they are hatched, the chicks are fed small lizards which they swallow head first. Sometimes the tail of a lizard hangs out of the chick's tiny mouth, but a series of gulps suffice to send it down.

The roadrunner leaps high into the air to seize that choice morsel, the land snail, from the spiked leaves of a yucca plant. It solves the problem of cracking the shell to obtain the tender flesh in a different way from the eagle or hawk, which drop the snail on rocks from the air. The roadrunner simply pounds the snail against the stone with abrupt motions of its long sinewy neck and strong beak.

GROOVE-BILLED ANI

THE groove-billed anis seem to like company so much that they not only live in colonies but several females may even share the same nest. Their home is frequently in a bush, orange tree, or lemon tree in southern Texas. The ani is a queer-looking bird, its black color trimmed with a violet sheen on wings and tail, and purple and green on its neck.

Its tail feathers blow in the wind as the ani flies awkwardly and heavily after the herds of cattle in river valleys. The birds are a help to the beasts for they pick off and eat the parasites on the bodies of the cattle.

The anis comprise three species, all similar in appearance, and all indigenous to the warm parts of North America. Although they bear no resemblance, they are related to the cuckoo.

YELLOW-BILLED CUCKOO (*Coccyzus a. americanus*). Length: 1 foot. Range: Suitable sections of North and South America.
American Museum of Natural History

BLACK-BILLED CUCKOO

THE black-billed cuckoo has an unenviable reputation in the bird kingdom. It is so hated as a nest robber who eats other birds' eggs, that, according to one observer, groups of robins will set upon a cuckoo and kill it.

However, the cuckoo is an aid to farmers, one of its chief staples being tent caterpillars. This olive-brown, white-breasted bird is heard more often than seen. Its weirdly harsh notes, which often emanate from dense foliage, are believed by some to indicate the coming of rain.

Related species are the widely distributed yellow-billed cuckoo, with similar habits; Maynard's cuckoo of southern Florida and the Keys; and the California cuckoo, found from the Pacific coast to Colorado and western Texas.

Parrots

Only two species of the large order of parrots inhabit the United States; and one of these, the Carolina paroquet, is believed to be extinct. The other, the thick-billed parrot, is little more than a visitor from Mexico to the southern border of Arizona.

Parrots are among the world's most admired birds, not only for the extravagant hues of their plumage, but also for their voices which sometimes utter harsh duplications of words. Most of the five hundred and fifty living species inhabit only the tropical and semi-tropical regions of the world.

Years ago the Carolina paroquet was a familiar sight in the cypress swamps of the Southeast where large flocks of these vividly colored birds would congregate. In the early eighteen hundreds Alexander Wilson saw these flocks on the Ohio River in the month of March. They had rich green bodies and their yellow heads were further decorated with red and orange.

Paroquets would use their strong bills to swing themselves from branch to branch, and they would eat as they went along. Most of their activity was in the coolness of the morning and evening, for they preferred a siesta in the

CAROLINA PAROQUET (*Conuropsis carolinensis*). Length: 1 foot. Range: Formerly ranged over much of the eastern United States especially throughout the southern part of the Atlantic Coastal Plain. Extinct since 1904.
New York Zoological Society

shade during the burning heat of midday. As they ate they gossiped in a low mumble, but as soon as they took flight their soft talk was transformed into raspy screaming. Many of them would spend the night in the same hollow tree, jamming its opening to such an extent that the late comers were forced to hang halfway out the entrance.

However, the paroquets were considered wasteful foragers, and this furnished fruit growers an excuse to set about exterminating them. Trappers captured and shipped the decorative creatures to market. Some people even killed paroquets to eat, though the birds were only a foot long and when further reduced by plucking and cooking were not at all a large portion. The paroquets seemed to have such a group solidarity that, when one of their number was shot by a hunter, the others would perhaps sympathetically, but very foolishly, gather about the victim. Consequently, the once large flocks of Carolina paroquets have not been observed for many years, nor have individuals since 1904, so it is believed that the species is completely extinct. Moreover, it is reliably reported that a famous naturalist deposited the last breeding members of the species on the dusty shelves of his museum.

THICK-BILLED PARROT

A NATIVE of sunny Mexico, the thick-billed parrot sometimes sneaks across the border for a spell. It strays about the canyons of southern Arizona. Thanks to such excursions into United States territory, this country can claim a member of the parrot family; this is the only one now here either as resident or visitor, excluding, of course, those in cages.

The thick-billed parrot is sixteen inches of that gaudy color usually associated with tropical birds. Its rich green plumage is set off with dabs of red, black, and lemon-yellow.

It exhibits a charmingly naïve curiosity, and sometimes small flocks will scurry inquisitively about travelers. However, it then becomes impossible to locate any other wildlife, since constant chattering and screaming of the parrots drive their animal neighbors to cover.

Sometimes flocks of several hundred wing their way through Arizona's canyons. The loudness of their joint squawking is outdone only by the loudness of their massed color. They fly in couples, one pair above the other, packed as closely as possible. The presence of such wayfarers overhead, according to a miner's tradition, augurs well for the future prosperity of mining. Their presence is announced so noisily that occasionally the winged caravan is heard before it swoops into view. Among the trees high in the mountains they eat the seeds of the hard green pine cones.

At home, in Mexico, they make their habitations in trees eighty feet above the ground, using the abandoned holes of imperial woodpeckers. Sometimes the nests are covered with sawdust. Observers have found both young birds and eggs in the same nest. It has been concluded, therefore, that breeding is done on a stagger system, the eggs being laid and hatched over a long period of time.

Birds of Prey

Our chapter on birds of prey embraces such widely divergent groups as the fast-flying majestic eagles and the little burrowing owls. All of them, though, from the great horned owl to the low-born buzzard, have the common characteristic of being flesh eaters, although the owls are placed in an order separate from that of the other birds of prey.

These birds include such nocturnal creatures as the owls, as well as the vultures whose eyes, though sharp, need daylight to discern a victim. Their food is obtained in a variety of ways. They may prey upon their fellows, catch their quarry on the run, devour a decayed bit of carrion, or appropriate the catch of other birds.

They have the questionable distinction of being, as a group, the most feared and hated of all birds. Their appearance is conducive to such reactions. The eyes of many of them are sunk beneath projecting ridges in a most sinister fashion. Their beetling brows, hooked beaks, and harsh cries all seem to aid in sending a shaft of icy terror into their victims' hearts even before an aggressive act has been committed.

Because of their rapacious character, purely mythical stories have been told about them, such as that which attributes to the condor and eagle the ability to carry off children in their claws. On the whole, though, birds of prey are quite helpful to man through their eating of carrion as well as their control of such pests as mice and other grain-eating rodents. Thus they play their role in the economy of nature by killing off the weak, checking over population of other species, cleaning of animal debris.

OWLS

UP IN the branches of a tree perches the owl, the night marauder. Its burning eyes, set in a round death mask of a face, pierce the gloom of the forest; its keen ears discern the slightest stirring of mouse or marmot.

Once the prey is located the owl flies, silent as a shadow, until it can drop swiftly upon the victim and hook it securely in its long talons. Its tearing beak severs the larger game into pieces that can easily be swallowed, the indigestible portions being ejected in the form of pellets from the sides of the mouth. These pellets are perhaps the best indication of the diet of the predatory birds. Into the enormous gullets go chickens, hares, and even baby deer, the smaller owls living on the smaller mammals, reptiles, birds, and insects.

Their eccentric appearance, their daytime lethargy, their large immovable eyes, the dead silence of their flight, and the dismal spots they frequently haunt, all have furthered the persistent legend that owls possess necromantic powers. Well-known hunters, owls are themselves denied the protection of game laws in many States; as a result, the popular spleen is freely vented upon all the species, harmful as well as comparatively beneficial. No doubt, the larger birds like the great horned owl may occasionally develop a taste for poultry, or more frequently poach upon a grouse or ptarmigan. But when the fields are overrun by grasshoppers or mice, the owls strive mightily side by side with human agencies to keep the natural balance intact. Owls are frequently seen on some city dumps preying on the pestilential gray rat.

BARN OWL (*Tyto alba pratincola*). Length: 1½ feet. Range: "Greater part of United States and Mexico" (Pearson).
New York Zoological Society

Owls are enabled to move noiselessly through the air because of the velvety consistency of the feathers which are so fluffy that the bird is given an appearance of greater bulk than it actually possesses. Two distinct families of owls are recognized by science—barn owls and typical owls. The barn owls are known by their heart-shaped faces. The round-faced typical owls include all the rest—horned owls, barred owls, screech owls, and so forth.

The fifty-six species and subspecies of the philosophical bird vary in size between the six-inch elf owl at one extreme and the two-foot-long horned owl at the other. Owls of the same species may show different colors, but in any dress they may be attacked by flocks of smaller birds who recognize an enemy. Owls' eggs are often found in abandoned nests of crows and hawks.

AMERICAN BARN OWL

THE nest of the eighteen-inch barn owl or monkey-faced owl is placed in any location that affords shelter anywhere in the United States. They have been found in prairie-dog burrows and church steeples. The fertile female of the species lays as many as eleven eggs or as few as three in the nest of hay, bones, twigs, and other refuse. The birds often return to the same nest year after year. Barn owls are voracious birds, spending the whole night eating where there is sufficient food. Sometimes the total weight of the food equals that of the bird. They rarely molest other birds; one specimen even lived peaceably with pigeons.

AMERICAN LONG-EARED OWL

WHEREVER the forests are dense enough to afford shelter and concealment, the long-eared owl is found in this country. This bird suffers greatly from the persecution of bounty hunters. In the more arid sections of the West, the long-eared owl is somewhat gregarious. In the coniferous woods of the East its coloration blends with the sylvan background and it can doze safely during the day.

Its nest of twigs, bark, pine needles, and assorted rubbish may be a squirrel's renovated domicile or even a hawk's hand-me-down aerie.

It is usually rather high in a tree. Here the three to eight eggs are laid, one every two days. After a three-week interval they are hatched and the young birds show by their priority their difference in size. The young are fed by the parents until they are about two months old, after which they hunt for themselves. These gray-yellow birds subsist largely on harmful rodents and are therefore deserving of protection. Because of their retiring habits during the day they are hard to find. However, they are not wary and only when their nest or young is disturbed do they seem to awaken and fly into a tantrum.

Like all the other owls, this bird's only real enemy is man, and it often suffers from the bounties paid as a result of ignorance of its useful habits.

SHORT-EARED OWL

THE short-eared owl hunts often during the day. It may be found all over the United States but its preferred habitat is usually sandy wasteland or marsh. Sometimes the bird is gray, sometimes brown. When a plague of field mice descends upon a certain area, the short-eared owl can be depended upon to do yeoman work in halting their ravages.

During the mating season the male flies at a great height, using slow jerky wing movements, and occasionally plummeting downward to earth again as he beats his wings across his belly.

The nest is a shallow hole in the ground lined with soft grasses and weeds. Five or six eggs are usually laid. When the young are hatched the parents protect them by feigning injury if an intruder comes by. The short-eared owl, a twenty-four-hour hunter, catches cat naps at odd hours in thickly covered trees or dense grass.

BARRED OWLS

FROM the prairies to the east coast the most common member of the family is the barred owl. A solitary bird, the barred owl utters a hoot and flies away if disturbed. Twenty inches long, with brownish-white striped plumage, this bird, also known as the hoot

NORTHERN BARRED OWL *(Strix v. varia).* Length: 1½ feet. Range: Middle eastern North America.
New York Zoological Society

owl, frequently takes over the abode of the hawk or the crow. When it makes its own home, that is usually in the hollow of a tree. Here the two to four eggs may be laid, to be hatched some three or four weeks later and here the young live.

Its diet consists of mice and other rodents, as well as birds, frogs, lizards, and insects. The Florida barred owl is much the same as the northern bird except that its toes are almost naked. The Texas variety is somewhat paler. It frequents the sagebrush area of the central portion of that State.

SPOTTED OWLS

THE mild-mannered California spotted owl refuses to become angry even when its nest with young is approached by an intruder. Spending the daytime in some shady spot, it rarely moves unless disturbed, and then flies but a short distance to a new perch near by. In addition to the various rats and mice it devours, it succumbs to the delights of melons, eggs, and even mutton chops, which it may filch from the bears in the western parks. Its range is through the western United States and Mexico.

GREAT GRAY OWL

DURING severe winters this thirty-inch monster of owldom finds its way into the United States from the frozen northlands in numbers. Its fluffy feathers lend it an even more imposing bulk than it actually possesses. The great gray owl is grayish-brown in color. It nests high in an evergreen tree, bringing sticks and moss to make its home.

RICHARDSON'S OWL

ABOUT the same color as the saw-whet and two inches larger, the related Richardson's owl comes to the United States only infrequently. Its call is more liquid than that of its American cousin and is comparable with the "splat" made by water dropping from a height. When this northern bird, also known as the Arctic saw-whet owl, is unable to find a hollow tree, it nests in thick bushes.

SAW-WHET OWL

EXCEPT in the deep South, the white-streaked, brown, eight-inch saw-whet owl is found all over the United States. Its call sounds like the rasping of a saw being sharpened. This bird sleeps so soundly that it is often killed by its dreaded enemy, the barred owl. It doesn't remain long in one locality, but shifts about in search of better food. It settles down in the spring, however, to lay its three to six white eggs in the hollow of a tree. This peaceful bird prefers mice to smaller birds. Its feathers blend into the bark of its sylvan perch.

SCREECH OWLS

THE cry of the screech owl is not a screech at all but rather a mournful wail. In the South the people call it the shivering owl because of its quavering whistle. This ten-inch bird is said to remain with the same mate for years. Their eggs are frequently laid in outbuildings or in man-made bird boxes. The nest itself is a slipshod affair of sticks, grass, leaves, and rubbish strewn about in a careless manner.

The Florida screech owl is somewhat smaller and darker than the common variety; midway between them in size is the pale Texas

SCREECH OWLS *(Otus asio)*. Length: 10 inches. Range: Eastern North America.
New York Zoological Society

variety. The California or Bendire's screech owl is a pronounced gray. The lightest of the screech owls is the Rocky Mountain breed. Also found in the Northwest, Kennicott's screech owl is a dark-colored bird. Other related screech owls are the Arizona screech owl, the spotted screech owl of southern Arizona, the flammulated screech owl of the Southwest, and the Idaho screech owl.

Screech owls are adept fishermen even in winter when they catch their meals through holes in the ice. Their chief food, however, is insects, according to Dr. A. K. Fisher. They also feed on crawfish, toads, frogs, and lizards and on the whole are useful to agriculture, doing a great deal of good.

HORNED OWLS

THE bold and powerful great horned owl is one of the largest of the owls, measuring a good two feet in length. Its white-barred chest distinguishes a generally sooty brown plumage mottled with grayish-white. Called the "tiger of the air," its courage and rapacity cause it to be dreaded by even so comparatively large an animal as the woodchuck. Of one hundred and forty-six great horned owls' stomachs examined, only thirty-one contained poultry, eight contained other birds, and the majority contained the remains of various mammals and insects. It is one of the few birds that have no objection to feeding on the remains of a skunk.

GREAT HORNED OWL *(Bubo v. virginianus)*. Length: 2 feet. Range: Eastern North America.
American Museum of Natural History

Found in the eastern States, it has often been known to lay its eggs while the snow still flies. These are laid one at a time at successive intervals of days in the nest of grasses, twigs, and roots. The nest is usually destroyed once the young are able to fly, in order not to attract other hunting birds to the vicinity. While its most familiar cry is a *hoot,* it also indulges in feline and canine noises.

Related species and subspecies are the western, the Pacific, dwarf, dusky, Arctic, Labrador, and St. Michael's horned owl of Alaska, a tawny bird.

SNOWY OWL

ALSO known as the great white owl and the ermine owl, this two-foot-long bird of the far North comes occasionally to the more northerly States. Sometimes it arrives in large migrations when dozens of specimens are seen.

It is strong and swift, capable of catching and killing hares, waterfowl, and fishes. Its habits are chiefly diurnal as a result of the long days of its northern habitat. One individual, caught on board a ship off Cape Race, lived in captivity for about twenty-five years.

AMERICAN HAWK OWL

HUNTING by day, this hawklike bird flies straight and swift, skimming the ground to alight on a bush or shrub. Then it pounces on a mouse or rat.

If its nest is disturbed it will fight vigorously. Its claws can strike through clothing to lacerate the flesh.

Medium-sized for an owl, this bird has short, pointed wings, is dark above and transversely barred across the chest and abdomen. Found throughout the northern United States and Canada, this American member of a circumpolar species winters in Alaska.

BURROWING OWLS

BETWEEN five and ten feet from the opening of a deserted animal burrow, the burrowing owl, only land bird to nest under the ground, builds its nest of weeds and animal refuse. It is set in an enlarged chamber in the cut-out sides of the channel. In this underground nursery are laid the half dozen or so eggs. These nine-and-a-half-inch birds are usually found in the more wide open sections of the United States. These brown, light-spotted birds are predatory and fearless. Lurking in the dark of their underground homes, they sally forth to pounce upon reptiles, mammals, and birds even up to the size of the nighthawk. Even when young these owls possess enormous appetites. Two subspecies are known — t h e western and the Florida. The former inhabits southwestern Canada east through the plains, while the latter variety is found in the prairie region of Florida.

WESTERN BURROWING OWL (*Speotyto cunicularia hypugaea*). Length: 9 inches. Range: Western and central North America.
J. W. Jackson

PYGMY OWLS

PYGMY owls or gnome owls of the western United States are the dwarfs of the tribe. Only six and a half inches long, it has no hesitation in attacking larger birds or mammals. Unlike all the other American owls, its wings make a whistling noise in flight. It also hunts more often during the day than other owls, its body blending with the pine trees on which it is usually perched.

Sometimes a reddish gnome owl is seen and these are among the handsomest of the owls.

Three to four eggs are hatched in the nest which may be between ten and eighty feet up in the branches or in the hollow of a tree. Sometimes the abandoned hole of a woodpecker is used for a nesting site.

ELF OWLS

NO larger than sparrows, the six-inch owls of southern California are the smallest members of the owl family. They may be seen in either brownish-gray, yellow-spotted plumage, or in a more somber dress of dark brown. They like to nest high above the ground, but when large trees are not handy they will occupy a hole in the giant cactus. These small birds subsist mainly on insects, rarely eating other birds or animals.

Whitney's elf owl is now found only in southern Arizona and New Mexico in the United States. It likes to skim across the hot, dry river bottoms.

The Texas elf owl frequents the lower Rio Grande Valley. Nothing has been published regarding its habits. A third subspecies inhabits Lower California.

OSPREY

THE grayish brown osprey, or fish hawk, flies slowly above the water, sometimes at considerable height, keeping a keen lookout for fishes which may approach the surface. Spying a likely victim, it races downward at lightning speed, strikes the water with a resounding splash, and seizes the fish in its claws. So firm is its grip that occasionally, when the prey is too large, the osprey is dragged underwater before it can open its claws, and in this case both bird and fish perish. But more often the fish, sometimes weighing as much as eight pounds, is drawn from the water and carried off to some perch where the osprey devours it. In catching small fishes the bird sometimes merely grazes the water.

OSPREY

This thirty-inch hawk lives exclusively on fish, which it hunts in oceans, lakes, and rivers. Though the above described is the usual fishing procedure, sometimes the bird sits for as much as an hour on a limb overhanging a body of water, waiting for its dinner to appear below.

Often the osprey's prey is appropriated by the eagle. The eagle pursues the smaller bird, forcing it to circle higher and higher, until in its eagerness to save its own skin the osprey drops its burden, which the eagle catches in mid-air.

Unlike other birds of prey, ospreys are gregarious. Year after year they return to the same nesting grounds, where numerous pairs may make their nest in the same tall tree or cliff. Their appearance in the spring of the year is welcomed by fishermen, partly because ospreys are regarded as birds of good omen, largely because their coming coincides with the arrival of great shoals of shad, herring, and other food fishes. The osprey is friendly in the presence of man, and does not attack other wild birds or domestic poultry.

OSPREY *(Pandion haliaetus carolinensis)*. Length: 2 feet. Range: North and South America. Diminishing.
New York Zoological Society

OSPREY WITH CATCH.
American Museum of Natural History

The fish hawk's nest is a simple platform of loosely arranged sticks usually placed on the top of a very high tree. Dallas Lore Sharp reported that one nest grew to such enormous proportions, as successive generations of ospreys added to it, that when it finally dropped it made three cartloads of material.

Sometimes blackbirds, sparrows, and grackles take residence in one of these huge structures. Sparrows, as they increase in numbers, have even been known to displace all of the former intruders, including the fish hawk itself. Its eggs number two to four and vary considerably in color. Sometimes they are a dull white, sometimes buff marked with chocolate color, sometimes an almost solid chocolate. Their length is about two and one-half inches. The male osprey is very attentive to his nesting mate, and to the young who require care and feeding for a considerable period. When frightened, the osprey utters a long plaintive whistle.

The osprey remains in northern latitudes until its fishing grounds begin to freeze over. Then it departs for subtropical regions, wintering from Lower California to the West Indies.

Because of its fishy diet, the osprey's flesh is oily and unpalatable; its eggs likewise have a distinctly fishy odor.

AUDUBON'S CARACARA

THOUGH Audubon's caracara lives chiefly on carrion, it attacks living prey with zest and cunning. When this bird is cruising, its flight is leisurely, accompanied by turns, risings, and fallings, but when it sets out to pursue a jack rabbit or prairie-dog, it flies swiftly and directly with occasional loud flappings of its white-tipped wings.

The caracara is a pirate and a bold fighter. It attacks crows and even hawks in mid-air, and on at least one occasion was seen assailing the formidable American eagle, though the combatants disappeared behind a hill before the observer could see the outcome of the battle. Caracaras eat other birds, including some good-sized ones, and also snakes. In one case a snake struggled and twined itself round the caracara's neck, but the bird was in the end victorious. A remarkable

AUDUBON'S CARACARAS (*Polyborus cheriway auduboni*). Length: 2 feet. Range: "Northern Lower California, southwestern Arizona, Texas, and Florida south to Mexico and Central America" (A.O.U. Check List, IV ed.). Almost extinct over much of its range.
American Museum of Natural History

gift of these birds is their ability to eat turtles. The father of a caracara family was seen to bring a five-inch mud turtle home for his chicks; the provider lingered by the nest for thirty-five minutes, drawing the meat out from under the shell. In general these birds feed their young on raw meat, instead of regurgitating baby food as do the vultures.

Caracaras are quite at home on the ground. They walk about by the roadsides in search of animals run over by automobiles and assemble in large numbers near slaughterhouses and garbage dumps. A bird with a broken wing can run swiftly in case of danger. Where food is scarce, caracaras fight among themselves and engage in wild chases after one of their number that has secured a tempting morsel.

These fierce birds of prey are found principally in Texas and Florida, more rarely in Arizona where they are known as Mexican eagles or Mexican buzzards. They inhabit prairies, swamps, and ponds, making their nests principally in cabbage palmettos and oak trees. The nest is placed on an upright branch, eight to fifty feet from the ground, in a position giving the bird a good view of the surrounding country. The nests are made of almost any material available—corn husks, broom weed, small sticks, mesquite twigs. No lining is used. Sometimes a hawk's abandoned nest is occupied.

The caracara lays two or three white eggs, clouded or splotched with buff, ochre, or brown. Four weeks are required for incubation. The chicks, which are a downy buff color at birth, remain in the nest for some weeks. Egg collectors, or oölogists, have gathered the eggs of Audubon's caracara with such persistence that the species is threatened with extinction. In order to circumvent this practice, game wardens of the Audubon Society now "beat the oölogists to it" by the simple but effective device of stamping each egg with indelible ink: "Property of the Audubon Society." This defaces the eggs in the eyes of the collectors but does not seem to upset mother caracara who hatches them out as stamped.

The only serious animal enemy of the caracara is the scissor-tailed flycatcher, which in Texas clings to the larger bird's back, biting it and pulling out its feathers.

When the caracara's nest is approached by humans, the parent bird noiselessly vanishes, soon to reappear with its mate on a nearby tree top where they watch the proceedings. The caracara is a noiseless bird, except for a harsh cry it emits when startled.

Caracaras have been tamed. They become amusing pets and learn to recognize their master even after a long absence.

GUADALUPE CARACARA

THE Guadalupe caracara, a close relative, was abundant fifty years ago on Guadalupe Island off Lower California, but is now extinct. It has never inhabited the United States and is mentioned here only to show what will happen to our own caracaras if we do not extend efforts to conserve them.

Though this bird was a valuable scavenger, the Mexicans persecuted it because of its way with domestic poultry, kids, and lambs. The Guadalupe caracara was exceedingly fierce and cruel in its attack. Chickens at the very door of the barnyard were unsafe. It often attacked newborn kids by pulling their tongues out by the roots. A jackass imprisoned beneath a fallen boulder had its eyes pecked out. However, it must be remembered that all this ferocity took place under the peculiar conditions of isolation that existed on the island and was directed solely against defenseless and domesticated creatures.

DUCK HAWK

SWIFTEST of all fliers is the duck hawk. Accurately timed at one hundred and eighty miles an hour from an airplane, this species holds the record. Though only a foot and a half in length, the slate-gray duck hawk, or peregrine falcon, attacks and kills wild geese and other powerful game birds. Its presence is so rare, however, that its destructiveness is of but slight economic importance. Soaring easily among the clouds, the falcon picks out its victim and then descends almost perpendicularly, sending the frightened flocks of game fowl scurrying in all directions. If the prey is not too heavy, the falcon

DUCK HAWK *(Falco peregrinus anatum).*
Length: 1½ feet. Range: North America.
New York Zoological Society

seizes it in its powerful talons and carries it off to a secluded spot, there to devour it. In addition to birds, the duck hawk's diet includes rabbits, mice, and insects. The peregrine often attacks its fellow marauder, the kite, sometimes to rob it of its prey, sometimes apparently just for the fight.

Duck hawks arrive at the breeding grounds in early February, though they do not actually mate until March. This month is spent in an elaborate courtship. The male performs complex acrobatic flights, usually centering about a cliff which he has chosen for his future home. To this spot he strives to attract his chosen female. He flies from ledge to ledge, goes through the motions of building a nest, and calls to her with a note resembling the sound of a broken hinge. Both birds go on foraging parties but whichever secures the prey, it seems to be the female who eats first. As the female's interest increases, the two birds sit for hours side by side wailing at each other. After mating, the male's solicitude for the home somewhat wanes, while the female's increases, and it is she who builds the nest that is actually used. Some females remain unmated and lead a vagabond life somewhat in the manner of the male hooligan seals.

The duck hawk lays from two to four eggs. The young are at first fed on mice and other small morsels brought them by their parents. When the parents feel that the chick has taken its ease long enough, they try to tempt it from the nest by dangling food in their claws. Sometimes a young hawk falls to earth and is killed when this maneuver is performed too early in its career. This bird is found throughout the United States, though it is nowhere abundant, and is most common in the New England and North Atlantic States.

Among the European nobility the duck hawk was much used in falconry and was known as the "noble peregrine." The birds were tamed and trained to hunt down game birds for their masters. A good hunting falcon brought immense prices; some hunters became so attached to their birds that they gave them royal funerals when they died. The duck hawk, also called the American peregrine, breeds in the mountains of California and Oregon and along the northern top of our country. It winters in many parts of the United States and even goes as far south as Panama. It deserves protection.

PIGEON HAWK

THE blackish-brown pigeon hawk is smaller than the great falcons, being scarcely a foot in length. Its rapid flight resembles that of the wild pigeon, and its posture when in repose also recalls that game bird, so that hunters sometimes mistake it for the latter. The pigeon hawk is less shy than most birds of prey, and may often be approached at quite short range.

This bird summers from Maine to the Great Plains, making its home in open country, at the edge of woods, and near large bodies of water. The pigeon hawk lives chiefly on small birds and mice. However, it often attacks larger birds. One was seen killing a ptarmigan and another was shot in the act of slaying a hen. According to some observers, it follows in the wake of small migrating birds, such as pigeons, robins, and blackbirds, picking off the stragglers and the weak. Pigeon hawks are said to be very inquisitive, showing a lively interest in human activities. In winter this falcon migrates to the southern States and South America.

SPARROW HAWK

THE ten-inch eastern sparrow hawk perches on the limb of a dead tree, waiting for a grasshopper or mouse to appear below. Sighting a victim, it flies down, hovers over it until the right moment arrives and rapidly strikes. The grasshopper's armor is no match for the hawk's beak thrust. Bearing its prey in its talons, the predator then returns to its perch to devour it. The hawk attacks sparrows and other small birds, and also eats snakes, toads, and spiders. It is therefore regarded as highly beneficial to farmers.

The general color of this bird is reddish, barred with black; the head of the male is bluish-ash with a reddish patch on the crown. In some regions the sparrow hawk is called killy-killy, because of its high-pitched cry.

The desert sparrow hawk, a somewhat larger variety, inhabits the western deserts from Montana to Arizona. The little sparrow hawk of Florida is of interest to ornithologists because of its very short tail.

The sparrow hawks are the tamest of the hawks, often nesting in dead trees in orchards or along the roadside.

EASTERN SPARROW HAWK (*Falco s. sparverius*). Length: 11 inches. Range: North America east of the Rockies.
New York Zoological Society

GYRFALCONS

THE white gyrfalcon, somewhat larger than the duck hawk, can be recognized by the pure white of its head and under-tail coverts. The gyrfalcon beats its wings rapidly in flying, and close observers are not greatly impressed by its swiftness. It often seems to tire out a prey which a duck hawk would easily overtake and attack. They are, however, powerful and courageous birds, with no fear of creatures twice their size. In Asia the Mongols still use them in falconry, though American falconers have gone over to swifter varieties. It is a northern species, restricted in this hemisphere chiefly to Greenland and Labrador, but sometimes seen along the coast of northern New England during the winter.

The black gyrfalcon is a bluish-ash or brownish-black color, and consequently the darkest of the gyrfalcons. It descends as far southward as New York and is sometimes seen in the Dakotas and other northwestern States. It nests either in tall pine trees or on rugged cliffs. One nest was found surrounded by a stockade of heavy icicles. This falcon does not seem

WHITE GYRFALCON *(Falco rusticolus candicans)*. Length: 2 feet. Range: Arctic America. Winters in southern Canada and Maine.
New York Zoological Society

to kill its prey with its talons but collides with it and seizes it at the moment of shock.

Like it the gray gyrfalcon breeds in the Arctic and sometimes winters as far south as Kansas. It also has been seen wintering in Wisconsin and Maine.

MacFarlane's gyrfalcon is another casual visitor which has been recorded from Minnesota as well as Maine.

The prairie falcon, the foot-and-a-half male of which is often called the American lanneret, and the somewhat larger female, the American lanner, flies like a duck hawk, taking short and rapid wing beats. It eats a greater proportion of mammals than the duck hawk, probably because of its preference for prairie regions where small mammals, particularly rodents, abound. They are able to kill jack rabbits fully twice their size. Ground squirrels are perhaps the most important item in their diet. In the United States these falcons inhabit the Great Plains, Washington, Oregon, and the plains of central California. Sometimes these falcons stray into the mountains and then they appear to live largely on birds.

The brown and white aplomado or lead-colored falcon, inhabiting Mexico and Central America, occasionally crosses the border into Texas, New Mexico, and Arizona. In habits this small species resembles the sharp-shinned hawk.

The small brown kestrel is a European falcon, accidental on the coast of Massachusetts. One was seen at Nantasket Beach in 1887.

AMERICAN EAGLE

THE American or bald eagle is most often seen soaring high in the air on the lookout for something to eat. Its flight is truly majestic; its great wings seem scarcely to move. The eyesight of this bird is proverbial. Often it sights a possible meal at a distance of as much as three miles and makes for it in a beeline, moving effortlessly, yet often with the breath-taking speed of a mile a minute.

The wingspread of an adult bald eagle may reach nearly eight feet. Yet despite its great size and strength and the majesty for which it is famed, this bird lives chiefly on carrion. By the ocean shores and on the banks of great rivers it finds dead fish. It often joins the crows and ravens in their noisy scavenging expeditions. The male eagle emits a loud and clear *cac-cac-cac*, while the f e m a l e utters a harsh-sounding half scream, half laugh.

The eagle is a clumsy fisherman. Where dead fish are not available, it often robs the skillful osprey. The osprey circles higher and higher in its efforts to escape and finally drops its catch, which the sky pirate seizes in mid-air.

Eagles also eat various snakes and rodents, but they c a n n o t be classed among the most b e n e f i c i a l birds to farmers. On the other hand, they are not the most harmful, though they do occasionally steal a chicken, lamb, or small pig. They do not kidnap babies, being unable even to carry such weight aloft in their weak claws.

AMERICAN EAGLE *(Haliaeetus l. leucocephalus)*. Length: 3 feet. Range: United States. Fast becoming rare and in danger of extinction. Deserves protection.
Ralph De Sola (NZP)

Eagles apparently mate for life and are very affectionate in their home lives. Year after year a pair returns to the same nest, which they repair slightly each spring. In the central States the eggs are laid in February or March. The nest is a large platform of loosely woven sticks, lined with roots and grass, usually situated high up in a tree or, in regions where tall trees are not available, in a cranny of a cliff. The eggs are ivory-white and are usually two in number, though occasionally three are found. About one month is required for incubation.

At birth the chicks are covered with a whitish down. Three years are required before the adult plumage is donned, and until that time the birds differ appreciably from their parents. In their first year they are almost entirely black. The following year the head and neck are still black and there is a black and gray mixture in the remaining plumage, which in the adult is an almost pure dark brown. Seeing this phase, John James Audubon thought he had discovered a new bird, which he modestly called the Washington eagle, instead of having some other ornithologist name it for himself. In the adult bird the head and neck are a pure white, and it is this white head, which looks like a bald pate in the distance, that has won the bird its misnomer. It is this bird which is the national emblem of the United States.

AMERICAN EAGLES NESTING.
Academy of Natural Sciences of Philadelphia

The American eagle is found throughout the United States and Alaska, though it is rare in California. Two subspecies are recognized —a northern and a southern bald eagle. In Alaska a bounty has been placed on our national emblem. Captive eagles have lived thirty-three years.

GOLDEN EAGLE

THE golden eagle inhabits the Appalachian and Rocky Mountains and the northwestern plains States. It may be distinguished from the American eagle by the presence of feathers on its ankles, which in the bald eagle are bare, and by a golden tinge about the neck. Its speed is twice as fast. The golden eagle prefers live food to carrion. It is expert at hunting small mammals, the ever-present prairie-dog and the furtive mouse. In many regions they seem to subsist largely on ground squirrels. In North Dakota, where the bird still nests in the Badlands, it is persecuted and unless hunters are forced to stop their ceaseless killing it will soon disappear entirely—never to appear again except on museum shelves and in books dealing with recently extinct animals. Forty-six years was the age attained by one golden eagle kept in a zoo.

HAWKS

A BEVY of small birds flutter from one sheltering bush to another; field mice and rabbits scamper unconcernedly along their narrow lanes. Then suddenly there is a terrifying rush of wings. A hawk swoops down, its victim utters a short screech, and the hawk sinks its death-dealing claws into one of the little creatures as the others flee in panic. The hunter rips its prey with its hooked beak, swallowing large pieces at a time without removing feathers or small bones. Later these inedible parts form pellets which are regurgitated.

Belonging to a family possessing an almost insatiable appetite, hawks must hunt during most of their waking hours, especially when they have young to feed. Because some hawks eat almost noth-

GOLDEN EAGLE (*Aquila chrysaetos canadensis*). Length: 3 feet. Range: Western and central North America. No longer breeds east of the Mississippi. Rare.
New York Zoological Society

ing but birds, whether poultry or songsters, all have been popularly branded as vicious creatures which should be executed on sight. Nothing could be more untrue, as most hawks are decidedly useful to mankind as killers of rodents, and some are so beneficial that their extinction would be a serious menace to the very farmers who indiscriminately slaughter them now. Though cats have a greater popular reputation as mouse killers, the hawk in reality destroys far more of these harmful rodents. Mice do tremendous damage to trees of all sorts, and annually consume about 3,000,000 tons of hay and staggering quantities of alfalfa in the United States. Moreover, these prolific creatures may bring forth as many as seventeen litters a year, and the young begin to breed for themselves at the tender age of twenty-five days. It has been estimated that the annual progeny of a single pair may run to one million, hence it is not surprising that if unchecked they may constitute a dreadful plague. In many localities the rough-legged hawk, for instance, subsists ninety-five per cent on mice; and a single hawk may daily devour hundreds of the destructive rodents.

SHARP-SHINNED HAWK

Grasshoppers form another leading item in the diet of many hawks. The importance of leaving these birds of prey unmolested can therefore hardly be overestimated. Only three species live chiefly on birds useful to man: the sharp-shinned hawk, which is too small to be destructive to game birds; Cooper's hawk; and the goshawk; all of which are found in most sections of the United States. In general the beneficial hawks, which subsist largely on meadow mice and other pests, may be recognized by their broad wings; these are the rough-legged hawk, the red-shouldered, the broad-winged, the red-tailed, and the marsh hawk. Those species that prey largely on other birds have conspicuously short wings; these are the goshawk, Cooper's hawk, and the little sharp-shinned hawk which we will take up in reverse order.

SHARP-SHINNED HAWK

THOUGH sharp-shinned hawks are smaller than most members of the family—females are no longer than fourteen inches and the males even shorter—they are fast and fearless. Immature sharp-shinned hawks are even more daring than adults. Because these young birds are colored brown, many people think they belong to another species. Sharp-shinned hawks build bulky nests of sticks, usually high in an evergreen tree but sometimes on a mountain ledge where it is exposed to the weather.

COOPER'S HAWK

THE most numerous of the destructive hawks are the Cooper's hawks. Aside from its darker head and its larger size, a Cooper's hawk looks almost exactly like a sharp-shinned hawk. Males of this species are eighteen inches, females twenty. So bold are these hawks that they will swoop down and seize a fowl while the owner stands watching near-by. Their red eyes seem to glow defiantly. Doves, grouse, rabbits, squirrels, and all kinds of domestic poultry are included among their prey. They are among the few real enemies of farmers among the birds.

GOSHAWKS

STILL larger, sometimes reaching a length of two feet, are the goshawks which fortunately are not very common in most parts of their range. They usually live in sections remote from towns, nesting in great evergreens and feeding chiefly on game birds. These gray birds have slate-colored bars across their white breasts. Similar, but more mottled in appearance, are their close relatives, the western goshawks, that live in the Pacific States.

MARSH HAWKS

THE marsh hawks are methodical hunters, sailing low over meadows and brushland on the lookout for squirrels, lizards, rabbits, and especially field mice. In the spring they hunt in pairs. When he has eaten his fill, the gray and white male sometimes performs for his brown and buff mate. He flies high and allows him-

YOUNG MARSH HAWKS *(Circus hudsonius)*. Length: 1½ feet (adults).
Range: North America.
A. C. Reneau, Jr.

self to fall, goes into a tailspin and only rights himself when he seems about to strike the earth. Together they build a nest on the ground, first providing a foundation of sticks if the soil is too damp. Both parents incubate the eggs and both feed the young birds and fight to defend them. In the fall the whole family hunts together, sometimes joining other families to form a small flock. Mature marsh hawks are about nineteen inches long.

Marsh hawks are found throughout most of the country and their habits vary considerably. In some sections they are destructive of bird life, but for the most part they are very useful. A single pair will destroy about a thousand field mice in a season and by thus saving the farmer's crops repay him well for a few chickens.

FEMALE GOSHAWK *(Astur atricapillus)*.
Length: 2 feet. Range: North America mainly in northern United States and southern Canada.
Academy of Natural Sciences of Philadelphia

RED-TAILED HAWK

EACH year the red-tailed hawk returns to the same nest in the crotch of some large tree, and each year the nest is strengthened and enlarged. Red-tailed hawks are large, slow-flying birds, the females being two feet long and the males about two inches shorter.

They are easily recognized by the red tail, banded with black, which contrasts with the gray-dappled body, brown above and white below.

Though this species is found only in the East, from Florida to Wisconsin, a similar though darker bird, the western red-tailed hawk, ranges from the Great Plains to the Pacific. Krider's hawk of the Great Plains is much lighter and has a white breast, while Harlan's hawk of the Mississippi Valley is almost black with a brown-and-white mottled tail.

HARRIS'S HAWK

HARRIS'S hawk adapts itself to the sparse animal and plant life of its southwestern home. Its nest is placed on a cactus or among the tangled thorny branches of a desert shrub. It flies low over the wasteland, moving lazily. But when it spies a chipmunk or a wood rat it can dart with great speed. When living food is not available, Harris's hawk is satisfied to feed on carrion. The females of this species are twenty-three inches in length and the males twenty.

RED-SHOULDERED HAWK

USUALLY the red-shouldered hawk remains in the shelter of the eastern forests. It has no difficulty in finding food as it will eat grasshoppers, fishes, mice, snakes, centipedes, and many other small animals. The males of this useful species are about twenty inches long and the females twenty-two. These brown and gray birds are splashed with red on the shoulders, and a lighter red on the breast. Somewhat smaller are the Florida red-shouldered hawks which are found in the southeastern and Gulf States. Another variety is the red-bellied hawk of the Rocky Mountains and Pacific coast.

The red-shouldered hawk is one of the most valuable birds to the farmer because of its omnivorous diet. It is estimated that ninety per cent of its food consists of injurious mammals and insects.

SWAINSON'S HAWK

VERY quietly the Swainson's hawk goes about its business of ridding the prairies of gophers, mice, and grasshoppers. This brown and white bird is about the same size as the red-tailed hawk, and is even less deserving of the accusations of poultry raisers. It is most common in eastern Washington and Oregon, but is occasionally seen in almost every other State. It usually nests in the branches of tall trees, but sometimes is satisfied with a bush or even the ground for its home where two eggs are laid.

YOUNG SWAINSON'S HAWK (*Buteo swainsoni*). Length: 1¾ feet (adult). Range: Western North America; casual in Northeast.
Adrian C. Fox

ROUGH-LEGGED HAWK

IN THE winter the rough-legged hawk may be found almost anywhere in the United States, but it breeds in Alaska. This brown bird with its heavy feather stockings often hunts at twilight or by the light of the moon. It prefers meadow mice to other food. Males are twenty inches long and females twenty-two. The rusty-colored rough-leg breeds and lives in the western States. It is a black and brown bird, much streaked with white, and similar in habits to the rough-leg.

BROAD-WINGED HAWK

A BROAD-WINGED hawk may seem almost a part of the tree on which it perches motionless for long periods, its brown feathers concealing it from the squirrels, gophers, and toads which it hopes to capture. This eastern bird is most useful in destroying caterpillars and insects.

SENNETT'S WHITE-TAILED HAWK

SENNETT'S white-tailed hawk is rare in its small range in southern Texas, as it is actually a Mexican bird. Also little known is the zone-tailed hawk, a black bird with white zone bands on the lower side of its tail.

ROUGH-LEGGED HAWK (*Buteo lagopus sancti-johannis*). Length: 1½ feet. Range: Northern United States, Canada, and Alaska.
J. W. Jackson

SWALLOW-TAILED KITE

THE swallow-tailed kite soars and twists, giving an impression of easy lightness. It is considered by many the most graceful of American birds, and in speed it is second only to the duck hawk. Gifted with unusual surface of wing and tail, it spends nearly all its time in the air. It dives down to earth to seize a frog or water snake, a grasshopper or caterpillar, and then quickly rises to devour its prey on the wing. This is accomplished by bending forward its talons which hold the food and slightly inclining its head. Like the swallow, this bird drinks by merely grazing the water's surface in its flight. Sometimes it is seen soaring above forest fires, hunting the insects that have been driven upward by the flames.

The wings, tail, and back of the swallow-tailed kite are black, while the rest of its plumage is pure white. It is two feet in length, but this includes the long, deeply forked tail. The wings are slender and when folded reach the tip of the tail.

This bird nests in the tops of tall trees, usually near watercourses. The nest is composed of dry twigs, hay, and sometimes moss. Two or three white or buff eggs, much splotched or speckled, are laid.

In the early fall these birds migrate to Central America and the West Indies. Before leaving they collect in small companies and perform amazing aerial maneuvers, circling about slowly and ascending in long spirals. Their call is a shrill *ke-wee-wee*.

Residents of the eastern, southern, and midwestern States should protect this bird, both for its beauty and its value in controlling snakes and insect pests. It does not attack other birds.

WHITE-TAILED KITE

THE white-tailed kite was for a time almost extinct as a result of persecution by ignorant hunters and ranchers, but today its numbers are again increasing. Though sometimes guilty of killing small birds, it lives chiefly on rodents, snakes, and grasshoppers. This bird inhabits almost the entire southern portion of the United States from Florida to California. It is about seventeen inches long, it has small claws and feet, and its wings are twice the length of its tail. Its general color is bluish-gray, but its square tail and lower parts are white. A live oak is the usual site of its grass and twig nest. Its three to five dull whitish eggs are sometimes so heavily marked with red and brown that the white cannot be detected.

MISSISSIPPI KITE

SMALLEST of kites is the Mississippi kite, which attains a length of only fourteen inches. This blue-gray bird is tireless on the wing and in full flight it can skillfully nip beetles from a tree branch or a serpent from the rock where it is sunning itself. Swift in its flight, it soars with grace and dexterity. It is stronger than the other kites and said to be more determined in the hunt. The female lays two or three blue-green eggs in a nest high in a tree. Usually these birds rehabilitate an old nest built by some other avian, adding a fresh lining of moss and leaves. Mississippi kites inhabit the Gulf States and the southern part of the Mississippi Valley.

EVERGLADE KITE

THE bluish-gray Everglade kite, as its name indicates, lives in the swamps of Florida. It feeds chiefly on a genus of land snail restricted to that area and has a needle-pointed bill adapted for pricking, paralyzing, and removing the creature from its shell. It returns again and again to the same hummock to feed, and its presence can be detected by the piles of empty snail shells it leaves. Everglade kites are about eighteen inches long and may be recognized most readily by a white line at the base of their tail. They nest in the bushes of their swamp home, laying two or three splotched white eggs. On the west shore of Lake Okeechobee they are protected by the National Association of Audubon Societies, but face depletion through swamp drainage and destructive fires in that area.

It is a rather tame bird, permitting observers to come within twenty-five or thirty feet before flying off. In flight it resembles the marsh hawk.

CALIFORNIA CONDOR

WITH its wings spread majestically to their full span of eleven feet, the California vulture, or condor, soars high in the sultry air. Largest flying land bird, not only in the United States but perhaps in the world, the condor watches the earth far below with sharp eyes.

It rivets its gaze upon a stalking beast of prey. When the carnivore has pounced upon a smaller animal and eaten its fill, down swoops the condor to peck away hungrily at the torn and bleeding carcass. The bird, whose main staple is carrion of all sorts, can devour a cow in surprisingly short time, though its own weight is but thirty pounds at most.

Sometimes the bird flies swiftly over the California mountains and joins the gulls in a sumptuous feast on some dead whale that has been cast ashore by the surf. The condor occasionally makes its own kill, as many small mammals and birds have learned. But it certainly does not deserve its reputation for flying off with young children, because its claws are quite weak and can

EVERGLADE KITE *(Rostrhamus sociabilis plumbeus)*. Length: 1½ feet. Range: Peninsular Florida, Cuba, Mexico, and Central America.
American Museum of Natural History

CALIFORNIA CONDOR *(Gymnogyps californianus)*. Length: 4 feet. Range: Restricted to the Coast Ranges of southern and Lower California. Almost extinct. Largest bird of prey in North America. Wingspread averages ten feet.

New York Zoological Society

carry comparatively little weight. In fact there is little basis for any birds carrying off babies.

In the winter the female lays a single egg, about four by two inches in size. The chicks when hatched are covered with white down, but their heads are bare. They hiss and growl in a display of emotion never exhibited by adults. Condors probably have the longest infancy in birddom, since they are not full grown for more than two years. Then they are brown or black birds, with orange heads.

The nest of a pair of condors is usually a cave in the sloping mountains, and is marked by the stench of rotting flesh and bones. This cave is their castle, and the couple vigorously resent any attempt at intrusion, defending themselves vigorously against bird, beast, and man, alike.

These giants of the bird world are almost extinct. Many of them died when ranchers put out poison bait to kill such marauding beasts as bears and cougars. The innocent birds, desirous only of a bite to eat, fell victim to the doctored carrion. Though their range once extended to Oregon and Washington, condors are now found only in certain isolated areas of southern and Lower California. In the former region, less than ten families have been reported in recent years, and no doubt this magnificent bird will soon be lost to the American scene. One captive condor in the National Zoological Park has lived thirty-seven years in captivity.

TURKEY VULTURE

EFFORTLESSLY wheeling and soaring for hours without flapping its wings, over the still, burningly hot countryside the turkey vulture, or buzzard, scans the earth for food. It halts its graceful flight to swoop down when it sights a dead beast. Hastily it begins pecking the flesh to the bone, for the presence of one vulture below will soon bring watchful neighbors. As it devours the carrion, the bird fouls the site with its noxious ordure.

When it leaves the land, the buzzard, also called carrion crow, rises higher and higher in wide, open circles, making the most of every whim of the wind and upward air currents. Even when it attains an altitude of thousands of feet, it watches the ground with vigilant, far-seeing eyes. A sign of weakness on the part of some wounded or starving beast is enough to keep the long-tailed buzzard circling over it with gruesome patience. Sometimes it does not wait for death, but will begin tearing out the flesh of a weakened, helpless creature.

The turkey vulture not only acts but looks as if it had been born in a garbage can and doused with slop and ashes. It has a naked, crimson head, and its plumage is a grayish black.

It performs a valuable service to ranchers who slaughter cattle and leave the bones and entrails for the vultures to pick over. The bird occasionally departs from its customary diet to eat a live reptile, rodent, or bird. Dead salmon are also eaten along the banks of the

Columbia River after their annual run. Turkey vultures range from the Southwest to Minnesota, and eastward to New Jersey. In captivity their average age is thirty-two years.

BLACK VULTURE

THE black vulture, another unbeautiful bird, strolls about the streets of some southern cities, very much at home. It is almost as helpful as a scientifically managed department of sanitation, and will devour dead animals by eating the bones clean. Consequently, black vultures are protected in most places by law. They are found not only in the South but occasionally wander as far north as Maine, New York, and Ohio. The black vulture is distinguished from the turkey vulture by a shorter, squarer tail and more heavy-set appearance.

In bygone days the family of vultures, whose Latin name *Cathartidae* means cleanser, had easy pickings. Then, when millions of animals trampled the plains and valleys, plagues and fights left the earth strewn with carrion for these birds.

A common characteristic of vultures is that they walk, rather than hop, when on the

TURKEY VULTURE (*Cathartes aura septentrionalis*). Length: 2½ feet. Range: Widely distributed over much of the United States, southern Canada, and northern Mexico.
New York Zoological Society

ground. And, as a rule, vultures build no nests, but deposit their eggs in any such convenient place as a cave, tree hollow, or simply on the earth. The eggs are pale green or bluish-white marked with brown.

Pigeons and Doves

Sergeant Mike, wounded by flying shrapnel in World War action, cited and decorated by the Government for valor, was the pride of the soldiers on Governors Island until his death. The sergeant was a carrier pigeon, member of that long-lived, likable, and often domesticated family which is best represented in the United States by the mourning dove. Captive specimens of this order attain an average age of more than twenty years.

Though carrier pigeons have long served man as messengers, the best known of all once were the passenger pigeons. During their migrations thousands and even millions swept overhead, darkening the sky. One observer recorded more than two billion in flight, their column extending for two hundred and forty miles and more than a mile in width.

In 1605 Champlain recorded an "infinite number" of them in Maine. Throughout the East their winter roosting places, miles in area, were so densely populated that the weight of the birds roosting on the trees broke off heavy branches. As the Atlantic coast was built up, they were pushed farther west. By 1800 Wilson recorded columns eight or ten miles in length appearing in Kentucky and steering across the Ohio to Indiana. But when the white men went to work in earnest, slaughtering them commercially, their doom was sealed. By the end of the nineteenth century the unbelievable numbers of these pigeons were a thing of the past. Conservation was considered too late. The last member of this once-vast species died in the Cincinnati Zoo in 1914.

Today seventeen members of the family of pigeons and doves inhabit the United States or are seen here intermittently. Most common is the domestic pigeon or rock dove which is loved all over the country and is common on the public squares of many towns and cities.

MOURNING DOVE

THE male mourning dove may be a cynic, for his mating call is a series of slow plaintive coos. His cry appears to emanate from such a grief-stricken soul that the bird seems to be mourning an unhappy event when he courts a female. He also struts proudly and ostentatiously before the female, his brown, black-dotted plumage spread wide and his pink-tinted chest swelled.

MOURNING DOVE

Despite mournful crying, the pair appear happy during the romantic warmth of spring. So very happy, in fact, that they spend too much of their time in a honeymoon of billing and cooing. As a result, the more practical side of marital life is neglected. Their nest is a sloppy affair, loosely put together so that it is little more than

WESTERN MOURNING DOVES *(Zenaidura macroura marginella).*
Length: 1 foot. Range: Western and interior North America.
J. W. Jackson

a platform of twigs and grass, and ill-designed to protect the eggs. It is true, however, that their limbs are not well suited for such construction tasks as more industrious birds undertake.

They share the work during the nesting season. The male sits on the eggs by day, while the female takes over the night shift. Sometimes the streamlined male noisily flaps from its perch, shoots upward a hundred feet or so, then nonchalantly glides on unmoving wings back to its perch. This is supposed, perhaps, to impress his wife as a clever masculine stunt.

Two chicks are born in the nest which is frequently placed in an evergreen tree. The young are fed at first with a secretion called pigeon's milk. This is a juice formed in the pigeon's crop and regurgitated for the benefit of the youngsters.

When they are older, the pigeons learn how to drink by burying their bills in the water and sucking it in as though through a straw. They eat such things as the seeds of corn, wheat, and weeds and an occasional insect. They also swallow fine bits of gravel as a digestive aid to their gizzards.

Like other members of the family, mourning doves are usually monogamous and quite devoted. When one of them dies the mate seems forlorn and goes about cooing in its melancholy way. Two subspecies are described—the western and the eastern.

GROUND DOVE

THROUGHOUT the South Atlantic and Gulf States the six-inch dove walks blithely about, pertly stepping from side to side to seize a morsel of seed. It is an amiable bird and seems so unafraid of people that it will wait until they approach quite closely before it takes wing. In spite of their gentle nature, ground doves fight among themselves like quarrelsome neighbors, with, however, little damage done. In sections of the South there is a superstition that evil befalls anyone who kills a ground dove. Consequently these birds go about unmolested. In the Southwest lives a subspecies, the Mexican ground dove.

OTHER PIGEONS AND DOVES

THE band-tailed pigeon of the West has a broad tail crossed by a band of black and its head is of purplish hue. It almost suffered the unhappy fate of the passenger pigeon, but protective legislation was passed in time to preserve the species. The red-billed pigeon, a subspecies, is found in the lower Rio Grande Valley of Texas and southward.

The family of pigeons and doves also includes two subspecies of the white-winged dove of the South and Southwest and the Inca dove of the Southwest. The Inca doves often move to the city, and

OTHER DOVES

some voluntarily spend much of their time in country barnyards. Less frequently observed is the white-crowned pigeon of the Florida Keys and the Antilles; the white-fronted and the eastern white-winged dove of the lower Rio Grande Valley of Texas; the western white-winged dove of the Southwest; the ringed turtle dove and the Chinese spotted dove domesticated about Los Angeles.

Game Birds

At one time in American history, the forests were stocked with a variety of game birds which the Indians used as a prime source of food. The first white settlers, too, could usually find a meal on the wing right in the backyard. But as the countryside was hunted more systematically, and cities replaced the pristine forests, the order became smaller and smaller, until legislation was necessary to preserve even a few of them.

For thousands of years man has enjoyed both the destruction and the display of game birds. Such beautiful species as pheasants and peafowl have been used to adorn lawns, while stuffed turkey, grouse, quail, and partridge have been hung proudly on hunting lodge walls.

The heath hen, last specimen of which died on Martha's Vineyard in 1932, is another splendid example of man's powers of ruthless extermination. About a foot and a half long, rusty brown above and reddish white below, these game birds were long a target in their more plentiful era for the guns of man and the talons of the goshawk, not to mention the depletion they suffered from brush fires. In habits the heath hen resembled the prairie chicken, except that instead of booming, it tooted. It was found only amid barren and sandy acreage, living on insects, berries, and leaf buds. Some people, however, complained that it had a bad habit of ruining gardens by a too voracious appetite. The nest, which it built on the ground, held about half a dozen or ten eggs.

Most of the members of this order seldom fly long distances, and often take to their feet to escape trouble. Once in the air, however, some of them can fly quite rapidly. In a test, a turkey, urged on by a honking automobile, shot along at fifty-five miles an hour. Because of their short, concave wings, the take-off of game birds is noisy and awkward. In flight, the wings produce a whirring sound.

Domestic fowl are believed to be descendants of the wild jungle fowl of the Malay Peninsula. Scientific cross-breeding has resulted in such well-known varieties as white leghorn, Rhode Island red, and Orpington. In at least one respect, there is a similarity between the wild and domestic fowl; both obtain most of their food from the ground and consequently scratch the earth a good deal in search of a meal.

Several species of pheasants have been introduced into this country. The handsome Chinese or ring-necked pheasant, established here in 1882, has spread out in the farm States.

TURKEY

THE noblest game bird in all the world is not too extravagant a description for the eastern wild turkey. One hundred years ago, this great bird, three feet tall on its sturdy legs, was so abundant that large specimens sold for only twenty-five cents. The first Thanksgiving dinner in the New World featured the wild turkey.

During the spring, when wild turkeys mate, the male struts about and preens his plumage in self-conscious vanity. In this season his breast is laden with energy-lending fat, for he must fight other males to win his mate. Courting hens above one year old and

WILD TURKEY *(Meleagris gallopavo silvestris).* Length: 3½ feet. Range: Eastern United States except Florida where a separate subspecies resides. Wild turkeys are today somewhat mixed with domestic and western breeds.
New York Zoological Society

RING-NECKED PHEASANT (*Phasianus colchicus torquatus*). Length: 4 feet. Range: Introduced from eastern and southeastern China. Acclimated in many parts of the United States and Canada since 1880.
Nature Magazine

wooing younger debutantes require different tactics. With the ladies the male will affect indifference and strut about more pompously. But with the younger females he may rise from the ground and fly about, alighting later and dragging wings and tail along the earth. Then drawing near the frightened hen he soothes her by purring. His body plumage is expanded, his fan-shaped tail is raised and spread, his naked head ornaments are swelled while the wing quills droop and rattle.

The eight to fifteen eggs of the female are hatched in a hole scooped in the ground and lined with some leaves. The parents always try to conceal their work behind some natural camouflage, such as a fallen tree or bush, as owls, foxes, and other prowlers would make short work of the eggs and young. Even the father is said to kill his own offspring, though proof is lacking for this statement. At any rate, the females keep away from the males during the incubating period, as many as three mothers using the same nest.

The young, bothered by ticks, will often roll out of the nest upon an anthill where the ants' acid smell drives the ticks away.

Rapidly diminishing as a result of intensive hunting, these birds are still tracked by the more inveterate Nimrods. Flushed by a dog, the strong fliers will rise and scatter in all directions, but if the hunter is patient they will soon return to the same spot. In the presence of hunters the wild turkey sometimes walks unconcernedly, apparently feigning to be a tame bird. In the timbered bottom lands of eastern North America, the wild turkey sometimes tips the beam at as much as thirty pounds. Its recorded history in this country dates back to the time of Captain John Smith. However, the turkey most of us eat today is a domesticated offspring of the original bird which is now rare and seldom seen. The wild turkey gets its fine flavor from its mixed diet of berries, seeds, and insects.

The name of the bird is probably derived from its call *turk, turk, turk,* and not from its supposed Turkish origin. It was bred and domesticated by the Incas and Aztecs and first introduced into Europe by Vasco da Gama in 1530. Turkeys are short-lived and records for their longevity seldom exceed five years.

A cheerful symbol of American folkways, the turkey was once proposed by Benjamin Franklin as our national bird to replace the rapacious eagle. And although Franklin was aware of its pompousness he argued that the turkey's other virtues more than offset this.

Four subspecies of the turkey are recognized: the eastern, Florida, Rio Grande, and Merriam's; the last named inhabits the mountains of the Southwest and northern Mexico.

GROUSE

SLOWING down suddenly, putting one foot cautiously before the other, the bird dog comes to a dead stop. He strains forward, one forepaw raised in the air, tail rigidly extended—his whole body forming a line to indicate the presence of game.

Grouse!

Crouched close to the ground, the rough-footed plump birds attempt to conceal themselves, relying on their coloration which blends with the grasses, until the hunter approaches too close and flushes them. Then with a sudden whirring of wings they are off in a straight low line of flight. The hunter must be a quick and accurate marksman to fire both barrels with effect before the speedy birds are gone.

Grouse are primarily ground birds for it is on or near the ground that they find the seeds, berries, insects, snails, and worms upon which they feed. Their nests are built in low bushes and under fallen logs.

With the exception of the ptarmigan, grouse are polygamous; the cocks will sometimes fight savagely for the possession of a hen. The wooing male struts and dances before the female in an elaborate courtship ritual.

By and large, the grouse is a forest bird, although many species inhabit the plains and some even live in the deserts.

RUFFED GROUSE

WHEN the first white men began pushing their way into the wilderness haunts of the ruffed grouse, these birds were so tame they could be knocked from the boughs with a stick. Even today, in some portions of America where the guntoting biped is not too well known, the ruffed grouse is quite tame; the young, reared from the egg, have so little distrust of man that they may be trodden underfoot. Fortunately for the bird, it soon developed an acute suspicion of the man that walked through the woods like a bear, until today the ruffed grouse is one of the most shrewd and wily creatures of the woodland. It rises off the ground with such speed that the man with the gun is frequently too startled to take a shot at it. Then it may double in its tracks so as to get behind the hunter who stumbles hopelessly ahead through the brush.

A mile away, when conditions are favorable, the drumming of the ruffed grouse may be heard. No sure evidence is at hand to certify whether the sound is made by the feathers flapping against the air or against the breast of the bird. The drumming is an expression of the vitality of the male bird.

RUFFED GROUSE

Nesting on the ground, the mother grouse has less difficulty protecting her brood than might be expected. During the breeding season, she seems to have no scent, for even trained bird dogs have been known to pass nesting females by. She sits so close to the ground and blends so well with her background that sharp-eyed hawks fly overhead without taking notice.

RUFFED GROUSE NESTING.
Dr. A. D. Stoesz

One persistent enemy of the ruffed grouse is the red fox. This sly chap is not to be outfoxed by second-raters. At the first sign of danger, the mother bird may scatter her brood in safe hiding places and then betake herself to some limb where she is out of reach of the snapping jaws. The fox sits tight, and eventually patience nets a reward greater than virtue's—the little ones return and the fox gets a meal.

About half of the young ones survive. In about a week from the time they emerge from the egg, the young grouse have learned to fly. In about three weeks they have attained the size of young chickens and at this

RUFFED GROUSE (*Bonasa u. umbellus*).
Length: 1½ feet. Range: Eastern United States.
American Museum of Natural History

time they are able to fly to considerable heights. Now they sleep on the ground in a circle about their mother and by October are wandering about by themselves.

Preparing for winter, young grouse add a layer of fat and a downy covering for their body and legs. Horny growths like small chicken combs grow along the toes and these permit them to run along the surface of the snow. With the first cold snap they come down from the exposed heights to the shelter of the valleys where greenbrier leaves and fruits, oak buds and acorns, wild grapes, mountain laurel, and like plants are found. Sometimes they burrow into a snowdrift to sleep. Young grouse are said to be largely insectivorous; about ninety-five per cent of their diet is estimated to come from this source, but the taste for plant life grows with the bird.

The typical ruffed grouse is recognized in four forms: the eastern ruffed grouse, ranging eastward from Minnesota to the Atlantic coast; the Canada ruffed grouse of the Northeast; the gray ruffed grouse of the Northwest; and the Oregon ruffed grouse of the Pacific coast. These subspecies extend the range of the species over most of the wooded sections of the country and make it the most widely known of game birds, despite the appalling inroads of the hunters, which have made the bird more than justifiably shy and suspicious.

DUSKY GROUSE

THE dusky grouse of the Western States is the largest and finest of the American wood grouse. Five races of this bird make their home in the timbered mountain ranges; the dusky grouse of the Rockies; the sooty grouse of the Pacific coast ranges; Richardson's grouse of the Canadian Rockies, and the Northwest, extending down to Wyoming; the Sierra grouse of southern Oregon and California; and the Mount Pinos grouse of southern California.

Mystery shrouds the winter activities of the dusky grouse. It is believed to spend this season among the boughs of resinous trees where it obtains a sufficient if not a palatable food supply. The rain and snow falling through the boughs provide it with water.

SPRUCE GROUSE

ONLY two of the five spruce partridges ever reach the United States, and they touch only a few of the northernmost States. Almost extinct in this country now, the spruce partridge, by the gentleness and curiosity of its nature, appears to be with us for a

HEATH HEN *(Tympanachus cupido)*. Length: 1½ feet. Range: Formerly in many parts of the northeastern United States. Extinct since 1932. More than $70,000 was spent in a belated attempt to save the species.
American Museum of Natural History

day rather than for all time. Unlike other relatives, it refuses to learn that man destroys nearly every wild creature that confides in him. As the hunter approaches, the naïve birds merely step aside to make way for him. Full-grown birds have even been caught in the hand or brutally slaughtered with a stick.

In the north woods is Franklin's grouse which reaches Oregon, Idaho, and Montana; and the Canada spruce grouse of the Northeast. This bird too exhibits too much confidence in mankind.

SHARP-TAILED GROUSE

THE prairie sharp-tailed grouse is the only one of three North American sharp-tailed grouse still commonly found within the United States. The mating antics of this bird are wonderful to behold. All the birds are summoned to a meeting place by the booming of one of the males. Beating his wings together, one of these birds runs along the floor of the meeting place. Immediately all the others join the dance, some circling to the right, others to the left while still others merely charge back and forth within the rings of gesticulating, puffing birds. The dancers become more and more excited until some of them jump over the backs of others, thus starting fights. This ritual is comparable with an Indian war dance, wherein each participant tries to make as much noise as possible.

This bird inhabits the northern part of the western United States where it lives on grain, buds, and flowers. Many birds perish in the winter when the snows bury these foods beyond their reach.

In the plains of the Rocky Mountain States dwells a subspecies, the Columbian sharp-tailed grouse.

WHITE-TAILED PTARMIGANS *(Lagopus l. leucurus)*. Length: 1 foot. Range: Rockies of United States and Canada. Scarce.
American Museum of Natural History

PTARMIGAN

UNLIKE many of the grouse, the male willow ptarmigan contents himself with one mate. Even for her he must do battle with pugnacious male rivals. So strenuously and often do these birds fight that few are ever able to reach the happy condition of being fathers.

This migratory bird breeds in Alaska and Canada and finds its way south to Minnesota and the New England States. In summer it eats various insects and herbs, switching to berries in the fall, but in winter subsisting entirely on the buds and twigs of the dwarf alder and willow of its northern range.

On the top of the world, high among the Rocky Mountains, the white-tailed ptarmigan makes its home. A miracle of protective coloration takes place when the snow flies, for then the plumage becomes white. At other seasons this grayish-brown and white bird is decked out with a white tail. The white-tailed ptarmigan is classified into two subspecies: the Rainier of the Cascade Range of Washington, and the southern which is distributed through the American Rockies.

PRAIRIE CHICKEN

A GREAT friend of the agriculturalist is the prairie chicken of the central States. It is the scourge of many insects that make the life of the farmer miserable, although it will not scorn berries, wild flowers, and seeds.

Yellowish-brown and spotted with black above, they flock together during the fall. In spring, however, they are most interesting to observe. Then the strutting males preen themselves and prance about uttering a provocative *boom-boom* which is taken up as a challenge by other males. After the birds have fought it out with beak and claw, the victors claim their mates, although fights have occurred when no females were present. Eight to twelve eggs are laid in a shallow hollow in the ground, lightly lined with vegetable debris.

PRAIRIE CHICKEN *(Tympanuchus cupido americanus).* Length: 1½ feet. Range: Still found in parts of the central United States and Canada. "Probably extinct east of Indiana" (A.O.U. Check List, IV ed.).
American Museum of Natural History

The species are the greater prairie chicken whose range extends from eastern Colorado to Indiana; Attwater's prairie chicken of the Louisiana and Texas coastal region; and the lesser prairie chicken of the Great Plains.

SAGE HEN

AMONG the fowl-like birds, only the wild turkey can boast of a more lavish physique than the "cock of the plains," as the sage hen is frequently called. This largest of American grouse, from two to two and a half feet long, is an inhabitant of the sagebrush.

The courting male sucks air in and out of sacs on the side of his neck, giving vent to a sound not unlike that made by a leaking pump.

Sage hens are slow to take wing but, once aloft, fly well. In the fall they form into flocks and soon retire from the more exposed flatlands to the shelter of wooded valleys. Feeding largely on the leaves of the sagebrush as well as on alfalfa and garden plants, sage hens also aid in keeping down the insect population.

Ordinarily affected little by the variations of the weather over their exposed range, sage hens are sometimes drenched by severe rains or beaten down in heavy hailstorms, which may kill the young and even grown birds.

MOUNTAIN QUAIL

THOUGH the olive-brown mountain quail or plumed partridge is an excellent flyer, it makes more use of its feet than most other flying birds. When pursued by hunters it apparently is too wise to take at once to the air, where it would offer an easy shot. Instead, it runs away swiftly and does not begin to fly until it is well out of range.

Again, in its more or less regular migrations, this bird walks instead of flying. In colder winters, the California flocks leave the mountains and set off on foot down the paths and dried-up valleys for the warmer regions below. In spring they return to the upland in the same manner. In Washington and Oregon, where the climate is cooler, the mountain quail inhabit lower regions and do not appear to migrate at all.

The presence of this bird is most readily detected by its high, clear, but rather plaintive note—the plaintive quality being peculiar to all birds of this family. It also emits a sort of crow; when startled, a flock of mountain quail may begin to chuckle.

This bird raises only one brood a year, but the brood is large. The usual number of eggs is six to twelve, but sometimes clutches of eighteen to twenty are laid. The nest is merely a mat of dead leaves or grass laid out on the ground, protected by a bush or tuft of weeds.

The young chicks at birth have brown or yellow stripes down the back and are speckled with brown and black. They are exceedingly active and when startled will scatter into the bushes.

Like other quails these birds are excellent eating. In addition, they are beneficial to man as destroyers of insects and certain harmful weeds, and for this reason alone it is just as well that they be left unmolested by hunters.

Related to the mountain quail is the plumed quail of the Sierra Nevada and the Cascade Range.

SCALED QUAIL

THE scaled quail, inhabiting the southwestern deserts, is bluish-ash in color. Black lines at the ends of its whitish abdominal feathers give it a scaled appearance. Its head is surmounted with a short brownish crest. These birds are also swift runners. They raise two or three large broods each season. Scaled quails are considered excellent game birds. They are also called blue quails or cotton tops. Two subspecies are known: the Arizona scaled quail of that State, New Mexico, western Texas, southern Colorado, and western Oklahoma; the chestnut-bellied scaled quail of southern Texas and adjacent Mexico.

These birds raise two or three broods of eight to sixteen eggs in a season, the cock assisting in the care of the young.

CALIFORNIA VALLEY QUAIL (*Lophortyx Californica vallicola*). Length: 1 foot. Range: Found in a few valleys of Oregon, California, and Nevada.
American Museum of Natural History

CALIFORNIA QUAIL

THE California quail is divided into three rather similar subspecies, the California, the valley and the Catalina quails. In California all are called valley quail to distinguish them from the mountain type. The birds are also found in Oregon as well as in Washington and Colorado where they have been introduced.

These birds are ash-brown above, slaty-blue below, with a chestnut patch. Though they are quite tame and friendly in the closed season, they become most alert as soon as hunters appear on the scene.

California quails have a number of calls. The most common is a clear *coo-coo-coo*, with the accent and a rising inflection on the second syllable; others are a clicking and a scolding call that sounds somewhat like cursing in Spanish. They seem to be constantly conversing. The large flocks appear to post sentinels to warn of danger.

The importance of nature's balance is strikingly demonstrated in the case of California quail. The widespread killing of hawks has depleted the number of quail, for the hawks had limited the number of ground squirrels which feed on quail eggs.

OTHER QUAILS

OTHER North American quails are the Gambel's quail, conspicuous for its curved dull bluish crest; and Mearn's quail which is spotted black, reddish, and brown and looks rather like a guinea hen. The last two species both inhabit the arid regions of the Southwest.

BOB WHITE

THE chestnut and black bob-white is the only eastern quail. Known to northerners as quail, to southerners as partridge, its name arises from the cheery interrogating cry which, however, is interpreted by many farmers, not as "bob-white" but as "more wet," meaning that rain is on its way. This is the game bird par excellence of the eastern United States, and it is estimated that 400,000 persons

BOB-WHITE (*Colinus v. virginianus*).
Length: 10 inches. Range: Eastern North America.
American Museum of Natural History

hunt it each year. Yet the hunters do not much deplete its numbers for, like other quails, it is highly prolific. These birds like to live in cultivated areas, and, though they eat some grain, they live to a far greater extent on harmful insects and weeds. Bob-whites are gentle, affectionate birds, but in the mating season the males are often quarrelsome. Sometimes these quails practice polygamy. The chicks leave the nest as soon as their down is dry.

Bob-whites move in flocks. When the numbers of a bevy are scattered by an enemy, they at once raise a plaintive cry.

The plumage of the masked bob-white, an Arizona species, is a mixture of reddish-brown, black, and gray. One time common in the vicinity of Tucson, this bob-white was seen in closely formed coveys of fifteen to twenty. So plentiful and so tame were the birds that people began to shoot at them with buckshot, often killing half a covey at one shot. It is not strange, therefore, that today the birds are rarely seen and their plaintive call, *how-ee*, is seldom heard north of the Mexican border. Subspecies of the eastern bob-white are the Florida bob-white, the now extinct Key West bob-white, and the widespread Texas bob-white which is also seen in eastern States.

Shore Birds

Beaches, marshes, and the banks of streams and lakes are the haunts of the five families of shore birds, many of which visit the United States only during their flights from northern breeding grounds. These birds figuratively stand with one leg in the water, the other on land.

Their food includes shellfishes, and aquatic mollusks seized on muddy shores, swamp-dwelling mosquitoes, and other insects such as locusts and grasshoppers. Most of their sustenance is derived in or near the water, some birds even plucking a morsel out of the rolling waters of the open sea.

Many of the shore birds travel incredible distances on their migrations. Some journey from northern Canada, pass the Equator, and go into Chile and Argentina in the southern hemisphere. As they fly overhead, or pause for a meal, they are frequently heard uttering their shrill, though rather sweet, cries.

Unfortunately these birds, of long thin legs and short tail, are considered excellent game birds and consequently great numbers were formerly wantonly killed by hunters. Most shore birds are now protected by legislation in Canada and the United States but may be killed without limit in their winter homes in the West Indies and South America.

OYSTER-CATCHER

OYSTER-CATCHERS live almost exclusively on shellfishes, oysters, clams, and mussels. Holding the victim in its three-toed feet, it cuts open the shell with its long, sharp red beak.

These birds inhabit the loneliest beaches of the South Atlantic and Gulf coasts of the United States, but their special preference is small sandy islets, inhabited only by shellfishes and all but covered with water at high tide. Here the oyster-catcher strides about with great dignity or runs swiftly when danger threatens. Its flight is graceful and rapid, but when startled it ordinarily flies but a short distance and then returns to the sands.

The oyster-catcher is nearly two feet in length and of striking appearance. Its lower parts are white, its wings and tail a dusky brown, while the head and neck are a glossy black.

AMERICAN OYSTER-CATCHER (*Haematopus palliatus*). Length: 1½ feet. Range: Atlantic and Gulf coasts of the United States.
New York Zoological Society

These birds nest from April to June, though the place where they lay their eggs can scarcely be called a nest. It is merely a shallow cavity in the sand, formed by the bird squatting and then revolving two or three times. The eggs number two or three, usually the former number, and are white or cream-colored with brown, black, or lavender spots and blotches. This color is an excellent camouflage against the sand strewn with shells and seaweed, and it is very difficult to find the eggs even when one is nearly walking on them.

The task of incubation is performed exclusively by the female, but it is said that she sits only at night or in cloudy weather, otherwise letting the sun do her work. Often the nesting site of the oyster-catcher is flooded by a rain squall or an unusually high tide, and then the eggs are floated away. The bird makes no attempt to salvage them.

The young are also very hard to find unless they are in motion, for their plumage is exactly the color of sand.

RUDDY TURNSTONE

THE nine-inch ruddy turnstones breed in summer in the Arctic tundra; then in August, as the northern winter approaches, the flocks set out for the South, flying usually in compact groups of a dozen or more, sometimes in a line, sometimes in a close formation. Autumn finds them making their way along both coasts of North America and occasionally crossing the interior. Their flight is rapid and, as they fly, they repeat a pleasant trilling note. Hunters call them calico birds because of their mottled chestnut, black, and white plumage.

By our winter—the summer of the southern hemisphere—they have passed through South America to the Antarctic, and then as this summer also draws to an end, they start on the way back. These birds are among the longest migrators, and they probably enjoy more daylight hours in the course of a year than any other living creature. In the month of May they pass along our shores in a northerly direction.

Turnstones have an upturned bill, somewhat shorter than the remainder of their head. It is with this implement that they obtain their food, by turning over pebbles and stones on the seashore. In the course of a single foraging expedition a bird may turn over hundreds of stones, shells, and even small boards, to feast on the slugs and worms beneath. In addition, however, these birds eat large quantities of grasshoppers.

SURF BIRDS *(Aphriza virgata).* Length: 10 inches. Range: Pacific coast of North and South America.
William L. Dawson, National Association of Audubon Societies

The turnstone's nest is nothing more than a hollow scratched in the ground and lined with grass and seaweed. The female lays four greenish-gray eggs, spotted and splotched with various shades of brown.

The black, or black-headed, turnstone is somewhat smaller than the ruddy turnstone, whose habits it duplicates. Its summer plumage, which is the one seen on the Pacific coast, is black with a greenish-gray gloss on the top. The forehead and the sides of the head are spotted with white.

SURF-BIRD

THE ten-inch surf-bird is an ashy-white above and dull white below. In the United States it is seen only on the Pacific coast, and there but rarely. It frequents the outer beaches and sand reefs, where it stands in the shallow water permitting the surf to dash over it. It is a timid bird, fleeing at the approach of man, and like its relative, the turnstone, a swift flyer. Nothing is positively known either of its nest or its eggs. The Indians report that it nests in the lake regions of the Alaskan interior.

PLOVERS

RUNNING swiftly near the water's edge almost into the wash of the surf, alternately dashing after each receding wave and retreating up the beach before the foaming brine, plovers snatch succulent morsels of oyster, mussel, and clam cast up on the shore. Their short bills, sometimes thickened at the tip, are poorly adapted to digging so they eat only what they find on the surface of the sand.

Of the seventy-five species of this comparatively small, migratory shore bird, eight plovers are found in North America. These are related to the Egyptian plover that serves as an animated toothpick and watchdog for the crocodile of the Nile.

While the wary birds may be seen from a distance on the beaches or migrating across country in large flocks, it requires patience to observe them closely. Their four eggs are disguised with spots so that they are almost hidden in the sand and pebbles among which they lie, the nests being but small depressions on the beach. Protectively speckled with black, the young "freeze" still in their tracks at the approach of an intruder. The parent birds will flutter nearby on pretended broken wings, hoping thus to lure the menacing visitor from the vicinity.

KILLDEERS

KILLDEERS appear to be the self-appointed watchmen for other birds and game. Hunters and cameramen well know the cry of *killdeer* which these birds raise—the signal which drives all wildlife from the vicinity.

Though speedy and graceful in flight, killdeers give the impression of being constantly nervous and tense. Breeding from Canada to the Gulf coast of the United States, killdeers winter from California through the Southwest to New Jersey. They are attracted by smaller bodies of inland water, and may even be found in meadows, pastures, and cultivated fields, where they eat weevils, beetles, wireworms, and other insect pests like the tick that carries Texas fever to cattle.

The female protects her young from intruders by pretending to be injured and, moving slowly as if in pain, lures the enemy from the nest.

The ten-inch birds have a white collar and lower parts, olive-brown back, and four black bands, two across the back and two smaller ones across the face. Killdeers breed and winter in the southern portion of the United States.

GOLDEN PLOVER

ONCE the Mississippi Valley was host to myriads of golden plovers making their way in April and May to the Arctic Circle. On the way they consumed many insects in the newly plowed fields. In September they would return south, but this time along the eastern coast, far out to sea. Pausing in their long flight to South

UPLAND PLOVER *(Bartramia longicauda)*.
Length: 1 foot. Range: North and South America. Formerly abundant but now in some danger of extinction.
J. W. Jackson

America, they would come to rest upon floating masses of seaweed which they ate. Only a violent storm would drive them to land, but whenever they did seek the safety of the solid shore they were slaughtered in large numbers. So today the golden plovers still migrate over the old courses, but in sadly reduced numbers. Those that summer in the Northeast, however, appear to make a nonstop flight to far-off Brazil travelling seventy miles an hour.

Birds of this species are so named because of the golden markings on their upper parts, especially conspicuous in summer when the breast is black. In winter they are mottled grayish brown. They are about eleven inches long and particularly handsome

SEMIPALMATED PLOVER

LIKE robins hopping on a lawn, the semipalmated plovers scuttle along a sandy beach. The flocks are widely scattered while they seek the tiny marine animals which are their food, but when alarmed they fly together.

During their migrations there are probably more semipalmated plovers to be seen along the Atlantic seaboard than any other plover species. Where flocks of hundreds were once visible, now dozens meet the eye. Their breeding grounds in the far North extend beyond the Arctic Circle. The birds breed no farther south than the north shore of the Gulf of St. Lawrence.

The height of the breeding season is about the middle of June. The nests are slightly more complex than the usual hollows scooped by other plovers; semipalmated plovers usually add a few wisps of seaweed to the rim and occasionally to the floor of the hole. Four eggs, sometimes only three, are laid in the cavity. These are handsome and boldly marked.

SNOWY PLOVER

LOOKING like a bleached sparrow, the seven-inch western snowy plover makes its home among the sand dunes of California not far from the Pacific. It is also seen breeding in Washington and northern Utah. The grayish upper parts blend perfectly with the sand; the white breast resembles a fragment of shell. Until they are sure they have been seen, adults and young remain stock still when approached.

Both male and female snowy plovers incubate the eggs. While one is so occupied the other scours the sands for worms or crustaceans to bring to its mate. The nest is always approached on foot to avoid bringing attention to it by flying there directly. Many eggs are lost because of high tides which occasionally sweep up beyond the normal high-water mark. Sometimes there is a second brood.

WILSON'S PLOVER

UNLIKE most plovers, Wilson's plover never goes far north to breed. It is most often seen along the shores of the South Atlantic and Gulf States, where it seeks out the least frequented beaches. About an inch longer than the semipalmated plover, this bird is paler and duller, and its bill is heavy and long.

MOUNTAIN PLOVER

REALLY an inhabitant of the western plains, the mountain plover consumes grasshoppers as well as many other harmful insects. Also called the prairie plover, it is about nine inches long and winters in the Southwest or in Mexico. It has a snow-white breast.

Other American plovers include the piping plover found east of the Rockies and the black-bellied plover whose range is nearly cosmopolitan. In migration it has been observed throughout the United States.

WILSON'S SNIPE

WILSON'S snipe, inhabiting damp, marshy regions throughout the country, is a favorite game bird, because of its tasty flesh and the difficulty entailed in hunting it. The mottled and barred black, brown, buff, and white of its plumage blend with the dull

AMERICAN WOODCOCK *(Philohela minor)*. Length: 11 inches. Range Eastern North America. Suffering from overshooting.
New York Zoological Society

browns and greens of the marshland, and like other snipes it sleeps through the hours when the sun is brightest. Only toward evening, or in cloudy weather, does it issue from its retreat and begin to probe about in the mud for its insect dinners, including locusts, grasshoppers, diving beetles, and other species harmful to man. When flushed, this eleven-inch bird flies swiftly and noisily upward with a great whirring of wings which tends to disconcert novice marksmen.

In the mating season the male snipe flies high into the air and then plummets downward with terrific speed. Sometimes, it is believed, he is joined by the female in this exciting performance. Though at other times snipe travel about in small flocks, at this season they are not gregarious. Like other shore birds, they build their nests on the ground, simply digging a hole and lining it with grass. They lay three or four grayish-olive eggs ornamented with varicolored streaks and splotches.

WOODCOCK

THE woodcock, a variety of snipe, is most easily recognized by its enormous eyes. Woodcocks inhabit nearly all of eastern North America, but so discreet are their habits that their presence in many thickly settled regions is scarcely suspected. One ornithologist reports finding a family living within the confines of Brooklyn, New York, quite unrecognized by that borough's millions of human inhabitants.

At breeding time the male performs a strange aerial dance. Soon after sunset he starts to flutter about in circles, chirping and clucking, till he is some fifty feet off the ground. Then he rapidly descends. On the ground he struts about with drooping wings.

The mother woodcock, when frightened, often flies off with a chick between her legs, deposits it in a safe place, and then returns for the others.

This gentle bird is considered very tasty eating and is much hunted, despite the fact that it feeds on worms and insects.

The European woodcock is occasionally found from eastern Canada to Virginia.

EASTERN DOWITCHER

THIS cinnamon-brown bird is a gregarious species, inhabiting open meadows throughout eastern North America. The long-billed dowitcher, a somewhat larger variety, is found in the West. These birds are of an unsuspecting nature and uncommonly easy to hunt.

SANDPIPER

ALONG nearly any beach, particularly where the sand is packed hard, flocks of sandpipers may be seen running hurriedly about, uttering their distinctive piping cry. When startled, they take to the air, fly for a short distance, and then resume their running, pausing only occasionally to probe in the sand with their long grooved beaks for insects and crawfishes. These birds are rarely seen in the water, but are excellent swimmers. A wave dashing unexpectedly over the beach causes them no difficulty at all. They nest in the sand and lay either three or four eggs. Some of the larger sandpipers, measuring nearly a foot in length, are considered good game birds. There are more than twenty species of sandpipers in the United States.

The least and semipalmated sandpipers are the species most commonly seen along our seacoasts in the spring and fall. These grayish-brown creatures are barely six inches in length. The two species are hard to distinguish, though the least sandpipers are said to prefer marshes, while the semipalmated species are happiest on sandy beaches. Despite these alleged preferences, they are often seen together.

The eastern solitary sandpiper, which winters in the Midwestern States, is the only sandpiper which inhabits deep woods and avoids sandy beaches. It flies swiftly and gracefully, often with the twistings and turnings of a snipe. Most of its food consists of crawfishes and aquatic insects, which it obtains by wading in shallow ponds and bogs and stirring up the water with its feet. The western solitary sandpiper, a subspecies, is hard to distinguish from its cousin, but like many western species it is somewhat larger. Its range overlaps that of its eastern relative, but extends westward to the edge of the Rockies.

The spotted sandpiper in winter is of a uniform ash color, but in summer it dons a suit of black spots both above and below. This

LEAST SANDPIPER *(Pisobia minutilla).* Length: 6 inches. Range: North and South America.
William L. Dawson, National Association of Audubon Societies

sandpiper is one of the commonest American varieties, breeding throughout the country. Because of its distinctive piping, it is sometimes called peetweet or teeterpeep. It is also called tilt-up because of the way it wags its rump. This bird is most often seen near streams and ponds.

Other sandpipers include the knot, a ten-inch grayish-brown species, occasionally seen in winter along our Atlantic coast, although when migrating it is found on both coasts; the nine-inch stilt sandpiper, seen along the Atlantic coast and sometimes wintering in southern Texas; the purple sandpiper, which in reality is black, with grayish and brownish markings, which makes no prolonged residence in the United States, but is encountered on its migrations in the Great Lakes region and in Georgia and Florida; the brownish-black pectoral sandpiper, seen in the Mississippi Valley, but rarely on the Pacific coast; the white-rumped sandpiper, encountered on its migrations along the Atlantic coast, which does not associate in flocks of its own kind, but mingles with other sandpipers; the seven-inch brownish-black Baird's sandpiper, found in migration from the Rockies to the Mississippi Valley. The sanderling is a mottled, ash-colored sandpiper, found in winter on all the coasts of the United States; in September it visits the Cape Cod beaches, where it may be seen running nimbly from the breakers, then returning to see whether anything edible has been washed up; the lesser yellowlegs winter casually in the southern United States; the buff-breasted sandpiper, once frequently seen in migration in the Mississippi Valley, is now rare.

GODWIT

HUDSONIAN godwits are large members of the snipe and sandpiper family. Their usual color is brown-red, and their chief peculiarity is that the male, which is smaller than the female, hatches the eggs. Their nest is built on the ground, but not always near water. These birds were most frequently seen on the Atlantic coast in the autumn, in the Mississippi Valley in spring.

The marbled godwit, twenty-one inches in length, is one of the largest shore birds. It often makes its home in the alkali country of California and the Northwest, but it also is seen in Louisiana, Florida, and Georgia.

WILLETS

THE sixteen-inch willet is gray with dark markings. It is noted for its astonishing noisiness, particularly in the mating season, when it keeps up a loud and regular *yip-yip-yip* for hours on end. It resides chiefly by sloughs and ponds, where it wades about looking for worms and insects. The eastern willet breeds from New Jersey to Florida and along the Gulf coast.

The western willet, found in nearly every State west of the Mississippi, is somewhat larger in size.

UPLAND PLOVER

THE twelve-inch upland plover is a shore bird only in structure, for actually it avoids water and makes its home in the dry prairie. This was once a common game bird in scattered sections eastward from the Great Plains, but for some time it has been in danger of extermination; it is now protected by law. It is a valuable destroyer of locusts, grasshoppers, crawfishes, and other pests. The upland plover is blackish-brown edged with white. It nests in the prairie grass, its color forming an excellent camouflage.

CURLEWS

LARGEST of shore birds, the twenty-six-inch long-billed curlews were formerly common in the East, from Massachusetts to South Carolina. They were seen flying in great wedge-shaped flocks, and roosting at evening by the thousands in various marsh regions.

Today these birds breed chiefly in the northwestern alkali territory, in company with the marbled godwit. Their prevailing color is reddish, and they are easily distinguished by their large size and their long, down-curved bills. Their nests are hard to find because, at the approach of danger, the male gives the alarm and both parent birds fly away. The eggs are unusually large. These birds subsist largely on locusts and other noxious insects.

The smaller, dusky-brown hudsonian curlew is seen in the course of its migrations along both the Atlantic and Pacific coasts. It is still plentiful, perhaps because it breeds in the far North, thus molested only by occasional explorers, and avoids large centers of civilization.

The Eskimo curlew, practically, if not entirely, extinct, was formerly abundant along the Atlantic coast from Labrador to New Jersey. Considered good eating, these birds were mercilessly hunted.

LONG-BILLED CURLEW *(Numenius americanus)*. Length: 2 feet. Range: North America in suitable areas. In danger of extinction.
Nature Magazine

They were very fat in summer, and for this reason were known as dough birds.

The annual migrations of these birds were among the most extensive of any avians, extending from the Barren Grounds of northern Canada to Patagonia and the Falkland Islands.

BLACK-NECKED STILT

THE black-necked stilt, the only American stilt, stalks in shallow water or along the shores of lakes and ponds in the southwestern and Gulf States. It moves with sureness and grace with legs bent backward at the joint. This bird, usually about thirteen inches in length, has proportionately longer legs than any other bird. When in the water it raises the thin reddish legs carefully, feet folded so that the water will not be disturbed. It is a conspicuous bird, black above and white below, and makes no attempt to conceal itself.

AVOCET

Though the feet are webbed it seldom swims. But the stilt wades as far out as it can, snapping insects from the reeds or water with its long-pointed bill or dipping its head and neck beneath the surface to secure a snail or waterworm. Diving beetles which destroy the insect food of fishes are its special prey, and it is also very useful when on shore in catching grasshoppers and the billbugs which damage corn.

The nest of the stilt may be little more than a small hollow in the sand or earth, or the eggs may rest on a bundle of weeds and reed stalks. When threatened with a flood, the parents build up the nest to keep the eggs above the rising water. These resourceful birds sometimes build a platform as much as eight inches high.

BLACK-NECKED STILT (*Himantopus mexicanus*). Length: 1 foot. Range: Temperate parts of North America and northern South America.
New York Zoological Society

No birds raise a more raucous clamor when the nesting grounds are invaded, and none have developed more varied means of decoying the visitor. They pretend to have broken their wings and even to have fractured one of their long legs. They may tremblingly beg for mercy, or they may swoop and dive at the intruder. Within a few hours after hatching, baby stilts begin to totter about.

AVOCET

AVOCETS are similar in structure though larger, reaching a foot and a half in length. They are remarkable for the great length of their flexible up-curved bills. As the bird grows older, the bill usually becomes more and more curved, as a result of years spent

AVOCET *(Recurvirostra americana).* Length: 1½ feet. Range: North America. Rare east of the Mississippi and in many parts of its range.
J. W. Jackson

probing in the mud for small shellfish. The avocet also hunts by swinging its bill back and forth just above the surface of the water, now and then opening it wide and clamping it shut on some insect.

The avocets are exceedingly well equipped for their shore life. Their long legs make them expert waders and, when they get beyond their depth, they can paddle swiftly with their webbed feet. In flight the long blue legs trail like a rudder.

This bird is white with gray tail and brownish head and neck. Because it is large and easily seen and also makes excellent food, hunters have practically wiped out the avocet east of the Mississippi. Today it is protected, and its numbers are slowly increasing in the West. Some winter in the Southwest, while others migrate to Central America.

Nesting habits of the avocets are much like those of the stilts. The baby birds can run clumsily for cover almost as soon as hatched, and will not stir if their parents have warned them to be still. They even permit themselves to be picked up and tossed out on the water without moving a muscle.

WILSON'S PHALAROPE

THE duties which most female birds seem to accept as their lot in life are taken over by the male phalarope. Even before marriage it is the male who is coy and must be chased by the more brightly colored, determined lady who has decided to marry him. And after mating it is the male who assumes the burdens of home-making and housekeeping, building the nest, sitting on the eggs, and later feeding the children. While he wears the apron, his wife, who has a black and chestnut patch down the side of her neck, joins a group of gossiping women.

To add insult to injury, the female usually has two husbands. Frequently her two husbands sit alongside each other, hatching eggs in separate nests. Oddly, this polyandry is not the result of a shortage of females, since they are three times as numerous as the males; but most of the females are unable to breed because of

WILSON'S PHALAROPE (*Steganopus tricolor*). Length: 9 inches. Range: North and South America.
J. W. Jackson

diseased ovaries. Observations have shown that of eight chicks two are usually males, one a female able to breed, and five will be sterile females.

In the damp lowlands of the western States, these white-breasted gray birds skim over the marshy waters. When someone approaches, the male attempts to decoy him from the nest, deceptively popping in and out of clumps of grass. Should the anxious father finally be trapped on the nest, which is simply a thinly-lined hollow, he will attempt to frighten the intruder away. At such times the giddy female nobly rises to the full stature of motherhood, and rushes to the aid of her besieged mate and children.

Wilson's phalarope eats the tiny animals found in stagnant water. Sometimes it whirls about the water like a dervish, rapidly swallowing the minute creatures disturbed by the motion. William L. Dawson observed one bird making two hundred and forty-seven consecutive turns, but its sense of equilibrium was probably excellent for it did not appear to become dizzy.

These snipelike nine-inch birds, of long neck, thin bill, partly webbed feet, and short tail, undertake long migrations. They often winter as far south as Chile and Argentina. Many probably spend the winter in the open waters of southern seas. They are well adapted for such life since they have strong wings, a heavy feather covering, and easily locate food in the water. In the United States, Wilson's phalaropes range as far east as New England and New Jersey. They are the only one of the three species of phalaropes which breed in this country, nesting from central Washington and Alberta south to the central states.

RED PHALAROPE

IN THE summer the female red phalarope has under parts, throat, and neck of red, while in winter its under parts are whitish. It is also called the whale bird by whalers in northern oceans. The presence of these birds used to be regarded as an indication of the proximity of right whales, since both fed upon the same floating masses of small crustaceans and other marine life.

Red phalaropes dwell in the open oceans of both the northern and southern hemispheres. They live on shore chiefly during their breeding season, when they take to the Arctic wastes. During their migrations these eight-inch birds are found along both coasts of the United States as well as offshore.

NORTHERN PHALAROPE

LIKE Wilson's phalarope, the northern phalarope makes itself economically valuable to man by eating harmful insects. In fact, it is credited with being a prolific destroyer of that insect pest, the Jersey or salt-marsh mosquito.

In shallow pools these seven-inch birds stir up the insects by whirling about. However, in the ocean they float quietly along and apparently find enough to eat without indulging in strenuous motions. They, too, pass through the United States as they wend their way from the far North to spend the winter in warmer climes off the coast of West Africa and Peru.

Marsh Birds

There is little similarity among birds of this order as to size and appearance. The black rail of New England, five inches long, can be sought for hours in a very limited area where its song is heard, while the great sandhill crane of Florida, member of the same order, towers above the grass plumes, as tall as a man.

Young marsh birds emerge from their shells covered with down and are able to run about very soon after hatching. All make their home in the marshlands or low wet regions. Unlike herons, they fly with their necks extended. Their hind toes are elevated and they run easily in and out of the bog.

The marsh dwellers are separated into two superfamilies, the long-legged cranes and limpkins, and the hen-like rails, gallinules, and coots.

Four of the twenty species of cranes are found in North America. Most cranes utter booming cries which can be heard great distances. The note is formed in the bird's great windpipe which, coiled under the breastbone, sometimes reaches the length of five feet, as is the case with the whooping crane.

In addition to the whooping crane, the order includes the brown or sandhill crane of Louisiana and Florida, the little brown crane of Alaska, which winters in Texas, and the Florida crane of the Southeast.

In the United States, limpkins are found only in Florida; farther south they range through Central America, Mexico, and the West Indies.

Ground-nesting birds, the rails, gallinules, and coots lay large clutches of eggs as a rule. When threatened with danger they will run rather than fly, a predilection which in some species has led to loss of the power of flight, and subsequent extermination. These birds have rather compact bodies which slip easily through the rank weeds and grasses. Their calls are loud and in certain respects similar to the notes of barnyard fowl.

Rails and gallinules walk about with heads bobbing like chickens and fly feebly and only for short distances. Birds of this group are often called mud hens, a seemingly well-deserved appellation. The name covers the king, California, light-footed, Yuma, Farallon, clapper, Virginia, yellow, black, and Carolina rails, the latter bird also known as the sora; the purple and Florida gallinules; and the water-dancing coot.

COOT

COOTS paddle about the shallow water of a slough or pond like white-billed gray ducks. They are, however, related not to the ducks but to the rails; their feet are not webbed, but each toe has lobed webs which are as good for purposes of paddling. When

AMERICAN COOTS *(Fulica americana)*. Length: 1¼ feet. Range: North America. Rare in many parts of the East.
William L. Dawson, National Association of Audubon Societies

startled, the coots skitter along the water's surface for a considerable distance with the aid of both wings and feet, before rising in a rather heavy flight. Often coots share a pond with ducks, and then the ducks use them as scouts in case of danger.

The coot's usual nesting site is a cluster of water plants which help to support the woven dry stalks that form the nest. As soon as the first brown-freckled ivory egg is laid, the mother begins incubation. Each day a new egg is added until there may be as many as sixteen. When a baby coot hatches, it waddles from the nest without awaiting the birth of its brothers and sisters. Except for its red bill and a few orange hairs on its head, it looks at this stage like a ball of black down. But when the ball reaches the water, it swims nimbly away.

Although the flesh of the coot is not considered very palatable, the birds are tame and easily killed by even the most unskillful of sportsmen. They are fairly common wherever there are lagoons or bogs with plenty of water plants. Here they find not only shelter, but also plenty of food.

Coots are migratory, spending their summers in the low-lying northern States except where they have been almost exterminated and wintering throughout the South. They also pass across our boundaries into Canada and Mexico. Except when they are concerned with hiding their nests, their curiosity makes them easy to observe.

PURPLE GALLINULE (Ionornis martinica).
Length: 1 foot. Range: Tropical and subtropical America.
Ralph De Sola (SIM)

PURPLE GALLINULE

IN THE swampy country around the rice plantations of South Carolina, purple gallinules are often seen dashing across the roads on their way from one pond to another. This eleven-inch bird is one of our most beautiful species. Its head and neck are purple, its back olive-green. The wings are edged with blue, and there is a shield of the same color above the bill. The eyes are red and the bill, somewhat resembling a hen's, is marked on the tip with yellow.

In the mating season

these birds show great activity, walking over the lily pads, their longish yellow legs shining in the sun, their short tails bobbing abruptly up and down. All the while they cluck merrily, and sometimes they climb out on land to exhibit their splendid purple plumage, even scrambling to the tops of the bushes.

Though their feet are without webs, gallinules are good swimmers. Their flight is heavy and fluttering, and on short flights the legs are held downward as if the bird expected to make an emergency landing at any moment.

Purple gallinules build a nest of rushes in among the cattails and pond lilies. Their six to ten eggs are cream-colored with brown and lavender spots. The species breeds in the Gulf and South Atlantic States and southward into the tropics.

FLORIDA GALLINULE

THE Florida gallinule travels farther north than its foregoing relative. It breeds as far north as New York and Nebraska, and winters throughout the South from California to Georgia. About the same size as the purple gallinule, its feathers are slaty and its only bright spots are a red frontal plate and a yellow-tipped red bill.

Loud clucks and gurgles of all kinds fill the marshes where Florida gallinules live. Though all their notes are harsh, some authorities claim that they can distinguish expressions of love, despondency, curiosity, and other emotions. Not only in voice do these birds resemble chickens, but also in the way they hold their bodies when running. By continued use they often form paths and runways through the grass. Florida gallinules are poor flyers but swim fairly well. Like others in their family, they nest in clumps of water reeds.

RAILS

UNOBTRUSIVELY the rails tread through the maze of reeds in swampy solitudes or on the margin of still pools. They can press their narrow bodies through the thickest growth. When danger threatens, their swift strong legs carry these shy birds to safety; even when they do not run, they can scarcely be noticed as their drab speckled plumage blends well with their background. So much have rails come to depend for safety on their speed and the protective cover of water plants that they are very hard to flush, and are so clumsy on the wing that they seem to have almost lost the power of flight. Yet some species migrate for considerable distances. As a rule, it is only by night that they travel or even roam along the open shore.

VIRGINIA RAIL

VIRGINIA rails not only avoid human company, but each pair usually is isolated from others of its kind. They come to the northern marshes for the breeding season, living largely on the slugs and other creatures of the bogs. Though their loud, harsh calls are often heard, these secretive birds are seldom seen. Their nests are neatly constructed in bunches of grass upon a matted foundation of reeds, which keeps the six to twelve eggs away from dampness. If an incautious investigator handles her eggs, the mother Virginia rail may destroy them on returning to the nest. She is very solicitous for her young when they have hatched, ruffling her feathers and calling much like a hen. These birds range over the greater part of the United States. In the fall they tend to migrate to the southern States or to Central America, though some winter as far north as Oregon. Virginia rails are about eleven inches long and have a very long bill curved downward near the tip. Their feathers are olive-brown above and black-streaked chestnut below.

KING RAIL

VERY similar in appearance and habits is the king rail. However, it is about nineteen inches in length. It breeds in fresh-water marshes throughout the East, and winters in the Southeast. Many pairs of king rails appear to breed in a comparatively small area. Their nests are placed either on the ground or in low bushes. The female goes about the business of maternity in a very methodical

CLAPPER RAIL

KING RAIL *(Rallus elegans)*. Length: 1½ feet. Range: Eastern North America.
American Museum of Natural History

way, laying an egg a day for ten or twelve days and then setting out to incubate them.

CLAPPER RAIL

IN SEPTEMBER and October southern hunters row along inlets or mud flats, and as the tide rises shoot the clapper rails that are forced from the shelter of the water grasses. Since the birds fly slowly and heavily and are about sixteen inches long they are perfect targets. It is almost impossible to start them by using dogs. Clapper rails are gray-brown, with lighter breast feathers and light bars across the abdomen. They are the most abundant species of rails. Northern clappers travel north as far as Connecticut for the nesting season, but winter in the southern Atlantic States at which time they become a victim to the hunters.

Subspecies are the Louisiana or Henshaw's clapper rail, a darker variant of the Gulf coast; the Florida clapper rail, which is even darker; and Wayne's clapper rail which is not found north of North Carolina. Related species are the California clapper rail and the light-footed rail of the coast of that State. The latter are menaced not only by hunters but also by hordes of hungry rats, while some meet their death by being caught in the shells of mussels exposed at low tide. All of these subspecies are similar in habits.

SORA *(Porzana carolina).* Length: 9 inches. Range: North America.
American Museum of Natural History

SORA

THOUGH the sora or Carolina rail is small, rarely exceeding nine inches in length, it is also considered a game bird. This olive-brown bird with its gray breast and short bill is inconspicuous, and only at twilight does it leave shelter. During migration from the northern breeding grounds to the winter home, however, it is easy to hunt as large numbers may congregate in one region. The sora usually builds its nest in the grass a little distance from the water of a swamp. The nest is rather carelessly put together, but the grass stems are twisted together to form a roof above the seven to sixteen eggs. Soras surprised in their bog may set up a cackling that reminds one of a barnyard.

YELLOW RAIL

THE yellow rail is a good swimmer, though it seldom displays its prowess by daylight. This shy straw-colored bird is only about seven inches long. The bill is short and the feathers grow to its base. Because it is so seldom observed, little is known of its habits except that it delights in eating fresh-water snails. The breeding range is in the northern States from Minnesota to Maine, but there are also breeding records from California. Its winters are spent in the Gulf States.

BLACK RAIL

TINIEST of its family is the black rail. This six-inch black bird with white bars on the rear parts and a short bill is believed to be very rare in this country. It breeds in the Northeast and winters near the Gulf of Mexico and in Central America. It is said to run through the grain fields with the rapid mincing steps of a mouse. The Farallon rail is a subspecies of the black rail and is frequently found in the coastal marshes of California and sometimes in Oregon and Washington.

SANDHILL CRANE

TAKING a few running steps to gain momentum, the shapely sandhill crane ponderously leaves the earth. As it rises, the bird utters a loud, resonant croak whose carrying power is great enough to float back after the bird is out of sight. In bygone days large flocks of these lithe, long-legged, long-necked birds would fly in single file as though playing follow the leader. But their numbers have been sadly depleted. In 1938 John Storer reported that there were less than two thousand specimens left in Florida. Those now remaining breed chiefly in central Florida.

This slate-gray creature, whose plumage is streaked with brown, prefers flat grassy country. As it walks about in stately manner, it pauses now and then to eat corn, or perhaps a frog, snake, or mouse. It bends its long supple neck to earth as it noses about for food. At short intervals, however, the bird draws itself up to full height to scan the open countryside for signs of danger.

If it becomes worried, it may pause inquisitively for a moment, then take off. Should it be unable to fly because of a wing injury, the bird will replace its normal caution with courage. The sandhill crane has been known to stand its ground and fight back valiantly when attacked. Its chief weapon is its thin bill which stabs viciously at a foe. Dancing about dexterously and lunging deftly with its pointed

FLORIDA SANDHILL CRANES *(Grus canadensis pratensis)*. Length: 4 feet. Range: Swampy areas of Florida, Georgia, South Carolina, Alabama, and Louisiana. Rare.
American Museum of Natural History

bill, the crane is a dangerous antagonist. It has been known to pierce the eye of many a hunting dog.

In March males and females congregate in clearings and hold ceremonial nuptial dances. They hop and jump about, then bow to one another with dignity. As the happy prancing of their courtship goes on, the birds call out in low, deep tones. In the Southeast they build their nests along grassy ponds or on floating platforms; in the West, the open prairies are the site for their homes. Two to four eggs are laid by the females.

The embryos are equipped with an egg tooth which is used to crack open the shell at birth. In a few hours the chicks run about, and within a few weeks they can run fast enough to escape capture. Fully grown, the cranes measure four feet and their wing spread is more than six feet. Their flesh is considered delicious eating and has accounted to some extent for the depletion of the species.

WHOOPING CRANE

THE whooping, or white, crane is the giraffe of American birddom. This graceful bird, considered one of the handsomest and most impressive in demeanor, is five feet tall when its neck is stretched to full length. Its shapely body rests in almost vertical position on its long slender legs, all in all making the crane a picture of aristocratic dignity and avian grace.

Called the whooping crane because of the hoarseness of its voice, the crane has an odd vocal organ. More than five feet of windpipe extends from its lungs to its throat, half of this being coiled about under its breastbone like a French horn. The voice of the crane rolls through the length of the pipe, emerging with the deep resonance of a low organ note.

Because of its size and the outstanding whiteness of its body, the whooping crane has fallen an easy prey to man. In New England it may have been wiped out by farmers who resented its desire for corn. Consequently it, too, like the sandhill crane, strays warily about in open country where it has a long view of possible enemies and can escape rapidly.

WHOOPING CRANE *(Grus americana).* Length: 4½ feet. Range: Breeding grounds restricted today to southern Mackenzie and northern Saskatchewan. Formerly not rare on the Atlantic and Gulf coasts when migrating. Almost extinct.
Louis Agassiz Fuertes

On short hops the whooping crane often flies low over the land, but on longer journeys it may soar to great heights. In the early nineteenth century, observers reported vast numbers of them flying overhead during migration periods. For hours the flocks streamed by, uttering such a cooperative clamor as to be almost deafening. But these scenes are no more; the whooping crane is now confined in small numbers to isolated spots mainly in the North, although during their migrations a few may sometimes be observed in eastern and central States.

The only other species of crane in this country is the little brown crane, similar to but smaller than the sandhill. It breeds in the far North but migrates through the United States to the Southwest.

LIMPKIN

THE limpkin, or courlan, flies with "a jerky motion, strongly suggestive of the movements of the wings of a mechanical beetle," according to Dr. Pearson's observations. This bird, of olive-brown

LIMPKIN

color splotched with white, flies about Florida's wilder regions, and is occasionally sighted in other southeastern States.

Limpkins divide their time between the swamps and treeless plains, sometimes many hundreds of them traveling together. Their favorite food is a fresh-water snail which the birds secure by wading in shallow water. They deftly seize the snails in their thin, elongated bills.

Like their relatives, the cranes, limpkins are quite noisy. Their cry has a sad and melancholy ring which has caused Floridians to call them crying birds. Although hunted for their flesh, the secluded nature of their range has protected them from severe decimation. In the hidden retreats of Florida, they successfully build their nests on vine-covered tree stumps. They, at least, because of their inaccessibility, do not appear to face imminent extermination, although Dr. Robert Cushman Murphy warns that, like the Everglade kites, they are endangered by "unnecessary drainage operations."

LITTLE BROWN CRANE *(Grus canadensis)*. Length: 3 feet. Range: Breeds in Arctic North America and winters in the southern United States and Mexico. Rare.

New York Zoological Society

LIMPKIN *(Aramus pictus).* Length: 2 feet. Range: Southeastern Georgia, peninsular Florida, and Cuba. In danger of extinction.

William L. Dawson, National Association of Audubon Societies

Wading Birds

Long-legged and long-necked, the birds of this order are usually observable along muddy inlets and marshes. They bend their necks into an S-shaped loop, the better to spear their prey with a single accurate stroke of the bill. The food they eat consists of fishes in the main, plus whatever reptiles, amphibians, mollusks, and marine animals fall their way.

Their four unwebbed toes permit them to perch well and they generally nest in trees. The young are born nearly naked.

The bills of the spoonbill and ibises are grooved along the sides while the storks and wood ibises have bills that are thick at the base and end in a rather blunt curved tip. Herons, egrets, and bitterns have straight bills ending in points.

This order of birds contains more than its share of beautiful creatures who are shot for their feathers or just for fun, with some of them well-nigh extinct a few years ago. The rippling flight of roseate spoonbills is today seen but rarely in Louisiana, and even in Florida there are no more than a thousand of these brilliantly plumed birds.

The fate of the egret and the snowy egret are too well known to require discussion here.

GREAT BLUE HERON

OF ALL the excuses offered by sportsmen for the extermination of a species, those brought forward in the case of the great blue heron seem the weakest. This statuesque and beautiful bird nests in colonies along the banks of streams, high in the branches of trees, from Canada to Lower California and in the southern Atlantic States except Florida. An excellent fisher, it uses this ability to bring it the greater portion of its food supply. Hence, in streams where trout are numerous, the blue heron is alleged to destroy trout. Therefore, the blue heron must be eradicated so that sportsmen may eradicate the trout.

Ellsworth D. Lumley, writing for the Emergency Conservation Committee, described the process as follows: "When fishing upon lakes or streams, the heron is a wary bird, seldom allowing man to approach within gun range. Man has therefore found it much easier and more effective to kill the birds at the rookeries during the nesting season. Here the birds forget some of their caution in their anxiety for their young. It is easier for hunters to wipe out an entire rookery by shooting the old birds as they fly about over the trees.

GREAT BLUE HERONS *(Ardea h. herodias)*. Length: 4 feet. Range: North America and northern South America. Decreasing because of persecution by fishermen.
Winton Weydemeyer

The young are left to starve or bake in the hot sun. Sometimes to make sure that no eggs or young survive, shots are fired through the bottom of each nest."

In addition to the spawn, eggs, and adult trout eaten by herons, the amount of which many naturalists believe to be insignificant, the great blue heron eats other fishes, as a rule the slow ones, or the smaller ones like minnows. Carps, suckers, and bullheads which come into the shallow water where the bird stands are also weighty items in the bird's fare. Sometimes the blue heron will stalk out upon pasture land or cultivated land and get a meal of gophers, field mice, snakes, salamanders, or grasshoppers.

The long neck of the bird, coiled back in an S-shaped loop, gives it a considerable striking range. It stands in the shallow water and, when a frog or fish traverses the rim of an imaginary circle, the neck uncoils like a steel spring, the prey disappears down the bird's gaping bill.

Known in some sections as old cranky, and mistakenly as the blue crane, the great blue heron's crested head rises four feet from the ground. Predominantly slate-blue, its under surfaces are white. It is rumored that a phosphorescent clump of feathers at the breast lures fishes at night into the maw. Young herons have been known to disgorge morsels of fish down on the heads of passersby under their high nests.

LITTLE BLUE HERON

THE little blue heron is little only by comparison with the larger great blue heron. It measures two feet in length. During the first two years of their lives, little blue herons are white and in this phase are commonly mistaken for egrets.

A bird of the Atlantic and Gulf coasts, and casually inland, the little blue heron gathers in large flocks along the edge of a lake or shallow pond. They spend the day fishing slowly and deliberately, and when evening comes they take off to marshy island or swamp where they roost with other members of the heron family. Water moccasins, alligators, and fish crows are a constant menace to the eggs and young of the little blue heron.

GREEN HERON

ONLY eighteen inches long, the green heron is probably the best known of the herons. Also known as the green bittern, it is dark green above and dark brown beneath. Awkward and clumsy in flight, it is swift and stealthy when there are fishes to be caught or salamanders to be speared on the long sharp bill. Startled, it gives vent to a sharp cry and flies a short distance away. Its courtship cry is a sucking, rasping gulp.

The eastern green heron breeds from Wisconsin east to Quebec and south to the West Indies. Anthony's green heron is a subspecies found on our Pacific coast and in southern Arizona.

LOUISIANA HERON

FROM the Gulf States to Delaware, Louisiana herons pitch their frail nests, merely platforms of sticks, in wooded swamps or on wooded or bushy islands. This is perhaps the most abundant of all the species of herons. They appear to be rather tame and are not easily driven from a vicinity by the intrusion of humans.

Trim and neat, purple feathers of the back and sides contrast with the pure white of the under sides. Louisiana herons live in a state of utter disorder and slovenliness in their rookeries. The odor of one of these places is said to be unforgettable. Yet, despite the manner in which they live, these herons always present a trim and neat appearance, the result of constant preening.

GREAT WHITE HERON *(Ardea occidentalis)*. Length: 4 feet. Range: Southern Florida and the Florida Keys. Rare and in danger of extinction.
New York Zoological Society

GREAT WHITE HERON

OFTEN mistaken for the American egret, the great white heron had been slaughtered almost to the point of extinction a few years ago. When the Audubon Society began its protection of the bird, its numbers had dwindled to two hundred; in 1938 six hundred specimens were under the society's protection.

Also known as the Florida heron, the birds are making their last stand down on the country's southernmost tip. Fifty inches long, the Florida heron has a long beak which it uses to defend itself. Even the young know the value of this weapon. Nestlings have been known to pierce the eyes of unwary trespassers.

LEAST BITTERNS *(Ixobrychus exilis)*. Length: 1 foot. Range: Temperate North America and northern South America.
American Museum of Natural History

BITTERN

MOST frequently seen in the midst of marshes and bogs, the bittern comes also to upland meadows and pastures. Here it seeks grasshoppers to add to the larder of fishes and frogs accumulated in wetter places. These retiring birds are seen singly or in couples, but never in flocks. Their dull plumage tends to blend with their surroundings, the reedy water grasses and marsh weeds. The American bittern breeds from Canada to California, extending eastward to North Carolina.

BLACK-CROWNED NIGHT HERON *(Nycticorax n. hoactli).* Length: 2 feet. Range: North and South America.
J. W. Jackson

Long-billed and long-necked, when danger threatens they puff up their loose feathers and are able to look much larger and more formidable than they really are. At night when they are generally active they plump about the shallows, at home in the difficult footing of the fen. When attempting to hide from interlopers, they stand motionless among the reeds, head back, bill tilted at an angle, so that the entire tableau assumes a lifeless look.

The least bitterns, of which two varieties are known—the eastern and western—breed throughout temperate North America where water conditions are suitable. These foot-long birds are known for their secretive disposition.

EGRET

FORTUNATELY it is still possible to speak of the egret as a thing of beauty. Recently it seemed hardly destined to remain a joy forever. Hunted for their plumes by avaricious milliner's agents, the bird was almost exterminated in its Florida haunts. The birds were always shot at when guarding the newly-hatched young, for then young and old alike had to perish. Now, under vigilant protection, they are holding their own.

The forty-inch pure-white American egret nests high in the limbs of a cypress tree overlooking a bog or marsh. A few birds are still found in California and Oregon.

The related snowy egret, much smaller and delicately beautiful with the spotless white of the feathers offsetting the black bill and legs and yellow feet, once bred as far north as New Jersey. Now they breed no farther north than North Carolina.

These birds too suffered for their possession of aigrettes, the soft plumes once used in millinery. Now, under protection, they are increasing in the vicinity of Charleston, South Carolina.

Brewster's egret is a

AMERICAN EGRET *(Casmerodius albus egretta)*. Length: 3½ feet. Range: Temperate and tropical America. Saved from extinction by the National Association of Audubon Societies.
New York Zoological Society

subspecies of California, Utah, and the Southwest. Another is the reddish egret of the Gulf coast.

OTHER HERONS

NEITHER the black-crowned nor the yellow-crowned night heron is strictly a nocturnal bird. The yellow-crowned bird is solitary, and only a few pairs are seen in one place, except perhaps in Florida where twenty pairs of the birds have been observed together. During the nesting season, the black-crowned herons collect in an isolated neck of the woods in hundreds of pairs. Since these birds often have two broods a year, it is not unusual to come upon adults feeding nestlings while older fledglings climb about squawking for food. The black-crowned bird is found living under a variety of climatic conditions from Canada to South America; the yellow-crowned is a southern species and never breeds north of Illinois.

Other herons, subspecies of the great blue herons, are Ward's heron of the Southeast; Treganza's heron of the West; the northwestern coast heron known from Cape Flattery, Washington, to Alaska; and the California

YOUNG EGRETS.
M. H. Oldham, National Wildlife Federation

heron known to that State and to Oregon. All are similar in appearance and habits.

WOOD IBIS

WITH wings spread majestically, the wood ibis wheels aloft and soars in sweeping circles, gaining altitude with each wing stroke until its mazes and loops obscure it from view. The flight of this large powerful bird is an impressive and awe-inspiring spectacle. It goes through the most intricate aerial evolutions, soaring on motionless wings or moving in a straight line with alternate flapping and sailing.

Selecting the tallest tree in the vicinity, the wood ibis builds its nest on a platform, reinforces the sides with Spanish moss, leaves, and vines, and lines the interior with green leaves or sprigs of green cypress. Usually the nests are built in cypress trees growing in water, and in Florida on mangrove trees as well. The nest completed, the ibis lays two or three eggs and begins to incubate.

Gregarious and sociable, the ibis always travels and nests in large flocks, each flock sometimes containing as many as 15,000 birds. As this bird platoon rises into the air, the roar of their wings, according to Dr. Edward Howe Forbush, resembles a clap of thunder. Ordinarily silent and slow in its movements, the wood ibis produces a rough guttural croaking sound when frightened.

The wood ibis is thirty-five to forty-seven inches long, and is essentially a stork with a down-curved bill. It is pure white in color, its tail rimmed with black. The head and most of the neck are scaly and without feathers; the bill is yellow, and the gawky long legs are blue.

The wood ibis is supposedly a stupid bird, and has been described as such because of its gluttonous nature. However, in procuring food it seems to be quite shrewd and methodical, as well as somewhat ruthless.

Gathering in a shallow pool of water, a large company of ibises will dance and prance about, thus stirring up the mud until the helpless and alarmed fishes, frogs, and young alligators rise to the

YOUNG WOOD IBIS (*Mycteria americana*). Length: 4 feet (adults). Range: Breeds along the South Atlantic and Gulf coasts of the United States, West Indies, Mexico, Central, and South America. Also found casually in other parts of the United States. Needs protection.
Allan D. Cruickshank, National Wildlife Federation

surface. In the course of fifteen minutes hundreds of these aquatic animals, frightened and suffocating, become the victims of the birds. The prey in sight, the ibises strike the heads of the victims with their large powerful beaks. Knocked unconscious, they are left to float on the surface of the water, and one by one the birds swallow them. Satiated, they move to the nearest margin of the lake, and stand about sunning themselves in smug, serious-faced rows, with breasts turned upwards.

The only stork in America (also called the American wood stork, Colorado turkey, flathead, ironhead, gannet, preacher, and Spanish buzzard) the wood ibis breeds and usually winters along the Gulf coast from Texas to Florida and north to South Carolina. After the breeding season it migrates irregularly to the western, central, and eastern States. Protected by the Audubon Society, this rare species occupies a breeding colony in southern Florida, where its only enemies are rapacious fish crows, which at times destroy its eggs and young.

GLOSSY IBIS

ALTHOUGH described as a "worm-eating shag on stilts" by W. L. Dawson, the white-faced glossy ibis is one of the most rhythmically graceful birds on land or in water. Its rich purplish chestnut coloration shimmers and gleams in the sun; when it floats lazily on the surface of the water, its silhouette framed against the background of green and brown reeds, its gliding, almost fragile movements are perfect in their beauty and symmetry. The flight is rapid and orderly, alternated by periods of sailing. Moving in columns or in a single file, the entire flock may be seen spiraling at great height, and plunging downward with great speed.

The white-faced ibis is gull-size, its length varying from twenty-two to twenty-seven inches. Its bill is curved downward, slaty-blue in color, red-tipped. The feet and legs are long, spindling, and colored dark wine purple. Its plumage is white with the exception of the somewhat blackish primaries. It is a strongly gregarious bird that nests and flies in flocks throughout the breeding season.

Called by such a variety of misnomers as the water turkey, swamp turkey, black curlew, Spanish curlew, and stone curlew, the ibis, contrary to popular misconception, is not a game bird; its meat is decidedly unpalatable. Still the species is being widely exterminated, and its once large numbers have been reduced to small flocks now found in the West from Oregon and Utah to southern Texas. It is also found locally in Louisiana and Florida; winters in southern California, Arizona, Texas, and Louisiana.

It builds its nest of broken reeds and attaches it to living reeds, sawgrass, or other vegetation. Its nest when completed is deeply cupped, and contains three to four green eggs. It feeds on aquatic animals, the long curved bill of this bird probing in the mud for crustaceans, insects, and frogs.

Somewhat smaller than the white-faced glossy ibis, the eastern glossy ibis, measuring twenty-three inches, is found in central

Florida and Louisiana; infrequently it has been seen in Iowa, Minnesota, Nebraska, Kansas, and New Mexico; it winters in southern California, Arizona, Texas, and Louisiana.

It is a pugnacious creature, and will chase any white ibis or heron that attempts to approach closer than a few feet. To the members of its own species, however, it is quite amicable, while the male and female bill and coo for hours at a time.

Its food consists of crawfishes, grasshoppers, and young snakes, including the poisonous cottonmouth moccasin. In two days' time it constructs its nest in elder bushes. Its young remain at home for six weeks before learning to fly.

Sometimes seen in the South from Texas to South Carolina is the white ibis. Its range is casual in more northern States.

SPOONBILL

ON the southwest tip of Florida, the spoonbills raise their splendid wings, cutting a silhouette of rose and carmine-tinted symmetry against the deep blue of the subtropical sky and the rich, warm green of the Gulf of Mexico. In a lazy, undulating motion, beginning at the shoulder and rippling downward to the tips, the pinions flap; the yellow legs trail behind, balancing the outstretched neck. The bird comes to rest in the dark foliage of a mangrove tree.

Reduced to a pitiful three hundred and fifty individuals in Florida and less than one thousand in Texas by the end of 1938, the spoonbill has become, like so many other beautiful native species, a rarity. Hunted for their plumes, shot by natives for food, persecuted by the bird stuffers of museums whose avidity increased with the steady fall in the numbers of this wonderful bird, the roseate spoonbill can now be saved from extermination only by the most vigilant protection. The Audubon Society has employed a special warden to devote full time to this long-delayed task. Luckily the south Florida locality where these birds now breed is somewhat removed from civilization, being accessible only by a dirt road; their only human neighbors, except for the warden, are a half-dozen lighthouse keepers.

SPOONBILL

In dense tropical marshes, among the cypress and mangrove trees, spoonbills erect a platform of sticks from eight to twenty feet above the ground. Here three or four brown-spotted eggs are laid. At first the young have feathered heads and wings edged with dark brown. It is three years before the adult plumage grows in, at which time the deep brown has paled to brownish-yellow, and the head has become quite bald.

Wading on their long legs in shallow lagoons, spoonbills thrust the spoon-shaped member, for which they are named, into the rich muck and root around for food. In the nest the baby spoonbills wait, alert and agitated, lined up in a row at the edge, swinging their heads and necks up and down. As the parent approaches, the young birds whistle and trill louder and louder until the older bird opens wide its mouth and the most impatient of the offspring plunges its smaller bill into the mouth of the parent. For at least ten seconds it waggles its bill around in the larger cavity as if famished, until the older bird shakes it loose and proceeds to feed the others.

Flying in long diagonal lines, the thirty-two-inch spoonbills

ROSEATE SPOONBILL *(Ajaia ajaja)*.
Length: 2½ feet. Range: Southern United States, West Indies, Mexico, Central, and South America. Very rare today.
American Museum of Natural History

travel in flocks, sometimes being seen with ibises. They are usually silent, although when near their nests a low croaking, almost conversational note is often heard.

Spoonbills, also called pink curlews, were formerly found as far north as Wisconsin, as far west as California, although in the main their American range favored the southeastern coastal and Gulf States. Southward they have been observed in the West Indies, Central America, and in South America down through lower Patagonia.

FLAMINGO

SHAKING his dark webbed foot to free it of clinging mud, the male parent flamingo places it on the rim of his conical, truncated mud nest, raises himself to a standing position over the top, preserving his balance by stretching his long neck and putting his curiously curved beak on the other nest edge; then he solemnly and ponderously shakes the other foot, stands with both feet on the edge of the nest, takes time out to preen himself with a gyration of his characteristic corkscrew neck, again balances with the aid of neck and bill, and suddenly plops down to parental duty so hard that an observer might expect the egg to break.

Male and female of this lovely vermilion species share in incubation, which requires four weeks. A grayish-white, dusky, downy youngster then pecks its way with parental aid to its new aerial environment. Before it is dry the newly hatched flamingo will leave its mud cradle, if enemies approach, and within a few hours it can run and fly a bit. If undisturbed, the chicks will remain in the nest for about four days.

The old bird feeds almost exclusively on small mollusks. The five-inch yellow-black bill, bent sharply downward in the middle, is thrust upside down into muddy water, which the bird stirs up by a dancing movement of its long dark legs. This leg action loosens the small invertebrates from the bottom, the bird seizes a billful of mud and mollusks, and strains them through a sievelike attachment on its lower jaw. The young are fed with regurgitated fluids from the mollusks. The immature flamingo has a straight beak and short

FLAMINGO

FLAMINGOES *(Phoenicopterus ruber)*. Length: 4 feet. Range: Atlantic coast of subtropical and tropical America and the Galapagos. Rare in the United States.
New York Zoological Society

legs at birth, and imitates its elders by trying to feed the neighbors' young. It produces a sound like a puppy's bark, and a whistling squeal.

When hurricanes and floods cover the large colony of mud nests, the casualties are excessive; floods and turkey buzzards rival man as the flamingoes' chief enemies. These gregarious brightly colored birds build colonies of hundreds; in rookeries where they have not been killed wholesale, thousands of their curious nests, five to fourteen inches high, are found. New nests are built atop old ones, about two feet apart, with water at high tide flooding around the connected pyramids. On the hollowed top one dull white egg is laid—rarely two. There are three main breeding rookeries on the islands of Great Abaco and Andros, in the Bahamas, and on small islands near Moron, off the north coast of Cuba.

Audubon recorded, in 1832, flocks of five hundred and more of the Florida species of flamingo at Key West and Indian Key, and northward as far as Pensacola, then moulting and unable to fly, hence helpless in the face of man's depredations. W. E. D. Scott saw a flock of about a thousand near Cape Sable, Florida, where they resided in 1890. Other ornithologists subsequently witnessed flocks of five hundred to one thousand visiting southern Florida in winter; as late as 1932 there were still large flocks, but more rarely seen. In 1905 the Audubon Societies began their belated guardianship of this and other birds threatened with extinction. Bahama authorities were convinced of the birds' value and extended legal protection; wholesale killing for plumage and food was largely stopped. Other governments have since taken similar measures of preservation in most breeding places which, for this Florida visitant, are in Cuba, Haiti, Yucatan, Guiana, Brazil, and Peru. Thus it can be reasonably hoped that the beautiful flamingo will survive.

The Florida flamingo migrates from season to season along the Atlantic and Gulf coasts of tropical and subtropical America; most numerous in the Florida Keys and Bahamas, it ventures only occasionally as far north as South Carolina and Alabama. A closely related species is found, strangely enough, in that curious natural zoo, the Galapagos Islands, eight hundred miles from the nearest other breeding place.

The length of these birds is forty-two to forty-eight inches; the wing spread about sixty-five inches. They inhabit shallow bays, lagoons, and mud flats that are flooded at high tide. Although most flamingoes are tropical in range, some venture into Patagonia and lakes high up in the Andes, where natives roast their eggs by the thousand for sale in the lowlands.

There is one large captive colony in a sanctuary at Hialeah, Florida; the gaudy birds are often paraded over the race track like bathing beauties. In captivity the flamingoes live to be thirty years of age.

In flight the flamingo's neck is stretched forward, legs backward, and the flame-colored bird becomes a miracle of dynamic symmetry. "One of the most stirring sights in the ornithological world,"

Dr. Frank M. Chapman called it after watching two thousand flying in formation at sunrise over Andros Island.

Three other species of flamingoes are found in South America. Another ranges from the Cape Verde Islands to India and Ceylon, visiting Lake Baikal in the north, and Madagascar in the south; another lives in South Africa. The European, African, and Asiatic flamingoes have a vermilion-to-scarlet color while the Florida species is pink-white.

Certain characteristics of the flamingo ally it with ducks and geese, but it is more closely related to storks, herons, bitterns, ibises, and spoonbills. None of its relatives has the flamingo's peculiarly crooked bill.

Ducks, Geese, and Swans

For beauty, variety of color, and economic importance, few orders surpass this group of birds. Fifty-six of the approximately two hundred species in the world are found in the United States. The total native population runs into many millions.

In varied formations, great numbers of these birds fly together during their long migrations. Every part of the country has its group of these semiannual visitors, even if only for a few fleeting moments as they call out a greeting and pass overhead. Ducks and geese, though often endowed with beauty and grace, are primarily considered for their tasty flesh and as hunter's targets; the swan, however, is often fortunate enough to win admirers for purely aesthetic reasons. In fact, the mute swan of the Old World has been naturalized in lakes and ponds of the New York City area.

These aquatic birds, best symbolized perhaps by the ducks whose dense oily plumage is justly responsible for the overworked simile, "like water off a duck's back," are much more at home in water than on land where their customary gait is a grotesque waddle. The webbed front toes act as paddles propelled by the powerful legs. Their long bills are used as sieves; when a mouthful of water, mud, and vegetation is seized, the mud and water are strained through the narrow apertures in the bill, leaving the desired morsel to be swallowed.

Geese and swans often live to ripe old ages, especially when domesticated. Longevity records of a swan which died at the traditional age of three score and ten, and that of a goose which lived for eighty years are not uncommon. However, these great ages are open to question and many authorities do not believe that the average age exceeds twenty-five years. Ducks seldom average more than fifteen years.

DUCKS

CLINGING to their course with the tenacity of pilgrims journeying to a shrine, countless hordes of ducks brave every element and run the gantlet of watchful hunters to complete their seasonal flights from breeding grounds to winter quarters. In small groups or flocks large enough to darken the sky, in wedge-shaped formations guided by flight leaders or in loosely organized bands, they set their route through trackless space as accurately as if proceeding along a broad, well-marked highway.

As they wing along during migrations or casual flights, they announce their presence with a variety of sounds, sweet or disturbing, loud or soft, depending upon the species and the hearer's sense of musical appreciation. Some ducks are dull in plumage, others of such gaudy hues as to create a joyful pattern of color against the blue and white of the sky.

Several years ago this popular bird group was beset by adverse weather conditions which made dust bowls of former feeding grounds; they were driven from swampy breeding places by reclamation projects. Concern was felt for their future. Then the forces of nature fortuitously lavished rains on parched regions. And man stepped forward to safeguard the ducks and ensure their unhindered reproduction—even if only to provide future targets for hunters. As a result of these combined agencies, it is estimated that there are about 65,000,000 ducks in North America. However, their killing by mass-production methods is permitted in Mexico where many of the species winter.

Ducks are heavy-bodied birds which waddle, not because of any inherent lack of dignity, but rather because their legs are placed so far back on their bodies. However, this physical structure permits sturdier swimming strokes and aids them in diving. The ducks have a wide flat bill, longish neck, sturdy pointed wings, and thick, warm feathers. The males, or drakes, are usually more highly colored than the females, but when they molt in late summer they become less distinctive. During this period the birds are unable to fly.

The birds and their eggs are preyed upon by such creatures as coyotes, crows, owls, muskrats, and even large fishes. Those that survive these hazards must still avoid the man with a gun. Duck mortality, nevertheless, is high and it is estimated that only ten to forty per cent of the eggs laid will result in ducklings which survive their first year.

Ducks are separated into two broad divisions, the river or surface-feeding ducks and the diving or sea ducks. However, some diving ducks may feed on the surface, and surface feeders may occasionally take a dive for a meal. The divers, distinguished by a small lobe like a paddle on the hind toe, usually are found in or near salt water.

There are about thirty-five North American species of ducks. Most of them feed on plants, particularly pondweed, bullock, smartweed, widgeon-grass, muskgrass, wild millet, wild celery, wild rice, duckweed, eel grass, sedge, bur reed, and cultivated grains. Mollusks and insects comprise the chief animal food, which is especially important in the case of the diving types, a large group of these being primarily meat eaters. The sago pondweed is probably the greatest single item of duck food.

MALLARD DUCK

THE mallard is the world's most famous and most useful duck. It is the sportsmen's prize of today, as well as yesterday's ancestor of the modern varieties of domestic ducks.

Mallards migrate in V-shaped flocks, green head and neck outstretched full length as they course along a mile a minute, buff-gray wings spread to full width. The two-foot male is further adorned with a white collar at the base of the green on its neck, a chestnut breast, and patches of purple and white on its wings.

The female is clothed in drab colors, but compensates by quacking loudly enough to be heard a mile away, while the gorgeous male has little of that vocal strength. The drake shows off all his fancy flying to the females in the mating season. When a female is captivated by his courtship, she assumes the offensive and pursues him.

Their nest is built on the ground and is made of feathers and vegetation. After the six to ten eggs have been laid, the wife is kept busy sitting on them. Meanwhile her husband, faithless and carefree, may either fly off in pursuit of another female, or join a few other husbands who likewise have deserted their families. In the summer the drake sheds his brilliant plumage and becomes as lusterless as the female; this molting is usually termed the "eclipse."

After hatching, the ducklings tag along after their mother who does her best to protect them. Major Allan Brooks, who intruded upon a family of mallards, observed: "One fine June day I came suddenly on a mallard with her day-old brood in a recently flooded

MALLARD DUCKS AND DRAKE *(Anas platyrhynchos)*. Length: 2 feet.
Range: Northern hemisphere.
New York Zoological Society

pool of crystal clear water. At the warning quack of the mother, every little duck dived, and as the surface became still I could see the youngsters dotted over the short turf that formed the bottom of the pool. They were not stretched out, but were sitting on the bottom with heads up, their wide-open, beady eyes regarding me through the limpid water. After watching them for what seemed to me two minutes, I waded in and touched each little form in turn. Instantly they rose buoyantly to the surface and pattered away to join the anxious mother, making no further effort at concealment."

As they float about the surface of ponds and marshes, mallards seize small frogs, fishes, worms, and plant life. They use their flattened bill to take up a mouthful of mud. Then by moving the tongue, they strain out the mud and water while retaining the desired food. Their southern jaunts in winter are appreciated for they eat crayfishes which undermine river dikes, and also destroy large quantities of insects.

Mallards breed in Asia, Europe, and the Arctic, as well as in the western and midwestern United States. Although found in most parts of our country, they are predominant inhabitants of the region west of the Appalachians.

BALDPATE

ANOTHER westerner, though sometimes found in the East, the baldpate or American widgeon is a devotee of plant life which grows underwater. Since it is not a proficient diver, it mingles with such ducks as the canvasback and scaup, waits until they dive and emerge with a mouthful of roots, and then steals the food right from their bills.

BALDPATES *(Mareca americana).* Length: 1½ feet. Range: North America in general.
Paul J. Fair, National Wildlife Federation

In swimming, flying, and even running on the ground, this bird has a freedom and grace singular in ducks. It is colored a mottled gray and brown, with white breast and gray legs. The drakes have a patch of white feathers on the top of their head, giving the impression of a bald pate—hence their name. A green patch on the white somewhat enlivens the color scheme.

A group of baldpates flies in close formation, sometimes so tightly packed that their wings almost clash. They may also proceed in a straight line, one abreast another. As they wheel through the air, the male whistles clearly and pleasantly, but when the females speak, it is in a harsh discordant croak. If one member of the group senses danger, it utters a louder whistle of warning, the signal to scatter or take to the upper regions.

SHOVELER

THE shoveler of the West, also known as the spoonbill, is most adept at using its long bill as a strainer. With its mouth full, it swings its head from side to side at the water level. As the water swishes through its bill, the undesired matter is drained off leaving behind the tasty mollusk, worm, or seeds. This method, which bears a marked resemblance to placer mining, is a characteristic of the whole order and accounts for the large amount of gravel—usually as much as a third—found among the stomach contents of most ducks.

The green-headed, white-breasted shoveler leaps out of the water with a peculiar rattling of its wings, and the whirring sound is also audible when it alights on the surface. Its landing is smoother than that of a seaplane, for it comes down almost vertically and barely stirs up a ripple. Some of the twenty-one-inch shovelers traverse more than two thousand miles of open ocean in migrating from Alaskan breeding grounds to their tropical and Hawaiian summer resorts.

It is rather more delicate than other ducks, and accordingly start their migration early and go further south. In their southern feeding grounds, they grow plump and are considered a great delicacy.

CANVASBACK

THE canvasback, pride and joy of hundreds of thousands of duck shooters, has never been seen wild outside of North America. The delectable flavor of its flesh is attributed to a diet of wild celery; but canvasbacks in regions where this plant is unavailable are just as delicious a dish as any other ducks—unless they be fish eaters.

To obtain the celery, the duck dives headlong into the water. When it emerges, it may fly for a while with graceful swiftness, dive for celery, reappear, and dive again. When it rests on the surface its heavy white body, long neck, and slender head form a picture of dignity and charm. On migrations the red-headed canvasbacks fly with strength and speed, sometimes in a line, at other times in dense mass formation, moving seventy miles an hour.

So efficiently and persistently has man hunted canvasbacks, that only the present and recently adopted limitations of the hunting season permit them to survive.

SCAUP DUCK

ANOTHER lover of wild celery, the greater scaup duck, or broadbill, sometimes stays under water for a full minute as it dives for the tasty vegetable. This swift-flying, skillful diver has fore parts of black with greenish beams, and its whitish body is mottled with black. It breeds north of the United States, but winters in both our eastern and western States. It is most often seen in salt-water bays.

OLD-SQUAW

INCESSANT chattering was responsible for the old-squaw's name, for it talks and talks like a garrulous old Indian woman. In various parts of the country it has also been descriptively dubbed old wife and old granny; and perhaps talkative local characters were used as the bird's namesake, for it is also called Old Billy, Old Molly,

John Connolly, and Uncle Huldy. The male's call, considered by some to resemble the phrase *south-south-southerly,* is uttered with a repetitiousness saved from monotony only by its musical form.

The loquacious male is also known as the long-tailed duck for obvious reasons. The long, thin tail usually lies loosely on the surface of the water, but when the male goes courting, it becomes erect.

The old-squaw is a proficient diver and has been inadvertently caught in fish nets as much as a hundred feet below the surface of the water. It sometimes flies with crazy irregularity, and during the mating season old-squaws are apt to chase one another about, even continuing the chase underwater.

This bird, which breeds in the far North, but winters along the coasts of the United States or in the Great Lakes region, is contrastingly colored in white and black or brown. The long-tailed male is not quite two feet long, while the less gorgeous female is six inches shorter.

EIDER

FROM the eiders come the well-known fluffy feathers which have stuffed so many pillows and comforters. The female lines her nest with the downy material after plucking it from her breast. In Iceland and European countries, industries have been established to collect eider down, and the birds consequently have been safeguarded. However, the rugged carelessness characteristic of the early American settlers almost exterminated the eiders, for when eighteenth-century seekers for eider down located these ducks, they procured the down by wantonly slaughtering the birds. As a result the industry soon waned in the United States.

The American or common eider breeds from Maine northward, and in winter extends its range to Delaware. It frequents the rocky coasts of the Atlantic, and many of them stay at Cape Cod where they dive for mussels. The males are white above and black below; the females are yellowish brown. Other eiders include the king eider which visits Maine and sometimes Massachusetts, and the Pacific eider of Alaska which is casual on the coast of Washington.

TEAL

SEVERAL species of teals are found in the United States. The green-winged teal, with bright chestnut head and neck, breeds in the West but winters as far east as Rhode Island. It is little more than a foot long, but one of the fleetest of birds. It has been clocked at thirty-five miles an hour. And it is a hardy bird, remaining in northern States late in the autumn, and sometimes far into the winter if unfrozen waters are available. The blue-winged teal is similar in many respects, but takes the precaution of heading south before the rigors of winter are felt. The cinnamon teal of the West was first observed in the United States in Louisiana, but today is just about a total stranger to that State.

BUFFLEHEAD

THE widely distributed bufflehead was so named because of the fluffy feather cap which adorns its head. It is a naïve bird in that it displays a fatal fondness for the decoys of hunters. However, this smallest of sea ducks has learned a certain wariness so that when a few are together in the water, one keeps watch while the others dive for food. The bufflehead, ambushed by hunters, dives rather than flies off to escape.

During the mating season the male erects his fluffy purple and green feathers as he struts before the females.

RUDDY DUCK

THE ruddy duck, found mostly in northern States, also is so much at home in the water that it prefers diving to flying as an escape. A surprised group will dive with each shot fired by a hunter. But then they all can be picked off when, in despair, they finally try to fly away, since their take-off from the water is slow and awkward. Hunters regard the ruddy duck's confused fright as so silly that they call the birds fool ducks.

Dr. Forbush describes the red and white male as a comical bird, handsome in the breeding season, but presenting "a ridiculous appearance in mating time as he swims pompously about with his head lifted proudly and drawn away back toward the spread tail, which is raised and thrown forward as if to meet it."

OTHER DUCKS

A NUMBER of other species have made the duck family familiar to residents of every part of the country. The black duck cf eastern and central States, which is not black but dusky brown, is similar to the mallard duck, though somewhat wilder. The New Mexican and Florida duck are little different from the black duck, except for their lighter colors. The related mottled duck inhabits much of the Gulf coast. The gadwall species, some of whose members touch almost every section of the country either during the breeding season or migration, is a swift flyer and a capable diver. A foreign bird, related to our baldpate, is the European widgeon which occasionally appears in the United States during migrations. The thirty-inch gray and white pintail of the West begins to move north after the first thaws, and its melodious whistling is one of the first signs of spring. The attractive male wood duck, gaily colored in green, blue, purple, red, yellow, and white—though the females are less colorful—frequents ponds and streams in wooded districts, eating insects and large numbers of acorns which it swallows whole. The redhead is often found together with the canvasback whose diving and flying ability it equals. The ring-necked duck has a lustrous black head and neck with a chestnut collar on its lower neck. The golden-eyed duck, or whistler, makes a whistling sound with its wings as they cut through the air. The scoters, or coots, are heavy sea ducks, strongly muscled and of sturdy build, as they must be to dive deep beneath the surface of the ocean. They include the scoter, or black coot; the white-winged, or velvet, scoter; and the surf scoter. Other ducks seen here are the perching tree ducks of the Southwest and Gulf regions and the colorful harlequin ducks of which there are two subspecies—an eastern and a western.

And, of course, an equally important division of duckdom are the domestic ducks, which are raised and admired on farms throughout the entire country from Long Island to Los Angeles.

CANADA GEESE

FLOCKS of Canada geese make their southern advance in autumn, winging ceaselessly onward like long lines of infantry which charge forward in rapid succession. Row after row, each silhouetted in irregular V-formations against the blueness of the heavens, appear in sight, pass overhead, and disappear into the southern horizon.

These three-foot-long geese call out with that well-known resonant *honk* of as varied range as an erratic auto horn. Found throughout most of North America, they are known in the North as gray geese because of their color, and in the West as honkers because of their characteristic call.

They swim on the surface of quiet waters in stately fashion, maintaining an air of dignity. They obtain food at the bottom of shallow ponds by bending their long necks under the surface. As they pluck vegetation they are virtually in an upside-down position so that only their tail emerges from the water, and stands upright in the air. Geese frequently swallow sand as a digestive aid.

On land they are less dignified in appearance. They waddle about, eating grain, and pause occasionally to make sure of their safety by stretching their long necks and looking around. At such times they are easily recognizable by the distinctive white patches on their cheeks. As an added precaution, a band of geese may station a sentry or two to warn the flock of the approach of suspicious characters.

They breed in the North from Alaska to Labrador, choosing such varied sites for nests as cliffs, trees, and marshes. Sometimes they exercise squatters' rights to the nest of an osprey which is away on a fishing trip. However, when the osprey returns it attacks them viciously. The interloping goose stretches its neck to full length, hisses, and beats at the enemy with its wings. When vanquished, the goose may have to leave so hurriedly that it even leaves its eggs be-

CANADA GOOSE AND GOSLINGS *(Branta c. canadensis)*. Length: 3 feet. Range: North America in general.
New York Zoological Society

hind. The osprey then unconcernedly lays its eggs alongside those of the Canada goose. Four subspecies of this goose are known: the common Canada goose, the lesser Canada goose of the west coast, Hutchins' goose of the East, and the cackling goose of California.

Under more normal circumstances the mother goose hatches her five to nine eggs while father gander stands by protectively. He will lay down his life in defense of his family. As soon as the young geese are hatched they are able to walk about and even swim. The parents molt at this time.

OTHER GEESE

ABOUT a dozen species of geese are found in the United States. The two-foot lesser snow geese once covered western prairies, according to Dr. Forbush, "like banks of snow." They come down from Canada to the western States in the fall, while a similar but larger bird, the greater snow goose, visits the East. Another eastern species is the blue goose, whose grayish plumage is surmounted with head and neck of white.

The emperor goose, a casual visitor to California, is described by Dr. Edward W. Nelson as the "least known and most beautiful." Its bluish gray plumage is dashed with yellow and black, its head and tail are white, and its feet are yellowish. The emperor goose winters in Alaska where the Eskimos use its skin in making clothing. It was saved from extinction only by prompt governmental action which made sanctuaries of its main breeding grounds.

Other species include the thirty-inch white-fronted goose, scattered in winter throughout many parts of the country, and the related tule goose which winters in the Sacramento Valley of California; its breeding range is unknown but is believed to be the Arctic. A few casual visitors are Ross's goose and the barnacle goose, the common brant of the eastern and central States, and the black brant whose head and breast are black and whose American range is from the west coast into the interior of Oregon and Nevada. Stragglers have been reported in the Northeast.

LESSER SNOW GOOSE *(Chen h. hyperborea)*. Length: 2 feet. Range: Winters in western United States and southern British Columbia.
Natasha Smith

LAST STAND OF THE TRUMPETER SWAN.
W. F. Kubichek, U. S. Bureau of Biological Survey

WHISTLING SWAN

THE whistling swan nests in summer on the frozen islands of the Arctic Ocean. An immense bird, often exceeding four feet in length, the swan builds a huge nest of grasses, moss, and plant stalks. When the parents leave the nest to search for food, consisting mainly of aquatic plants, they conceal the eggs under a covering of moss.

Unhappily these birds molt their flight feathers in early summer, and at that time they fall an easy prey to Eskimo hunters. In September, when the midnight sun begins to set at six o'clock, the feathers of the survivors are restored, and the young are able to fly. Then they join in great flocks and make their way southward. Apparently they divide into three main groups, one flying down the Atlantic coast, one down the Pacific, and the third choosing a central route over the Midwestern States. They fly in extended straight lines and at great heights, for they have learned what to expect if they draw too near civilization. Aviators have timed these flights at fifty-five miles an hour. Occasionally a great flock has been brought down by a blizzard, and then the unfortunates are usually shot or clubbed to death by farmfolk. Some swans have found a safe haven on the islands of the Great Lakes, but the only region in the United States where they commonly winter is along the coast of North Carolina.

The whistling swan does not make a habit of whistling. Its usual note is a deep *boom-boom,* but sometimes the high-flying flocks produce a high-pitched gasping cry.

The swan song was long regarded as a mere myth; but in recent years there have been reliable reports of mortally wounded swans singing for half an hour or more in soft, pleasing, melodious notes unlike any sound they normally produce. Gunners, unmoved by this death cry, continue to aim, maim, and slaughter the fast-vanishing birds.

TRUMPETER SWAN

THE trumpeter swan, now exceedingly rare, is the largest of North American wild fowl, attaining a length of fully five feet, a wingspread of eight, and a weight of thirty-five pounds. Unlike the smaller whistler, it prefers fresh water to salt, and so in its migrations it follows the Mississippi Valley, together with great flocks of cranes, wild geese, and other water fowl. The remaining swans fly steadily in V-shaped formations, uttering loud, raucous cries that can be heard at a great distance.

However, the mass migrations of past years have ceased. Once these birds were seen in the Middle West from Illinois south to Texas, in southern California, New York, and Delaware. Today their breeding grounds in the United States are restricted to but two localities—one in Wyoming, the other in Montana. In 1936 only one hundred and fifteen trumpeter swans were known to be in the entire United States. By 1939, owing to extraordinary conservation measures, the population increased to one hundred and ninety-nine—a gain of eighty-four. No effort should be spared to save this beautiful species for posterity.

Trumpeter swans were formerly much hunted for their down and their soft breast skins which were made into hats and other garments. A trumpeter swan received in the Philadelphia Zoo in 1895 died in 1925 after twenty-nine years of captivity.

MERGANSERS

MERGANSERS, also called fishing ducks, sheldrakes, and even sea pheasants, are perhaps most appropriately designated as sawbills. The saw-toothed edges of their long cylindrical bills enable them to cope with fishes of considerable size although this fish fare

TRUMPETER SWAN *(Cygnus buccinator)*. Length: 5 feet. Range: Interior and western North America. Only one hundred and forty-eight of these largest of American waterfowl are left alive in the United States. They are under the protection of the Bureau of Biological Survey in Montana and Wyoming.
New York Zoological Society

RED-BREASTED MERGANSER *(Mergus serrator).* Length: 2 feet. Range: Northern part of northern hemisphere.
Ralph De Sola (SIM)

tends to render their flesh unpalatable. Their habits, however, are so similar to those of ducks that little need be said concerning them.

The three native species of mergansers include the American merganser or goosander, a two-foot-long ducklike bird that breeds throughout most of our northern and southwestern States. It winters as far south as Lower California, Florida, and Louisiana. The red-breasted merganser or sheldrake of the same size breeds in the United States from Minnesota to Maine, winters as far south as Cuba, and is often seen in the southern States in company with the common or American merganser and the third American species— the widely distributed hooded merganser.

The hooded merganser, water pheasant, or hairy-crown is perhaps the most beautiful member of the merganser family. A group of them imparts a peculiar charm to any pond or stream that they may chance to alight upon. The fan-shaped crests of the birds, their playful splashing, their hoarse croakings—all combine to form an arresting and unforgettable picture.

Pelican Group

Pre-eminently fishers, the birds of this group include the pelicans, snakebirds or water turkeys, boobies and gannets, cormorants, and man-o'-war birds. They inhabit the seacoast, the open ocean, rivers, bays, estuaries, and, to some extent, inland lakes and swamps. The pelican, often found hundreds of miles from the ocean, is the most adaptable to the life of the interior; the cormorants, gannets, snakebirds or water turkeys, and man-o'-war birds follow. Excellent fliers, it is strange that these birds do not venture farther inland. Most often seen far out on the sea is that naïvely trusting bird, the booby.

These related birds resemble each other more during the fledgling stage than as adults. The bill of the pelican is pouched, that of the cormorant is hooked, while the booby's bill is pointed. They differ from each other also in the lengths of their necks and sizes of their heads. Similarities include the backward position of the legs, the webbed four-toed feet, and their long and pointed wings. Because of the posture of the young man-o'-war bird—it holds the tip of its bill against its breast—it has been called the frigate pelican. Young boobies and pelicans look alike too.

The high divers—boobies, gannets, and pelicans—are protected from the shock of their swift plunges into the sea by air-filled pads of tissue under the skin, which act as shock absorbers.

In the man-o'-war bird and the booby families, the female is much the larger partner, whereas the male brown pelican overshadows his mate. The parent birds of this group refuse to feed their offspring once they have acquired their first feathers.

MAN-O'-WAR BIRD

THOUGH an excellent fisherman, the haughty man-o'-war bird, or frigate bird, prefers to get its food by piracy. Soaring at a great height above the ocean, this giant bird sights a tern or booby with a fish in its beak. Darting down like a meteor, it forces the smaller bird to relinquish its prey, usually by the mere threat of its presence. When the victim does not permit itself to be terrorized, it may be disabled by a swift peck on the wing. Despite its great size, the air pirate can maneuver swiftly enough to catch the falling fish in mid-air, and then and there devour it. A man-o'-war bird has been known to alight on a pelican's head and help itself to dinner from that bird's pouch.

When necessary, however, the frigate bird will swoop low over the waves to catch the flyingfishes as they leap from the water, or dive down from great heights to seize the fishes swimming near the surface. It also feeds on young sea turtles. An infant man-o'-war bird has disgorged as many as seven flyingfishes.

The adult frigate bird has a wingspread of more than six feet. Its tail, controlled by seven separate sets of muscles, is used as a rudder in the bird's aerial gyrations. The male is a glossy black in color, with bluish-green head. A red sac, hanging from his neck, is distended in the mating season. The female is duller in color and has a brownish breast. The adult's body is scarcely larger than that of a good-sized chicken.

Despite their great powers of flight, the frigate birds do not venture far out over the ocean but remain close to their breeding grounds on the shore. They do not often land on the flat beach, for they have difficulty in rising unless they can drop for a short distance. Solitary in the hunt, they are sociable in roosting and breeding. Observers, who

MAN-O'-WAR-BIRDS SOARING.
Ralph De Sola (AMNH)

MAN-O'-WAR-BIRD *(Fregata magnificens)*. Length: 3 feet. Range: Tropical and subtropical coasts of the Americas.
New York Zoological Society

have seen their great colonies roosting in the mangrove swamps, describe them as lazy birds, sleeping for long hours and rising well after sun-up.

They breed in February in the West Indies and nest in rocks, low bushes, or tussocks. The building materials are sticks which the birds tear from the trees in full flight. Their one egg is about the size of a hen's. Both parents share in incubation and guard duty, the latter made necessary by these birds' habit of stealing one another's eggs.

In the United States the frigate birds winter in Florida, Louisiana, Texas, and southern California. Stragglers are sometimes seen in more northerly States. It is not definitely known whether these birds breed in the United States, although there is good reason to believe they do. Herbert K. Job has reported finding their eggs on the islands off Louisiana.

BROWN PELICAN

THE brown pelican is a large bird with a large appetite. The Florida variety attains a wingspread of six and a half feet, while the California subspecies, as would be expected, goes it one better with a spread of eight and a half feet. The length of bill is about one foot.

Every morning these birds set out on fishing expeditions, usually several miles from home. The daily diet usually consists of six to nine fishes averaging about eight inches in length. The first caught are eaten immediately, while others are stored in the immense neck pouches for future use and for the young.

On their fishing expeditions the pelicans play about in the waves, avoiding the water with great dexterity until they sight a fish. Then they bounce down with a terrific splash and swish their pouch through the water. The pouch gathers in several gallons of fish-

EASTERN BROWN PELICANS *(Pelecanus occidentalis)*. Length: 4½ feet. Range: South Atlantic and Gulf coasts of the United States; Atlantic coast of Central and South America. Unjustly persecuted by fishermen.
New York Zoological Society

containing water; the water strains out and the fishes remain. At evening the birds return homeward in groups of three to seven, flying in unison, alternating five or six wingbeats with a long glide.

Sometimes a gull is seen riding on the pelican's head, and now and then the gull even helps itself to a fish from the pelican's pouch; but even so, the birds seem to live together on excellent terms. The pelican on the whole is a sweet-tempered bird, beloved even by man. Such is its preoccupation with food that it seems to enjoy captivity as long as it gets enough to eat.

Pelican Island in Florida has been set aside by the Government as a bird sanctuary, and there, on an area of little more than three acres, two thousand brown pelicans build nearly one thousand nests in the low tangled mangroves. The nests are large structures of loosely woven sticks. Egg laying begins in February and goes on until May, though each female lays no more than three or four. During this season there is great activity in the nesting ground, with chicks of varying ages tottering about, and new ones constantly emerging.

At birth the young are helpless and covered with a thick, fluffy down. They are fed on a regurgitated fish soup from the parental gullet. As they grow older they also grow bolder, and shortly before weaning they climb halfway down their parents' mouths in feeding.

The Florida or eastern brown pelican frequents the Atlantic and Gulf coasts. Formerly it was much persecuted as a rival to fishermen, but a survey disclosed that it subsisted largely on the Gulf menhaden, an oily unpalatable fish, and since then they have been protected in many regions. The California brown pelican resides in southern California and breeds on islands off the coast.

The pelican's note is much like the croak of a frog.

WHITE PELICAN

WHITE pelicans are more co-operative-minded than their brown brothers. In large numbers they haunt the shores of lakes and rivers, forming "fishing trusts." They wade shoreward in a wide semicircle, which they narrow as they advance. They hold their heads back and their bills just above the surface, ready to strike and scoop up schools of minnows and other small fishes, sometimes gliding along without disturbing the fishes, sometimes beating the water with their wings at a signal from their leader. At other times

WHITE PELICAN *(Pelecanus erythrorhynchos)*. Length: 5 feet. Range: Temperate North America. In danger of extinction and in great need of more adequate protection.
Ralph De Sola (CPM)

they form two lines which approach each other, and catch the fishes as they waddle along. After these efforts they sit on shore or on sand bars, leisurely digesting their meal, after which they rise high in the air in great flocks, many of the adult birds achieve a wingspread of nine feet.

White pelicans migrate by day, in flocks ranging from five to a hundred, at great height and sometimes sailing in wide circles. Occasionally they form common flocks with the cormorants, alternating in line and beating their wings in synchronized flight, according to Dr. William Beebe.

WHITE PELICAN TAKING OFF.
J. S. Daily

White pelicans often share their breeding grounds with herons and cormorants.

These birds have grown rather rare in the United States. They are protected in a sanctuary in Yosemite Park and are sometimes seen in Texas and along the lakes and rivers of the Middle West as far north as Illinois. Formerly they were common in Florida.

CORMORANTS

FROM a low perch at the edge of a lagoon the cormorant plops into the water. Down, down toward the sandy bottom, it pushes with sturdy webbed feet, using its short wings like fins, until it comes upon the sleepy eel moping in the half-light. It seizes the elongated fish where best it can, and rises with it securely grasped in its hooked bill. Reaching the surface, it flings the prey into the air with a swift backward toss of the head, nimbly catches it in a more convenient position, and gulps it down.

Agile and muscular, the cormorant can give chase if it must, propelling itself beneath the water at a good rate. Sometimes the three-foot-long aquatic bird stays submerged for almost a minute.

Of the eight species found in the United States, the common or European cormorant is the most numerous. Along the Atlantic seaboard and by the shores of estuaries and lakes, its rough nest of seaweed, placed on the ground or in mangrove and cypress trees, may often be seen. This member of the pelican family, with its dense dark plumage tinted with a greenish-blue sheen, is known in different localities as the shag or the lawyer. The name cormorant is derived from *corvus marinus*, meaning sea crow.

During the building of the nest in the spring, the male bird takes some seaweed in his mouth and passes it to the female. She

BRANDT'S CORMORANTS (*Phalacrocorax penicillatus*). Length: 2½ feet. Range: Vancouver Island, British Columbia to Magdalena Bay, Lower California.
American Museum of Natural History

utters a mating call which must sound like music to her mate who puffs out the plumage on his head and neck and extends his neck sac. The female spreads her tail like a fan and bends it forward; her head is bent backward, upside-down, and swings from side to side. Both birds have their mouths open.

The female bird lays three to five oval, two-inch-long, greenish-blue eggs. Naked and dusky when they first emerge, the fledglings are soon covered with a soft brownish down. They feed by thrusting their avid bills down the throat of the parent bird who regurgitates half-digested food. The young are preyed upon by raiding sea gulls and on the west coast of South America by sea lions as well. In this region cormorant dung comprises a high percentage of the guano deposits which are so valuable as fertilizer and for their high nitrate yield.

Eventually the fledglings leave the nest and join their elders, flying in V-shaped squadrons low over the water. Acting in unison, they drive fishes into shallow water where they are easily scooped up. Many people believe that cormorants destroy valuable food fishes in harmful quantities. The fact is that, far from being a destroyer of valuable sea food, the cormorants aid the fishing industry by ridding the waters of countless "vermin" fish such as sculpins, gunnels, sand lance, and capelin; no fair-minded person should deny them the occasional flounder, herring, and eel that varies this diet. Once in a while the cormorant goes ashore to take a salamander or frog into its elastic, pouched bill; sometimes even mollusks and crawfishes.

Before the cormorant can swallow its catch it must rise to the surface. In China cormorants are made use of by fishermen. The leashed birds are set out to do the fishing, but a leather collar or ring about the neck prevents the bird from swallowing the catch.

OTHER CORMORANTS

THE double-crested cormorant, distinguished by the orange and yellow area on its face, gives birth to young which have whitish breasts. Subspecies of the double-crested cormorant are the Florida cormorant, white-crested cormorant, and Farallon cormorant.

On the Pacific coast, Brandt's cormorant has a fawn-colored patch on the throat. The Florida cormorant is slightly smaller than the double-crested species and inhabits North Carolina, Florida, and the Gulf coast; the white-crested cormorant is found mainly in Alaska; the Farallon cormorant makes its home on the coast and inland lakes of the Pacific slope. Other species found in the Pacific area are Baird's cormorant and the Mexican cormorant which also is seen along the Gulf.

WATER TURKEY

THE three-foot water turkey, snakebird, or darter swims rapidly underwater with the help of its curved webbed feet. The bird's long sinuous neck is drawn in a multiple kink. On approaching a fish, the kinks straighten out with the force of a released bowstring, and the darter's long sharp beak is driven straight through the unsuspecting victim. Then the snakebird, which cannot eat underwater, rises to the surface to enjoy its meal among the sheltering rushes. Tossing the fish into the air, it catches the head first in its gullet. So elastic is the snakebird's neck that, though it is only one inch in diameter, the bird has been seen to swallow a fish eight inches long and one and one-half inches across.

Frequently this bird swims along the surface, with only its sinuous neck and head above the water. At such times it truly resembles a water snake twisting and twining along. At the approach of a stranger, the darter will submerge, but instead of diving like most aquatic birds, it simply sinks down feet first. It can remain under water for some minutes, and when it finally reappears, it often does so with neck pointed straight upward, to simulate a stick. It requires some time before even an ornithologist can distinguish this "stick" from others in the bog by its roving eye. At other times it swims with its body submerged and only its long snaky neck out of water.

The plumage of the adult snakebird is a glossy black with green glints and a streak of white on neck, wings, and tail. The firm elastic feathers somewhat resemble large fish scales. The immature bird is blackish-brown.

WATER-TURKEY

WATER-TURKEYS *(Anhinga anhinga)*. Length: 3 feet. Range: Southern United States and tropical America. Rare in United States.
American Museum of Natural History

In the river bogs and fresh-water lakes near the Gulf coast, the snakebirds perch silently for hours in branches overlooking the water, either in flocks or in pairs. They are good flyers, and when surprised in their roosts they may take to the air instead of diving. Then they fly upward and circle about at a great height like hawks.

Snakebirds build large nests close to the water's edge. Their two to four eggs are light blue with chalky white covering. Often these birds breed in groups with herons and ibises.

In the United States snakebirds inhabit chiefly Florida, the Gulf coast, Georgia, and South Carolina, but some have been known to breed as far north as Illinois. This bird has been much persecuted as a competitor of fishermen. However, it operates in spots little used for commercial fishing and subsists chiefly on mullets, sunfishes, and minnows. It should be protected as a great devourer of aquatic insects.

Snakebirds thrive in captivity and, if put in a glass tank with fishes, give free exhibitions of their hunting technique. Sometimes, however, they accidentally spear one another, inflicting serious injury.

COMMON GANNET

SOARING lightly in the rose-tinged sky, the gannets scan the sea on tireless wings. Their sharp eyes peer beneath the waves, searching out the moving shoals of fishes down in the green depths.

When the finny prey is sighted, the anserous fishers rise in the air to a height of one hundred feet or so, each bird then plummeting downward, wings folded to its sides, gathering momentum as it falls until it strikes the water with a terrific impact which shatters the wave in a ten-foot column of spray. Carried far beneath the surface by the power of the dive, the gannet gets down to where the fishes are swimming, selects its catch, and stuffs it into its gullet. Burdened with a large herring or pilchard, it beats its six-foot pinions against the wind, rises with its catch, and flies with it to the face of the cliff where thousands of the white birds pitch their precarious nests.

On Bonaventure and Anticosti Islands and on Bird Rock just off the Gaspé Peninsula in the Gulf of St. Lawrence, these sea birds have their best-known rookeries. Few dare trespass on these massive seabound stone promontories with the rough beach at their feet. The colony here numbers twelve thousand adult birds, but the birds are also seen in less-known locations along the shore of eastern North America where they winter from North Carolina to the Gulf.

In the seaweed-reinforced nest one chalky white egg (infrequently two) is laid during the middle of May. The female incubates the egg, holding it between her webbed feet while her mate fishes. While engaged in this task, she will not leave the nest even at the approach of humans. Near the end of June, a black-skinned naked fledgling is hatched, shapeless and blind. The newcomer thrusts its head down the neck of the tan-headed parent and extracts a partially digested meal. After a week or so the down begins to grow, clothing the chick in a fluffy wrapping.

Three months later, fat, stiff, and hesitating, the young gannet takes off on its first flight. Fully grown, the bird will be three feet long, its tail containing from twelve to eighteen feathers which are black at the tips. The legs are short and stout; the feet completely webbed.

Related to the pelicans, the gannets are noted for their longevity, some of them reaching fifty years of age. The name gannet is derived from the Anglo-Saxon *ganot*, meaning sea fowl.

GANNET *(Moris bassana)*. Length: 3 feet. Range: Coast of North Atlantic; breeds on Bird Rock and Bonaventure Island in Gulf of St. Lawrence.
New York Zoological Society

BOOBY

A TROPICAL and subtropical variation of the gannets, the white-bellied booby appears infrequently on the coasts of the southern Atlantic and Gulf States except Texas, occasionally coming as far north as South Carolina. Sailors gave it its name because it was so witless that it could be caught by hand. It can inflict injury, however, with its cylindrical beak when sufficiently annoyed although this is not often.

The chief characteristics distinguishing the boobies from the gannets are that gannets are migratory while boobies are permanent; boobies are dark brown on top and white beneath while gannets are nearly all white except for their black wingtips. An exception, of course, is the red-footed booby which looks very much like a gannet.

In a hastily constructed nest of sticks and weeds, the booby lays as many as three eggs. When brooding, the female squawks and grunts hoarsely, while the male, strangely enough, peeps like an overgrown chick.

The white-bellied, brown-backed boobies of the Bahamas were among the first birds seen by Columbus and his crew as they approached the shores of the New World. One of these even perched, much to the delight of the argonauts, on the *Santa Maria*.

TROPIC-BIRD

THE yellow-billed and the red-billed tropic-birds fly for great distances over the ocean, and often accompany ships in the South Atlantic and Caribbean. Mariners call them boatswain birds, perhaps merely because they fly in the shipping lanes, perhaps because they utter a shrill cry resembling a boatswain's whistle. However it is by no means certain that they do this.

The flight of these great white birds, measuring more than thirty inches in length, is graceful in the extreme. They do not glide and soar with imperceptible wing motions like the albatrosses and man-o'-war birds, but beat their wings in steady, regular cadence. They have been likened to large white doves with two long tail feathers trailing behind. It is perhaps because of their manner of flight that they sometimes show signs of fatigue, pausing to rest in the rigging of ships. They do not rest on the decks, because their legs are weak and they are unable to stand on level surfaces; their gait is a wobbling roll, and that may be still another reason for calling them boatswain birds.

The tropic-birds subsist on fishes and squids, which they get by diving. Their dive is swift and sudden and their prey has little chance to escape.

Tropic-birds lay but one egg a year, and this is placed in a hole in the sand. The parents share in incubation and are extremely reluctant to abandon their p o s t s even in the presence of danger. Humans, it is alleged, exploit this characteristic to pluck out the long tail feathers to decorate women's hats.

Tropic-birds nest in the West Indies. The red - billed tropic - bird has been seen off southern California and the yellow - billed off the Atlantic coast.

The tropic-bird is one of the most attractive of the sea birds.

WHITE-BELLIED BOOBY *(Sula leucogaster)*. Length: 2½ feet. Range: Atlantic coasts of tropical America; sometimes seen off Florida.
New York Zoological Society

Albatrosses, Petrels, and Shearwaters

Creatures of the open ocean, this group of birds rarely comes to shore except to breed. They select a lonely island in the North Atlantic or Pacific and here the female bird lays a single egg in a burrow or cavity.

Tubinares they are sometimes called because their nostrils are enclosed in external tubes, one on each side of the bill in the albatrosses; in the other birds of this group, the tubes are connected and placed on top of the bill.

From the smallest of the tube-nosed swimmers, the stormy petrel, to the largest, the giant albatross, these birds are the strongest and most enduring flyers of all the feathered race. Scudding like sea spume before the gale they scour the ocean for marine life and oily substances. When the sea is stormy they remain in the air for days at a time. Adaptations for this strenuous life include a dense and oily plumage, three webbed front toes, long narrow wings, and hooked horny bills.

Albatrosses follow ships for days, seemingly with no wing exertion, feeding on the refuse dumped overboard. Even though a large albatross may have an eleven-foot wing span, they are hardly ever more than eighteen pounds in total weight. These birds are rarely seen north of the subtropical seas although of the sixteen known species, three, the Laysan, the short-tailed, and the black-footed albatrosses, sometimes find themselves as far north as Alaska.

While the albatross settles into the water rather heavily, with outstretched wings and feet, the shearwater disappears under the surface in a swift plunge. In contrast with the steady soaring flight of the albatross, the shearwater curves and skims the surface.

The larger shearwaters exceed the smaller albatrosses in size, although as a group they are smaller. Largest of the shearwaters is the great shearwater of the Atlantic Ocean. This bird often reaches a length of twenty inches and spreads its wings for almost four feet.

The sooty shearwater reaches our Atlantic coast from the southern hemisphere in the summer.

Petrels are found on both the Atlantic and Pacific coasts of this country.

Fulmars also belong to this order. However, their distribution on the New England coast is generally limited to the Georges fishing bank off Massachusetts. They nest from here, northward, in colonies as do the gulls.

ALBATROSS

PATROLLING the surface of the sea in great circles, the black-footed and short-tailed albatrosses of the North Pacific pounce swiftly on squids, fishes and their eggs, seaweed, and edible refuse. They follow ships for days on end, never tiring, with scarcely perceptible soaring wing motion. At least one of these birds was known to fly for three thousand miles.

In the wake of a vessel an albatross plunges down into the churning foam after a morsel and is left far behind. But with a few strokes of its long pinions it is again circling over the masts and funnels. Sometimes a dozen of them, unexcelled by any bird in beauty of flight, seem to act as a convoy.

White tails and splashes of white about the face offset the black plumage of the black-footed albatross. Fairly common off the Pacific coast of the United States, these twenty-inch birds are known by sailors as goonies.

Unlike most birds, these groove-beaked coursers pair in the early winter in great colonies which dot the islands of the Pacific from Hawaii far to the west. Here they go through the motions of their elaborate ritual dance, a ceremony quite apart and distinct from the courtship activities. It may even be indulged in by two or more males or as many females. Even the bowing of a human being is liable to set them off, posing, swaggering, curtsying, with stately and dignified movements. Long after the breeding season is over the peculiar dance is performed by the birds. Frequently these imitative birds attempt to enter into the courtship ritual of other species with which they share the island breeding places, but they succeed only in looking ridiculous as their stately motions ill match the agile grace of smaller birds.

During the actual courtship, the birds touch beaks in almost human fashion, the male giving vent to harsh and unmusical groans which have been called bovine. At this time of the year the birds resent interference and become irritated at the intrusion of humans.

On at least one island of the mid-Pacific, the arrival of the breeders is the occasion for much excitement, for at that time the

WANDERING ALBATROSS AND WILSON'S PETRELS *(Diomedea exulans* and *Oceanites oceanicus).* Length: 4 feet, 7 inches. Ranges: Pacific and South Atlantic Oceans; all oceans except the North Pacific. The wandering albatross is the largest sea bird and attains the remarkable wingspread of eleven and one half feet.
F. L. Jaques from Murphy's "Oceanic Birds of South America"

betting pool, engaged in by the inhabitants as to the time of arrival of the birds, is settled, bringing its windfall to the lucky guesser.

Laid in the open sun, the eggs of the albatrosses are in danger of being cooked and the parents attempt to keep them covered with their bodies as much as possible.

Fossil specimens prove that the albatross once battled the winds of the North Atlantic. These sea creatures never fare well in captivity; seemingly they find it impossible to exchange the great range and sweep of their ocean habitat for even the biggest flying cage.

The name albatross is derived from an Arabic root meaning bucket, referring to the bucket on a water wheel. Originally applied to the pelican, for obvious reasons, the name began to be applied to any large bird, and finally it stuck, in corrupted form, to the albatross.

This bird is the center of many sailors' superstitions, the best known being that an albatross following a ship brings good luck, and to kill such a bird brings evil.

WILSON'S PETREL

FROM the cold silences of Antarctica, Wilson's petrel beats its way northward along the Atlantic coast as far as Labrador. Dancing and skipping over the surface of the water, it chases merrily through the valleys formed by wave on wave, looking for floating scraps of fish and oily marine substances.

Most authorities are agreed that the petrels were so named because they appear to walk on the water, but the exact link is debated. Some insist that petrels were named for St. Peter, who, the New Testament has it, walked on the water on one occasion. An earlier spelling of their name—pitteral—leads many to believe that the pitter-patter of the bird's gait on the sea is the original source. Mother Carey's chickens, a name loosely applied to all the petrels, but more specifically to Wilson's, is probably a corruption of the prayerful *mater cara*, or dear mother, breathed by devout sailors in dire peril. Mother Carey, it is also alleged, was the wife of Davey Jones who presides over the gloom-pervaded seafarers at the bottom of the sea.

Wilson's petrel nests on little islands near the Antarctic Circle in February. A single white egg is laid in crevices in the rocks, which abound in that region. Sometimes the mother bird will take the trouble to dig a burrow, close under the surface. The wintry winds of that high latitude are so fierce that fledglings are often frozen before they have had a chance to take wing—sometimes even before they have left the egg. The breeding places are littered with these frozen remnants.

Guarding the nest, the mother bird waits for the return of her spouse with food for herself and the young. Strangely enough the fledgling, after a few healthy meals have been tucked into its crop, seems larger than its seven-inch parents. By this time it is almost ready to fend for itself.

Like all petrels, Wilson's has a slender hooked beak. Its wings are fairly long and its tail boasts a bit of a fork. Almost entirely black, the plumage of this bird is offset by a patch of white near the tail. The long web-footed legs are yellow. The webbing between the toes, with the assistance of the fluttering wings, permit the remarkable wave walking.

Along our Atlantic coast, Wilson's petrel is the most common. It comes here, directly after its breeding cares have been attended to. Patient followers of ships, they wing their way behind them for hours waiting for food scraps to be thrown overboard. Then they leap into the water, to be left far behind, their small black forms punctuating the great expanse of ocean. Finishing their meal, they rush forward once more to pursue the floating commissary.

LEACH'S PETREL

THE northern islands of both the North Atlantic and North Pacific Oceans are the nesting places of Leach's petrel. An inch larger than Wilson's petrel, Leach's is almost identically colored except that its plumage tends to darkish brown rather than somber black. Its legs are black and its tail is noticeably forked.

More fastidious than its Antarctic counterpart, Leach's petrel lays its single egg in a makeshift nest of feathers and stray bits of grass. The nest may be either in a burrow or beside a rock. Sometimes the nest is shared with a puffin. Leach's petrel is the only petrel to breed on our shores. In the period before the egg is laid, male and female stay near the nest, but when the fledgling arrives, the male takes the responsibility for feeding it. During the nesting season the voice of the male is heard frequently at night.

Like Wilson's petrel, these birds are at the mercy of the storms which blast up the coast lines. Sometimes after a severe blow their bodies litter the beaches.

FORK-TAILED PETREL

DISTINCTIVELY attired in pearly-gray plumage, the nine-inch fork-tailed petrel is difficult to confuse with the other petrels. Its tail is as sharply cleft as a two-tined pitchfork. Breeding in the frigid archipelagoes of the North Pacific, it courses to the coast of Asia on the west and to southern California.

The fork-tailed nests in a variety of locations; the grass-grown slopes of the Aleutians, the basalt rocks of another group of Alaskan islands, and the evergreen forests of an island near Sitka seemingly find equal favor with it.

These petrels mate during June and July. Especially in their woodland haunt, they await the coming of twilight before emerging from their underground burrows. Then, in the somber forest they rend the silence with their cries. All during the night these sounds are likely to fill the air. They resent encroachment to the extent of flying in the face of the intruder. They have been known to put out a small campfire by flying right into it. With the coming of the first streaks of dawn the wood becomes noticeably quieter. The birds take off, a few at a time, to the open sea.

KAEDING'S PETREL

KAEDING'S petrel breeds on islands in the Pacific off the coast of Lower California and is sometimes seen off southern California. Emerging at twilight, these petrels fly in large flocks with a great whirring of wings and squeaking like bats.

The nestlings are fed by either the male or the female, who squirt a yellow fluid down the open mouth of the chick.

A related subspecies is Beal's petrel of the west coast. Other American species include the black petrel of the California coast whose range extends to Peru, the ashy petrel, and the Socorro petrel which breeds on islands off the coast of California.

SHEARWATERS

TO THE tiny islands of Tristan da Cunha, far down in the South Atlantic Ocean, the greater shearwaters come by the thousands. Here, surrounded by the tossing open ocean, the black-capped eighteen-inch riders of the sea breed in such great numbers as to blanket their base from sight. The pressure of population on these sequestered shoals is literal—the birds are forced to stagger their egg-laying activities in order to provide nesting room for the whole colony.

In flight, their long narrow wings ripple almost imperceptibly before the encouraging breeze. In small bands they skim the waves, the long lower mandibles of their beaks dipping into the water, the movable upper mandibles closing and opening as they swallow scraps of food. Shearwaters follow whales and porpoises, as the excreta of these marine mammals constitute a delicacy for them. Sometimes a school of unwary fishes riding near the surface is raided. On a foggy day squids often lose their bearings and come to the top, whereupon the shearwaters seize them.

Up and down the Grand Bank where the codders ply their craft, the fisherman calls these birds hagdons. Mixing business and pleasure they catch the shearwaters with barbed hooks baited with fish entrails, thus assuring themselves food and bait. In this case rapacity gets its due, for in order to get at the alluring fish entrails, the hook-billed shearwaters chase away great numbers of other birds.

MANX SHEARWATER (*Puffinus puffinus*). Length: 1½ feet. Range: Northeastern North Atlantic; accidental on the American coast from Greenland to New York.

New York Zoological Society

CORY'S SHEARWATER

LIKE the greater shearwater, Cory's shearwater lays its eggs out in the open without benefit of nest. Called borealis, this bird was once believed to come from the Arctic to the South Atlantic, but now it has been identified as the common shearwater of those small groups of islands which stipple the sea off the west coast of Europe and Africa, the Azores and the Madeira group.

Cory's bird is as large as the greater shearwater. Its brownish cap is not as well demarcated from the whitish neck as that of its cousin. Laying its eggs in April and May, Cory's shearwater abandons its young when they have reached the fledgling stage.

In early autumn both Cory's and the greater shearwater come to the vicinity of New York and are sometimes seen dipping over the ferries in the harbor.

SOOTY SHEARWATER

PREDOMINANTLY brown and black with a black bill, the sooty shearwater merits its name. Because it breeds in the vicinity of New Zealand, it also goes by the unlovely appellation of mutton bird. At any rate, it looks like a crow from a distance.

The single egg is laid in a burrow tunneled through damp ground. The young hatch out in a chamber at the end of the boring, and, vigilantly guarded by their parents, they are soon fat and appetizing. Despite the courageous fight waged by the parents, the Maori tribesmen used to gorge themselves on the young birds.

This species of shearwater, unlike the preceding two, is found in both the Atlantic and Pacific Oceans. They find their way as far north as Alaska on the Pacific side and to Canada on the Atlantic. To the south, their nests have been discovered on Cape Horn, and in places along the California coast the rocks are splattered with their pearly black excrement.

Observers state that after diving under the water, the sooty shearwater moves its wings in such a way as to be actually "flying" in the deep.

Other shearwaters sometimes seen off our coasts are the slender-billed, the black-vented, the pink-footed, and the New Zealand—all on the Pacific; Audubon's and the Manx on the Atlantic.

Gulls and Terns

The common features shared by these birds are their long and pointed wings, their free and bare legs extending from near the center of the body, and their sturdy bills. Found in every quarter of the globe, this order of water birds is marked also by their open lateral nostrils.

Skuas, jaegers, and gulls have hooked, rapacious-looking bills. The bill of the skimmer is edged like a blade and the tern's bill is pointed. Fish is the chief food of all these birds although they secure their diet in different ways. The skuas and jaegers have been called sea hawks and robber gulls for obvious reasons. They are swift and aggressive enough to overtake weaker sea birds in the air and force them to disgorge their catch.

Almost always found near the seacoast, gulls, of which there are twenty American species, sometimes travel far inland, as during their beneficent visit to Utah in the early days of settlement. From 1848 to 1850 the settlers were threatened by great numbers of black crickets which almost made farming impossible. The noxious insects were driven off or eaten in great numbers by gulls "which came to save the day." The grateful and progressive State has erected a bronze monument to these birds.

HERRING GULL

OVER the harbors and rivers of the Atlantic coast States, the two-foot-long herring gull wheels and dips, scanning the water for bits of refuse and garbage. This bird, the common gull or sea gull so familiar in the East, is the most abundant of the gulls in that region.

Unlike the petrels which spend most of their time on the wing, the herring gull rests frequently on the surface of the water where it may be seen bobbing about like a celluloid toy on the wavelets near docks and piers. A typical gull, the herring gull's feet are webbed, thus enabling it to swim easily. In swift-running streams and eddies this gregarious bird floats with the current until it is dragged downstream and away from the other birds which usually cluster about a reliable source of food supply, such as a garbage-dumping platform. Then it picks itself from the water with a few measured

HERRING GULLS *(Larus argentatus smithsonianus)*. Length: 2 feet. Range: Breeds in northern North America; winters along coasts of United States, Cuba, and Mexico.

James McAlpin Pyle

strokes of its long wings and may fly directly upstream to take the ride all over again.

Heard overhead, the low whistling call of the herring gull seems like a disembodied voice; it is hard to connect the thin note with this robust soaring bird.

On low sand bars and mud flats the birds collect by the hundreds to pry out clams with their slightly down-curved bills. Then they fly with the catch to a hard strip of sand or a concrete highway where they drop the clams, breaking their shells and exposing the meat.

On the rocky islands off the northeastern coast herring gulls breed by the thousands, notably on Great Duck and No-Man's Land, islands where upward of ten thousand of the birds pitch their nests annually, mated pairs faithfully returning to the same spot year after year. Each couple occupies its private site and drives intruders away without ceremony; a couple may even drive an interloper from the site of a neighbor. Before actually starting hostilities, however, the gull assumes a threatening pose, neck outstretched and head pointed downward. This usually suffices to send an intruding bird scurrying away. Clashes also occur among the colony of gulls when one oversteps his boundary and enters a neighbor's domain.

The nests often consist of a mound of tightly packed seaweed with a neat cup-shaped depression in the top, hidden in clumps of grasses or behind boulders. The three eggs are pale blue to olive-brown in color. Here, amid a stench of decomposing fish brought by the carrion-eating gulls to their young, the chicks, dirty little balls of fluff, scatter about before the intruder. The greatest danger to the chicks, however, does not come from any human agency but from the adult herring gulls themselves. Sparing their own offspring, these birds seem to take delight in punching in the skulls of young birds who mistake them for their parents. The chicks, when hungry, tap at the red spot on the parents' bills, a signal that they feel it is time to eat.

Before the passing of laws which protect herring gulls in every State where they occur, hundreds of thousands were killed to satisfy the requirements of the millinery trade.

In summer the head, neck, and tail of the herring gulls are pure white, and the mantle is grayish-blue; in winter the head and neck take on dusky streaks and the yellow bill is somewhat dulled.

GREAT BLACK-BACKED GULL

RETIRING and wary, the great black-backed gull of the North winters in this country from the Great Lakes to the Delaware River. Also known by the doleful title of coffin carrier, it remains in the neighborhood of offshore sand bars. Timid where humans are concerned, this gull shows no hesitation in stealing food from the nests of other birds and killing and eating the eggs and young.

Although thirty inches long, it is easily scared away from its feeding grounds by intruders. It takes to the air uttering a *ha-ha-ha* not too loudly. On other occasions its calls vary. The repertory of the great black-backed gull includes at least four separate types of cry.

Its nest is placed in a cupped hollow generally situated on the shore of a small island. Here two to three eggs are laid, the young remaining immature until their fourth year.

The bird is so called because of the deep slate-colored mantle which surmounts its white body.

CALIFORNIA GULL

NESTING in colonies in inland lakes of the western United States, the twenty-three-inch California gull sports a pearly-gray topcoat over its white body. The nests of small sticks and grasses are placed on the ground.

RING-BILLED GULL

WHITE with a blue-gray mantle is the decorative scheme of the ring-billed gull. Making the rounds with herring gulls, these birds, similar in appearance, are often mistaken for their scavenging cousins. A distinguishing characteristic is the black ring on its beak.

Also known as the lake gull, this bird breeds across the entire continent, generally in reedy marshes.

In addition to fishes, the ring-billed gull will eat worms and insects, sometimes flying far inland for them. A rather intelligent bird, it will follow boats and even garbage trucks.

HEERMANN'S GULL

SAID to be lazy, these white-headed, blue-gray, twenty-inch birds of the Pacific coast pester the pelicans for an occasional handout. When the larger birds snare their fish, Heermann's gull is often there to snatch the catch from their jaws.

Breeding off the coast of Mexico, these birds fly north to Washington in June. In their northern range they seem to display no domestic or amorous instincts whatsoever. Their low-pitched cries are mellow and sweet.

HERRING GULL.
C. W. Schulz

LAUGHING GULL

ONE of the more beautifully plumaged gulls, the laughing gull wears a black hood and dark gray upper parts to set off its lower white parts. Playful and gregarious, flocks of these birds are often seen chasing porpoises and diving for smaller fishes without coming to rest on the surface at all. The bird's name was suggested by its loud call which is said to be mirthful. Breeding along the Atlantic and Gulf coasts, the laughing gull builds a substantial nest of grasses and weeds in the northern part of its range, but contents itself with a mere hollow in the sand farther to the south.

These birds harry the pelicans too, often alighting on their very heads as they prepare to filch the prey.

FRANKLIN'S GULL

ANCHORED lightly to the floor of the marsh, the nests of Franklin's gulls float at the surface. These gulls breed together in great colonies, the nests being sometimes only two to three feet apart. Two or three eggs are laid during the latter part of May and the young take to the water shortly after they have been hatched out. Soon the margin of the lake or fen is alive with chicks trying out their natatorial skill.

Often Franklin's gulls fly in flocks over the countryside in the Midwestern States uttering fluted cries. They follow the furrow made by the plow to pick up the worms and grubs that are turned up. This peculiar representative of a maritime family is rarely seen on either seaboard.

Startlingly beautiful in their slate-colored hoods with white eyelids peering forth, they look like members of a secret order. On the wing, a dainty rose color is seen on the under parts. This delicate flush has given the bird the name of the rosy gull. People of the plains know it as the prairie pigeon.

During the warmer part of the year, Franklin's gulls are largely insectivorous, feeding on cutworms, grubs, the larvae of the dragonfly and grasshoppers. This is the bird that saved the Mormons from a plague of grasshoppers and was rewarded, as a species, with a monument.

BONAPARTE'S GULL

WHILE Bonaparte's gull is seen more often than Franklin's on the seacoast, it too finds the inland reaches of the countryside much to its liking. Fourteen inches long, it has a slate hood and bluish-gray mantle.

Known as sea pigeons, one of their favorite stunts is to fly high over marshes, catching insects on the wing. Occasionally they dip to the sod for a worm. In the coastal sections they wheel gracefully overhead, keeping a sharp lookout for shoals of fishes.

SABINE'S GULL

SABINE'S gull, an Arctic bird, migrates to both coasts of the United States. Also known as the hawk-tailed gull, it has a forked tail. Sabine's gull feeds on aquatic insects thrown up on the beaches.

They usually lay their two or three eggs on moss, occasionally on dry sand. The nest itself is a depression scooped out of the earth and lined with dry grass.

KITTIWAKE

THE kittiwake is the most seagoing gull of a maritime family. Sometimes it stays at sea for seven or eight months at a time. Kittiwakes follow the right whale, waiting for this monster to rise to the surface for air. At that time the industrious and graceful eighteen-inch bird can get the morsels of fish falling from the whale's mouth. A fish eater in the main, the kittiwake will eat almost anything at all if it has to. It prefers drinking salt water to fresh and actually sleeps on the great waves of the bounding main, its head neatly enfolded by a protecting wing. Closely related and quite similar, the Pacific kittiwake comes down from the Arctic to northern Lower California.

GLAUCOUS GULL

FOLLOWING the fishing fleets along the eastern seaboard, the thirty-inch glaucous gull not only plagues the fishermen, but robs smaller gulls of their pickings as well. These weaker birds are lucky if their eggs and young are not gorged in addition. Occasionally these burgomaster gulls, as they are also known, come into New York harbor.

For some reason, glaucous gulls prefer not to rest on the surface of the water like other gulls, but seek a jut of land or rock emerging from the sea to repose on.

SKIMMER

AT TWILIGHT, or on moonlit nights, black skimmers flit near the surface of the sea, their knife-thin lower mandibles scooping the water for shrimps and fishes. These birds, also known as scissorbills, have mandibles that meet edgewise, the lower one longer than the upper. Black above and white beneath, the eighteen-inch body of the bird is nicely streamlined, permitting the long wings to maneuver gracefully.

Highly gregarious, black skimmers collect near the shore line where the minute creatures they eat are most likely to be found. Their four eggs are laid in a mere hollow in a sand bank where the birds lounge about waiting for their favorite feeding time—dusk. Fishermen along the Atlantic and Gulf coasts often go through these nurseries collecting the tasty eggs.

With little ability or instinct to defend themselves, the unaggressive creatures are usually satisfied with an abandoned tern's nest for breeding.

Black skimmers are the only species of the five that inhabit the earth to be found in the United States.

ROYAL TERN

SQUAWKING a hoarse *kak-kak,* the twenty-inch royal tern cleaves into the sea from a height of several yards. After remaining submerged for a few seconds, it rises with a small fish in its beak and retires to a sand bar or jut of ground where others of its species stand about in groups.

Royal terns are rarely found far from the coast. Their nesting place is usually a hollowed-out cup of sand large enough to accommodate two or three eggs. So many royal terns nest in such a small space that the colony becomes almost a vast communal home.

White, with a mantle of bluish-gray, the royal tern flashes a diadem of greenish-black along the crest of the head. There was a time when these birds were much sought after by manufacturers of ladies' hats, which resulted in greatly reducing their numbers.

Like all terns, the royal tern flies with its bill pointed downward, distinguishing it from the smaller gulls which carry their bills horizontally. Their flight is strong and generally steady. In the autumn small flocks are to be seen coursing together, the larger flocks congregating in winter on the shores of southern California and the Gulf of Mexico.

CABOT'S TERN

With royal indifference, this tern has been known to take over breeding ground already occupied by black skimmers, merely throwing sand over the skimmer's eggs and proceeding to incubate their own. The brown pelican too has suffered from the "taking ways" of the royal tern when the smaller bird was too lazy to do its own fishing.

CABOT'S TERN

CABOT'S tern is sometimes called the boy's tern. It is sixteen inches long and wears a mantle and tail of bluish-gray over its white body.

Among the swiftest and most powerful of the terns, Cabot's tern returns to the same nesting site year after year. The same constancy is shown in taking a mate; the birds, unlike other terns, remain together for life. These birds breed from North Carolina to Florida and Texas, in densely packed colonies.

COMMON TERN *(Sterna hirundo)*. Length: 1 foot. Range: Nearly cosmopolitan.
Ralph De Sola (SIM)

COMMON TERN

FISHERMEN take their cue from the sight of the common tern circling in flocks over the water. Schools of large fishes drive the smaller ones to the surface where they are fair game for the fifteen-inch sea swallow, as the common tern is also known.

These black-headed, pearl blue and white birds, while not particularly beautiful on the ground, are exceedingly graceful aloft. At one time they perched in great numbers, in a state of *rigor mortis*, on the high peaks of feminine headwear. Now, fortunately, they are protected.

Breeding through the north central States to North Carolina, the common tern either nests in a bare sandy hollow or lines this depression in the most perfunctory manner. Its red bill, legs, and feet have given the bird the additional name of red shank.

ARCTIC TERN

WINGING its way each year from the Arctic to the Antarctic regions and back, the Arctic tern accomplishes the greatest migration known in the bird world. This trip begins once the breeding duties in the North have been disposed of. The hardy birds have been known to nest within eight degrees of the North Pole.

Arctic terns make their long journey in order to avoid the oncoming Arctic winter, but incidentally they also take advantage of both the Arctic and Antarctic daylight seasons, thus enjoying twenty-four sunlit hours each day for at least eight months of the year.

ROSEATE TERN

ONCE almost exterminated along the Atlantic coast, the roseate or graceful tern is now increasing under protection. Fifteen inches long, with gray upper parts, it is during the bird's leisurely flight that the rosy-pink under parts show to best advantage. The long streamers adorning the tail were a potent factor in the avidity with which millinery hunters persecuted these terns. They have been called the longest, the slenderest, and the most highly specialized of the terns.

Roseate terns resemble common terns in their nesting habits, often sharing the same nesting locations with those birds.

LEAST TERN

SLIGHT and dainty, the nine-inch least or minute tern comes from the tropics in the spring to both the Atlantic and Pacific coasts. Swift and graceful in flight, they show a solicitude for each other that is rare among birds. When one of their number is wounded, the rest of the flock gather about squeaking plaintive and concerned cries. This trait facilitated the near extermination of the least tern. Mated pairs are very devoted; the males frequently feed the females during the incubation of the one to four eggs.

BLACK TERN

THE nine-inch black tern is not to be intruded upon lightly. In their nesting grounds in the western part of the country these insect eaters dash fiercely at an interloper, pecking him violently.

Black terns may be found wherever Franklin's gull ranges and in many places where this gull is not to be seen. To the north these birds frequent fresh-water marshes, while in the southern part of their range they seem partial to salt-water bays and inlets. Generally flying about in large groups, they catch their insect fare on the wing.

Two years after birth, these birds are ready to mate. Sometime in June they lay their two to four eggs in a slipshod nest of dead reeds.

NODDY

MERELY by adding new materials, the noddy uses the same nest year after year on the Louisiana and Florida coasts. In these aggregations of sticks, leaves, and grasses the one egg is laid which when hatched will be fiercely defended by both parents.

The brown and gray sixteen-inch birds do their fishing in groups, preying on the unfortunate fishes which may have been forced to leap from the water by larger ones.

The noddy is so called because of its habit of greeting other noddies with a nod of its head. Noddies have a distinctive courtship ritual. After nodding to each other, the female thrusts her bill down the opened throat of the male and helps herself to some morsels of fish which he has regurgitated. At this point, he runs off to find a stick which he brings back to the female.

SOOTY TERN

THE sooty terns or wide-awakes diet on small fishes and are known to drink sea water. Always moving, the sixteen-inch birds never seem to get any rest.

Along the South Atlantic and Gulf coasts, where they breed, sooty terns fight among themselves over the choicer breeding locations. Male and female take turns incubating their one to three eggs, the sitter usually being fed by the other bird.

Entirely black above, with a slight green gloss, the sooty tern has a white crescent on the forehead extending above the eyes and cut off from the white cheeks by a black band.

GULL-BILLED TERN

SOMETIMES called the Egyptian tern, the gull-billed tern is fourteen inches long, colored white with a saddle of bluish-gray. This bird of the Atlantic and Gulf States has greatly diminished in number in recent years. It will defend its nest with great courage.

CASPIAN TERN

THE Caspian tern is so large, twenty-two inches, that it has often been mistaken for a gull. The large bluish-gray and white bird is the largest of the tern family. Gull-like too, it soars aloft in great circles. However, the Caspian tern feeds like a tern, not like a gull.

Their deep red bills emitting a harsh *crack-a-day-o* they chase over the water, their slightly forked tails streaming behind in the wind. They nest in great colonies, each pair making a small hollow for their two or three eggs.

FORSTER'S TERN

FORSTER'S tern feeds less on fish than most terns. It favors insects, catching them on the wing. These fork-tailed, fifteen-inch, bluish-gray and white coursers nest in great colonies in the West, the Gulf, and southern Atlantic States. Occasionally, however, a fifteen-inch Forster's tern will drive a western grebe from its nest and appropriate the place for itself. The usual colony of these terns is so crowded that the parents refuse to allow the fledglings to leave the nest as they might get lost among the neighbors' children.

In all some thirteen kinds of terns are found in the United States.

SKUA

KNOWN also as the sea hawk, the twenty-two-inch killer, the northern skua, merits the name. Blackish-brown, it looks very much like a hawk in the air, pursuing its solitary way many miles from the nearest shore. It is a wanderer of the high seas and the fishing banks, a bird of striking beauty in flight, rapacious in activity. Large and strong, it chases gulls that have just made a catch, annoying the smaller birds until they drop their prey, whereupon the skua leaps and catches it.

Bully that it is, the skua is no coward. It will courageously defend its little grass-lined depression in the ground with the two or three eggs in it. Even the massive golden eagle will be fought off if it should intrude during the nesting season.

Although web-footed, skuas seemingly are indifferent to the feel of the water, they prefer to seize their prey in the air. They come down to the fishing banks off the northern States. On the Pacific coast the Chilean skua is sometimes seen.

POMARINE JAEGER

THIS bird's German name means hunter, although robber would be much more accurate. Like the larger skuas, these birds seemingly prefer to steal fish instead of catching it for themselves. Breeding in the Arctic, they come each winter to the North Atlantic coast where they gather on the fishing banks.

Faster and fiercer than the pomarine jaeger, the parasitic jaegers often hunt in pairs and will attack even the pomarine jaeger and such a formidable opponent as the glaucous-winged gull. These birds are twenty inches long, slightly smaller than the pomarine jaegers, are found off both coasts and even in the interior.

LONG-TAILED JAEGER

THE enormously elongated and pointed tail feathers distinguish the long-tailed jaeger from the pomarine and parasitic jaegers. It is more frequently seen inland, generally about the swamps and marshes of mountain regions. Here it hunts down mice, small birds, and insects, and raids the nests of near-by birds for eggs and young.

On the sea this jaeger is the especial nemesis of the kittiwake, and since the long-tailed variety is the most graceful and adept aerialist of the jaegers, the smaller bird must get away fast if it is to keep its meal. Twisting and circling in the sky, this acrobatic fighter is one of the most agile of all birds.

Twenty-three inches in length, the long-tailed jaeger is a purplish slate-colored bird, with white under parts. Its two to three eggs are spotted with brown. These are laid in a small depression in the earth, lined with leaves and dry grasses.

Diving Birds

Down at the bottom of the evolutionary tree of birds are the diving birds. These fish eaters are the closest allied of all birds to their common reptilian ancestors. They are found at almost all times in the water, since they live on fish and marine life only. Their flesh is tough and generally unpalatable except to Eskimos.

On land these birds are awkward and ungainly, their legs being placed in such a rearward position as to force the birds to stand or squat almost perpendicularly. Clothed in dense plumage, colored alike in both sexes, and provided with a warm layer of body fat, diving birds are further adapted for their aquatic life by having webbed or lobed feet. The body and neck of a diving bird are, as a rule, elongated so that the bird has a boat-shaped appearance.

Their bills are without pouches to carry fish in, but they can be opened quite wide.

Of the two suborders of diving birds, the family of grebes comprise one by themselves; the other is formed by the family of loons and that of the auks, murres, and puffins.

Grebes and loons both are skillful swimmers and clumsy walkers. The smaller grebes are found farther inland than the loons, in bodies of fresh water, although they are quite at home on the ocean. Swift flyers, the grebes for some reason prefer to dive and swim underwater when threatened.

Extinct member of the group is the great auk. Unable to fly, it was shot for its down and salted away in barrels of provision ships. Its eggs were stolen in a relentless persecution which began in earnest when white men first reached the shores of this continent. It became extinct about 1844. Today only stuffed specimens exist, to the number of eight birds and seventy eggs.

Dr. Hornaday states in his *American Natural History:* "When Funk Island was visited by Mr. F. A. Lucas in 1887, in quest of auk remains, he found deposits of bones several feet in thickness, evidently where the bodies of slaughtered birds had been heaped up, and left to decay. Out of these deposits, several barrels of mixed bones and peaty earth were taken which yielded several complete skeletons of that species."

The great auk had extremely keen hearing and was quick to take alarm. However, it was awkward on land and could easily be overtaken by men. It was never studied systematically so little is known of its feeding habits.

AUKS

WITH the first warm breath of spring, the auks return by the thousands from their migrations, to the sheer cliffs and rocks of their northern breeding grounds. Here, along the shores of the Atlantic and Pacific Oceans, the birds gather for courtship. Bowing and waddling, cooing, gurgling, and hoarsely croaking, the squat and boisterous birds plight their troth.

Among the fallen rocks or in a shallow hole each pair of mating birds lay a single egg which differs greatly in color in different species.

When the fledgling is hatched it is covered with a dark gray or brown down, and depends upon its parents for food until fully grown.

But there comes a time when the patience of the parents is overtaxed and then the adolescent is seized by the back of the neck like an overgrown lout and dragged off into the sea to be ducked. Once, twice, three times, the mother auk dives with the youngster until the chick breaks away from its parent's grip and proceeds to dive and swim by itself.

GREAT AUKS *(Plautus impennis)*. Length: 2½ feet. Range: Formerly found on coasts and islands of the North Atlantic. Extinct since 1844.
R. Bruce Horsfall

Seven to about seventeen inches in length, the species of this small Arctic sea bird live exclusively on fishes and crustaceans. They not only dive well but swim expertly beneath the surface of the water, using both feet and wings. The auk seems almost to prefer this mode of locomotion to flying, which it does heavily. Sometimes when pursued it will skim along the water, fluttering its wings as if unable to fly.

Dull and unsuspicious, these gregarious birds have many enemies, not only the Eskimos but foxes, gulls, and ravens as well. Many of them fall victim to the fury of the Arctic blizzards.

Auks have three-toed webbed feet which they use as brakes both in the air and under the water.

RAZOR-BILLED AUK

ON the North Atlantic and adjacent parts of the Arctic Ocean the sixteen-inch razor-billed auk is found. This bird, also known as the tinker, icebird, and sea crow, has a sharply compressed bill and a wedge-shaped tail containing twelve feathers. Black above, it has a narrow white line connecting the base of the bill with the eye. Breeding in the Gulf of St. Lawrence, the razor-billed auk finds its way as far south as the coasts of North Carolina.

LITTLE AUK

ANOTHER auk of the North Atlantic that makes the southern jaunt for the winter is the little auk or dovekie, measuring but eight inches. This smallest of the Atlantic auks swims low in the water and may be distinguished by its short, stout bill and flesh-colored feet. It breeds in Arctic Canada, Greenland, and Iceland.

Still smaller, the seven-inch least auklet is the midget of the entire species. It drifts down to the State of Washington from the North Pacific and Bering Sea.

Covering the same range, the nine-inch Cassin's auklet is nocturnal during the breeding season. Its upper parts are dusky gray, with small white spots above and below the eyes.

DOVEKIE *(Alle alle)*. Length: 8 inches. Range: Coasts and islands of North Atlantic.
New York Zoological Society

Two more of these North Pacific auks find their way to the Californias during the winter; the sooty blackish, fourteen-inch rhinoceros auklet, and the somewhat smaller paroquet auklet whose gray sides and flanks turn white during the cold season.

PUFFINS

UTTERLY grotesque in appearance, this sea bird of the North Atlantic and Pacific coasts waddles along like a penguin, bolt upright, its enormous caricature of a beak, emblazoned with yellow, red, and blue bands, swaying before its face. Its call has been described as a "low mirthless laughter."

Comical as the bird is normally, during the breeding season it becomes a cartoonist's dream. Its beak is much larger then, and redder. The faces of both male and female turn from blackish to white, until they look like masked tipplers, placing one red foot,

PUFFIN

webbed and clawed, before the other. After the breeding period the "nose" is considerably reduced in size, as sixteen of the eighteen horny plates which give it its bulk fall away. The remaining plates are then a brownish color. The brilliant reddish nuptial tint of the eyelids also fades.

Only one chick is born to each nesting pair of puffins. Male and female have divided the labor of preparing for it, the father bird excavating the burrow in the hillside which serves as the nest, the mother bird incubating the egg. Small as it is, the fledgling puffin is covered with black down, an inch long at birth, looking like a black powder puff.

Aloft, the adult birds fly well, although they tend to labor a bit. Puffins do not rise easily from the water, especially when the surface is calm. In rough weather, aided by a gust of wind, they flap their wings, dip into the water several times, and finally take off.

ATLANTIC PUFFINS *(Fratercula a. arctica)*. Length: 1 foot. Range: Coasts and islands of North Atlantic.
Allan D. Cruickshank, National Wildlife Federation

The special providence that looks after puffins must work overtime, as these sea parrots escape danger, when they escape it at all, seemingly by sheer inadvertence and muddling through. Many a puffin's feathery hide has gone into the manufacture of the warm parkas which keep the Eskimos of the Northland warm.

The cry of the puffin is heard only when the bird is frightened or excited. Otherwise it is silent as it goes about its fishing.

TUFTED PUFFIN

SIXTEEN inches long, the tufted puffin roams the Bering Sea. With the coming of winter, the bird flies down the west coast of North America to southern and Lower California where it nests in rocky crevices and burrows in the Santa Barbara Islands from April to July.

Black above, the tufted puffin has a brown chin, cheeks, throat, and foreneck. Its under parts are a deep grayish brown. During the breeding season it develops yellow tufts on the side of the head as well as an enlarged bill. Its feet become salmon-red.

OTHER PUFFINS

SOMEWHAT smaller, the horned puffin accomplishes the same migration each winter. This bird has white under parts and white cheeks.

Smallest of the puffins, the Atlantic puffin measures eleven and a half to fourteen inches. During the winter it leaves the bleak shores of the North Atlantic to come as far south as Massachusetts.

GUILLEMOTS

ARDENT lovers, the pigeon guillemots think nothing of killing each other in a dispute over a female. A spectral gray in the winter, when it is found in Lower California, the pigeon guillemot is solid black during the mating season. Ordinarily mild and gregarious, these birds are irate and bellicose during the mating season. In fights the weaker bird is frequently dragged beneath the water and held there by its stronger opponent. Sometimes the embattled birds break through the surface of the sea into the air, like flyingfishes, still chasing each other.

Graceful and adroit in the water, a good diver and swimmer, the guillemot flies and walks awkwardly.

Pigeon guillemot chicks are afraid of light and refuse to rest until safely tucked into the subterranean holes which serve as their nests.

BLACK GUILLEMOTS

ALSO called the sea pigeon, the black guillemot male pursues the female on land, sea, beneath the sea, and in the air. Eventually she yields.

This buoyant bird rises by striking the water with its feet. Under water it prefers to use its wings.

High in the most inaccessible portions of the rocky coast line of Maine, the Gulf of St. Lawrence, and Labrador, black guillemots make their nests in little rocky caves. Jet black and covered with down, the two little offspring are fed with

PALLAS'S MURRES *(Uria lomvia arra).* Length: 1½ feet. Range: Alaska, Arctic Ocean, and Japan. Similar species are found wintering in the United States.
American Museum of Natural History

shellfishes which the parent birds get by diving, which they do expertly.

Almost extinct, the common murre or guillemot has been intensively hunted for twenty-five years. A few are still seen in Maine and southern California. This sixteen-to-eighteen-inch bird has a white face marked with a black line from the base of the bill to the eye.

BRÜNNICH'S MURRE

LARGEST of the murres, Brünnich's murre is a very common waterfowl seen in great numbers in Maine. This eighteen-inch bird broods erect over its eggs in penguin fashion. The eggs have a tendency to roll in a circle when they are dislodged, their ends being sharply tapered.

The head, neck, and upper parts of this bird are grayish-black; the throat, foreneck, breast, and abdomen are white. Its bill is long and stout, blackish in color.

The common murre may be distinguished from Brünnich's murre by its slenderer bill and the pale line along its upper mandible.

ANCIENT MURRELET

VAST colonies of ancient murrelets form upon the islands of the Arctic. Here the young fledglings, but two days out of the shell, are initiated into the mysteries of the sea. Chirping like English sparrows, they tumble down the slopes and race for the water to which they take with amazing aptitude. They seem to need no prompting from their parents. Ancient murrelets find their way to California during the winter. The short stout bills of these birds are bluish-white.

In the Bering Sea the natives call these birds the "Old Man" because of the feathered appearance of its head. These feathers are molted in the winter, however, when the birds reach southern waters.

Other winter visitors to California from the Arctic are the marbled murrelet, Xantus' murrelet, and Craveri's murrelet.

COMMON LOONS *(Gavia immer)*. Length: 2½ feet. Range: Northern part of northern hemisphere. Needs protection.
American Museum of Natural History

LOONS

THE solitary loon travels alone or, at most, in pairs. Nesting near the water's edge, it is prepared to slip instantly under the surface where its enemies cannot follow. Often the loon rests under the water tucking one foot under the feathers of the flank, and paddling in circles with the other—its bill placed under its scapulars.

Those who have hunted in the northern woods know how thrilling and eerie the call of the loon can be. If there is a voice of the forest primeval, this is it—an age-old call that haunted these same forest spaces many thousands of years ago. Fossil loons give credence to this last statement.

Supple and vigorous, loons move with little effort over the surface of the water, wholly or partly submerging their bodies at will. Their flattened legs and toes, connected by webs, churn the birds along with such speed that hunters are often unable to catch up with them as they move through swamp and lake. Loons dive so rapidly that hunters swear they are able to dodge a bullet. Their short wings working like fins, the diving loons can get down sixty feet below the surface where they pounce upon fishes with their daggerlike bills. The catch is brought to the surface where it is battered and crushed into pancake shape before being swallowed. Sometimes a fish six inches in diameter, a quarter as large as the bird, is swallowed in this manner.

Its feet placed far to the rear, the loon is even clumsier than a duck while on land. Forced to remain upright while walking, it makes its visits to shore infrequent and short. It shows great speed, however, when it must scamper into the water.

The loon's flight is strong, but it requires the assistance of a head wind to rise. The young learn to swim almost as soon as they are out of the shell.

COMMON LOON

A LARGE heavy bird, the common loon, also called the great northern diver, is said by Dr. Forbush to "typify savagery." Sometimes three feet long, these startling birds have black bills, feet, and legs, and are black above, with white under parts.

While at sea, the shrill voice of the great northern diver is still. But during the breeding season its insane-sounding laughter pierces the stillness of the woods.

It lays two or three eggs, elliptical in shape, oily brown in color, and makes no apparent effort to conceal them. In this country loons are found mainly in California, Iowa, New York, New England, and, in the winter, occasionally in Florida. With the melting of the ice they begin their return trip to the Arctic regions. Along the Atlantic coast the staple item in the loon's diet is fish. Inland they eat frogs, crabs, mollusks, leeches, insects, and also various water plants.

The common loon and the related black-throated and red-throated loons are hunted extensively and are considered excellent game.

BLACK-THROATED LOON

KNOWN also as the Pacific loon and Pacific diver, the black-throated loon is somewhat smaller than the common loon. Its eggs are also somewhat narrower and darker.

In the winter it comes inland to the central States and sometimes ventures as far east as Long Island. It breeds in deep lakes, on vegetation near water, or on bare ground, in much the same fashion as the common loon. Its one or two eggs are olive-green.

RED-THROATED LOON

THE red-throated loon is the smallest of the species. It is also called the tutchmunk, scapegrace, and little loon.

Distinguished from the common loon by the bluish-gray coloring on the crown and the back of the neck, these birds are rather gregarious for loons, and may be seen at times in small flocks. They range through the southern part of California, up and down the Atlantic coast from Maine to Florida, and across country to the Great Lakes region.

GREBES

POSSESSED of great rapidity of movement and an ability to sink out of sight instantaneously, the grebe has exasperated many sportsmen, caused them to chase it for hours at a time, and has earned for itself the appropriate and graphic names of hell-diver and waterwitch. It never seems to be ruffled at the approach of danger, and its escape (always in the water) is methodical and mysterious, on many occasions leading the hunter to believe that he never saw the bird at all. It gently lowers itself in the water until only its head and long neck protrude, looks hastily about, and then submerges with a quick downward motion of its head.

The javelin-beaked grebe is closely related to the loon in habits and physical characteristics. Long-necked and with feet placed far back under its body, its most recorded occupation is playing tag with the hunter, diving only a split second ahead of a gun shot, submerging casually without leaving a ripple in its trail.

In diving below the water's surface, the grebe seems to rise and describe a loop similar to the surface dive of man; it plunges forward, and with the aid of its short concave wings pierces the water. For its food supply it follows schools of fishes which form a substantial portion of its diet, and crushes them before swallowing. When the grebes dive for fish one bird is usually placed as lookout. This method of watching for danger seems to be peculiar to the grebes.

When alighting, the grebe spreads its wings, and with feet far behind, crashes into the water. Taking off into the air is a difficult process, requiring the striking of water with the wings, much churning and splashing, and a tail wind.

WESTERN GREBE

MEASURING twenty-four to twenty-nine inches, the western grebe inhabits western North America. Frequenting ponds, lakes, and rivers during the breeding season, it moves northward toward estuaries and the open sea in the winter.

The sexes are alike in plumage. They construct the nest from a variety of vegetation, push it into the water to create a floating island, and anchor it to shore or to vegetation on shore.

When courting, the male and female tread water, standing in an upright position with wings spread apart, and necks drawn out and arched as they thresh violently with their feet. Thus standing about three feet apart, facing each other, they churn the water until they both collapse from exhaustion, then they dive head first.

Subsequently three to five greenish-blue eggs are laid by the female. These soon become discolored and mud-stained. Unlike the loons, the grebes somehow manage to conceal their eggs at the approach of danger, plastering them with soft mud. Serving a triple purpose, the mud disguises the eggs, furnishes protection against the sun's rays in the daytime, and keeps them warm at night. The nests and eggs of the grebes are frequently destroyed by terns, ravens, and by storms which break the nest from its anchorage and capsize its contents.

When the chicks are hatched, they are given a ride on mother's back. Clambering upon her wing feathers, they are taken to the shore and dipped into the water. The mother, while acting as a ferryboat, twists her extremely long neck backward in order to feed her brood.

Male and female grebes are extremely faithful (that is, for the one breeding season), and may be constantly seen together. They are brownish-black above, satiny-white below, and the head is crested on top.

WESTERN GREBE *(Aechmophorus occidentalis)*. Length: 2 feet. Range: Western North America.
William L. Finley, Nature Magazine

The western grebe, also called western dabchick and swan grebe, is in constant danger of being exterminated for the millinery trade, since its feathers are long and conspicuously colorful. A most peculiar habit of the grebe is to eat feathers. As a matter of fact, feathers seem to constitute a major portion of its diet.

W. L. Finley has reported his observation of the hatching of these grebes. The chick cuts his way around the shell until the whole cap falls off and the chick steps out.

HOLBOELL'S GREBE

HOLBOELL'S grebe, also known as the American red-necked grebe and Holboell's diver, is noted for its speed and savagery. It can easily detect and overtake any small fish which it devours by the battering method.

Its coloration varies with the seasons. It is greenish-black above in the summer, grayish-brown above in the winter and white below. Its neck is shorter than that of the western grebe, and its body is stouter and shorter.

Ordinarily silent, the male produces a great many raucous dinning sounds during the breeding season, giving out long wailing cries. It is at all times, however, a solitary bird. It covers its eggs with mud, and in many other of its habits strongly resembles the western grebe. Its distribution is not restricted to North America, however, as it is also found breeding in Siberia.

PIED-BILLED GREBE

THE widespread pied-billed grebe, also known as didapper and helldiver, lays seven or eight eggs at the rate of one a day. In the daytime it covers the eggs with mud, and carries out this process during the entire period of incubation. The chicks, when first hatched, resemble little skunks. Almost immediately they are taken into the water, attaching themselves to the feathers and back of the mother who dives and swims with her little brood clutching desperately to her throughout the journey.

The nest is a mass of reeds and soaking vegetation attached to the shore. The food supply consists of fishes and other aquatic animals, and feathers. It is brown-black above, light brown and white below, and measures thirteen inches in length. At the approach of danger this grebe prefers to sink instead of diving, and aided by air cells in various parts of its body it is quite adept at this method of escape.

This grebe is widely distributed and is the only one to breed in the eastern United States.

Pronouncing Index

* Indicates an Illustration

Pronunciation: The symbols are those in common use; the more frequently used are given at the foot of the page. The pronunciation is in every case taken from *Webster's New International Dictionary*.

A

Acadian Chickadee (chĭk'á·dē), *477
Albacore (ăl'bȧ·kōr), 206
Albatross (ăl'bȧ·trôs), 701, *702
Alligator (ăl'ĭ·gā″tēr), 294, *295, *297
Alligator and Crocodile, *298
Alligator Gar, *261, 263
Alligator Snapping Turtle, 394, *395
Allison's Tuna, *see* Yellowfin Tuna
Amberjack, 177
American Bison, *25
American Eagle, 582, *583, *584
American Perch, *see* Yellow Perch
American Sable, *see* Marten
American Toad, *436
Amphioxus (ăm'fĭ·ŏk″sŭs), *see* Lancelet
Anchovy (ăn·chō'vĭ), 253
Ancient Murrelet, 730
Angelfish, 173
 Black, *173
 Queen, 173
Angler (ăng'glēr), *145, 146
 Deep Sea, *148
 Oceanic, 148
Ani, Groove-Billed (ä'nē), 557
Anole (á·nō'lē), *see* Chameleon
Antelope, Pronghorn (ăn'tḗ·lōp), 28
Antelope Ground Squirrel, 83
Aplomado (ăp″lȯ·mä'dō), 582
Arctic Tern, 718
Argentine (är'jĕn·tĭn), 245
Arizona Vine Snake, 377
Armadillo (är″mȧ·dĭl'ō), 16
 Texas, 17
Atlantic Puffin, 728
Audubon's Caracara (kä″ra·kä'ra), *575

Auk (ôk), 724
 Great, 724
 Little, 725
 Razor-Billed, 725
Avocet (ăv'ȯ·sĕt), 633, *634
Axolotl (ăk'sȯ·lŏt'l), *see* Tiger Salamander

B

Badger (băj'ēr), 105, *106, *107
Bailey's Collared Lizard, 313
Bald Eagle, *see* American Eagle
Baldpate (bôld'pāt″), *672
Baleen (bȧ·lēn'), 8
Baltimore Oriole, 522
Band-Tailed Pigeon, 602
Banded Gecko (gĕk'ō), 303, *304
Banded Ground Snake, 368
Bank Swallow, 505
Barbero, *see* Surgeonfish
Barking Squirrel, *see* Prairie Dog
Barn Owl, *563, 564
Barn Swallow, *506
Barracuda (băr″ȧ·kōō'dȧ), 207
 California, 209
 Great, 208
Barred Owl, 565, *566
Barren Ground Caribou (kăr'ĭ·bōō), 33
Basking Shark, 269
Bass (băs), 184
 Black, 184
 Large-Mouthed, 184
 Mud, 187
 Rock, 184, 187
 Sea, 182
 Small-Mouthed, 184
 Strawberry, 187
 Striped, 187
 White, 187
Bassarisk (băs'ȧ·rĭsk), *see* Ringtail Cat

Bat (băt), 126
 Big-Eared, 129
 Brown, 128
 Free-Tailed, 129
 Jackass, 129
 Leaf-Nosed, 129
 Lump-Nosed, 129
 Mastiff, 129
 Northern, 128
 Pipistrelle, 129
 Silver-Haired, 129
Batfish, *143, *144
Bear (bâr), 123
 Black, 123
 Brown, 124
 Cinnamon, 124
 Grizzly, 124
Beaver (bē'vẽr), 67, *69
 Dam, *68
 Mountain, 57
Bell Toad, 440, *441
Bellbird, *see* Wood Thrush
Bendire's Thrasher, 489
Berlander's Tortoise, 409
Bewick's Wren, 485
Big-Eared Bat, 129
Bighorn, *see* Mountain Sheep
Bison (bī's'n), 24, *27
 Eastern, 28
 Plains, 28
 Wood, 28
Bittern (bĭt'ẽrn), 655
Black-and-White Warbler, 497
Black Angelfish, 173
Black-Banded Skink, 335
Black Bass, 184
Black Bear, 123, *124, *125
Black-Billed Cuckoo, 558
Black-Capped Vireo, 499
Black-Chinned Hummingbird, 540
Black-Chinned Sparrow, 515
Black-Crowned Night Heron, *656, 658
Black Dogfish, 274
Black Duck, 677
Black Fox, 101

āle, chȧotic, câre, ȧdd, ăccount, ärm, ȧsk, sofȧ; ēve, hẹre, ėvent, ĕnd, silẽnt, makēr; īce, ĭll, charĭty; ōld, ȯbey, ôrb, ŏdd, sŏft, cȯnnect; fōōd, fōŏt; out, oil, cūbe, ūnite, ûrn, ŭp, circŭs, menü; chair; go; sing; then, thin; nature, verdure.

737

PRONOUNCING INDEX

Black Guillemot (gĭl'ė.mŏt), 729
Black Iguana (ĭ.gwä'na), 308
Black Marlin, 199
Black-Necked Stilt, 632, *633
Black Rail, 645
Black Rat, 64, 67
Black Swift, 542
Black-Tailed Deer, 41, 42
Black Tern, 719
Black-Throated Loon, 733
Black-Throated Sparrow, 515
Black Turnstone, 622
Black Vulture, 598
Black Wolf, 105
Blackbird, 519
  Red-Winged, 520
  Rusty, 520
  Yellow-headed, 520
Blackburnian Warbler, 497
Blackcat, see Fisher
Blackfish, 11
Blacksnake, 352, 354, *355
Blanding's Turtle, 403, *404
Bleak, 235
Blind Worm, 325
Blow Snake, see Hog-Nosed Snake
Blowing Viper, see Hog-Nosed Snake
Blue Bull Snake, 352
Blue Catfish, 230
Blue Goose, 680
Blue Grosbeak, 510
Blue-Headed Vireo, 499
Blue Jay, 528, *529
Blue Marlin, *199
Blue Shark, 270
Blue-Throated Hummingbird, 540
Blue Whale, 4
Blue-Winged Warbler, 497
Blueback Mullet, 212
Bluebird, 470, *471
Bluefin Tuna, 204
Bluefish, 177
Blunt-Headed Gecko, 305
Boa (bō'à), 342
  Dwarf, 342
  Rosy, 342
  Rubber, 342
Boat-Tailed Grackle (grăk''l), 522
Bob-White, 617, *618
Bobcat, 92
Bobolink (bŏb'ȯ.lĭngk), 523
Bohemian Waxwing, 502
Bonaparte's Gull, 714

Bonito (bȯ.nē'tō), 206
Booby (boo'bĭ), 697, *699
Boomer, see Mountain Beaver
Borer, 283
Bottlenosed Porpoise, *10
Bowfin, 258, *259
Bowhead Whale, 8
Box Snake, 360
Box Terrapin, see Mud Turtle
Box Turtle, 404, *406
Boxfish, see Porcupinefish
Brandt's Cormorant (kôr'mô-ränt), 694
Brant, 680
Bream, see Dace
Broad-Winged Hawk, 592
Bronzed Grackle, 522
Brook Stickleback, 217
Brook Trout, *249
Brotulid (brō.tū'lĭd), *143
Brown Bat, *127
Brown Bear, 124
Brown Creeper, *482
Brown Pelican, *688
Brown Skink, *333
Brown Snake, 350
  See also Storer's Snake
Brown Thrasher, *486, 487
Brown Trout, 250
Brunnick's Murre, 730
Brush Rabbit, 52
Buffalo (bŭf'à.lō) see Bison
Buffalofish, *238, 239
Bufflehead, 676
Bull Frog, *425
Bull Snake, 357
Bull Trout, 250
Bullhead Catfish, *229
Bunting (bŭn'tĭng), 516
  Indigo, 516
  Painted, 517
  Plumed, 517
  Snow, 517
Burrowing Owl, 570, *571
Burrowing Squirrel, see Prairie Dog
Bush Snake, 378
Bush-Tit, 478
Butterflyfish, 172
Buzzard (bŭz'ẽrd), see Turkey Vulture

C

Cabot's Tern, 717
Cacomistle (kăk'ȯ.mĭs'''l), see Ringtail Cat

Cacomitl (kăk'ȯ.mĭt'''l), see Jaguarundi
Cactus Wren, 483
Ca'ing Whale, see Blackfish
Calico Bass, see Strawberry Bass
California Barracuda, 209
California Condor, 595, *596
California Flyingfish, 225
California Gull, 712
California Hagfish, see Borer
California Jay, 530
California Quail, 617
California Sea Lion, 85, *86
California Thrasher, 489
California Valley Quail, *616
Camas Rat (kăm'ăs), see Pocket Gopher
Camp's Frog, 431
Canada Goose, 678, *679
Canada Jay, 530
Canada Lynx, 90
Canvasback, 674
Cape Striped Lizard, 331
Caracara (kä''rà.kä'rà), 575
  Audubon's, *575
  Guadalupe, 577
Carcajou (kär'kà.jōō), see Wolverine
Cardinal, 518, *519
Caribou (kăr'ĭ.bōō), 31, *32
  Barren Ground, 33
  Mountain, 33
  Woodland, 33
Carolina Paroquet (păr'ȯ.kĕt), *559
Carolina Rail, see Sora
Carp, 235
  Gold, 237
  Leather, 237
  Mirror, 237
  Scaled, 237
Carp Sucker, see Sucker
Carrion Crow, see Turkey Vulture
Caspian Tern, 720
Cat Squirrel, 80
Catbird, 487, *488
Catfish, 228
  Blue, 230
  Gafftopsail, 230
  Sea, 230
  White, 230
Cattalo (kăt'à.lō, 26
Cave Salamander, *447, *450
Cedar Waxwing, 502, *503
Cerulean Warbler, 495
Chameleon (kȧ.mē'lė.ŭn), 305, *307

āle, châotic, câre, ădd, ăccount, ärm, àsk, sofà; ēve, hẽre, ėvent, ĕnd, silėnt, makēr; īce, ĭll, charĭty; ōld, ȯbey, ôrb, ŏdd, sôft, cȯnnect; fōōd, fŏŏt; out, oil, cūbe, ūnite, ûrn, ŭp, circŭs, menü; chair; go; sing; then, thin; nature, verdure.

PRONOUNCING INDEX

Channel Bass, see Drum
Chaparral Cock (chăp″ȧ·răl′), see Roadrunner
Cheekpockets, see Pocket Gopher
Chestnut-Sided Warbler, 497
Chicaree (chĭk′ȧ·rē), see Pine Squirrel
Chickadee (chĭk′ȧ·dē), 477
    Acadian, *477
    Eastern, 477
Chicken Snake, 360
    See also Rat Snake
Chicken Terrapin, 401
Chimera (kī·mē′rȧ), 279, *280
Chimney Swallow, see Chimney Swift
Chimney Swift, 540, *541
Chinook (chĭ·nōōk′), 248
Chipmunk (chĭp′mŭngk), 78, *79
Chipping Sparrow, 515
Chippy, see Tree Sparrow
Chorus Frog, 433
Chub, see Dace
Chub Mackerel, 203
Chuck-Will's-Widow, 543
Chuckwalla (chŭk′wŏl″ȧ), *310
Cinnamon Bear, 124
Clapper Rail, 643
Clear-Nosed Skate, *279
Cliff Swallow, 505
Coachwhip Snake, 352, 355
Cobia (kō′bĭ·ȧ), see Sergeantfish
Codfish, 220, *221
    Common, 220
    Tom, 221
    Wachna, 221
    Wall-Eyed, 221
Collared Lizard, 311, *312
Collared Peccary (pĕk′ȧ·rĭ), 43, *44
Collared Swift, see Spiny Swift
Colorado Turkey, see Wood Ibis
Common Dolphin, 10
Common Eel, *243
Common Gar, 263
Common Loon, *731, 732
Common Murre (mûr), 730
Common Porpoise, 11
Common Sea Drum, 176
Common Tern, *717, 718
Condor, California, 596
Conger Eel (kŏng′gēr), 241, 243
Congo Eel, 451, *452
Cony (kō′nĭ), see Pika

Cooper's Hawk, 587
Cooper's Tanager, 508
Coot, *639
Cooter Terrapin, 401
Cope's Hook-Nosed Snake, 368
Copperhead, 382, *383
Coral Snake, 378, *379
Coral Snake, False, see King Snake
Cormorant (kôr′mô·rănt), 691, *692
    Brandt's, 694
    Double-Crested, 693
Corn Snake, 360, 362
Cornetfish, 215
Cory's Shearwater, 707
Cotton Rat, 63, 64
Cottonmouth Moccasin, 380, *381
Cottontail Rabbit, 50, *51
Couch's Swift, see Spiny Swift
Cougar (kōō′gēr), 97
Courlan (kōōr′lăn), see Limpkin
Cowbird, 521
Cowfish, *155, 156
Cow-Nosed Ray, *276
Coyote (kī′ōt), 101, *103
Crampfish, see Torpedo
Crane (krān), 645
    Little Brown, 648
    Sandhill, 645
    Whooping, 647
Crappie (krăp′ĭ), 187
Creeper, 482
    Brown, 482
    Mexican, 483
    Rocky Mountain, 483
    Sierra, 483
Cricket Frog, 432
Crissal Thrasher, 489
Croaker, see Drum
Crocodile (krŏk′ô·dĭl), 299, *300
Crocus (krō′kŭs), see Fresh Water Drum
Cross Fox, 101
Crossbill, 510
Crow, 525, *527
    Common, 525
    Fish, 527
Cuckoo (kōōk′ōō), 558
    Black-Billed, 558
    Yellow-Billed, 558
Curlew (kûr′lū), 631, *632
Cusk, 222
Cut-Throat Trout, 250
Cutlass Fish, 210

D

Dab, see Fluke
Dace (dās), 231
    Horned, 234
Daddy Sculpin, 171
Darter, 190
Tessellated, 191
Deep-Water Moray, 241
Deer, 38
    Black-Tailed, 41, 42
    Mule, 41
    Virginia, 38
    White-Tailed, 38
DeKay's Snake, 351
Demoiselle (dĕm″wä·zĕl′), 163
Desert Iguana (ĭ·gwä′nȧ), *308, 309
Desert Swift, see Spiny Swift
Desert Tortoise (tôr′tŭs), *409
Devil Fish, see Manta
Diamond-Backed Rattlesnake, 386
Diamondback Terrapin, *399
Dickcissel (dĭk·sĭs′ĕl), 517
Dipper, *489
Doctorfish, see Surgeonfish
Dog Snapper, *179
Dogfish, 273
    Black, 274
    Smooth, 274
    Spiny, 273
Dolphin (dŏl′fĭn), 11
    Blackfish, 11
    Common, 10
    Killer, 9
Dolphin (fish), 194, *195
Double-Crested Cormorant, 693
Dove (dŭv), 600
    Ground, 602
    Mourning, 600
Dovekie (dŭv′kĭ), *726
Dowditch (dou′dĭch), 628
Downy Woodpecker, 546
Drum, *175
    Common Sea, 176
    Fresh-Water, 176
Duck, 668
    Baldpate, 672
    Black, 677
    Bufflehead, 676
    Canvasback, 674
    Eider, 675
    Gadwall, 677
    Golden-Eyed, 677
    Mallard, 670
    Old-Squaw, 674
    Pintail, 677

āle, chȧotic, câre, ădd, ȧccount, ärm, ȧsk, sofȧ; ēve, hęre, ėvent, ĕnd, silẽnt, makēr; īce, ĭll, charĭty; ōld, ȯbey, ôrb, ŏdd, sȯft, cȯnnect; fōōd, fŏŏt; out, oil, cūbe, ûnite, ûrn, ŭp, circŭs, ₥enü; chair; go; sing; then, thin; nature, verdŭre.

739

PRONOUNCING INDEX

Redhead, 677
Ring-Necked, 677
Ruddy, 676
Scaup, 674
Scoter, 677
Shoveler, 673
Teal, 676
Wood, 677
Duck-Gill Eel, 244
Duck Hawk, 577, *578
Duckbill Cat, see Paddlefish
Dusky Grouse (grous), 610
Dwarf Boa, 342
Dwarf Pocket Rat, 66

E

Eagle (ē'g'l), 582
  American, 582
  Golden, 585
Eared Grebe (grēb), 737
Eastern Bison, 28
Eastern Chickadee, 477
Eel, 241
  Common, 243
  Conger, 243
  Congo, 451
  Duck-Gill, 244
  Long-Necked, 244
  Parasitic, 244
  Snake, 244
  Spiny, 244
  Thread, 244
  Worm, 244
Eel-pout, *284
Egret (ē'grĕt), *657, *658
Eider Duck (ī'dēr), 675
Elephant Fish, see Ratfish
Elf Owl, 572
Elk, see Wapiti
Elver, see Eel
Emperor Goose, 680
English Sparrow, 512, *513
Ermine (ûr'mĭn), see Weasel
Ermine Owl, see Snowy Owl
Escolar (ĕs"kô·lär'), 210
Evening Grosbeak (grōs'bēk"), 510
Everglade Kite, 594, *595
Everglade Water Rat, 62
Eyra (ā'ra), see Jaguarundi

F

Falcon, Prairie, 582
Fallfish, 235
Fan-Tail Mullet, see Blueback Mullet

Ferret, see Weasel
Field Mouse, 62
Filefish, 156, *157
Finback Whale, 8
Finch (fĭnch), 509
  Gold-, 511
  House, 509
  Purple, 509
  Rosy, 511
Fish Crow, 527
Fish Hawk, see Osprey
Fisher, 119
Fishing Duck, see Merganser
Five-Lined Skink, 332, *334
Flamingo (flȧ·mĭng'ō), 664, *665
Flapjack Turtle, see Soft-Shelled Turtle
Flasher, see Sea Bass
Flat-Nosed Snake, 356
Flatfish, 217
Flathead, see Dace
Flathead, see Wood Ibis
Flicker, 550, *551
Florida Gallinule (găl'ĭ·nūl), 641
Florida Jay, 529
Florida Manatee (măn"ȧ·tē'), *14
Flounder, see Flatfish
Fluke, 219
Flycatcher
  See also Gnatcatcher
  Phoebe, 536
  Scissor-Tailed, 534
  Vermilion, 536
Flying Squirrel, 84
Flyingfish, 222, *223, *224
  California, 225
  Monroe's, 225
Forest Salamander (săl'ȧ·măn"dēr), 448
Forked-Tailed Petrel (pĕt'rĕl), 704
Forster's Tern, 721
Four-Eyed Butterflyfish, 172
Four-Spined Stickleback, *216
Fowler's Toad, *439
Fox, 99
  Black, 101
  Cross, 101
  Gray, 101
  Red, 99
  Silver, 101
  Tree, 101
Fox Sparrow, 516
Fox Squirrel, 81
Franklin's Gull, 713

Free-Tailed Bat, 129
Fresh Water Drum, 176
Frigate Bird, see Man-O'-War Bird
Frigate Mackerel, 203
Frogs, 424
  Bull, 425
  Camp's, 431
  Chorus, 433
  Cricket, 432
  Gopher, 429
  Green, 428
  Leopard, 426
  Marnock's, 431
  Northern, 429
  Pickerel, 428
  Ricord's, 431
  Robber, 429
  Tree, 432, 434
  Western, 429
  White-Lipped, 431
  Wood, 428
Frostfish, see Cutlass Fish
Fur Seal, 87

G

Gadwall Duck, 677
Gafftopsail Catfish (găf·tŏp's'l), 230
Gallinule (găl'ĭ·nūl), 640
  Florida, 641
  Purple, 640
Gannet (găn'ĕt), 696, *697
  See also Wood Ibis
Gar (gär), 263
  Alligator, 263
  Common, 263
  Short-Nosed, 263
Gar-Pike, 260
Garter Snake, 343, *344
Gecko (gĕk'ō), 302
  Banded, 303
  Blunt-Headed, 305
  Mediterranean, 305
  Reef, 305
  Warty, 303
Gila Monster (hē'lȧ), 325, *327
Gizzard Shad, 252
Glass Snake, 323, *324
Glaucous Gull, 715
Globefish, see Puffer
Glossy Ibis (ī'bĭs), 661
Gnatcatcher, 475
Gnome Owl, see Pygmy Owl
Goby (gō'bĭ), 162
Godwit (gŏd'wĭt), 630
Gold Carp, 237

āle, châotic, câre, ădd, ȧccount, ärm, ȧsk, sofȧ; ēve, hẽre, ĕvent, ēnd, silẽnt, makēr; īce, ĭll, charĭty; ōld, ôbey, ôrb, ŏdd, sôft, cŏnnect; fo͞od, fo͝ot; out, oil, cūbe, ûnite, ûrn, ŭp, circŭs, menü; chair; go; sing; then, thin; nature, verdûre.

740

PRONOUNCING INDEX

Golden-Crowned Kinglet, *474
Golden-Crowned Sparrow, 515
Golden Eagle, 585, *586
Golden-Eyed Duck, 677
Golden-Mantled Ground Squirrel, *84
Golden Plover, 623
Golden Trout, 250
Golden-Winged Warbler, 497
Goldfinch, 511
Goldfish, see Gold Carp
Goosander (gōōs·ăn′dẽr), see Merganser
Goose (gōōs), 678
  Blue, 680
  Brant, 680
  Canada, 678
  Emperor, 680
  Snow, 679
Goosefish, see Angler
Gopher, Pocket (gō′fẽr), 71
Gopher Frog, 429
Gopher Snake, *353
  See also Indigo Snake
Gopher Tortoise, 407
Goshawk (gŏs′hôk″), 588, *589
Grackle (grăk′'l), 520
  Boat-Tailed, 522
  Bronzed, 522
  Great-Tailed, 522
  Purple, 520
Graham's Lizard, 331
Grasshopper Mouse, 63, 65
Grasshopper Sparrow, 514
Gray Fox, 101
Gray Perch, see Fresh Water Drum
Gray Snapper, 180
Gray Squirrel, 80, *81
Gray Whale, 8
Gray Wolf, 105
Grayling (grā′lĭng), 245
Great Auk (ôk), *724
Great Barracuda (băr″à·kōō′då), *208
Great Black-Backed Gull, 711
Great Blue Heron, 651, *652
Great Gray Owl, 567
Great-Tailed Grackle, 522
Great White Heron, *654, 655
Great White Owl, see Snowy Owl
Grebe (grēb), 733
  Eared, 737
  Holboell's, 736
  Horned, 737
  Pied-Billed, 736
  Western, 734

Green Frog, 428
Green Heron, 653
Green Jay, 530
Green Moray, 239, *240
Green Snake, 368
Green Tree Frog, *433
Green Turtle, 411, *412
Greenland Whale, see Bowhead
Greenlet, 499
Grenadier (grĕn″à·dēr′), *143
Grosbeak (grōs′bĕk″), 510
  Blue, 510
  Evening, 510
  Pine, 510
  Rose-Breasted, 510
Groove-Billed Ani (ä′nē), 557
Ground Dove, 602
Ground Lizard, see Brown-Backed Skink
Ground Snake, see Storer's Snake
Ground Squirrel, 83
Groundhog, see Woodchuck
Grouper (grōōp′ẽr), 180, *181
Grouse (grous), 607
  Dusky, 610
  Ruffed, 608
  Sharp-Tailed, 612
  Spruce, 611
Guadalupe Caracara (gwä″dà-lōōp′ kä″rà·kä′rà), 577
Gudgeon (gŭj′ŭn), see Dace
Guillemot (gĭl′ē·mŏt), 728
  Black, 729
Guitarfish, 278
Gull (gŭl), 712
  Bonaparte's, 714
  California, 712
  Franklin's, 713
  Glaucous, 715
  Great Black-Backed, 711
  Heermann's, 712
  Herring, 709
  Kittiwake, 715
  Laughing, 713
  Ring-Billed, 712
  Sabine's, 714
  Skimmer, 715
Gull-Billed Tern, 720
Gurnard, Flying (gûr′nẽrd), 164
Gyrfalcon (jûr′fôl″kŭn), *581

H

Hackleback Sturgeon, 267
Haddock (hăd′ŭk), 221
Hagdon (hăg′dŭn), see Shearwater
Hagfish, 283
Hairy Woodpecker, 546
Hake, 222
Halfbeak, 225
Halibut, 219
Hammerhead Shark, 272
Hammond's Spadefoot Toad, 438
Harbor Porpoise, see Common Porpoise
Hardhead Trout, 250
Hare, 50
  See also Jack Rabbit
  Snowshoe, 50
  Varying, 50
Harlequin Snake (här′lĕ·kwĭn), see Coral Snake
Harris's Hawk, 590
Harris's Sparrow, 515
Harvest Mouse, 63, 65
Hawk (hôk), 585
  Broad-Winged, 592
  Cooper's, 587
  Duck, 577
  Goshawk, 588
  Harris's, 590
  Marsh, 588
  Pigeon, 579
  Red-Shouldered, 590
  Red-Tailed, 589
  Rough-Legged, 591
  Sennett's White-Tailed, 592
  Sharp-Shinned, 587
  Sparrow, 580
  Swainson's, 591
Hawk Owl, 570
Hawksbill Turtle, *412, 413
Hayden's Skink, 334
Headfish, see Sunfish
Heath Hen, *611
Heermann's Gull, 712
Hellbender, *459
Henslow's Sparrow, 514
Hepatic Tanager (hē·păt′ĭk tăn′à·jẽr), 508
Hermit Thrush, 470
Hermit Toad, see Spadefoot Toad
Heron (hĕr′ŭn), 651
  Black-Crowned Night, 658
  Great Blue, 651
  Great White, 655
  Green, 653
  Little Blue, 653
  Louisiana, 654
  Yellow-Crowned Night, 658
Herring (hĕr′ĭng), 250, *251
  Thread, 251
Herring Gull, 709, *710, *713

āle, chåotic, câre, ădd, *a*ccount, ärm, àsk, sof*a*; ēve, hêre, ĕvent, ẽnd, silĕnt, makẽr; īce, ĭll, charĭty; ōld, ȯbey, ôrb, ŏdd, sȯft, cȯnnect; fōōd, fŏŏt; **out**, **oil**, cūbe, ûnite, ûrn, ŭp, circ*u*s, menü; chair; go; sing; then, thin; nature, verdure.

741

PRONOUNCING INDEX

Herring Hog, see Common Porpoise
Hickory Shad, 252
Hieroglyphic Terrapin (hī′ĕr-ŏ-glĭf″ĭk), 400
Hog-Nosed Snake, 373, *374, *375
Holboell's Grebe, 736
Holbrook's Spadefoot Toad, 439
Hooded Warbler, 497
Hoot Owl, see Barred Owl
Horned Dace, 234
Horned Grebe, 737
Horned Lark, 533
Horned Lizard, 318, *319
Horned Owl, 569
Horned Puffin, 728
Horned Toad, see Horned Lizard
House Finch, 509
House Mouse, 67
House Wren, 483, *484
Hummingbird (hŭm′ĭng-bŭrd″), 538
  Black-Chinned, 540
  Blue-Throated, 540
  Rivolis', 540
  Ruby-Throated, 538
Humpback Whale, *5, 8

I

Ibis (ī′bĭs), 659
  Glossy, 661
  White, 662
  Wood, 659
Iguana (ĭ·gwä′nȧ), 308
  Black, 308
  Desert, 309
Indigo Bunting, 516
Indigo Snake, 352
Ipswich Sparrow, 514
Ironhead, see Wood Ibis
Ivory-Billed Woodpecker, 546

J

Jack Rabbit, 47, *48
  White-Tailed, 50
Jackass Bat, 129
Jaeger (jā′gĕr), 722
  Long-Tailed, 722
  Pomarine, 722
Jaguar (jăg′wär), *95
Jaguarundi (jăg′wär·rŭn′dĭ), *94
Jay (jā), 528

Blue, 528
California, 530
Canada, 530
Florida, 529
Green, 530
Pinon, 530
Steller's, 529
Jefferson's Salamander, 458
Jewfish, see Grouper
Jumping Mouse, *56
Junco (jŭng′kō), 516

K

Kaeding's Petrel (pĕt′rĕl), 705
Kangaroo Mouse, 56
Kangaroo Rat, *66
Kemp's Loggerhead Turtle, *412, *413
Killdeer (kĭl′dēr″), 623
Killer Dolphin, 9
King Rail, 642, *643
King Salmon, see Chinook
King Snake, 363, *364, *365
Kingbird, 535, *536
Kingfish, see Drum
Kingfisher, 553, *554
Kinglet, 473
  Golden-Crowned, 474
  Ruby-Crowned, 474
Kite (kīt), 593
  Everglades, 594
  Mississippi, 594
  Swallow-Tailed, 593
  White-Tailed, 593
Kittiwake (kĭt′ĭ·wāk), 715
Knot Sandpiper, 629

L

Lake Herring, see Whitefish
Lake Lamprey (lăm′prĭ), 282
Lake Sculpin (skŭl′pĭn), 171
Lake Sturgeon (stûr′jŭn), 267
Lake Trout, 250
Lamperina, see Borer
Lamprey (lăm′prĭ), 281
  Lake, 282
  Sea, *282
  Silver, 283
Lancefish, see Surgeonfish
Lancelet, 285, *286
Lanneret (lăn′ĕr·ĕt″), see Prairie Falcon
Large-Mouthed Bass, 184
Lark, Horned, 533

Lark Sparrow, 514
Laughing Gull, 713
Leach's Petrel, 704
Leaf-Nosed Bat, 129
Leaf-Nosed Snake, 356
Least Bittern, *655, 656
Least Sandpiper, *629
Least Tern, 719
Leather Carp, *236, 237
Leathery Turtle, see Trunkback Turtle
LeConte's Snake, 367
LeConte's Thrasher, 489
Lemming Mouse, 63
Leopard Cat, see Ocelot
Leopard Frog, 426
Leopard Lizard, 313
Limpkin, 648, *650
Ling, 222
Little Auk (ôk), 725
Little Blue Heron, 653
Little Brown Crane, 648, *649
Little Chief Hare, see Pika
Lizards, 302
  Bailey's Collared, 313
  Cape Striped, 331
  Collared, 311
  Graham's, 331
  Horned, 318
  Leopard, 313
  Night, 327
  Plated, 322
  Reticulated, 313
  Sand, *315
  Spotted, 316
  Striped, see Racerunner
  Tessellated, 331
  Wormlike, 336
  Zebra-Tailed, 317
Log-perch, see Darter
Loggerhead, see Shrike
Long-Eared Owl, 564
Long-Necked Eel, 244
Long-Tailed Jaeger, 722
Longtailed Swift, see Small-scaled Swift
Loon (loon), 731
  Black-Throated, 733
  Common, 732
  Red-Throated, 733
Louisiana Heron, 654
Louse Fish, see Sharksucker
Lump-Nosed Bat, 129
Lumpfish, *167
  See also Lumpsucker
Lumpsucker, 166
  Spiny, 168
Lungless Salamander, 445

āle, chåotic, cåre, ădd, ȧccount, ärm, ȧsk, sofȧ; ēve, hĕre, ĕvent, ĕnd, sil*e*nt, makĕr; īce, ĭll, char*i*ty; ōld, ȯbey, ôrb, ŏdd, sŏft, cȯnnect; fo͞od, fo͝ot; out, oil, cūbe, ůnite, ûrn, ŭp, circ*u*s, menü; chair; go; sing; then, thin; natūre, verdûre.

PRONOUNCING INDEX

Lynx, Canada (lĭngks), 90
Lyre Snake, *377
  See also Rear-Fanged Snake

M

Mackerel (măk′ẽr‧ĕl), 202
  Chub, 203
  Frigate, 203
  Monterey Spanish, 203
  Pacific, 203
  Sierra, 203
  Spanish, 203
Mackerel Shark, 270
Magnolia Warbler, 497
Magpie, *531
Mallard Duck, 670, *671
Man-Eater Shark, 270
Man-O'-War Bird, 685, *686, *687
Manatee (măn″à‧tē′), 13
Manta (măn′tà), 278
Many-Lined Skink, 334
Map Turtle, see Slider Terrapin
Marbled Salamander, 457, *458
Marlin, 198
  Black, 199
  Blue, 199
  Striped, 199
  White, 199
Marmot (mär′mŭt), see Woodchuck
Marnock's Frog, 431
Marsh Hawk, *588
Marsh Wren, 483
Marten, 117, *118
  Pine, 119
Martin, Purple, 505
Maryland Yellow-Throat Warbler, 494
Mastiff Bat (màs′tĭf), 129
Meadow Mouse, 62
Meadowlark, 523, *534
Mediterranean Gecko (gĕk′ō), 305
Menhaden (mĕn‧hā′d′n), 251
Merganser (mẽr‧găn′sẽr), 683, *684
Milk Snake, 366
Miller's Thumb, see Sculpin, Scaleless
Mink, *119, 120
Minnow, 231
Mirror Carp, 237
Mississippi Kite, 594
Mitchell's Toad, 423
Mockingbird, 485
Mole, 130, *131

Mole Salamander, 457
Monkey-Faced Owl, see Barn Owl
Monroe's Flyingfish, 225
Monterey Spanish Mackerel, 203
Moonfish, see Spadefish
Moos (mōōs), 33, *34, *35
Moray (mō′rā), 239
  Deep-water, 241
  Green, 239
  Spotted, 241
Mosssbunker (môs′b̯ŭngk″ẽr), see Menhaden
Mountain Beaver, 57, *59
Mountain Caribou, 33
Mountain Goat, 22
Mountain Lion, see Cougar
Mountain Quail, 615
Mountain Rover, 626
Mountain Sheep, 19
Mourning Dove, 600, *601
Mourning Warbler, 497
Mouse (mous), 56
  Field, 62
  Grasshopper, 63, 65
  Harvest, 63, 65
  House, 67
  Jumping, 56
  Kangaroo, 56
  Lemming, 63
  Meadow, 62
  Pocket, 66
  Red-Backed, 63
  Spiny Pocket, 65
  White-Footed, 63, 65
Mud Bass, 187
Mud Dab, see Fluke
Mud Eel, see Siren
Mud Puppy, 444, *445
Mud Salamander, 449
Mud Turtle, 398
Mudfish, see Bowfin
Muhlenberg's Turtle, 403
Mule Deer, *40, *41
Mullet (mŭl′ĕt), 211
  Blueback, 212
  Striped, 212
  White, 212
Murre (mûr), 730
  Brunnich's, 730
  Common, 730
Musk Hog, see Collared Peccary
Musk Turtle, 396, *397
Muskallunge (mŭs′kĕ‧lŭnj), 226, *227
Muskrat, 60, *61
  Florida Round-Tailed, 62

Musquash (mŭs′kwŏsh), see Muskrat
Myrtle Warbler, 497

N

Narrow-Mouthed Toad, 421, *422
Newt, Spotted (nūt), 453
Night Lizard, 327, *328
Nighthawk, 544
Nine-Spined Stickleback, 217
Noddy, 719
Northern Bat, 128
Northern Frog, 429
Northern Phalarope (fà‧lă′rōp″), 637
Norway Rat, 64, 67
Nurse Shark, 271
Nutcracker, 530
Nuthatch (nŭt′hăch), 480
  Pygmy, 481
  Red-Breasted, 481
  White-Breasted, 480

O

Ocellated Flounder, *218
Ocelot (ō′sĕ‧lŏt), 92, *93
Old-Squaw, 674
Olive Swift, see Small-Scaled Swift
Opossum (ô‧pŏs′ŭm), 134, *135
Orange-Crowned Warbler, 497
Orchard Oriole, 523
Orcutt's Swift, see Spiny Swift
Oriole (ō′rĭ‧ōl), 522
  Baltimore, 522
  Orchard, 523
Ornate Swift, see Small-Scaled Swift
Osprey (ŏs′prĭ), 572, *573, *574
Otter, 112, *114
  Sea, 114
Ovenbird, 494
Owl, 562
  Barn, 564
  Barred, 565
  Elf, 572
  Great Gray, 567
  Hawk, 570
  Horned, 569
  Long-Eared, 564
  Pygmy, 571
  Richardson's, 567

āle, chàotic, câre, ădd, ăccount, ärm, àsk, sofà; ēve, hẽre, ėvent, ĕnd, silĕnt, makẽr; īce, ĭll, charīty; ōld, ȯbey, ôrb, ŏdd, sôft, cŏnnect; fōod, fŏot; out, oil, cūbe, ûnite, ûrn, ŭp, circŭs, menü; chair; go; sing; then, thin; natûre, verdûre.

743

PRONOUNCING INDEX

Saw-Whet, 567
Screech, 567
Short-Eared, 565
Snowy, 570
Spotted, 566
Oyster-Catcher, 619, *620

P

Pacific Harbor Seal, *88
Pacific Mackerel, 203
Pacific Swift, see Spiny Swift
Pack Rat, 64
Paddlefish, *264
Painted Bunting, 517
Painted Turtle, *402
Painter, see Cougar
Pallas's Murre, *729
Palm Warbler, 497
Panther, see Cougar
Parasitic Eel, 244
Paroquet, Carolina (păr'ȯ·kĕt), 559
Parrot, 559
  Thick-Billed, 560
Parula Warbler (păr'ū·lȧ), 497
Peccary, Collared (pĕk'ȧ·rĭ), 43
Peewee, 537
Pekan (pĕk'ăn), see Fisher
Pelican (pĕl'ĭ·kăn), 688
  Brown, 688
  White, 689
Pennant, see Fisher
Perch, 187
  Sacramento, 187
  Wall-Eyed, 189
  Yellow, 187, 189
Peregrine (pĕr'ė·grĭn), see Duck Hawk
Petrel (pĕt'rĕl), 703
  Forked-Tailed, 704
  Leach's, 704
  Kaeding's, 705
  Wilson's, 703
Phainopepla (fā·ĭ"nō·pĕp'lȧ), see Silky Flycatcher
Phalarope (făl'ȧ·rōp), 635
  Northern, 637
  Red, 636
  Wilson's, 635
Phoebe (fē'bē), see Sea Bass
Phoebe Flycatcher, 536
Pickerel, 228
Pickerel Frog, 428
Pied-Billed Grebe, 736
Pigeon, Band-Tailed (pĭj'ŭn), 602

Pigeon Hawk, 579
Pika (pī'kȧ), 52, *53
Pike, *226
Pike-Perch, *189
Pileated Woodpecker, *548
Pilot Blacksnake, 360, 361
Pilot Whale, see Blackfish
Pilotfish, 176, *177
Pine Grosbeak, 510
Pine Lizard, *314
Pine Martin, 119
Pine Siskin, 512
Pine Snake, *358
Pine Squirrel, 81
Pine Warbler, 497
Pink Curlew, see Spoonbill
Pink Salmon, 248
Pinon Jay (pĭn'yŭn), 530
Pintail Duck, 677
Pipefish, 214
Pipistrelle (pĭp"ĭs·trĕl'), 129
Pipit (pĭp'ĭt), 490, *491
Plains Bison, 28
Plated Lizard, *322
Plover (plŭv'ẽr), 622
  Golden, 623
  Mountain, 626
  Semipalmated, 624
  Snowy, 625
  Upland, 631
  Wilson's, 625
Plumed Bunting, 517
Pocket Gopher, 71
Pocket Mouse, 66
Polecat, see Skunk
Pollock (pŏl'ŭk), 221
Pomarine Jaeger, 722
Pompano (pŏm'pȧ·nō), 191, *192
Poor-Will, 542
Porbeagle (pôr'bē"g'l), see Blue Shark
Porcupine (pôr'kū·pīn), *54
  Canada, 55
  Western, 55
Porcupinefish, 153, *154
Porgy (pôr'gĭ), see Spadefish
Porpoise (pôr'pŭs), 4, *9, 11
  Common, 11
Portuguese Man-o'-War Fish, *193
'Possum, see Opossum
Prairie Bird, see Horned Lark
Prairie Chicken, 613, *614
Prairie Dog, 76, *77
Prairie Falcon, 582
Prairie Warbler, 497
Prairie Wolf, see Coyote

Preacher, see Wood Ibis
Pronghorn Antelope, 28, *30
Prothonotary Warbler (prŏ·-thŏn"ȯ·tẽr"ĭ), 495
Ptarmigan (tär'mĭ·găn), 613
  White-tailed, 613
  Willow, 613
Puff Adder, see Hog-Nosed Snake
Puffer, 151, *152
Puffin, 726, *727
  Atlantic, 728
  Horned, 728
  Tufted, 728
Puma (pū'mȧ), *98
  See also Cougar
Purple Finch, 509
Purple Gallinule, *640
Purple Grackle, 522
Purple Martin, *504, 505
Pygmy Nuthatch, 481
Pygmy Owl, 571
Pygmy Rabbit, 52
Pyrrhuloxia (pĭr"ōō·lŏk'sĭ·ȧ), 518

Q

Quail (kwāl), 615
  California, 617
  Mountain, 615
  Scaled, 616
Queen Angelfish, 173

R

Rabbit, 47
  Brush, 52
  Cottontail, 50
  Jack, 47
  Pygmy, 52
  Swamp, 52
Raccoon (ră·kōōn'), 120, *121
Raccoon Perch, see Yellow Perch
Racer, 352
Racerunner, 329, *330
Rail, 641
  Black, 645
  Clapper, 643
  King, 642
  Sora, 644
  Virginia, 642
  Yellow, 645
Rainbow Snake, 371
Rainbow Trout, 250

āle, chåotic, câre, ădd, ȧccount, ärm, ȧsk, sofȧ; ēve, hẽre, ėvent, ĕnd, silĕnt, makẽr; īce, ĭll, chȧrȧty; ōld, ȯbey, ôrb, ŏdd, sôft, cǒnnect; fōōd, fǒǒt; out, oil, cūbe, ūnite, ûrn, ŭp, circŭs, menü; chair; go; sing; then, thin; natûre, verdûre.

PRONOUNCING INDEX

Rat, 63
  Black, 64, 67
  Cotton, 63, 64
  Dwarf Pocket, 66
  Kangaroo, 66
  Norway, 64, 67
  Pack, 64
  Rice, 63, 65
  Roof, 67
  Trade, 64
  Wood, 63
Rat Snake, 359
Ratfish, 280
Rattlesnake, 384, *385, *386
  Diamond-Backed, 386
Rattlesnake Pipe, see Sauger
Raven, 532
Ray, 275
  Cow-Nosed, *276
  Sting, 275
Razor-Billed Auk, 725
Rear-Fanged Snake, 375
Red-Backed Mouse, 63
Red-Bellied Dace, *232
Red-Bellied Snake, 373
  See also Storer's Snake
Red-Bellied Woodpecker, 550
Red-Breasted Nuthatch, 481
Red-Cockaded Woodpecker, 547
Red-Eyed Vireo, 498
Red Fox, 99, *100
Red-Headed Woodpecker, 550
Red Phalarope (făl'ȧ·rōp), 636
Red Salamander, 450
Red-Shouldered Hawk, 590
Red Snapper, 180
Red Squirrel, 81
Red-Tailed Hawk, 589
Red-Throated Loon, 733
Red-Winged Blackbird, *520
Red Wolf, 105
Redhead Duck, 677
Redpoll, 511
Redstart, 494
Reef Gecko, 305
Reindeer, see Caribou
Remora (rĕm'ô·rȧ), see Shark-sucker
Reptiles, 291
Reticulated Lizard, 313
Ribbon Snake, *346, 347
Ribbonfish, see Drum
Rice Rat, 63, 65
Richardson's Owl, 567
Ricord's Frog, 431
Right Whale, 7
Ring-Billed Gull, 712
Ring-Necked Duck, 677

Ring-Necked Pheasant, *606
Ring-Necked Snake, 369
Ringed Ground Snake, 368
Ringed Perch, see Yellow Perch
Ringtail Cat, *122
Rivoli's Hummingbird, 540
Roadrunner, 555, *556
Roadtrotter, see Horned Lark
Robber Frog, 429, *430
Robin, 468, *469
Rock Bass, 184, 187
Rock Hind, see Grouper
Rock Rabbit, see Pika
Rock Wren, 485
Rockchuck, see Woodchuck
Rocky Mountain Creeper, 483
Rocky Mountain Goats, *23
Rocky Mountain Sheep, *20, *21
Rodents, 46
Roncador (rŏng"kȧ·dōr'), 176
Roof Rat, 67
Rose-Breasted Grosbeak, 510
Roseate Tern (rō'zė·ȧt), 718
Rosy Boa, 342
Rosy Finch, 511
Rough-Legged Hawk, 591, *592
Royal Tern, 716
Rubber Boa, 342, *343
Ruby-Crowned Kinglet, 474
Ruby-Throated Hummingbird, 538, *539
Rudderfish, see Pilotfish
Ruddy Duck, 676
Ruddy Turnstone, 620
Ruffed Grouse, 608, *609
Rusty Blackbird, 520
Rusty Dab, see Fluke
Rusty Flounder, see Fluke

S

Sabine's Gull (sā'bīnz), 714
Sacramento Perch, 187
Sage Hen, 614
Sage Thrush, 489
Sailfish, *196
Salamander (săl'ȧ·măn"dēr), 445
  Forest, 448
  Jefferson's, 458
  Lungless, 445
  Marbled, 457
  Mole, 457
  Mud, 449
  Red, 450
  Slimy, 448

  Spotted, 457
  Tiger, 455
  Tree, 449
  Two-Lined, 450
Salamander, see Pocket Gopher
Salmon (săm'ŭn), 245, *247
  King, see Chinook
  Pink, 248
  Spring, see Chinook
Sand Dab, see Fluke
Sand Lizard, *315
Sand Perch, see Sauger
Sand Shark, *273, 274
Sandpiper (sănd'pīp"ēr), 638
  Knot, 629
  Spotted, 629
  Stilt, 629
Sanderling (săn'dēr·lĭng), 630
Sandhill Crane, 645, *646
Sapsucker, 552
Sardine (sär·dēn'), 253
Sauger (sô'gēr), 189
Savannah Cricket, see Cricket Frog
Savannah Sparrow, 514
Saw-Whet Owl, 567
Sawbill, see Merganser
Sawfish, 278
Scaled Carp, 237
Scaled Quail, 616
Scaled Sculpin, 171
Scaleless Sculpin, 171
Scarlet Snake, 367
Scarlet Tanager, 506, *507
Scaup Duck (skôp), 674
Scissor-tailed Flycatcher, 534
Scorpion Mouse, see Grasshopper Mouse
Scoter (skō'tēr), 677
Screech Owl, 567, *568
Sculpin (skŭl'pĭn), 169
  Daddy, 171
  Eighteen-Spined, *170
  Lake, 171
  Scaled, 171
  Scaleless, 171
Sea Bass, *183
Sea Bass, Rock, *182
Sea Catfish, 230
Sea Cow, 13
  Steller's, 13
Sea Hawk, see Skua
Sea Lamprey, *282
Sea Lion, 85
  California, 85
  Steller's, 87
Sea Otter, 114
Sea Parrot, see Puffin

āle, châotic, câre, ădd, a̐ccount, ärm, ȧsk, sofȧ; ēve, hęre, ėvent, ĕnd, silĕnt, makēr; īce, ĭll, charĭty; ōld, ôbey, ôrb, ŏdd, sôft, cȯnnect; fōod, fo͝ot; out, oil, cūbe, ûnite, ûrn, ŭp, circŭs, menü; chair; go; sing; then, thin; nature, verdure.

745

PRONOUNCING INDEX

Sea Pheasant, see Merganser
Sea Robin, Red-Winged, *165
Seahorse, *213
Seal, Fur, 87
Seaside Sparrow, 514
Semipalmated Plover, 624
Sennett's White-Tailed Hawk, 592
Sergeant Major (sär'jĕnt), *162
Sergeantfish, 177
Seven-Spined Stickleback, 217
Shad, 252
Shark, *271
  Basking, 269
  Blue, 270
  Hammerhead, 272
  Man-Eater, 270
  Nurse, 271
  Sand, 274
  Thresher, 270
  Tiger, 272
  Whale, 274
Shark Pilot, see Pilotfish
Sharksucker, 159, *160
Sharp-Nosed Snake, 366
Sharp-Shinned Hawk, 587
Sharp-Tailed Grouse, 612
Sharp-Tailed Sparrow, 514
Shearwater, 705, *706
  Cory's, 707
  Sooty, 707
Sheldrake (shĕl'drāk), see Merganser
Shiner, *233
  See also Dace
Short-Eared Owl, 565
Short-Nosed Gar, 263
Shoveler, 673
Shovelnose, 267
Shrew (shrōō), 132
Shrike (shrīk), 500, *501
Shypoke, see Green Heron
Sidewinder Rattlesnake, *388
Sierra Creeper, 483
Sierra Mackerel, 203
Siffleur (sē″flûr′), see Woodchuck
Silky Flycatcher, 502
Silver Carp, see Sucker
Silver Fish, see Tarpon
Silver Fox, 101
Silver-Haired Bat, 129
Silver Lamprey, 283
Silver Perch, see Drum
Silversides, see Mullet
Silver-Tip Bear, see Grizzly
Siren (sī'rĕn), 442, *443
Siskin, Pine (sĭs'kĭn), 512

Skate (skāt), 277
  Clear-Nosed, *279
Skate eggs, *277
Skilton's Skink, 335
Skimmer, 715
Skink, 332
  Black-Banded, 335
  Brown-Backed, 335
  Five-Lined, 332
  Hayden's, 334
  Many-Lined, 334
  Skilton's, 335
  Sonora, 334
Skipjack, 177, 205
Squa (skū'ă), 721
Skunk, 110, *111
  Spotted, 112
Slider Terrapin, 401
Slime Eel, see Hagfish
Slimy Salamander, 448
Small-Mouthed Bass, 184
Small-Scaled Swift, 316
Smelt, 245
Smooth Dogfish, 274
Snake, 338
  Arizona Vine, 377
  Banded Ground, 368
  Black, 352, 354
  Blue Bull, 352
  Box, 360
  Brown, 350
  Bull, 357
  Bush, 378
  Coachwhip, 352
  Cope's Hook-Nosed, 368
  Copperhead, 382
  Coral, 378
  Corn, 360, 362
  Cottonmouth Moccasin, 380
  De Kay's, 351
  Flat-Nosed, 356
  Garter, 343
  Green, 368
  Hog-Nosed, 373
  Indigo, 352
  King, 363
  Leaf-Nosed, 356
  Le Conte's, 367
  Milk, 366
  Pilot Black, 360
  Pine, 358
  Rainbow, 371
  Rat, 359
  Rattle-, 384
  Rear-Fanged, 375
  Red-Bellied, 373
  Ribbon, 347
  Ring-Necked, 369

  Ringed Ground, 368
  Scarlet, 367
  Sharp-Nosed, 366
  Storer's, 352
  Strecker's Hook-Nosed, 368
  Swamp, 350
  Taylor's, 367
  Water, 348
  Western Gopher, 359
  Worm, 341, 367
  Yellow Ground, 367
Snake-Bird, see Water-Turkey
Snake Bite, 338
Snake-Eel, 244
Snapper, 179
  Gray, 180
  Red, 180
Snapping Turtle, 391, *393
Snipe, Wilson's (snīp), 626
Snipefish, 215
Snow Bunting, 517
Snow Goose, 679, *680
Snowshoe Hare, 50
Snowy Owl, 570
Snowy Plover, 625
Soapfish, see Grouper
Soft-Shelled Turtle, 414, *415
Sole, 219
Song Sparrow, 516
Song Thrush, see Wood Thrush
Sonora Skink, 334
Sooty Shearwater, 707
Sooty Tern, 720
Sora (sō'rà), 644
Southern Bull Frog, *427
Spadefish, *174
  See also Paddlefish
Spadefoot Toad, 437, *438
Spanish Buzzard, see Wood Ibis
Spanish Mackerel, 203
Sparrow (spăr'ō), 512
  Black-Chinned, 515
  Black-Throated, 515
  Chipping, 515
  English, 512
  Fox, 516
  Golden-Crowned, 515
  Grasshopper, 514
  Harris's, 515
  Henslow's, 514
  Ipswich, 514
  Lark, 514
  Savannah, 514
  Seaside, 514
  Sharp-Tailed, 514
  Song, 516
  Swamp, 516

āle, chåotic, câre, ădd, ȧccount, ärm, åsk, sofȧ; ēve, hẹre, ĕvent, ĕnd, silĕnt, makēr; īce, ĭll, charĭty; ōld, ȯbey, ôrb, ŏdd, sŏft, cŏnnect; fōōd, fŏŏt; out, oil, cūbe, ŭnite, ûrn, ŭp, circṳs, menü; chair; go; sing; then, thin; nature, verdure.

PRONOUNCING INDEX

Tree, 515
Vesper, 513
White-Crowned, 515
White-Throated, 515
Sparrow Hawk, *580
Sperm Whale, 6
Spiny Dogfish, 273
Spiny Eel, 244
Spiny Pocket Mouse, 66
Spiny Swift, *314
Spoonbill, 662, *663
Spoonbill Cat, see Paddlefish
Spoonbill Duck, see Shoveler
Spotted Lizard, 316
Spotted Moray, 241
Spotted Newt, 453, *454
Spotted Owl, 566
Spotted Salamander, *456, 457
Spotted Sandpiper, 629
Spotted Turtle, 403
Spreading Adder, see Hog-Nosed Snake
Spring Bird, see Horned Lark
Spring Salmon, see Chinook
Spruce Grouse, 611
Squirrel (skwûr'ĕl), 80
  Antelope Ground, 83
  Cat, 80
  Flying, 84
  Fox, 81
  Golden-Mantled, 84
  Gray, 80
  Ground, 83
  Pine, 81
  Red, 81
  Tufted-Eared, 80
Squirrelfish, see Sea Bass
Stanbury's Swift, see Small-scaled Swift
Starling, 523, *524
Steelhead Trout, 250
Stejneger's Chameleon, 307
Steller's Jay, 529
Steller's Sea Cow, 13
Steller's Sea Lion, 87
Stickleback, 215
  Brook, 217
  Four-Spined, 216
  Nine-Spined, 217
  Seven-Spined, 217
  Two-Spined, 216
Stilt (stĭlt), 632
Stilt Sandpiper, 629
Sting Ray, 275
Stoat (stōt), see Weasel
Stoneroller, see Dace
Storer's Snake, 352
Strawberry Bass, 187

Strecker's Hook-Nosed Snake, 368
Striped Bass, 187
Striped Ground Squirrel, *82
Striped Lizard, see Racerunner
Striped Marlin, 199
Striped Mullet, 212
Striped Snake, see Garter Snake
Striped Tunny, see Bonito
Sturgeon (stûr'jŭn), *265
  Hackleback, 267
  Lake, 267
Sucker, 238
  White, 237
Sulphur-Bottom Whale, 4, 8
Summer Tanager, 508
Sunfish, *186
Sunfish, Ocean, 149, *150
Surf Bird, *621, 622
Surgeonfish, 171
Swainson's Hawk, *591
Swallow, 504
  Bank, 505
  Barn, 506
  Cliff, 505
  Tree, 506
Swallow-Tailed Kite, 593
Swamp Rabbit, 52
Swamp Robin, see Wood Thrush
Swamp Snake, 350
Swamp Sparrow, 516
Swan, 681
  Trumpeter, 682
  Whistling, 681
Swan Grebe, see Western Grebe
Swellfish, see Puffer
Swift (bird), 540
  Black, 542
  Chimney, 540
  White-Throated, 542
Swift (lizard), 313
  Small-Scaled, 316
  Spiny, 314
Swordfish (sōrd'fĭsh"), 200, *201

T

Tailless Hare, see Pika
Tanager (tăn'ȧ-jẽr), 506
  Cooper's, 508
  Hepatic, 508
  Scarlet, 506
  Summer, 508
  Western, 508
Tang, see Surgeonfish
Tarpon (tär'pŏn), 254, *255, *256

Taylor's Snake, 367
Taylor's Toad, 423
Teal (tēl), 676
Tench (těnch), 235
Tern (tûrn), 718
  Arctic, 718
  Black, 719
  Cabot's, 717
  Caspian, 720
  Common, 718
  Forster's, 721
  Gull-Billed, 720
  Least, 719
  Roseate, 718
  Royal, 717
  Sooty, 720
Terrapin (tĕr'ȧ·pĭn), 399
  Chicken, 401
  Cooter, 401
  Diamond Back, 399
  Hieroglyphic, 400
  Slider, 401
  Troost's, 400
Tessellated Darter, 191
Tessellated Lizard, 331
Texas Armadillo, *17
Texas Narrow-Mouthed Toad, 423
Thick-Billed Parrot, 560
Thrasher (thrăsh'ẽr), 489
  Bendire's, 489
  California, 489
  Crissal, 489
  Le Conte's, 489
Thread Eel, 244
Thread Herring, 251
Three-Toed Woodpecker, 549
Thresher Shark, 270
Thrush (thrŭsh), 470
  Hermit, 470
  Sage, 489
  Townsend's Solitaire, 472
  Water, 497
Wood, 471
Thunderpumper, see Fresh Water Drum
Tica (tĭk'ȧ), see Tench
Tiger Lizard, see Graham's Lizard
Tiger Salamander, 455
Tiger Shark, 272
Timber Wolf, *104
Toad (tōd), 435
  Bell, 440
  Hammond's Spadefoot, 438
  Holbrook's Spadefoot, 439
  Mitchell's, 423
  Narrow-Mouthed, 421

āle, chåotic, câre, ădd, ȧccount, ärm, ȧsk, sofȧ; ēve, hĕre, ĕvent, ẽnd, silĕnt, makẽr; īce, ĭll, charĭty; ōld, ôbey, ôrb, ŏdd, sôft, cŏnnect; fōod, fŏot; out, oil, cūbe, ûnite, ûrn, ŭp, circŭs, menü; chair; go; sing; then, thin; nature, verdure.

747

PRONOUNCING INDEX

Spadefoot, 437
Taylor's, 423
Texas Narrow-Mouthed, 423
Tom Cod, 221
Torpedo, 276
Tortoise (tôr'tŭs), 407
  Berlander's, 409
  Desert, 409
  Gopher, 408
Towhee (tou'hē), 517
Townsend's Solitaire Thrush, 472
Trade Rat, 64
Tree Fox, 101
Tree Frog, 432, 434
Tree Salamander, 449
Tree Sparrow, 515
Tree Swallow, 506
Triggerfish, 158, *159
Tripletail, see Sea Bass
Trogon (trō'gŏn), 555
Troost's Terrapin, 400, *401
Tropic-Bird, 698
Trout, 248
  Brook, 249
  Brown, 250
  Bull, 250
  Cut-Throat, 250
  Golden, 250
  Hardhead, 250
  Lake, 250
  Rainbow, 250
  Steelhead, 250
Trumpeter Swan, *681, 682, *683
Trumpetfish, 215
Trunkback Turtle, 410, *411
Trunkfish, 155
Tufted-Eared Squirrel, 80
Tufted Puffin, 728
Tufted Titmouse, 480
Tuna, 203
  Allison's, see Yellowfin Tuna
  Bluefin, 204
  White, see Albacore
  Yellowfin, 205
Tunny (tŭn'ĭ), *204
Turkey, *605
Turkey Vulture, 597, *598
Turnstone (tûrn'stōn″), 620
  Black, 622
  Ruddy, 620
Turtles, 390
  Alligator Snapping, 394
  Blanding's, 403, *404
  Box, 404
  Green, 411
  Mud, 398

Muhlenberg's, 403
Musk, 396
Painted, 402
Snapping, 391
Soft-Shelled, 414
Spotted, 403
Trunkback, 410
Wood, 403
Two-Lined Salamander, 450
Two-Spined Stickleback, 216

U

Upland Plover, 631, *624

V

Varying Hare, 50
Veery (vēr'ĭ), 472
Verdin (vûr'dĭn), 479
Vermilion Flycatcher, 536
Vesper Sparrow, 513
Vireo (vĭr'ḗ-ō), 498
  Black-Capped, 499
  Blue-Headed, 499
  Red-Eyed, 498
  White-Eyed, 500
  Yellow-Throated, 499
Virginia Deer, 38, *39
Virginia Rail, 642
Vole, see Meadow Mouse
Vulture (vŭl'tûr), 597
  Black, 598
  Turkey, 597

W

Wachna Cod (wäk'nä), 221
Wall-Eyed Cod, 221
Wall-Eyed Perch, 189
Wall-Eyed Pike, see Pike-Perch
Walleye, see Pike-Perch
Wapiti (wŏp'ĭ-tĭ), 36, *37
Warbler (wôr'blēr), 492
  Black-and-White, 497
  Blackburnian, 497
  Blue-Winged, 497
  Cerulean, 495
  Chestnut-Sided, 497
  Golden-Winged, 497
  Hooded, 497
  Magnolia, 497
  Maryland Yellow-Throat, 494
  Mourning, 497
  Myrtle, 497
  Orange-Crowned, 497

Palm, 497
Parula, 497
Pine, 497
Prairie, 497
Prothonotary, 495
Worm-Eating, 497
Yellow-Throated, 496
Warmouth (wôr'mouth), 187
Water Shrew, *133
Warty Gecko, 303
Water Ouzel (ōō'z'l), see Dipper
Water Snake, 348, *349
Water Thrush, 497
Water-Turkey, 694, *695
Waxwing, 502
  Bohemian, 502
  Cedar, 502
Weakfish, see Drum
Weasel, 115, *116
Western Dabchick, see Western Grebe
Western Frog, 429
Western Gopher Snake, 359
Western Grebe, 734, *735
Western Tanager, 508
Whale (hwāl), 4
  Blue, 4
  Bowhead, 8
  Finback, 8
  Gray, 8
  Humpback, *5, 8
  Right, 7
  Sperm, 6
  Sulphur-Bottom, 4, 8
Whale Shark, 274, *275
Whalebone, 8
Whaling, 4
Wheat Bird, see Horned Lark
Whip-Poor-Will, 542, *543
Whistler, see Mountain Beaver
Whistling Rabbit, see Pika
Whistling Swan, 681
White Bass, 187
White-Breasted Nuthatch, 480, *481
White Catfish, 230
White-Crowned Sparrow, 515
White-Eyed Vireo, 500
White-Footed Mouse, 63, 65
White-Headed Woodpecker, 550
White Ibis, 662
White-Lipped Frog, 431
White Marlin, 199
White Mullet, *212
White Pelican, 689, *690, *691
White Perch, see Fresh Water Drum

āle, châotic, câre, ădd, *a*ccount, ärm, àsk, sof*a*; ēve, hęre, ęvent, ĕnd, silĕnt, makēr; īce, ĭll, charĭty; ōld, ôbey, ôrb, ŏdd, sôft, cŏnnect; fōod, foŏt; out, oil, cūbe, ûnite, ûrn, ŭp, circ*u*s, menü; chair; go; sing; then, thin; nature, verdûre.

748

PRONOUNCING INDEX

White Sucker, 239
White-Tailed Deer, 38
White-Tailed Kite, 593
White-Tailed Ptarmigan, *612, 613
White-Throated Sparrow, 515
White-Throated Swift, 542
White Tuna, see Albacore
Whitefish, 244, *245
Whooping Crane, 647, *648
Wild Canary, see Goldfinch
Wildcat, *91
Willet, 630
Willow Ptarmigan, 613
Wilson's Petrel, *702, 703
Wilson's Phalarope, *635
Wilson's Plover, 625
Wilson's Snipe, 626
Wilson's Thrush, see Veery
Wishtonwish (wĭsh'tŏn·wĭsh), see Prairie Dog
Wolf, 103
  Black, 105
  Gray, 105
  Red, 105
Wolverine (wŏŏl"vẽr·ēn'), 108, *109
Wood Bison, 28
Wood Duck, 677
Wood Frog, 428

Wood Ibis, 659, *660
Wood Rat, 63
Wood Robin, see Wood Thrush
Wood Stork, see Wood Ibis
Wood Thrush, 471, *472
Wood Turtle, 403
Woodchuck, 73, *74
Woodcock, *626, 627
Woodland Caribou, 33
Woodpecker, 545
  Downy, 546
  Hairy, 546
  Ivory-Billed, 546
  Pileated, 548
  Red-Bellied, 550
  Red-Cockaded, 547
  Red-Headed, 550
  Three-Toed, 549
  White-Headed, 550
Worm-Eating Warbler, 497
Worm Eel, 244
Worm Lizard, *337
Worm Snake, 325, *341, 367
Wormlike Lizard, 336
Wormlike Snakes, 341
Wren (rĕn), 483
  Bewick's, 485
  Cactus, 483
  House, 483
  Marsh, 483

Rock, 485
Wren-tit, 475

Y

Yarrow's Swift, see Spiny Swift
Yellow-Banded Swift, see Spiny Swift
Yellow-Billed Cuckoo, *557, 558
Yellow-Breasted Chat, 497
Yellow-Crowned Night Heron, 658
Yellowfin Tuna, 205
Yellow Ground Snake, 367
Yellow-Headed Blackbird, 520
Yellow Ned, see Yellow Perch
Yellow Perch, 187, *188
Yellow Rail, 645
Yellow-Tail, see Fluke
Yellow-Tail Salmon, 177
Yellow-Throated Vireo, 499
Yellow-Throated Warbler, *496
Yellow Warbler, *493

Z

Zebra-Tailed Lizard, 317

āle, chăotic, câre, ădd, ȧccount, ärm, ȧsk, sofȧ; ēve, hẹre, ėvent, ĕnd, silẽnt, makēr; īce, ĭll, charĭty; ōld, ȯbey, ôrb, ŏdd, sôft, cȯnnect; fōōd, fŏŏt; out, oil, cūbe, ūnite, ûrn, ŭp, circŭs, menü; chair; go; sing; then, thin; natûre, verdûre.

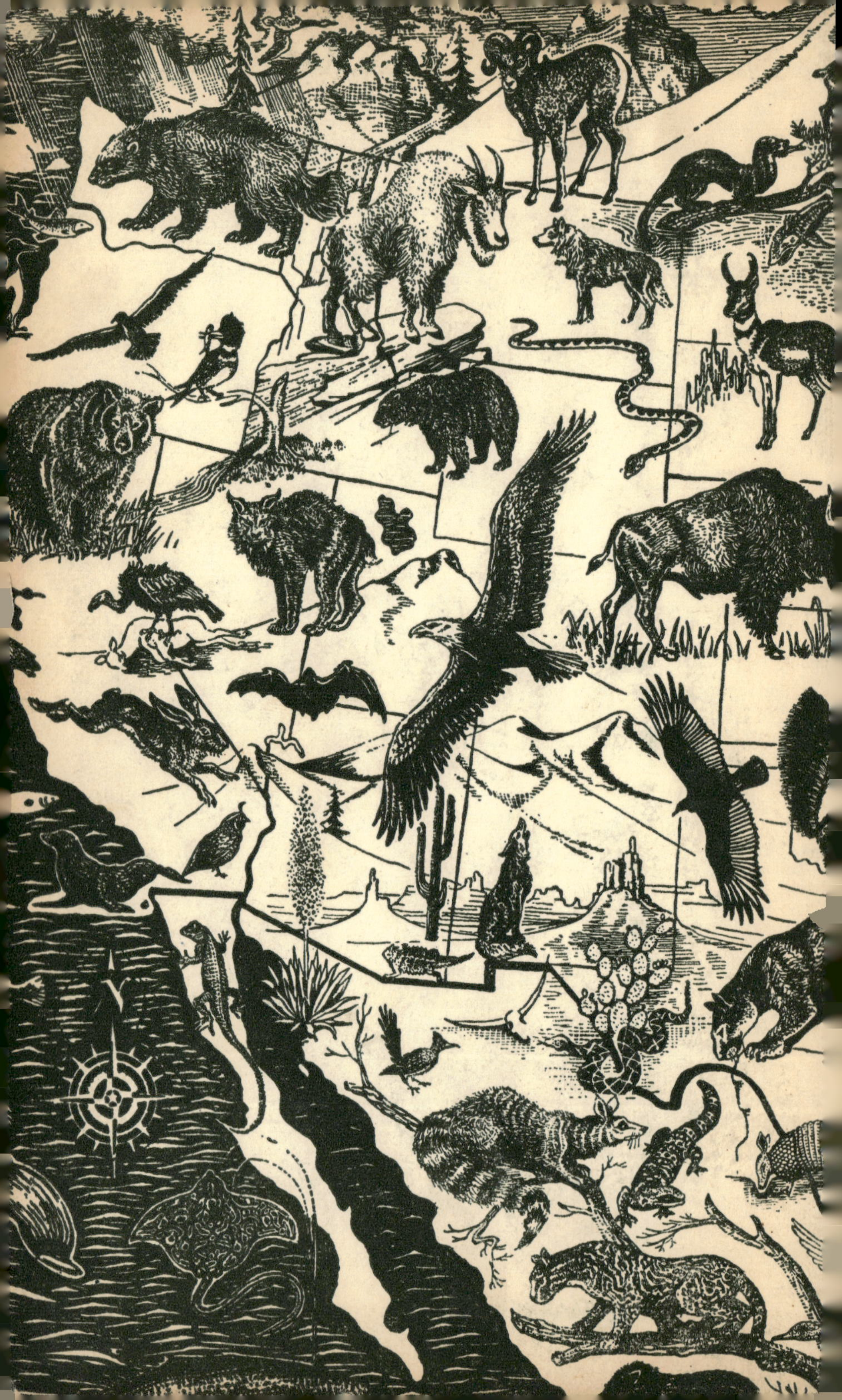